DESIGN OF URBAN STORMWATER CONTROLS

Prepared by the **Design of Urban Stormwater Controls Task Force** of the **Water Environment Federation** and the **American Society of Civil Engineers/ Environmental & Water Resources Institute**

Daniel E. Medina, Ph.D., P.E., D. WRE, CFM,
    Co-Chair
Christine A. Pomeroy, Ph.D., P.E., *Co-Chair*

John A. Aldrich, P.E., D. WRE
Steve Apfelbaum
Tom Ballestero, Ph.D.
Billy Barfield
Michael Barrett, Ph.D., P.E., D. WRE
Michael Borst (ASCE/EWRI Blue Ribbon Review
    Panel member)
David Brandes (ASCE/EWRI Blue Ribbon Review
    Panel member)
Tai Bui, Ph.D., P.Eng.
Chein-Chi Chang, Ph.D., P.E.
Ni-Bin Chang
Gregory R. Chol, P.E.
Shirley Clark, Ph.D., P.E., D. WRE
Suzanne Dallman, Ph.D.
Thomas Davenport (ASCE/EWRI Blue Ribbon
    Review Panel member)
David D. Dee, Jr., P.E., D. WRE (ASCE/EWRI Blue
    Ribbon Review Panel member)
Randy Dymond, Ph.D., P.E. (ASCE/EWRI Blue
    Ribbon Review Panel member)
Andrew Earles, Ph.D., P.E., D. WRE (ASCE/EWRI
    Blue Ribbon Review Panel member)
Bruce K. Ferguson (ASCE/EWRI Blue Ribbon
    Review Panel member)
Patricia Flood, P.E.
Rod Frederick, P.E., D. WRE (ASCE/EWRI Blue
    Ribbon Review Panel member)
William H. Frost, P.E., D. WRE
Jeffry S. Glenn, P.E., D. WRE (ASCE/EWRI Blue
    Ribbon Review Panel member)
John Gulliver, Ph.D., P.E.
A. R. Jarrett, Ph.D., P.E. (ASCE/EWRI Blue Ribbon
    Review Panel member)
Kathlie S. Jeng-Bulloch, Ph.D., P.E., D. WRE (ASCE/
    EWRI Blue Ribbon Review Panel member)
Barry Johnson, P.E.
Charlene E. Johnston, P.E. (ASCE/EWRI Blue
    Ribbon Review Panel member)

Cory LaNeave Jones, P.E.
Jonathan Jones, P.E., D. WRE (ASCE/EWRI Blue
    Ribbon Review Panel member)
Hayes Lenhart
James H. Lenhart, P.E., D. WRE (ASCE/EWRI Blue
    Ribbon Review Panel member)
Vachara Limtrajiti, P.E.
Peter Mattejat, P.E.
Gary Minton, Ph.D., P.E.
Brian N. Neilson, P.E.
Thomas P. O'Connor
Mira Olson (ASCE/EWRI Blue Ribbon Review
    Panel member)
Bryan Pariseault, P.E. (ASCE/EWRI Blue Ribbon
    Review Panel member)
Ian Paton, P.E., CPESC, CFM
Scott Perry
Robert Pitt, Ph.D., P.E., D. WRE
Michael A. Ports, P.E., PH, D. WRE (ASCE/EWRI
    Blue Ribbon Review Panel member)
David B. Powers, P.E., PH, D. WRE
Srinivasan Rangarajan, Ph.D., P.Eng., D. WRE
Louis C. Regenmorter
Jeffrey M. Rice, P.Eng.
Virginia A. Roach, P.E., BCEE
Domenic Rocco (ASCE/EWRI Blue Ribbon Review
    Panel member)
James M. Rossi, CPESC, CPSWQ
James E. Scholl
Marc A. Schulte, P.E., D. WRE, CFM, CPSWQ
Earl Shaver (ASCE/EWRI Blue Ribbon Review
    Panel member)
Rachel Small
Ken J. Susilo, P.E., D. WRE, CPSWQ
Scott Taylor, P.E., D. WRE
Robert G. Traver, Ph.D., P.E., D. WRE (ASCE/
    EWRI Blue Ribbon Review Panel member)
Aditya Tyagi, Ph.D., P.E., D. WRE
Thomas M. Walski
David W. Watkins, Ph.D. (ASCE/EWRI Blue
    Ribbon Review Panel member)
Kenneth Wright, P.E., D. WRE
Tess Wynn, Ph.D.

Under the Direction of the **Watershed Subcommittee** of the **Technical Practice Committee**

2012

Water Environment Federation
601 Wythe Street
Alexandria, VA 22314-1994
http://www.wef.org

American Society of Civil Engineers/
    Environmental & Water Resources Institute
1801 Alexander Bell Drive
Reston, VA 20191-4400
http://www.asce.org

DESIGN OF URBAN STORMWATER CONTROLS

WEF Manual of Practice No. 23
ASCE/EWRI Manuals and Reports on Engineering Practice No. 87

*Prepared by the Design of Urban Stormwater Controls
Task Force of the Water Environment Federation and the American
Society of Civil Engineers/Environmental & Water Resources Institute*

WEF Press

Water Environment Federation   Alexandria, Virginia

American Society of Civil Engineers/Environmental &
Water Resources Institute   Reston, Virginia

New York   Chicago   San Francisco   Lisbon   London   Madrid
Mexico City   Milan   New Delhi   San Juan   Seoul
Singapore   Sydney   Toronto

McGraw-Hill books are available at special quantity discounts to use as premiums and sales promotions, or for use in corporate training programs. To contact a representative, please e-mail us at bulksales@ mcgraw-hill.com.

Design of Urban Stormwater Controls

1 2 3 4 5 6 7 8 9 0   DOC/DOC   1 8 7 6 5 4 3 2

ISBN   978-0-07-170444-1
MHID   0-07-170444-2

Water Environment Research, *WEF*, and *WEFTEC* are registered trademarks of the Water Environment Federation. *American Society of Civil Engineers, ASCE, Environmental & Water Resources Institute*, and *EWRI* are registered trademarks of the American Society of Civil Engineers.

Printed and bound by RR Donnelley.

This book is printed on acid-free paper.

IMPORTANT NOTICE

The material presented in this publication has been prepared in accordance with generally recognized engineering principles and practices and is for general information only. This information should not be used without first securing competent advice with respect to its suitability for any general or specific application.

The contents of this publication are not intended to be a standard of the Water Environment Federation (WEF) or the American Society of Civil Engineers (ASCE)/Environmental & Water Resources Institute (EWRI) and are not intended for use as a reference in purchase specifications, contracts, regulations, statutes, or any other legal document.

No reference made in this publication to any specific method, product, process, or service constitutes or implies an endorsement, recommendation, or warranty thereof by WEF or ASCE/EWRI.

WEF and ASCE/EWRI make no representation or warranty of any kind, whether expressed or implied, concerning the accuracy, product, or process discussed in this publication and assumes no liability.

Anyone using this information assumes all liability arising from such use, including but not limited to infringement of any patent or patents.

About WEF

Formed in 1928, the Water Environment Federation® (WEF®) is a not-for-profit technical and educational organization with members from varied disciplines who work toward WEF's vision to preserve and enhance the global water environment.

For information on membership, publications, and conferences, contact:

Water Environment Federation®
601 Wythe Street
Alexandria, VA 22314-1994
(703) 684-2400
http://www.wef.org

About ASCE/EWRI

Founded in 1852, the American Society of Civil Engineers (ASCE) represents more than 140,000 members of the civil engineering profession worldwide, and is America's oldest national engineering society. Created in 1999, the Environmental & Water Resources Institute (EWRI) is an Institute of the American Society of Civil Engineers. EWRI services are designed to complement ASCE's traditional civil engineering base and to attract new categories of members (non-civil engineer allied professionals) who seek to enhance their professional and technical development.

For information on membership, publications, and conferences, contact:

ASCE/EWRI
1801 Alexander Bell Drive
Reston, VA 20191-4400
(703) 295-6000
http://www.asce.org

Manuals of Practice of the Water Environment Federation

The WEF Technical Practice Committee (formerly the Committee on Sewage and Industrial Wastes Practice of the Federation of Sewage and Industrial Wastes Associations) was created by the Federation Board of Control on October 11, 1941. The primary function of the Committee is to originate and produce, through appropriate subcommittees, special publications dealing with technical aspects of the broad interests of the Federation. These publications are intended to provide background information through a review of technical practices and detailed procedures that research and experience have shown to be functional and practical.

Water Environment Federation Technical Practice Committee Control Group

R. Fernandez, *Chair*
Jeanette Brown, P.E., BCEE, D. WRE, *Vice-Chair, Publications*
Stacy J. Passaro, P.E., BCEE, *Vice-Chair, Distance Learning*
Barton G. Jones, P.E., *Past Chair*

Akin Babatola
Paul A. Bizier, P.E., BCEE
Kevin D. Conway, P.E.
R. Copithorn
Victor A. D'Amato, P.E.
R. P. Dominak
Ronald Horres
Susan Moisio, P.E.
T. Page-Bottorff
Christine A. Pomeroy, Ph.D., P.E.
R. C. Porter
Eric P. Rothstein, CPA
A. T. Sandy
K. Schnaars
Andrew R. Shaw, P.E.
J. Swift
A. K. Umble, Ph.D., P.E., BCEE
Paula Zeller

Manuals and Reports on Engineering Practice

(As developed by the ASCE Technical Procedures Committee, July 1930, and revised March 1935, February 1962, and April 1982)

A manual or report in this series consists of an orderly presentation of facts on a particular subject, supplemented by an analysis of limitations and applications of these facts. It contains information useful to the average engineer in his everyday work, rather than findings that may be useful only occasionally or rarely. It is not in any sense a "standard," however; nor is it so elementary or so conclusive as to provide a "rule of thumb" for nonengineers.

Furthermore, material in this series, in distinction from a paper (which expresses only one person's observations or opinions), is the work of a committee or group selected to assemble and express information on a specific topic. As often as practicable, the committee is under the direction of one or more of the Technical Divisions and Councils, and the product evolved has been subjected to review by the Executive Committee of the Division or Council. As a step in the process of this review, proposed manuscripts are often brought before the members of the Technical Divisions and Councils for comment, which may serve as the basis for improvement. When published, each work shows the names of the committees by which it was compiled and indicates clearly the several processes through which it has passed in review, in order that its merit may be definitely understood.

In February 1962 (and revised in April 1982) the Board of Direction voted to establish a series entitled "Manuals and Reports on Engineering Practice," to include the Manuals published and authorized to date, future Manuals of Professional Practice, and Reports on Engineering Practice. All such Manual or Report material of the Society would have been refereed in a manner approved by the Board Committee on Publications and would be bound, with applicable discussion, in books similar to past Manuals. Numbering would be consecutive and would be a continuation of present Manual numbers. In some cases of reports of joint committees, bypassing of Journal publications may be authorized.

Contents

Chapter 1 Introduction

Chapter 2 Effects of Stormwater on Receiving Waters

Chapter 3   Performance Goals for Stormwater Controls

Chapter 4   Unit Processes and Operations for Stormwater Control

Chapter 5   Selection Criteria and Design Considerations

Chapter 6   Basins

Chapter 7   Swales and Strips

Chapter 8   Filters

Chapter 9 Infiltrators

Chapter 10   Gross Pollutant Traps and Mechanical Operations

Chapter 11   Maintenance of Stormwater Controls

Chapter 12   Whole Life Cost of Stormwater Controls

Chapter 13   Performance Assessment

Chapter 14   Analytical Tools for Simulation of Stormwater Controls

List of Figures

List of Tables

Table		Page

Preface

This manual is a revision of the Water Environment Federation's (WEF's) and the American Society of Civil Engineers' (ASCE's) Manual of Practice (MOP) titled *Urban Runoff Quality Management* (1998). Since publication of the previous edition of this manual, a paradigm shift in the way stormwater is viewed and managed has begun. Traditionally viewed as a nuisance to be disposed of quickly through pipes and into central detention facilities, in some parts of the United States stormwater is now viewed as a resource to be used beneficially and returned to its natural pathways through a variety of distributed controls. The latter has become the pillar of an approach known by the popular names of *low-impact development* and *green infrastructure*. Another development was the recognition that both quantity and quality are inextricably linked. This MOP takes a holistic view and espouses the concept that systems of stormwater controls can be designed to meet the various objectives of stormwater management, including flood control; stream channel protection; groundwater recharge; water quality improvement; protection of public safety, health, and welfare; and multipurpose public benefits such as provision of open space, parks, playgrounds, trails, wildlife habitat, and enhancement of property values. However, this MOP does not provide an in-depth discussion of the well-established principles of flow attenuation and drainage design.

This MOP focuses on consolidating technologies under a comprehensive view of stormwater management in an attempt to foster a convergence between traditional stormwater controls and green infrastructure. This objective requires engineers to work side by side with urban planners, landscape architects, ecologists, soils scientists, regulators, and other professionals. This multidisciplinary view of stormwater can have a profound effect on development of sound land planning, which can be much more effective in protecting receiving waterbodies than engineered facilities to help designers meet the fundamental goals of minimizing effects to the environment, meeting applicable regulations, protecting public safety, and designing facilities in harmony with livable communities to enhance public spaces and provide recreation opportunities.

This Manual of Practice was produced under the direction of Daniel E. Medina, Ph.D., P.E., D. WRE, CFM, Co-Chair, and Christine A. Pomeroy, Ph.D., P.E., Co-Chair. The principal authors of this Manual of Practice are as follows:

Chapter 1   Daniel E. Medina, Ph.D., P.E., D. WRE, CFM
Chapter 2   Christine A. Pomeroy, Ph.D., P.E.
             Steve Apfelbaum
             Shirley Clark, Ph.D., P.E., D. WRE
             Daniel E. Medina, Ph.D., P.E., D. WRE, CFM
             Robert Pitt, Ph.D., P.E., D. WRE
Chapter 3   John A. Aldrich, P.E., D. WRE
             Daniel E. Medina, Ph.D., P.E., D. WRE, CFM
Chapter 4   Gary Minton, Ph.D., P.E.
Chapter 5   William H. Frost, P.E., D. WRE
Chapter 6   Virginia A. Roach, P.E., BCEE
             John A. Aldrich, P.E., D. WRE
             Vachara Limtrajiti, P.E.
Chapter 7   John A. Aldrich, P.E., D. WRE
             Daniel E. Medina, Ph.D., P.E., D. WRE, CFM
Chapter 8   Tom Ballestero, Ph.D.
             John A. Aldrich, P.E., D. WRE
Chapter 9   John A. Aldrich, P.E., D. WRE
Chapter 10   Cory LaNeave Jones, P.E.
             John A. Aldrich, P.E., D. WRE
Chapter 11   Michael Barrett, Ph.D., P.E., D. WRE
Chapter 12   Michael Barrett, Ph.D., P.E., D. WRE
Chapter 13   Aditya Tyagi, Ph.D., P.E., D. WRE
             Louis C. Regenmorter
Chapter 14   Srinivasan Rangarajan, Ph.D., P.Eng., D. WRE

Authors' and reviewers' efforts were supported by the following organizations:

Atkins, Calverton, Maryland

California State University—Long Beach, Long Beach, California

CDM Smith, Ann Arbor, Michigan; Cambridge, Massachusetts; Cleveland, Ohio; and Sacramento, California

CH2M HILL, Austin, Texas

City of Aurora Water, Aurora, Colorado

City of Houston, Houston, Texas

Contech Construction Products, Portland, Oregon

District of Columbia Water and Sewer Authority, Washington, D.C.

Drexel University, Philadelphia, Pennsylvania

EMHT, Minneapolis, Minnesota

Geosyntec Consultants, Los Angeles, California

HDR | HydroQual, Mahwah, New Jersey

Imbrium Systems Corporation, Rockville, Maryland

KCI Technologies, Inc., Sparks, Maryland

Malcolm Pirnie, Inc., Lansing, Michigan

Michael Baker Jr., Inc., Richmond, Virginia

Michigan Technological University, Houghton, Michigan

New York City Department of Environmental Protection, Staten Island, New York

Parsons Brinckerhoff, Baltimore, Maryland

Pennsylvania Department of Environmental Protection, Norristown, Pennsylvania

RBF Consulting, Carlsbad, California

Reynolds Smith and Hills, Inc., Orlando, Florida

Tetra Tech, Inc., Seattle, Washington

University of Central Florida, Orlando, Florida

University of Georgia, Athens, Georgia

University of Minnesota, Minneapolis, Minnesota

University of New Hampshire, Durham, New Hampshire

University of Texas, Austin, Texas

University of Utah, Salt Lake City, Utah

Urban Systems Ltd., Richmond, British Columbia, Canada

URS Corporation, Fort Washington, Pennsylvania; Germantown, Maryland; and La Jolla, California

U.S. Environmental Protection Agency, Chicago, Illinois, and Edison, New Jersey

Villanova University, Villanova, Pennsylvania

Virginia Polytechnic Institute and State University, Blacksburg, Virginia

Virginia Polytechnic Institute and State University Center for Geospatial Information Technology, Blacksburg, Virginia

Wescorp Consultants, Inc., Caledonia, Ontario, Canada

Wright Water Engineers, Inc., Denver, Colorado

DESIGN OF URBAN STORMWATER CONTROLS

Chapter 1

Introduction

1.0 URBAN STORMWATER MANAGEMENT OVERVIEW

Stormwater management continues to pose serious challenges in urban and suburban areas worldwide. The transformation of native and agricultural lands to urban land use has radically altered the hydrologic regime; this conversion is expected to accelerate as the population becomes denser in cities and surrounding areas. Also, existing urbanized areas are undergoing redevelopment. According to the National Research Council (NRC) (2008), 42% of urban lands in the United States will be redeveloped by the year 2030 (Nelson, 2004). Although it is inevitable that ecosystems in urban areas will be affected by increased runoff quantity and stormwater pollutants, opportunities are available to implement sound stormwater management practices for new development and take advantage of redevelopment for improving stormwater management.

The challenges of stormwater management are formidable. The negative effects of urbanization on aquatic ecosystem integrity are well documented throughout the United States (see Chapter 2). The physicochemical, biological, and thermal phenomena taking place within stormwater controls and their effectiveness in protecting urban streams from those effects are the subject of active research. However, there is uncertainty surrounding the causality of those effects and the potential benefits that an array of stormwater control measures can offer cumulatively over a watershed, especially when considering variability in climate and in physiographic and ecological conditions. Although models are useful tools for evaluating potential

1

benefits, they are based on approximations of highly complex processes that are not fully understood. There are also institutional and regulatory hurdles, the most significant of which is the disconnection between land use planning and stormwater management that is commonplace in public agencies. The cost of stormwater retrofits in older, urbanized areas developed without any stormwater controls will be very high based on the need to upgrade and relocate existing infrastructure. Finally, operation and maintenance and replacement of existing controls will also add to the financial burden on municipalities.

As a result of these complexities and challenges, stormwater management is a rapidly evolving field. The body of knowledge continues to widen and deepen as better understanding of the effects of stormwater becomes available through research worldwide and as industry innovation adds new options in stormwater management technology. Since publication of Water Environment Federation's (WEF's) and the American Society of Civil Engineers' (ASCE's) manual of practice (MOP) on *Urban Runoff Quality Management* in 1998, a paradigm shift in the way stormwater is viewed and managed has begun. Traditionally viewed as a nuisance to be disposed of quickly through pipes and into central detention facilities, in some parts of the United States stormwater is now viewed as a resource to be used beneficially and returned to its natural pathways through a variety of distributed controls. The latter has become the pillar of an approach known by the popular names of *low-impact development* and *green infrastructure*. Green infrastructure applications started in the early 1990s as small initiatives and pilot projects aimed at restoring hydrology; now, they are part of many development guidelines and regulations nationwide. For example, in December 2007, the U.S. Congress enacted the Energy Independence and Security Act (U.S. EPA, 2009). Section 438 of that legislation supports a holistic view of the effects of stormwater on receiving waters and requires that federal development and redevelopment projects "maintain or restore, to the maximum extent technically feasible, the predevelopment hydrology of the property with regard to the temperature, rate, volume, and duration of flow." Another parallel development was the recognition that both quantity and quality are inextricably linked, a realization crystallized in the NRC report *Urban Stormwater Management in the United States* (NRC, 2008). The report emphasizes addressing stormwater upstream by focusing on runoff minimization and reductions in sources of stormwater pollutants.

Past stormwater management practices have several decades of documented performance failures and successes, whereas green infrastructure is relatively new, with a limited amount of research supporting its applicability because of its short performance history. In some areas of the United States, detention-based technologies are still the predominant method of stormwater management; in other areas, "green" infiltration- and evapotranspiration-based controls are gaining momentum as a preferred stormwater management method and extensive research on the performance of green infrastructure practices is currently underway (Brown and Hunt, 2011; Carpenter and Kaluvakolanu, 2011; Clary et al., 2011; He and Davis, 2011; Lucas and Greenway, 2011; Machusick et al., 2011; Sileshi et al., 2010).

In addition to water quality protection and channel protection, flood control is often an objective of stormwater management. In many jurisdictions, stormwater management is synonymous with flood control for postdevelopment conditions, and some practitioners associate the term *quantity control* with flood control and drainage, and separately from *quality control*. This MOP takes a holistic view and espouses the concept that systems of stormwater controls can be designed to meet the various objectives of stormwater management, including flood control; stream channel protection; groundwater recharge; water quality improvement; protection of public safety, health, and welfare; and multipurpose public benefits such as provision of open space, parks, playgrounds, trails, wildlife habitat, and enhancement of property values.

However, this MOP does not provide an in-depth discussion of the well-established principles of flow attenuation and drainage design. Detailed information regarding hydrology of surface runoff, the hydraulics of conveyance infrastructure, and flood routing can be found in various publications such as *Design and Construction of Urban Stormwater Management Systems* (ASCE and WEF, 1992), *Handbook of Hydrology* (Maidment, 1993), *Municipal Stormwater Management* (Debo and Reese, 2002), and *Hydrology and Floodplain Analysis* (Bedient et al., 2008). Much of the relevant material in these references remains current.

The myriad of challenges associated with stormwater management make clear the need to use every tool available to provide flexible designs that meet management goals cost-effectively. No single approach is a panacea. For instance, infiltration is not always possible or desirable and detention has drawbacks such as thermal enrichment and increases in the duration of midrange flows. Irrespective of the stormwater management approach, hydrology-centric site planning, minimization of directly connected impervious areas, stormwater pollution prevention, and application of processes to minimize, slow down, infiltrate, evaporate, transpire, and detain runoff yield better functioning and cost-effective designs. This MOP focuses on consolidating technologies under a comprehensive view of stormwater management in an attempt to foster a convergence between traditional stormwater controls and green infrastructure. This objective requires engineers to work side by side with urban planners, landscape architects, ecologists, soils scientists, regulators, and other professionals. This multidisciplinary view of stormwater can have a profound effect on development of sound land planning, which can be much more effective in protecting receiving waterbodies than engineered facilities. Regardless of the approach, designers must meet the fundamental goals of minimizing effects to the environment, meeting applicable regulations, protecting public safety, and designing facilities in harmony with livable communities to enhance public spaces and provide recreation opportunities.

This MOP attempts to summarize the state of the practice of designing stormwater controls at a point when the practice itself is in a state of flux. Results of research on the effectiveness of stormwater controls generate design guidelines and the lessons learned as practitioners implement these designs suggest additional research topics, which in turn result in improved designs. The authors have combed the best available knowledge from academia and industry to develop the material in this publication, but the schedule for production of an MOP results invariably in a snapshot in time. The reader is encouraged to keep pace with the evolution of stormwater management technology through consultation of the journal papers, articles, and conference proceedings published by WEF, American Society of Civil Engineers, and other professional associations.

The following are some salient features of this MOP:

- The title of the MOP changed from *Urban Runoff Quality Management* to *Design of Urban Stormwater Controls*. This change is consistent with the NRC (2008) report and seeks to emphasize that quantity and quality are closely related and cannot be separated for effective stormwater management. Although some readers may consider stormwater quantity as referring primarily to extreme flood events, this MOP takes a broader view and considers the effects of, and solutions to, problems caused by too much surface water entering natural systems originally formed under a hydrologic regime with less runoff inputs.

- The term, *stormwater control*, replaces the popular best management practice (BMP) acronym. This terminology is consistent with the 2008 NRC report and is a good descriptor of the function of devices that are designed and constructed to manage stormwater. The term also emphasizes that these are engineered devices and seeks to differentiate them from "practices" that can involve numerous non-engineering approaches to stormwater management.

- Unit processes and unit operations are proposed as a rational approach for selecting stormwater controls to match given performance criteria. The MOP steers away from a "cookbook approach" often based on the concept of percent removal of a given pollutant. Instead, the MOP favors the approach followed by the water and wastewater treatment industries, in which unit processes are selected to address given water quality or quantity influent properties and effluent treatment goals. This approach is consistent with evolving strategies for selection of stormwater controls at a national level (Strecker et al., 2005).

- A taxonomy of stormwater controls and a simplified nomenclature are included in this MOP. The authors do not expect that this arrangement will become the industry standard, but believe that it will help the reader navigate the myriad of terms that pervade the industry. The taxonomy presented in this MOP demonstrates that most stormwater controls fall under a small number of categories that are logically aligned with the dominant unit processes that occur within them.

- Performance assessment for water quality receives special attention in this MOP. The stormwater industry has often focused on the misguided concept of measuring effectiveness of stormwater controls in terms of percent removal efficiencies for given pollutants (Jones et al., 2008). Given the significant investments in upcoming stormwater retrofits throughout the United States, it is imperative that the ability of stormwater controls to improve water quality be documented appropriately.

This MOP was written by a dedicated group of volunteer authors with a variety of personal experiences, expertise, and regional knowledge. The authors have attempted to generalize their writing to fundamental principles that are useful in all regions of the United States and the reader is cautioned to interpret the material in that light rather than as a suggestion that a particular regional approach is better than another. The reader must adjust the material in this MOP to match factors such as rainfall and evapotranspiration patterns, soil types, land cover, temperature, regulations, development practices, demographics and other relevant region-specific issues.

The contents of this MOP are as follows: Chapter 2, "Effects of Stormwater on Receiving Waters," presents the effects of stormwater and stormwater controls in broad categories, with key references presented at the end. The chapter was written primarily by engineers, for engineers, and is not an exhaustive treatment of the voluminous body of knowledge disseminated by the scientific and engineering communities. Space limitations in the MOP for this type of background material do not allow for full treatment of this important topic. Readers who wish to obtain additional information should consult these references and subsequent research.

Chapter 3, "Performance Goals for Stormwater Controls," describes the methodologies to size stormwater controls to meet desired goals of flood control, stream channel protection, groundwater recharge, and pollutant removal. Portions of this chapter remained unchanged from the preceding edition of this MOP as they continue to be relevant today. The chapter highlights the difference between the common approach of setting performance standards for every individual development site and the preferable watershed-based approach that takes a comprehensive view of runoff volumes, peak flows, and pollutant inputs to develop standards that are consistent with watershed-wide management goals. The MOP does not attempt to set national standards to be applied anywhere in the U.S. Instead, it presents a summary of selected approaches with pertinent commentary about their origins, strengths, limitations, and applicability.

Chapter 4, "Unit Processes and Operations for Stormwater Control," presents the adaptation of the concept of unit processes and unit operations to stormwater management. The concept is applied to both quantity and quality control, given that these two objectives frequently merge in many facilities. The objective is to help the reader identify the proper unit processes to address a given management goal, select a suitable stormwater control that provides those processes, and conceptualize a system of stormwater controls for effective operation. The aforementioned simplified nomenclature and taxonomy of stormwater controls is also presented.

Chapter 5, "Selection Criteria and Design Considerations," covers design principles and selection procedures for stormwater controls, resource protection measures, and measures to reduce runoff and pollutants. Regarding the deployment of stormwater controls, the chapter describes system configuration principles, performance, and implementation constraints. The authors caution that the actual application of all of these aspects is heavily dependent on regional and site-specific characteristics. Nevertheless, this chapter addresses essential concepts that should be easily modified depending on local conditions. ·

Chapter 6, "Basins"; Chapter 7, "Swales and Strips"; Chapter 8, "Filters"; Chapter 9, "Infiltrators"; and Chapter 10, "Gross Pollutant Traps and Mechanical Operations" comprise the core of the design material in the MOP. Each chapter includes the unit processes that the control provides, basic design principles, and specific design considerations for variants, including typical applications and their limitations. The design procedure for each stormwater control is also presented and describes typical configurations, design equations, and additional considerations, as appropriate (e.g., maintenance issues, aesthetics, safety, and access). Although a sizing example is presented, no engineering drawings with standard details are provided as these vary widely across the United States.

Chapter 11, "Maintenance of Stormwater Controls," summarizes maintenance requirements for various types of stormwater controls in the following two general maintenance categories: routine maintenance and intermittent maintenance. Routine maintenance consists of basic tasks done on a frequent and predictable schedule. Intermittent maintenance typically comprises more onerous and infrequent tasks needed to keep the controls in working order. The tasks needed are further arranged in levels of maintenance (i.e., low, medium, and high) and relate mainly to frequency of activities. Not all of the controls in Chapters 6 through 10 are documented here. The reason for this is that the information in Chapter 11 was compiled from a series of publications that did not include all types of controls. The reader may be able to infer processes for other controls based on this chapter and is encouraged to consult other sources for this purpose.

Chapter 12, "Whole Life Cost of Stormwater Controls," presents a methodology to estimate the expenditures associated with deploying and maintaining stormwater controls. The concept of whole life costs is used here to emphasize that stormwater controls are an investment that needs to be maintained to achieve the expected performance. The chapter summarizes the long-term investment requirements and capital costs needed for various stormwater controls throughout the deployment process. These include feasibility studies, commissioning, conceptual design, preliminary design, detailed design and development, construction, operation, and decommissioning. As with Chapter 11, not all stormwater controls have cost estimates in this chapter.

Chapter 13, "Performance Assessment," presents a methodology to evaluate the performance of stormwater controls. Performance assessment is challenging because of inconsistent study methods, terminology, lack of associated design information, and absence of reporting protocols. As stated earlier, the use of removal efficiencies to evaluate water quality treatment is highly problematic and has hindered the stormwater industry and the regulators (NRC, 2008). This chapter presents alternate, physically based, and statistically valid methods to evaluate performance, both for water quantity and quality. The chapter also outlines principles to plan and implement a data collection program.

Chapter 14, "Analytical Tools for Simulation of Stormwater Controls," describes analytical methods and computer models that are used for simulation and evaluation of stormwater controls, with a focus on the unit processes they provide.

2.0 REFERENCES

American Society of Civil Engineers; Water Environment Federation (1992) *Design and Construction of Urban Stormwater Management Systems;* ASCE Manuals and Reports of Engineering Practice No. 77; WEF Manual of Practice No. FD-20; American Society of Civil Engineers: New York.

Bedient, P. B.; Huber, W. C.; and Vieux, B. E. (2008) *Hydrology and Floodplain Analysis;* Prentice Hall: New York, 816 pp.

Brown, R. A.; Hunt, W. F., III (2011) Impacts of Media Depth on Effluent Water Quality and Hydrologic Performance of Undersized Bioretention Cells. *J. Irrigation Drainage Eng.,* **137,** 132.

Carpenter, D. D.; Kaluvakolanu, P. (2011) Effect of Roof Surface Type on Storm-Water Runoff from Full-Scale Roofs in a Temperate Climate. *J. Irrigation Drainage Eng.,* **137,** 161.

Clary, J.; Quigley, M.; Poresky, A.; Earles, A.; Strecker, E.; Leisenring, M.; Jones, J. (2011) Integration of Low-Impact Development into the International Stormwater BMP Database. *J. Irrigation Drainage Eng.,* **137,** 190.

Debo, T. N.; Reese, A. J. (2002) *Municipal Stormwater Management.* 2nd ed.; CRC Press: Boca Raton, Florida, 1176 pp.

He, Z.; Davis, A. P. (2011) Process Modeling of Storm-Water Flow in a Bioretention Cell. *J. Irrigation Drainage Eng.,* **137,** 121.

Jones, J.; Clary, J.; Strecker, E.; Quigley, M. (2008) 15 Reasons You Should Think Twice Before Using Percent Removal to Assess BMP Performance. *Stormwater,* **9** (1).

Lucas, W. C.; Greenway, M. (2011) Phosphorus Retention by Bioretention Mesocosms Using Media Formulated for Phosphorus Sorption: Response to Accelerated Loads. *J. Irrigation Drainage Eng.,* **137,** 144.

Machusick, M.; Welker, A.; Traver, R. (2011) Groundwater Mounding at a Storm-Water Infiltration BMP. *J. Irrigation Drainage Eng.*, **137**, 154.

Maidment, D. (Ed.) (1993) *Handbook of Hydrology*; McGraw-Hill: New York.

National Research Council (2008) *Urban Stormwater Management in the United States*; The National Academies Press: Washington, D.C.

Nelson, A. C. (2004) Toward a New Metropolis: The Opportunity to Rebuild America. Paper prepared for the Brookings Institution Metropolitan Policy Program, Brookings Institution: Washington, D.C.

Sileshi, R.; Pitt, R.; Clark, S. (2010) Enhanced Biofilter Treatment of Urban Stormwater by Optimizing the Hydraulic Residence Time in the Media. *Proceedings of American Society of Civil Engineers/Environmental & Water Resources Institute Watershed 2010: Innovations in Watershed Management under Land Use and Climate Change* [CD-ROM]; Madison, Wisconsin; Aug 23–27.

Strecker, E. W.; Huber, W. C.; Heaney, J. P.; Bodine, D.; Sansalone, J. J.; Quigley, M. M.; Pankani, D.; Leisenring, M.; Thayumanavan, P. (2005) *Critical Assessment of Stormwater Treatment and Control Selection Issues*; Report No. 02-SW-1; Water Environment Research Federation: Alexandria, Virginia.

U.S. Environmental Protection Agency (2009) Stormwater Management for Federal Facilities under Section 438 of the Energy Independence and Security Act. http://www.epa.gov/owow/NPS/lid/section438/ (accessed May 5, 2011).

Chapter 2

Effects of Stormwater on Receiving Waters

This chapter briefly summarizes the effects of stormwater on receiving streams and the aquatic ecosystems in them. This chapter is not intended to be a compendium of the state of current scientific knowledge on the effects of stormwater on receiving waters. Rather, the chapter presents a summary of basic concepts that the reader can explore further through the references at the end of the chapter and other publications.

Urban receiving waters include streams, lakes, rivers and oceans. There may be many types of planned uses for these waters, including

- Stormwater conveyance (flood risk reduction);
- Ecosystem integrity (habitat and biodiversity);
- Noncontact recreation (parks, aesthetics, and boating);
- Contact recreation (swimming); and
- Water supply.

Development in an urban watershed with no stormwater controls makes it unlikely that any of these uses can be maintained or sustained. Careful planning focused on water resources, sound development practices, and the incorporation of stormwater controls can make it possible for streams to become an asset to the urban community. However, it is important to set expectations for urban streams within the context of achievable benefits. For example, it is virtually impossible to return an urban stream to its pristine state before human influence. Stormwater conveyance and noncontact recreation could be basic goals for all urban waters. Healthy biota should also be a goal, but with the realization that the natural stream ecosystem will be affected by urbanization. Careful planning and optimal utilization and placement of basic stormwater controls, installed at the time of development, plus protection of stream habitat, may enable partial use of some of these basic goals in urbanized watersheds. Water contact recreation, consumptive fisheries, and water supplies may not be realistic goals for most urban waters. However, the other uses may be possible in urban areas where the receiving waters are large and drain mostly undeveloped areas so that the effects of localized urbanization will not cause significant degradation.

Despite the challenges outlined in the previous paragraph, science and engineering have made important strides in protecting streams. This chapter summarizes the effects of urbanization on receiving waters from the point of view of the following four categories of effects: water quantity, water quality, channel form, and aquatic biota. However, it should be noted that these effects do not take place separately; rather, they almost always happen concurrently. For example, in certain locations, this close interrelatedness is manifested as the process by which the increased flows and runoff volumes move a stream out of dynamic equilibrium with increased instream erosion and sedimentation. Sedimentation buries the alluvial material that serves as habitat for macroinvertebrates and erosion destroys the riparian habitat for fish and other aquatic life. Other situations are described in literature by Bledsoe et al. (2008) and Soar and Thorne (2001). These complex interrelationships require close collaboration between science and engineering. Palmer et al. (2003) emphasize that successful restoration of stream ecosystems is best accomplished by interdisciplinary teams of engineers, ecologists, and geomorphologists.

In summary, the division among the categories of effects in this manual is made to organize and present the information, not to imply that the phenomena occur separately. In addition to describing the categories of effects mentioned above, this chapter also summarizes mitigation effects that stormwater controls provide.

1.0   EFFECTS OF URBANIZATION ON WATER QUANTITY

The hydrologic effects of urbanization are well known by watershed engineers and scientists. During the process of urbanization, land is covered with impervious surfaces such as roads, parking lots, roofs, driveways, and sidewalks. These impervious surfaces reduce infiltration and evapotranspiration, and increase the volume of runoff, both of which work in combination to alter the natural flow regime of the system. General hydrologic changes include more frequent and higher peak flows (Booth and Jackson, 1997; Hollis, 1975; Konrad and Booth, 2002), flashier flows (Henshaw and Booth, 2000; Konrad and Booth, 2002; Walsh et al., 2005), and modified baseflows that can be either higher or lower than before development. On an individual storm basis, Figure 2.1 exhibits the behavior typically observed when comparing conditions before and after development. The figure shows the direct runoff for a 10-ha (25-ac) drainage area in Columbia, Missouri, being converted from pastureland to single-family residential land use with 1000-m^2 lots, which introduces 35% imperviousness. The addition of imperviousness increases peak flows and total runoff volume, represented by the area under the hydrograph. In addition, the time at which the peak occurs has been shortened because of the introduction of paved areas, catch basins, and storm drains that create fast pathways for water to reach the streams. For this small watershed, the five-minute reduction in the time to reach the peak flow is barely noticeable in the figure.

Multiple effects result from these watershed changes. Receiving channel and inundation-maintained morphologies are altered as described later in this chapter. Connections between the stream channel and its former frequently inundated floodplains are disrupted, leading to dewatering of the floodplain environment. This dewatering, which can also be caused by channelization or upstream impoundments, greatly diminishes the productivity, diversity, and functions of the floodplain as only rare flood events occupy the floodplain rather than the smaller events responsible for most of the systems' evolution. Urbanization effects are complex and sometimes lead

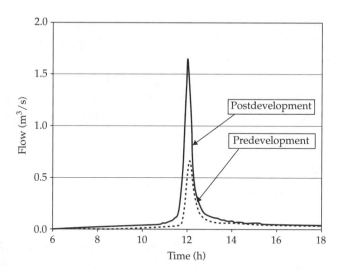

FIGURE 2.1   Effect of urbanization on the 1-year storm hydrograph for a 10-ha (25-ac) watershed being developed from pastureland to single-family residential near Columbia, Missouri (1 m^3/s = 35.31 cfs).

to baseflow increases, for instance, caused by leaky water infrastructure and lawn irrigation. Brandes et al. (2005) report that the mechanisms commonly cited do not always lead to decreases in baseflow; instead, baseflow reductions may be caused by other urbanization effects such as interbasin transfers and other water exports. In semiarid climates, urbanization can create baseflows where there were none. Return flows from excess irrigation have created permanent flow conditions in many streams, although the return flows often carry with them excess nutrients from fertilizer application (Tyagi et al., 2008). A related effect is the conversion of streams from historically supported baseflow hydrology to surface flow control. This change alters zones of dilution for ground and surface water-derived chemistry in addition to thermal and biogeochemical gradients supporting the diversity of aquatic life.

2.0   EFFECTS OF STORMWATER CONTROL PRACTICES ON WATER QUANTITY

Historically, the objectives of stormwater management have been to manage flows to protect life and property and to reduce pollution loads into waterways. Channel protection and aquatic habitat protection are additional goals now in place in many jurisdictions. A sensible approach to these goals is to attempt to replicate the original hydrologic patterns through reduction of runoff volumes and attenuation of peak flows, as opposed to flood control only, which typically seeks to detain water or increase conveyance to minimize flooding. Reduction of runoff volumes can be attained by creating opportunities for the water to return to the original infiltration and evapotranspiration pathways. Although this volume reduction also reduces peak flows, it may be necessary to create storage areas where the runoff can be detained temporarily, which further attenuates the peaks. Figure 2.2 shows the effect of a stormwater detention basin on a single storm (Ibendahl and Medina, 2008). The basin is designed to maintain the 1-, 2-, 10-, and 100-year peak flows at or below their predevelopment values. The Natural Resource Conservation Service synthetic storms were used for sizing the basin and its outlet works (U.S. Department of Agriculture, 1986). The figure shows how the basin attenuates the peak flow of the 1-year storm below the predevelopment condition and delays the occurrence of the peak; however, the basin does not reduce the total runoff volume. The resulting effect is a temporal

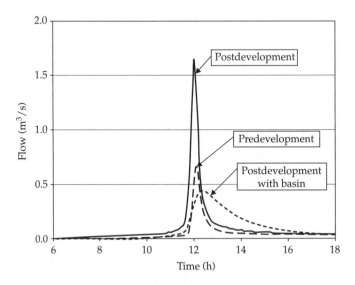

FIGURE 2.2 Effect of a basin on the 1-year hydrograph for a 10-ha (25-ac) watershed being developed from pastureland to single-family residential near Columbia, Missouri (1 m³/s = 35.31 cfs).

redistribution of the flows that may increase the duration of erosive flows or increase peak flows further downstream in the watershed as peak flows from other drainage areas combine. This effect is discussed further in Chapter 3.

Figure 2.3 shows the effect of applying green infrastructure controls. In this case, spatially distributed controls capture, infiltrate, and evapotranspire the first 33 mm (1.3 in.) of runoff. The figure shows that this level of control maintains the 1-year event to its predevelopment condition but only partially attenuates the 100-year event. These effects are often described using flow-duration curves (FDCs) like the one in Figure 2.4, which summarizes the modeled 15-minute direct runoff for the site under various control scenarios, using the statistics of a 40-year rainfall record (Ibendahl and Medina, 2008). A total of 5916 storms took place in that period, of which less than 1% was greater than 70 mm (2.75 in.); the 1-year storm is 76 mm (3 in.). The figure shows that a basin designed for attenuation of the 1-, 2-, 10-, and 100-year events using synthetic hyetographs provides some peak reduction for the higher flows in the historic rainfall record but the remainder is largely unaffected. The common strategy in many municipalities to detain the 1-year event and release the runoff over 24 hours has a marked effect on reducing high flows below predevelopment levels but increases low flows. In this case, the receiving stream will experience these flows for a longer period, which may increase channel erosion potential. Application of green infrastructure to infiltrate and evapotranspire 33 mm of runoff best approaches

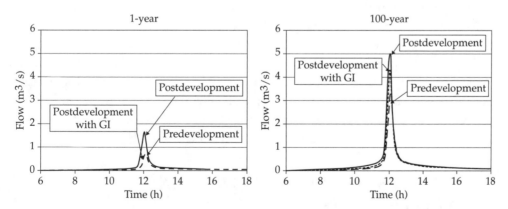

FIGURE 2.3 Effect of green infrastructure controls designed to capture 33 mm (1.3 in.) of runoff for a 10-ha (25-ac) watershed being developed from pastureland to single-family residential near Columbia, Missouri (1 m³/s = 35.31 cfs).

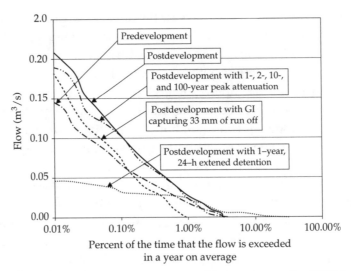

FIGURE 2.4   Effect of various stormwater control strategies on the FDC for a watershed draining 10 ha (25 ac) near Columbia, Missouri. The watershed changed from pastureland to single-family residential (1 m³/s = 35.31 cfs).

the predevelopment condition, although some additional attenuation is needed for high flows and less for low flows. The period of record analyzed did not include a significant flooding event, for which the behavior of control strategies would be similar to that depicted in Figure 2.3.

In conclusion, it is difficult if not impossible to mimic predevelopment conditions under any stormwater management strategy. Detention-based strategies do not reduce the volume of runoff and tend to lessen peak flows at the high end of the spectrum but amplify them at the lower end. Runoff volume-reduction strategies can approach predevelopment conditions for the smaller storms that compose the largest portion of annual runoff but cannot completely attenuate peak flows when required for extreme events. Chapter 3 further discusses these observations in connection with the development of performance goals for stormwater controls.

3.0   EFFECTS OF URBANIZATION ON WATER QUALITY

Runoff carries a number of pollutants into receiving streams depending on the land use. Nitrogen, phosphorus, heavy metals, hydrocarbons, sediments, pathogens, organic material, chloride, other particulates, and debris are among the most common urban runoff pollutants. The sources are varied and include fertilizer and pesticide application; automobile fluids and brake pad residue; feces from pets, livestock, and wildlife; sand and salt from snow removal operations; illicit connections into the storm drain system; lack of sediment control at construction sites; and littering along streets and highways. Stormwater flowing over hot paved surfaces also increases the temperature of receiving waters.

Lee and Jones-Lee (1995) found that relatively short periods of exposure to toxicant concentrations in stormwater are not sufficient to produce the receiving water effects that are evident in urban receiving waters, especially considering the relatively large portion of toxicants that are associated with particulates. However, investigations have identified acute toxicity problems associated with frequent, moderate-term (approximately 10- to 20-day) exposures to adverse toxicant concentrations in urban receiving streams (Crunkilton et al., 1997). In contrast, the most severe receiving water problems are likely associated with chronic exposures to contaminated sediment and to habitat destruction.

Pathogens in stormwater can potentially affect human health. Some epidemiology studies have examined increased health risks associated with contact recreation, including waterbodies affected by stormwater, although most studies have focused on wastewater contamination of surface waters. However, separate storm sewers could carry similar pathogens and, as reported by Craun et al. (1997), O'Shea and Field (1992a; 1992b), and Kay (1994), in most cases the levels of pathogens causing increased illness during these epidemiological studies were in the range found in waterbodies only affected by stormwater. Nonetheless, the results of environmental epidemiology studies have provoked controversy. Craun et al. (1996) present suggestions for better interpretation of existing data and design of future studies.

The effects of large discharges of relatively uncontaminated sediment on the receiving water aquatic environment were summarized by Barrett et al. (1995) and Schueler (1997). These large discharges are mostly associated with poorly controlled construction sites, where 75 to 750 tons of sediment per hectare per year of exposure may be lost. Much of this sediment reaches urban receiving waters, where massive effects on the aquatic environment can result. However, high rates of sediment loss are also associated with later phases of urbanization, where, in response to increased and more frequent flows, channels widen or incise depending on the resistance of the stream bed and bank materials. Sediment is typically listed as one of the most important pollutants causing receiving water problems in the United States.

4.0 EFFECTS OF STORMWATER CONTROL PRACTICES ON WATER QUALITY

Stormwater controls are deployed to remove pollutants found in stormwater. Many controls provide one or more mechanisms that remove one or more pollutant types. Depending on the type of stormwater control, one or more of the following pollutant removal processes may be present:

- Sedimentation,
- Flotation,
- Sorption,
- Precipitation (as a chemical reaction),
- Filtration,
- Photosynthesis,
- Nitrification and denitrification,
- Temperature reduction,
- Disinfection,
- Screening,
- Photodegradation, and
- Oxidation–reduction.

The processes involved in evapotranspiration- and infiltration-based controls decrease pollutant loads by reducing the total volume of runoff directly reaching the streams. Although infiltration may carry some pollutants into the subsurface, concerns over groundwater contamination should only arise in cases of high mobility of the pollutant in the vadose zone, high concentrations and high detection frequencies in stormwater, and high soluble fractions (Pitt et al., 1994). For example, chloride is highly soluble in water and is a conservative substance whose concentrations are only reduced by dilution. For such pollutants, source reduction by proper management practices is the best approach. These processes and the way in which they affect pollutants are discussed in detail in Chapter 4.

5.0   EFFECTS OF URBANIZATION ON CHANNEL FORM

Numerous factors affect the spatial and temporal response of a stream channel. These factors include various aspects of geomorphology and fluid mechanics such as sediment characteristics, discharge, sediment transport, channel geometry, and flow velocities. Urbanization disrupts the balance between sediment transport capacity and sediment supply. Increases in the magnitude and duration of peak flows that accompany development without stormwater controls allow a stream to carry more sediment than it could prior to watershed development. Increases in runoff volume and changes in the temporal distribution of flows accelerate channel erosion. When the supply of sediment is less than the carrying capacity of the stream, channel degradation can occur in the form of incision, lateral adjustment, or a combination of the two. Other effects of development also affect the balance of sediment availability and transport capacity. Removal of forests can increase sediment to streams, channel realignment increases the slope, dams and other impoundments trap sediments, and diversions for irrigation or water supply decrease instream flows. The introduction of these modifications quickly results in disruptions to the state of dynamic equilibrium, although some streams never reach a dynamic equilibrium state even without perturbation.

It is commonly believed that urbanization results in increased sediment yield from upland erosion in a watershed; however, after development, the additional sediment load frequently found in urbanized watersheds likely comes from inchannel erosion. Wolman (1967) found that whereas sediment yield increased by a factor up to 200 during the construction phase of urbanization, it declined to preurbanization levels after construction was completed. In addition, urbanization may reduce sediment production depending on the land use that it replaces. Douglas (1985) showed that a stable, urban environment will have a low-to-moderate sediment yield compared to a predevelopment agricultural condition, which supplies a moderate-to-heavy sediment yield. Trimble (1997) estimated that bank erosion accounted for about two-thirds of measured sediment load. In contrast, bank erosion in rural streams is only 5 to 20% of the annual sediment load (Caraco, 2000).

A survey of research since the early 1970s supports the notion that discharges that have become larger and more frequent because of watershed development cause enlargement of stream channels (Rohrer, 2004). Neller (1988; 1989) found that urban streams were, on average, 4 times larger than adjacent rural streams. However, site-specific conditions dictate the extent of these changes. For instance, Booth and

Henshaw (2001) studied channel changes in light to moderately urbanized watersheds in humid regions and showed that the geologic substrate strongly influenced whether or not significant channel change occurred, regardless of development intensity. Similar conclusions about this crucial geologic control were reached by Pavlowsky (2004), who studied streams in Missouri, and Kang and Marston (2006) in their stream studies in Oklahoma. Other types of human influence magnify the complexity and add to the uncertainty of the analyses. For example, Fitzpatrick and Peppler (2007) concluded in a Wisconsin study that detailed evaluation of geomorphic processes and responses to changes in runoff and sediment with local geologic and anthropogenic controls is needed to adequately predict urbanization effects.

Changes in the flow regime caused by urbanization lead to changes in the cross section and planform of stream channels. The increased flows and streambank erosion alter the stable configuration of a main channel and adjacent floodplains to a deeply incised channel disconnected from the floodplain. This channelization effect further increases the flow velocities because overbank flows are no longer able to access the floodplain where they could flow at a slower velocity. These changes trigger a process of erosion and channel enlargement that results in excess sediment supply from the eroding channels. When this supply rate exceeds the stream's transport rate, the sediment transport regime becomes unstable. This condition results in a cycle in which excess sediment creates depositional features that cause more erosion (Gracie and Thomas, 2004). This is a long-term effect in which instream sediment contribution continues to change over time, even after urbanization of the watershed has stabilized (Weber et al., 2004).

6.0   EFFECTS OF STORMWATER CONTROL PRACTICES ON CHANNEL FORM

Despite the ubiquitous degradation of urban streams, requirements specifically designated to control channel erosion are rare. The varied magnitudes, frequencies, and durations of discharges associated with different climates result in different sediment transport regimes. Streambed and bank materials are also essential in evaluating erosion potential. Therefore, these regional and site-specific factors are important when selecting stormwater controls that provide stream erosion control. Numerous methods are available for this evaluation, including the tractive shear force method (Lane, 1955), excess shear stress methods (Pomeroy et al., 2008), or evaluation of stream power (Watson et al., 2001).

Many municipalities have development ordinances that require large storms to be controlled so that the postdevelopment peak discharge for a given return interval storm does not exceed a given value. Often, this value is the corresponding predevelopment peak; however, some jurisdictions require "over control" and establish a lower discharge peak such as a percent of the corresponding predevelopment event or the peak discharge of a more frequent storm (Center for Watershed Protection). Peak discharge attenuation requirements vary widely, with practices ranging from control of the 100-year, 25-year, 10-year, or 2- or 1-year return interval storms, to a combination of return interval storms.

Peak flow attenuation reduces flooding immediately downstream, but it is not effective for reducing erosion in stream channels (Rohrer, 2004). Studies have shown that peak attenuation of the 2-year storm may actually worsen erosion (McCuen, 1979; Moglen and McCuen, 1988; MacRae, 1993; 1997). The reason for this phenomenon is that peak attenuation of a few relatively severe storm events achieved through detention basins subjects stream channels to erosive flows for a longer duration and at increased frequencies. Equally important is the observation in Section 2 that the facilities only attenuate the flow of the storms for which they are designed, whereas smaller, more frequent storms do not experience any attenuation (Roesner et al., 2001). The effect on the stream channel is that these attenuated discharges could be greater than the critical discharge for sediment transport and occur for a longer period of time than in predevelopment conditions, resulting in cumulative transport of more sediment. Even if the magnitudes of peak discharges are maintained from predevelopment to postdevelopment for a set of design flows, the duration and frequency of erosive flows can increase dramatically. As a result of this increase, the effective discharge in the channel is shifted to smaller runoff events that range from the half-year event up to the 1.5-year runoff event (MacRae and Rowney, 1992). MacRae (1993; 1997) also documented that a 2-year control triggers channel expansion, causing widening by as much as 3 times the predevelopment condition. In addition, MacRae (1997) found that overcontrol design criteria do not protect the stream channel from erosion and that, depending on the streambed and streambank material, the channel may either degrade or aggrade.

The addition of volume capture requirements for water quality control allows peak discharges of storms with a return interval of less than 2 years to be reduced; however, increased durations of discharge from basins and trapping of sediment may exacerbate channel erosion, especially in streams that are highly sensitive to changes in low flows (e.g., sand bed channels) and increase combined peak flows downstream

(Chapter 3). In contrast, gravel and cobble bed streams are typically less sensitive to changes in sediment load (Bledsoe, 2002a).

Recognition of changes in the magnitude and duration of flows, changes in sediment supply, and the potential response of different stream types are each important aspects of understanding channel erosion in urbanizing watersheds. Some jurisdictions now require runoff volume reduction through the application of green infrastructure principles to address stream channel effects.

Figure 2.5 illustrates the effect of several control strategies using shear-stress duration curves for the 10-ha watershed near Columbia, Missouri, introduced in Section 2. The area under each of the curves is the work by shear forces that the stream bed and streambanks experience cumulatively in a given year. Curves above the predevelopment condition indicate that the flow regime is further eroding the channel section, and vice versa. The area between a given curve and that for the predevelopment condition is the excess erosion if the curve is above the predevelopment curve or the erosion deficit if the curve is below the predevelopment condition. Figure 2.5 shows that the predevelopment condition exceeds the critical shear stress for silty loam, the material of the channel and streambanks, approximately 3% of the time. This critical threshold assumes no vegetation or armoring in the channel. The critical shear stress is exceeded some of the time as part of the natural dynamic geomorphic processes taking place in the stream. The postdevelopment condition increases the magnitude of the shear stresses; for a given value of the stress, the stream experiences it for a longer time than before development, although the critical shear stress is exceeded approximately the same 3% of the time. A basin sized to attenuate the 1-, 2-, 10- and 100-year event using synthetic design storms events keeps the shear stress virtually the same as the postdevelopment condition or slightly increases them for the most extreme events. A basin designed to provide 24-hour extended detention of the 1-year storm markedly reduces the shear stress for the higher range of events but increases them for the lower range. In this case, the critical shear stress is exceeded more than 18% of the time. The curve resulting from runoff volume reduction through green infrastructure application does not quite reduce the postdevelopment shear stresses in the high range of flows to the predevelopment condition, although it is closer than the detention curves. On the lower end of the range, green infrastructure produces less shear stress than the predevelopment condition; the critical stress is exceeded 0.9% of the time.

Knowledge of the erosional processes associated with development has led to a movement to design stormwater controls to address this issue. Moglen and

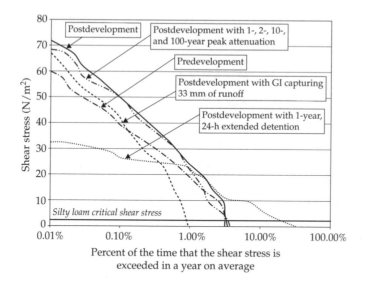

FIGURE 2.5 Effect of various stormwater control strategies on the shear stress for a watershed draining 10 ha (25 ac) near Columbia, Missouri. The watershed changed from pastureland to single-family residential (1 N/m² = 0.021 lb/sqft, 1 mm = 0.04 in.).

McCuen (1988) proposed an alternative detention basin design that limits the total bed-material load after development to that which existed before development. The Ventura County Watershed Protection District in Southern California has developed a Stormwater Quality Urban Impact Mitigation Plan that addresses stream erosion assessment and urbanization effects (Donigian and Love, 2005). The Santa Clara Valley Urban Runoff Pollution Prevention Program developed a method for predicting channel instability to establish instream stability criteria (Palhegyi and Bicknell, 2004). Pomeroy et al. (2008) suggested that the concept of shear stress reduction can be applied to the development of design criteria using detention basins. Additional examples of these initiatives are presented in Chapter 3.

In summary, the relationships between urbanization and stream instability are well known and can be traced to the increased magnitude and duration of flows. However, stormwater management design criteria seldom address this aspect adequately. With the exception of a few jurisdictions (e.g., in Washington and California) that are developing criteria based on geomorphic concepts, channel protection strategies, when they are in place, are typically limited to controlling a single event for channel protection (e.g., the 1-year storm) when, in fact, the performance of stormwater controls should consider the magnitude and duration of excess shear stress.

7.0 EFFECTS OF URBANIZATION ON AQUATIC BIOTA

Stormwater effects on aquatic life stem from the fundamental and often profound changes that occur where urban stormwater enters waterways and where the physical, chemical, thermal, light regime, and sediment conditions are altered. Urbanization and hydrologic changes associated with increased impervious cover degrade aquatic life to the extent that this pattern has been dubbed the "urban stream syndrome" (Meyer et al., 2005; Walsh et al., 2005). Numerous studies have documented the effects of stormwater on habitat and biota (May et al., 1997; Meyer et al., 2005; Moore and Palmer, 2005; Nelson and Palmer, 2007; Ney and Van Hassel, 1983; Paul and Meyer, 2001; Roy et al., 2006; Wang et al., 2000; Wellman et al., 2000) and the reader is directed to this literature for in-depth treatment. Other than direct and indirect ecotoxic effects and exceeded tolerance ranges (temperature, chemistry, light), the significant reasons biological organisms appear to be affected are summarized as follows:

- Increased unpredictable environment. Most ecological systems and biological organisms are not adapted to the range of physical, chemical, and thermal changes imposed by urban stormwater systems. The changes in FDC illustrated in Figure 2.4 create disruptions of most native species and the diversity, productivity, and dynamic tolerance ranges of healthy ecological systems.

- Life-cycle disruption. Species behaviors, foods, and other life histories are not favored by altered hydrological regimes, while invasive species have wider tolerance for new hydrological regimes and different reproductive strategies. Erosion and sedimentation from bed and bank loads and hydrologic changes restructure habitats, eliminating species, prey, habitat structure, and quality, and resulting in a replacement of plant and animal communities with tolerant species. For example, sedimentation favors carp and other bottom feeders and disfavors darters and other visual feeders.

- Riparian and shore system alteration. Riparian and shore systems that adjoin waterbodies contribute significantly to the maintenance of water quality and species populations of aquatic communities. Urban stormwater discharges may affect downstream refugia (hiding places) of biological organisms. While upstream ecosystem may not be directly affected by urban stormwater effects, disruptions in the stream continuum from an outfall to downstream reaches may effectively isolate the upstream ecosystem by restricting recolonization, gene flow, and seasonal spawning. For example, embankments for regional basins and stream crossings may create barriers for upstream movement of aquatic organisms and changes in clarity, temperature, or pH may disrupt cues for anadromous fish migration. Upstream reaches in a river typically harbor fishes and other organisms found where carbon-based detritus (branches, leaves, etc.) are larger and support macroinvertebrates that decompose these substrates. In downstream locations, macroinvertebrates and fishes are filter feeders that utilize small particles resulting from organic matter shredding organisms found upstream. This physical and biological continuum can be broken with urban stormwater effects. For example, removal of native riparian vegetation eliminates a significant primary food source in headwater streams. Furthermore, removal of riparian forests not only eliminates fallen leaves as a food source, but also moves the primary productivity to algae and periphyton, further altering the aquatic food web. Riparian vegetation removal also reduces shading, which increases water temperature.

- Habitat and microhabitat alteration. Channel changes from altered hydrology and hydraulics have resulted in channel dynamics and morphological changes that have directly affected many levels of habitat. Hydrologic sediment alterations can affect sand and gravel bar longevity, stability and quality of spawning areas, secure locations for surviving floods, and the structure of pools and riffles.

Numerous studies have documented these factors in the degradation of aquatic biota associated with urbanization. For example, during the Coyote Creek, San Jose, California, receiving water study, 41 stations were sampled in both urban and nonurban perennial flow stretches of the creek over 3 years to evaluate the effects of urban runoff on water quality, sediment properties, fish, macroinvertebrates, attached algae, and rooted aquatic vegetation (Pitt and Bozeman, 1982). These investigations found distinct differences in the taxonomic composition and relative abundance of the aquatic biota present. The nonurban sections of the creek supported a comparatively diverse assemblage of aquatic organisms, including an abundance of native fishes and numerous benthic macroinvertebrate taxa. In contrast, the urban portions of the creek (less than 5% urbanized), affected only by urban runoff discharges and not industrial or municipal discharges, had an aquatic community generally lacking in diversity and was dominated by pollution-tolerant organisms such as mosquito fish and tubificid worms.

Plant communities are also affected by urbanization. Cedar swamps in the New Jersey Pine Barrens were studied by Ehrenfeld and Schneider (1983), who examined 19 wetlands subjected to varying amounts of urbanization. Typical plant species were lost and replaced by weeds and exotic plants in urban runoff-affected wetlands. Increased uptake of phosphorus and lead in the plants were found. The authors concluded that the presence of runoff to the cedar swamps caused marked changes in community structure, vegetation dynamics, and plant tissue element concentrations.

In general, monitoring of urban stormwater runoff has indicated that the biological uses of urban receiving waters are most likely affected by habitat destruction and long-term pollutant exposures (especially to macroinvertebrates via contaminated sediment), while documented effects associated with acute exposures of toxicants in the water column are rare (Burton and Pitt, 2002).

Thermal effects affect biological communities in profound ways. Changes in temperature patterns of waterbodies can have significant effects on reproductive success, sex ratios of fishes, macroinvertebrates, and many other aquatic and wetland organisms. This change, coupled with chemistry and discharge changes, can also create intolerable habitat conditions, oxygen depletion, and depleted life, from the bottom of the food chain to the top trophic groups. Thermal changes can also favor the productivity of invasive algae, exacerbated oxygen depletion, and anoxia, which cause serious effects on other biological organisms.

In addition to fish and invertebrates, effects also extend to other living organisms including algae, microbes, and macrophytes. A concise summary can be found in literature by Paul and Meyer (2001).

Initial attempts to characterize these effects led to the determination of impervious area thresholds. Booth and Jackson (1997) examined numerous data from lowland streams in western Washington and concluded that development having about 10% imperviousness caused a readily apparent degradation of aquatic life in receiving waters. However, Booth et al. (2004) later reviewed the effects of land use, hydrology, biology, and human behavior in reviving urban streams in the Puget Sound lowlands in Washington. The authors propose that impervious area alone is a flawed surrogate of river health and propose that hydrologic metrics be used instead as they reflect chronic altered stream flows. Medina et al. (2007) showed an application of some of these metrics to fish habitat restoration in the Great Lakes.

Other research has specifically examined the role that large woody debris (LWD) has in stabilizing habitat in urban streams. Booth et al. (1997) found that LWD performs key functions in undisturbed streams that drain lowland forested water-sheds in western Washington. These important functions include energy dissipation of flow energy, channel bank and bed stabilization, sediment trapping, and pool formation. Urbanization typically results in the almost complete removal of this material. Logs and other debris have long been removed from channels in urban areas for many reasons, particularly because of their potential for blocking culverts or to form jams at bridges, increase bank scour, and elicit complaints from residents who favor "neat" streambank areas that are devoid of woody debris in and near the water and even with mowed grass to the water's edge.

8.0 EFFECTS OF STORMWATER CONTROL PRACTICES ON AQUATIC BIOTA

Literature documenting the direct effects of stormwater control practices on aquatic biota is limited. However, the biotic effects of stormwater control practices are driven by the hydrologic and morphologic effects of these practices. Numerous researchers have advocated use of hydrologic metrics that quantify altered stream-flow regimes to form mechanistic links between urbanization, hydrology, hydraulics, and biota (Booth et al., 2004; Cassin et al., 2005; Eisele et al., 2003; Kennen and Ayers, 2002; Kirby, 2003; Scoggins, 2000). Pomeroy et al., (2008) provide a protocol for examining linkages between stormwater controls, metrics describing instream flow regimes, and stream ecosystem health as measured by macroinvertebrates. Evaluation of the interrelationships between land use, runoff control strategies, hydrologic metrics, and ecologic health in streams allows for the development of stormwater management criteria that can provide protection of aquatic biota.

Understanding of the characteristics of the receiving waterbody is essential to select proper stormwater controls that should be used for the benefit of desirable biota or removal of undesirable species. For example, if a lake is the receiving water, it may be necessary to emphasize phosphorus and nitrogen control to avoid algal blooms. Conversely, if a trout stream is the receiving water, the focus of control practices may need to be on temperature and heavy metals.

9.0 SUMMARY

This chapter presented an abridged summary of the significant effects of uncontrolled stormwater on receiving streams and mitigating measures that stormwater controls can provide. The conversion of land from its original condition to urban uses has induced changes in the hydrologic regime that affect the geomorphology of streams and the integrity of the ecosystems in them. Findings point to the realization that "not all imperviousness is created equal," as stated by Bledsoe (2002b) to emphasize that percent imperviousness alone is not a predictor of stream health. Instead, connectedness of impervious areas, receiving stream order, soil characteristics, topography, vegetation cover, climatic variables, and presence of stormwater controls need to be considered. The nature and magnitude of the effect depends on complex interrelationships among the physical, chemical, and biological characteristics of the watershed. Realistic goals, careful planning centered on water resources, sound development practices, properly installed and maintained stormwater controls, and a commitment to stream protection are needed to mitigate these effects. The body of knowledge on this subject continues to expand with regard to understanding the effects of stormwater controls as they attempt to alleviate or reverse negative effects. The reader is encouraged to seek additional information in the references in the next section as well as in subsequent publications.

10.0 REFERENCES

Barrett, M. E.; Malina, J. F., Jr.; Charbeneau, R. J.; Ward, G. H. (1995) *Water Quality and Quantity Impacts of Highway Construction and Operation: Summary and Conclusions*; Report No. 266; Center for Research in Water Resources: The University of Texas at Austin: Austin, Texas.

Bledsoe, B. P. (2002a) Stream Erosion Potential and Stormwater Management Strategies. *J. Water Resour. Plann. Manage.,* **128,** 451.

Bledsoe, B. P. (2002b) Relationships of Stream Responses to Hydrologic Changes. In *Linking Stormwater BMP Designs and Performance to Receiving Water Impact Mitigation;* Proceedings of an Engineering Foundation Conference; Snowmass Village, Colorado; Aug 19–24, 2001; Urbonas, B. R., Ed.; American Society of Civil Engineers: Reston, Virginia.

Bledsoe, B. P.; Hawley, R.; Stein, E. D. (2008) *Stream Channel Classification and Mapping Systems: Implications for Assessing Susceptibility to Hydromodification Effects in Southern California;* Southern California Coastal Water Research Project: Costa Mesa, California.

Booth, D. B.; Jackson, C. R. (1997) Urbanization of Aquatic Systems: Degradation Thresholds, Stormwater Detection, and the Limits of Mitigation. *J. Am. Water Resour. Assoc.,* **33** (5), 1077.

Booth, D. B.; Montgomery, D. R.; Bethel, J. (1997) Large Woody Debris in Urban Streams of the Pacific Northwest. *Proceedings of the Effects of Watershed Development and Management on Aquatic Ecosystems Engineering Foundation Conference;* Snowbird, Utah; Aug 4–9, 1996; Roesner, L. A., Shaver, E., Horner, R. R., Eds.; American Society of Civil Engineers: New York; pp 178–197.

Booth, D. B.; Henshaw, P. C. (2001) Rates of Channel Erosion in Small Urban Streams. In *Land Use and Watersheds, Human Influence on Hydrology and Geomorphology in Urban and Forest Areas*; Wigmosta, M. S.; Burges, S. J., Eds.; American Geophysical Union: Washington, D.C.; pp 17–38.

Booth, D. B.; Karr, J. R.; Schauman, S.; Konrad, C. P.; Morley, S. A.; Larson, M. G.; Burger, S. J. (2004) Reviving Urban Streams: Land Use, Hydrology, Biology, and Human Behavior. *J. Am. Water Resour. Assoc.,* **40** (5), 1351.

Brandes, D.; Cavallo, G. J.; Nilson, M. L. (2005) Base Flow Trends in Urbanizing Watersheds of the Delaware River Basin. *J. Am. Water Resour. Assoc.,* **41** (6), 1377.

Burton, G. A., Jr.; Pitt, R. (2002) *Stormwater Effects Handbook: A Tool Box for Watershed Managers, Scientists, and Engineers;* CRC Press: Boca Raton, Florida; p 911.

Caraco, D. (2000) Dynamics of Urban Stream Channel Enlargement. In *The Practice of Watershed Protection*; Schueler, T. R., Holland, H. K., Eds.; Center for Watershed Protection: Elliott City, Maryland.

Cassin, J.; Fuerstenberg, R.; Tear, L.; Whiting, K.; St. John, D.; Murray, B.; Burkey, J. (2005) *Development of Hydrological and Biological Indicators of Flow Alteration in Puget Sound Lowland Streams*; Final Report; King County Water and Land Resources Division: Seattle, Washington.

Center for Watershed Protection, Inc., Stormwater Manager's Resource Center Home Page. http://www.stormwatercenter.net (accessed May 4, 2011).

Craun, G. F.; Calderon, R. L.; Frost, F. J. (1996) An Introduction to Epidemiology. *J.—Am. Water Works Assoc.,* **88** (9), 54.

Craun, G. F.; Berger, P. S.; Calderon, R. L. (1997) Coliform Bacteria and Waterborne Disease Outbreaks. *J.—Am. Water Works Assoc.,* **89** (3), 96.

Crunkilton, R.; Kleist, J.; Ramcheck, J.; DeVita, W.; Villeneueve, D. (1997) Assessment of the Response of Aquatic Organisms to Long-Term In-Situ Exposures to Urban Runoff. *Proceedings of the Effects of Watershed Development and Management on Aquatic Ecosystems Engineering Foundation Conference;*

Snowbird, Utah; Aug 4–9, 1996; Roesner, L. A., Ed.; American Society of Civil Engineers: New York.

Donigian, A. S.; Love, J. T. (2005) The Use of Continuous Watershed Modeling to Address Issues of Urbanization and Channel Stability in Southern California. *Proceedings of the World Environmental and Water Resources Congress;* Anchorage, Alaska; May 15–19; Walton, R., Ed.; American Society of Civil Engineers: Reston, Virginia.

Douglas, I. (1985) Urban Sedimentology. *Prog. Physical Geography,* **9** (2), 255.

Ehrenfeld, J. G.; Schneider, J. P. (1983) *The Sensitivity of Cedar Swamps to the Effects of Non-Point Pollution Associated with Suburbanization in the New Jersey Pine Barrens;* Report No. PB8–4-136779; U.S. Environmental Protection Agency, Office of Water Policy: Washington, D.C.

Eisele, M.; Steinbrich, A.; Hildebrand, A.; Leibundgut, C. (2003) The Significance of Hydrological Criteria for the Assessment of the Ecological Quality in River Basins. *Phys. Chem. Earth,* **28** (12–13), 529.

Fitzpatrick, F. A.; Peppler, M. C. (2007) Changes in Aquatic Habitat and Geomorphic Response to Urbanization, with Implications for Assessing Habitat Degradation. *Proceedings of the World Environmental and Water Resources Congress;* Tampa, Florida; May 15–19; Kabbes, K. C., Ed.; American Society of Civil Engineers: Reston, Virginia.

Gracie J. W.; Thomas, W. A. (2004) Sediment Transport in Some Eastern United States Streams. *Proceedings of the World Environmental and Water Resources Congress;* Salt Lake City, Utah; June 27–July 1; Sehlke, G., Hayes, D. F., Stevens, D. K., Eds.; American Society of Civil Engineers: Reston, Virginia.

Henshaw, P. C.; Booth, D. B. (2000) Natural Restabilization of Stream Channels in Urban Watersheds. *J. Am. Water Resour. Assoc.,* **36** (6), 1219.

Hollis, G. E. (1975) The Effect of Urbanization on Floods of Difference Recurrence Interval. *Water Resour. Res.,* **11**, 431.

Ibendahl, E.; Medina, D. E. (2008) A Practical Methodology to Evaluate Hydromodification Performance of Conventional and Low Impact Development Stormwater Controls. *Proceedings of the 3rd National Low Impact Development Conference;* Seattle, Washington; Nov 16–19; She, N., Char, M., Eds.; American Society of Civil Engineers: Reston, Virginia.

Kang, R. S.; Marston, R. A. (2006) Geomorphic Effects of Rural-to-Urban Land Use Conversion on Three Streams in the Central Redbed Plains of Oklahoma. *Geomorphology,* **79** (3–4), 488.

Kay, D. (1994) Predicting Likelihood of Gastroenteritis from Sea Bathing: Results from Randomized Exposure. *Lancet,* **344** (8927), 905.

Kennen, J. G.; Ayers, M. A. (2002) *Relation of Environmental Characteristics to the Composition of Aquatic Assemblages Along a Gradient of Urban Land Use in New Jersey, 1996–98*; Water-Resources Investigations Report 02–4069; U.S. Geological Survey: West Trenton, New Jersey; p 78.

Kirby, C. W. (2003) *Benthic Macroinvertebrate Response to Post-Development Stream Hydrology and Hydraulics*; UMI Microform 3079343; Ph.D. Dissertation, George Mason University, Fairfax, Virginia.

Konrad, C. P.; Booth, D. B. (2002) Hydrologic Trends Associated with Urban Development for Selected Streams in the Puget Sound Basin, Western Washington; Water-Resources Investigations Report 02–4040; U.S. Geological Survey: Tacoma, Washington.

Lane, E. W. (1955) Stable Channel Design. *Trans. Am. Soc. Civ. Eng.,* 120, 1234–1279.

Lee, G. F.; Jones-Lee, A. (1995) Deficiencies in Stormwater Quality Monitoring. In Stormwater NPDES Related Monitoring Needs. *Proceedings of an American Society of Civil Engineers Engineering Foundation Conference;* Mt. Crested Butte, Colorado; Aug; Torno, H. C., Ed.; American Society of Civil Engineers: New York.

MacRae, C. R. (1993) An Alternative Design Approach for the Control of Stream Erosion Potential in Urbanizing Watersheds. *Proceedings of the Sixth International Conference on Urban Storm Drainage,* Niagara Falls, Ontario, Canada; Sept 12–17; Seapoint Publishing: Victoria, British Columbia, Canada.

MacRae, C. R. (1997) Experience from Morphological Research on Canadian Streams: Is the Control of the Two-Year Frequency Runoff Event the Best Basis for Stream Channel Protection? In *Effects of Watershed Development and Management of Aquatic Ecosystems*; Roesner, L. A., Ed.; American Society of Civil Engineers: New York; pp 144–162.

MacRae, C. R.; Rowney, A. C. (1992) The Role of Moderate Flow Events and Bank Structure in the Determination of Channel Response to Urbanization.

Proceedings of the 45th Annual Conference on Resolving Conflicts and Uncertainty in Water Management; Canadian Water Resources Association: Kingston, Ontario, Canada.

May, C. W.; Horner, R. R.; Karr, J. R.; Mar, B. W.; Welch, E. B. (1997) Effects of Urbanization on Small Streams in the Puget Sound Lowland Ecoregion. *Watershed Protection Tech.*, **2** (4), 483.

McCuen, R. H. (1979) Downstream Effects of Stormwater Management Basins. *J. Hydraulic Div.*, **105**, 1343.

Medina, D. E.; Mittag, M.; Kealy, M. J.; Brown, B. (2007) Quantification of Aquatic Ecosystem Improvements through Flow Regime Restoration. *Proceedings of the 5th International Conference on Urban Watershed Management and Mountain River Protection and Development;* Chengdu, China; April 3–5.

Meyer, J. L.; Paul, M. J.; Taulbee, W. K. (2005) Stream Ecosystem Function in Urbanizing Landscapes. *J. North Am. Benthic Soc.*, **24** (3), 602.

Moglen, G. E.; McCuen, R. H. (1988) Effects of Detention Basins on In-Stream Sediment Movement. *J. Hydrology*, **104**, 129.

Moore, A. A.; Palmer, M. A. (2005) Invertebrate Biodiversity in Agricultural and Urban Headwater Streams: Implications for Conservation and Management. *Ecol. Applications*, **15** (4), 1169.

Neller, R. J. (1988) A Comparison of Channel Erosion in Small Urban and Rural Catchments, Armidale, New South Wales. *Earth Surf. Processes Landforms*, **13**, 1.

Neller, R. J. (1989) Induced Channel Enlargement in Small Urban Catchments, Armidale, New South Wales. *Environ. Geol. Water Sci.*, **14** (3), 167.

Nelson, K.; Palmer, M. A. (2007) Predicting Stream Temperature Under Urbanization and Climate Change: Implications for Stream Biota. *J. Am. Water Resour. Assoc.*, **43**, 440.

Ney, J. J.; Van Hassel, J. H. (1983) Sources of Variability in Accumulation of Heavy Metals by Fishes in a Roadside Stream. *Arch. Environ. Contam. Toxicol.*, **12** (6), 701.

O'Shea, M.; Field, R. (1992a) An Evaluation of Bacterial Standards and Disinfection Practices Used for the Assessment and Treatment of Stormwater. *Adv. Appl. Microbiol.*, **37**, 21.

O'Shea, M.; Field, R. (1992b) Detection and Disinfection of Pathogens in Storm-Generated Flows. *Can. J. Microbiol.*, **38** (4), 267.

Palhegyi, G. E.; Bicknell, J. (2004) Using Concepts of Work to Evaluate Hydromodification Impacts on Stream Channel Integrity and Effectiveness of Management Strategies. *Proceedings of the World Environmental and Water Resources Congress;* Salt Lake City, Utah; June 27–July 1.

Palmer, M. A.; Hart, D. D.; Allan, J. D.; Bernhardt, E. (2003) Bridging Engineering, Ecological, and Geomorphic Science to Enhance Riverine Restoration: Local and National Efforts. *Proceedings of a National Symposium on Urban and Rural Stream Protection and Restoration World Environmental and Water Resources Congress;* Philadelphia, Pennsylvania; June.

Paul, M. J.; Meyer, J. L. (2001) Streams in the Urban Landscape. *Annu. Rev. Ecol. Syst.*, **32,** 333.

Pavlowsky, R. T. (2004) Urban Impacts on Stream Morphology in the Ozark Plateaus Region. *Proceedings of the Self-Sustaining Solutions for Streams, Wetlands, and Watersheds Conference;* St. Paul, Minnesota; Sept 12–15.

Pitt, R.; Bozeman, M. (1982) *Sources of Urban Runoff Pollution and Its Effects on an Urban Creek*; EPA-600/S2-82-090; U.S. Environmental Protection Agency: Cincinnati, Ohio.

Pitt, R.; Clark, S.; Parmer, K. (1994) *Protection of Groundwater from Intentional and Nonintentional Stormwater Infiltration*; EPA-600/SR-94–051 PB94–165354AS; U.S. Environmental Protection Agency, Storm and Combined Sewer Program: Cincinnati, Ohio; p 187.

Pomeroy, C. A.; Postel, N. A.; O'Neill, P. A.; Roesner, L. A. (2008) Development of Stormwater Management Design Criteria to Maintain Geomorphic Stability in a Kansas City Metropolitan Area Stream. *J. Irrigation Drainage Eng.*, **134** (5), 562.

Pomeroy, C. A.; Roesner, L. A.; Coleman, J. C.; Rankin, E. (2008) *Protocols for Evaluating Wet Weather Practices and Urbanization Patterns;* Final Report No. 03-WSM-3; Water Environment Research Foundation: Alexandria, Virginia.

Roesner, L. A.; Bledsoe, B. P.; Brashear, R. W. (2001) Are Best-Management-Practice Criteria Really Environmentally Friendly? *J. Water Resour. Plann. Manage.*, **127,** 150.

Rohrer, C. A. (2004) Modeling the Effect of Stormwater Controls on Sediment Transport in an Urban Stream. M.S. Thesis, Department of Civil Engineering, Colorado State University, Fort Collins, Colorado.

Roy, A. H.; Freeman, M. C.; Freeman, B. J.; Wenger, S. J.; Ensign, W. E.; Meyer, J. L. (2006) Importance of Riparian Forests in Urbanizing Watersheds Contingent on Sediment and Hydrologic Regimes. *Environ. Manage.*, **37** (4), 523.

Schueler, T., Ed. (1997) Impact of Suspended and Deposited Sediment. *Watershed Protection Tech.*, **2** (3), 443.

Scoggins, M. (2000) Effects of Hydrologic Variability on Biological Assessments in Streams in Austin, Texas. *Proceedings of the National Water Quality Monitoring Council 2000;* Watershed Protection Department: Austin, Texas.

Soar, P. J.; Thorne, C. R. (2001) *Channel Restoration Design for Meandering Rivers;* ERDC/CHL CR-01–1; U.S. Army Corps of Engineers, Engineer Research and Development Center: Washington, D.C.

Tyagi, A.; Chongtoua, B.; Medina, D.; Patwardhan, A.; Slater, C. (2008) Management of Dry Weather Flows in Semi Arid Climates Using Low Impact Development Technology. *Proceedings of the World Environmental and Water Resources Congress;* Honolulu, Hawaii; May 12–16.

Trimble, S. W. (1997) Contribution of Stream Channel Erosion to Sediment Yield from an Urbanizing Watershed. *Science,* **278** (5342), 1442.

U.S. Department of Agriculture (1986) *Urban Hydrology for Small Watersheds; Technical Release 55;* Natural Resources Conservation Service, Conservation Engineering Division: Washington, D.C.

Walsh, C. J.; Roy, A. H.; Feminella, J. W.; Cottingham, P. D.; Groffman, P. M.; Morgan, R. P., II (2005) The Urban Stream Syndrome: Current Knowledge and the Search for a Cure. *J. North Am. Benthol. Soc.,* **24** (3), 706.

Wang, L.; Lyons, J.; Kanehl, P.; Bannerman, R.; Emmons, E. (2000) Watershed Urbanization and Changes in Fish Communities in Southeastern Wisconsin Streams. *J. Am. Water Resour. Assoc.,* **36**, 1173.

Watson, C. C.; Bledsoe, B. P.; Biedenharn, D. S. (2001) Specific Stream Power and a Risk-Based Design Approach. *Proceedings of the American Society of Civil Engineers Wetlands Engineering and River Restoration Conference,* Reno, Nevada, Aug 27–31.

Weber, D.; Sturm, T. W.; Warner, R. (2004) Impact of Urbanization on Sediment Budget of Peachtree Creek. In *Critical Transitions in Water and Environmental Resources Management,* Proceedings of the World Environmental and Water Resources Congress, Salt Lake City, Utah, June 27–July 1.

Wellman, J. C.; Combs, D. L.; Cook, S. B. (2000) Long-Term Impacts of Bridge and Culvert Construction or Replacement on Fish Communities and Sediment Characteristics of Streams. *J. Freshwater Ecol.,* **15** (3), 317.

Wolman, M. G. (1967) A Cycle of Sedimentation and Erosion in Urban River Channels. *Geografiska Annaler,* **49A,** 385.

11.0 SUGGESTED READINGS

Ashmore, P. E.; Day, T. J. (1988) Effective Discharge for Suspended Sediment Transport in Streams of the Saskatchewan River Basin. *Water Resour. Res.,* **34,** 864.

Federal Emergency Management Agency (1999) *Riverine Erosion Hazard Areas: Mapping Feasibility Study;* Federal Emergency Management Agency: Washington, D.C.

Kresan, P. L. (1988) The Tucson, Arizona Flood of October 1983—Implications for Land Management Along Alluvial River Channels. In *Flood Geomorphology;* Baker, V. R.; Kochel, R. C.; Patton, P. C.; Eds.; Wiley & Sons: New York.

Leopold, L. B.; Wolman, M. G.; Miller, J. P. (1964) *Fluvial Processes in Geomorphology;* W.H. Freeman and Co.: San Francisco, California.

Nash, D. B. (1994) Effective Sediment-Transporting Discharge from Magnitude-Frequency Analysis. *J. Geology,* **102,** 79.

Palmer, M. A.; Moglen, G. E.; Bockstael, N. E.; Brooks, S.; Pizzuto, J. E.; Wiegand, C.; VanNess, K. (2002) The Ecological Consequences of Changing Land Use for Running Waters: The Suburban Maryland Case. *Yale Bull. Environ. Sci.,* **107,** 85.

U.S. Army Corps of Engineers (1994) *Channel Stability Assessment for Flood Control Projects;* EM 1110–2-1418; American Society of Civil Engineers: New York.

Chapter 3

Performance Goals for Stormwater Controls

(continued)

1.0 INTRODUCTION

1.1 Basic Concepts of Stormwater Control

The objective of stormwater controls, as stated in Chapter 2, is to reduce the effect of development on receiving waterbodies by removing pollutants and attempting to replicate target hydrologic patterns through runoff volume reduction and attenuation of peak flows that may erode streams or cause flooding. Figure 3.1 illustrates that these objectives are met through integrated controls suited to the characteristics of the watershed. These objectives are addressed within the context of the following principles:

- Minimization of runoff by reduction of impervious areas and project footprint, protection of native soils to maintain infiltration capacity, and protection of native vegetation to maintain evapotranspiration potential.

- Source controls implemented at the point where precipitation reaches the ground to prevent stormwater from contacting pollutants and minimize runoff by promoting infiltration and evapotranspiration.

- Control systems distributed throughout the drainage system, close to the sources of runoff, to capture stormwater, remove pollutants, promote further infiltration and evapotranspiration, enable rainwater harvesting, and slowly discharge remaining runoff.

- Resource protection such as vegetated setbacks to protect the habitat and assimilative capacity of waterbodies while protecting the surrounding development from flooding and erosion.

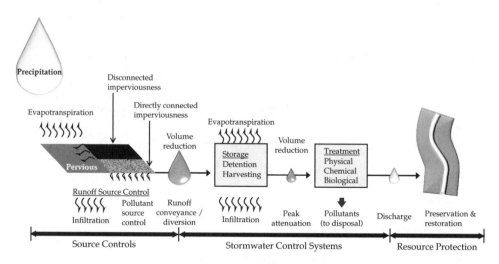

FIGURE 3.1   Illustration of an integrated stormwater management system.

- Protection of public safety, health, and welfare.

- Protection of infrastructure and public property by reducing flood hazards and erosion.

- Community enrichment by blending stormwater controls into the built environment to enhance active and passive recreation features, wildlife habitat, property value, pedestrian and bicycling trails, playgrounds, parks, and other assets that support livable communities and connect the public to natural resources.

- Technical feasibility, cost-effectiveness, public acceptance, and practicality.

Stormwater control systems are composed of one or more unit operations, each utilizing one or more unit processes to control runoff and remove pollutants, as described in Chapter 4. The effectiveness of each of these processes is governed by flow, volume, and configuration factors related to regional climatic and precipitation patterns; the variability of stormwater flows, volumes, and pollutant concentrations; the natural setting within which each of these controls is applied; and the integration of processes that occur in stormwater control systems.

Because of the complexity and limited historic understanding of these factors, an empirical set of design criteria has emerged for stormwater controls based on implementation experience. Many stormwater controls designed according to these empirical criteria do not effectively achieve stated stormwater management objectives because design criteria are often selected based on literature reviews rather than assessments of achievable performance goals and local hydrologic conditions (NRC, 2008).

This chapter provides an overview of several approaches used for developing performance goals and design criteria for stormwater controls. The practice of stormwater management varies substantially across the United States, and objectives and approaches must be evaluated on a case-by-case basis, accounting for such factors as climatic factors, designated uses of the receiving waters, water quality problems, flood hazards, applicable regulations, and nature of the proposed project. No one approach fits every situation and it should be emphasized that this MOP does not attempt to set national standards to be applied everywhere in the United States. The material presented in this chapter is a summary of selected approaches from various jurisdictions with pertinent commentary about their origins, strengths, limitations, and applicability. These methodologies can be used in sizing stormwater controls where local standards are lacking, provided they are properly adapted to consider site-specific factors. In addition, local and state agencies are encouraged to review their current performance standards and compare them to the criteria presented in this MOP to verify that maximum effectiveness is achieved through their investments in stormwater control infrastructure.

1.2 Relationship between Stormwater Control Objectives and Performance Goals

With the current paradigms of urban development, stormwater effects are virtually unavoidable in urbanized areas and it is difficult, if not impossible, to return to or maintain the hydrologic regime of a pristine environment. Stormwater management objectives are intended to mitigate these effects and are dictated by a number of drivers that include federal, state, and municipal regulations; regional or state goals to mitigate the effects of urban runoff; and special local needs such as cold-water fisheries protection, source surface water protection, groundwater protection, flood hazard reduction, and other locally important issues. The selection of the appropriate level of control is typically dictated by a local municipal regulation but can also be a federal decision driven, for example, by the Endangered Species Act or the Coastal Zone Management Act, targeted to a specific issue or sensitive waterbodies (Clar et al., 2004).

Individual states typically establish beneficial use designations for their receiving waters, issue water quality standards for each beneficial use designation, conduct receiving water quality assessments, define impaired waterbodies, determine total maximum daily loads (TMDLs) for pollutants causing water quality impairment, and direct regional planning agencies to develop area-wide water quality management plans under Section 208 of the CWA. Beneficial uses of receiving waters typically include aesthetic resources, aquatic habitat, water supply, and recreation. While state regulatory agencies have designated beneficial uses for most significant receiving waters, beneficial uses of many urban streams and lakes may not currently be designated. Beneficial uses of urban streams and lakes should reflect their municipal drainage functions and consider any previous or required future alterations for flood or streambank erosion control. Municipal stormwater management programs should be linked to confirming or designating beneficial uses of waters receiving urban runoff. Each receiving water "user" will have individual views on what these beneficial uses should be (e.g., swimming, surfing, fishing, boating, aquatic life habitat, or aesthetics) and local areas of concern. Certain waters will be seen as more valuable than others.

Attainment of seemingly obvious beneficial uses may involve significant cost considerations. Table 3.1 defines possible goals that may be established for attaining stream beneficial uses and the possible performance standards that may be established to attain those goals. For example, if goal 4 in Table 3.1 were selected, enormous costs would be incurred and current technology might be insufficient to meet standards for several constituents. Therefore, it is imperative to understand the implications of various goals and the costs associated with obtaining these goals. Technical studies are necessary to determine whether beneficial-use attainment is achievable at a reasonable cost and to quantify long-term control goals necessary to attain designated uses.

TABLE 3.1   Beneficial-use attainment related to performance criteria.

Attainment goals	Performance criteria	
	Pollutant loads	Stream habitat
1. No significant degradation	Reduce increase	Reduce deterioration
2. No degradation	No increase	No deterioration
3. Improved water quality	Lower than existing	Better than existing
4. Meet numeric water quality standards during storm events	Significantly lower than existing	Better than existing

A recent interpretation of goals toward beneficial use attainment is Section 438 of the Energy Independence and Security Set of 2007, which requires Federal agencies to reduce stormwater runoff from Federal development projects. The act requires such projects "...to maintain or restore to the maximum extent technically feasible, the predevelopment hydrology of the property with regard to temperature, rate, volume and duration of flow." The performance standard subsequently established by the U.S. Environmental Protection Agency (U.S. EPA) is to retain the 95th-percentile storm or an alternative performance design objective established through site-specific hydrologic analysis (U.S. EPA, 2009).

In many jurisdictions, the term "predevelopment" is taken to mean the existing conditions before a project is built, but there are existing conditions that are not desirable as a target; for instance, farmland with high nutrient discharges or an extensive paved area that is known to be causing stream channel erosion. As stated earlier, a return to pristine conditions is impossible because of cost, technical infeasibility, or practicality; therefore, this is not a realistic target either. As a compromise, some jurisdictions select a hydrologic condition that implies the presence of beneficial functions, for instance meadow or woods in good condition, regardless of the existing type and degree of urbanization currently on the site. In this MOP, the term "predevelopment" is used to designate a desirable target condition. This target must be selected carefully in the context of overall management goals and stakeholder priorities for a watershed and should represent protection of an existing valuable condition, or an improvement over existing conditions that are the source of impairments.

Once the predevelopment condition is defined, stormwater controls should be designed to achieve an explicit set of control objectives descriptive of the desired outcome; e.g., maintain chemical, physical, and biological parameters indicative of a desired beneficial stream-use designation; prevent structure flooding during a 25-year event; or prevent erosive velocities from damaging infrastructure.

The most common performance standards for stormwater controls consist of the following two interrelated parameters that are established to achieve each control objective based on site conditions and constraints:

- A design volume typically derived from precipitation, modeling, and analysis of runoff statistics; and

- A release rate for the design volume set to achieve the desired control objectives; for example, runoff discharge volume and peak-flow frequencies, hydraulic retention time, pollutant removal or effluent concentration, and postdevelopment peak flow limits for a particular design event, such as the 2-, 10-, or 100-year storm, or matching a specified flow duration curve.

In the future, an effluent concentration could be a third control objective for some specific situations. U.S. EPA has made it a priority to develop and implement numeric water-quality-based effluent limits in stormwater permits (e.g., Hanlon and Keehner, 2010), primarily to meet TMDLs. Despite the technical difficulties in setting reliable numeric limits for nutrients, some states have specified them in stormwater discharges in various forms. For example, North Carolina specifies maximum nutrient loads for sensitive waters, and Florida and Wisconsin have standards in place, although their effectiveness and appropriateness are still being evaluated. Unlike toxics, whose maximum limits are zero or very low concentrations, nutrients are building blocks of life and maximum concentrations are extremely difficult to establish because of the complex linkages between loads, indicators such as dissolved oxygen and chlorophyll, and aquatic ecosystem variables such as habitat, algae, macroinvertebrates, and fish. A study in Florida exemplifies the complexity of this subject and summarizes knowledge gaps (Anderson and Janicki, 2010). A review of this subject is beyond the scope of this MOP; however, the point to make is that this movement toward numeric criteria may translate to effluent limits expected from stormwater controls.

This MOP focuses on the volume and flow criteria stated in the bullets above. These two criteria can be the result of a watershed study that specifies volumes and flows for stormwater controls in various locations in the watershed. Alternatively, the two-criterion approach is applicable under the premise that meeting these criteria is equivalent to meeting technology-based effluent limits. The two-criterion approach is also consistent with conclusions from the analysis of the data in the International BMP Database (www.bmpdatabase.org) indicating that properly designed stormwater controls produce an approximately constant effluent concentration.

Stormwater management goals are not exclusive of each other but rather complementary, building on each other as shown in the example illustration of the unified sizing criteria in Figure 3.2. For instance, satisfying requirements for recharge and evapotranspiration also may partially or fully achieve those for water quality and channel protection. Table 3.2 lists objectives for each category of stormwater control

FIGURE 3.2   Unified stormwater sizing criteria and objectives (adapted from Minnesota, 2005).

presented in this MOP (Chapters 6 through 10). The following sections discuss the basis for each control objective listed in Table 3.2.

1.2.1   Groundwater Recharge and Evapotranspiration

An important stormwater control objective is to maintain groundwater recharge and evapotranspiration at predevelopment conditions, to the extent feasible, thereby reducing effects to the baseflow hydrology of streams and wetlands. Groundwater recharge in this context means the infiltration of stormwater to shallow and deep aquifers. Shallow infiltration becomes part of interflow, which is the source of baseflow. Some of this infiltrated water is evapotranspired by vegetation or evaporates directly from the soil. Excess infiltrated water that reaches deeper into the soil is stored in aquifers and becomes part of the regional groundwater system. However, many small storms only fill the pore space in the soil and are evapotranspired, with no infiltration past the vadose or root depth zone.

This performance goal consists of a recharge and evapotranspiration volume and the design depends on infiltration and evapotranspiration rates. Infiltration rates may be determined using the average annual recharge rate of the U.S. Department of

TABLE 3.2 Stormwater management objectives provided by stormwater controls*.

		Type of stormwater control				
Stormwater management control objective	Basis of performance standard	Basins (Chapter 6)	Swales and Strips (Chapter 7)	Filters (Chapter 8)	Infiltrators (Chapter 9)	Gross Pollutant Traps and Mechanical Operations (Chapter 10)
Recharge and evapotranspiration	Recharge rate, evapotranspiration rate	S	S		X	
Water quality control						
• Capture and release	Capture volume, drawdown time	X		X	X	
• Flow-through	Capture volume, design hydrograph		X	X		X
Channel protection	Shear stress	X	S	S	X	
Overbank flood control	Design storm, peak attenuation	X			S	
Extreme flood control	Design storm, peak attenuation	X			S	

*X = primary function; S = secondary function.

Agriculture, Natural Resources Conservation Service (NRCS) hydrologic soil groups at the site, hydrologic relationships between rainfall and stream flow, water-well withdrawal rates, modeling, or other appropriate methods. Evapotranspiration rates can be derived from site-specific data maintained by cooperative extension services. Continuous hydrologic simulation may be used to define predevelopment runoff, infiltration, and evapotranspiration statistics, and to establish a meaningful recharge and evapotranspiration volume for given climatic and subsurface conditions.

Potential factors that may reduce infiltration rates should be considered during design. Hydraulic conductivity is a function of soil properties and water temperature. Therefore, failure to incorporate soil physics and temperature as well as improper soil testing lead to inaccurate design infiltration rates. The design should also account for potential maintenance deficiencies that result in accumulated sediment and reduced infiltration rates. Evapotranspiration is often neglected in water budget computations and can be an important water removal mechanism, depending on geographic locations and climate.

There are some caveats that must be considered in selecting recharge and evapotranspiration volumes. In arid areas, water rights of downstream property owners may limit or preclude capture of upstream recharge and evapotranspiration volumes. Recharge goals must also incorporate criteria for protecting the quality of groundwater. U.S. EPA wellhead protection and underground injection regulations and programs under the Safe Drinking Water Act provide criteria for practices intended to recharge groundwater. For example, certain infiltration practices might be subject to these regulations if they cause polluted water to enter fractured rock aquifers (U.S. EPA, 2011). Typically, these regulations do not apply to most stormwater controls, unless they are deployed in karst terrain. In these circumstances, soil scientists and geologists should be included in the design process.

1.2.2   Water Quality

Removal of pollutants from stormwater before discharge to receiving waters is driven by federal and state regulations:

- The 1987 amendments to the Clean Water Act and promulgated by U.S. EPA and most often delegated to state and regional agencies, for example, require that operators of municipal separate storm sewer systems (MS4s) implement controls to the maximum extent practicable, including postdevelopment stormwater management, stormwater pollution prevention for industrial activities, sediment and erosion control for construction activities, and TMDL implementation.

- The 1990 Coastal Zone Act Reauthorization Amendments, which require states to address nonpoint source pollution affecting coastal waters, wetlands, and floodplains.

- The Endangered Species Act, which requires a biological assessment if an action involving the federal government has the potential to affect a threatened species.

- The Energy Independence and Security Act of 2007, which requires federal facilities to control the hydrologic effect of stormwater to the maximum extent technically feasible.

- State and municipal requirements.

- Specific cases in which there is a clear directive to treat stormwater before discharge, regardless of the regulatory need to do so.

- Applicable court cases that mandate specific conditions for stormwater treatment.

The water quality criterion defines the size and drawdown rate of a stormwater control needed to capture and treat a certain fraction of the average annual precipitation or runoff volume. This capture volume, commonly called the water quality volume (WQV), typically ranges from 80 to 90% of the average annual runoff, according to many stormwater management manuals developed in the United States. Specifications may state an explicit volume to be treated such as 80% of the average annual runoff volume, determined using a continuous hydrologic simulation model, through flow monitoring, or from statistical analyses. Alternatively, recommendations may prescribe a percentile storm to capture. For example, the 85th-percentile storm is the rainfall event for which 85% of all runoff-producing events have an equal or lesser precipitation depth. In this instance, the percentile storm volume is used to calculate the capture volume using hydrologic relationships that consider the potential roles of infiltration, evaporation, and transpiration. The underlying premise is that additional runoff beyond the specified storm depth occurs infrequently and thus contains a small fraction of the average annual runoff volume and pollutant load. The recharge and evapotranspiration volume and the WQV may be equal or nearly equal for drainage areas with relatively high infiltration rates.

Stormwater controls are sized using WQV in one of the following two ways, depending on the unit processes involved with pollutant removal (see Chapter 4):

- Effective pollutant removal of a *capture-and-release control* is governed by the time necessary to release the WQV captured by the facility. Such controls require a surface or subsurface storage volume because runoff under design conditions typically reaches the control much faster (often less than 1 hour) than the drawdown time, which is typically 12 to 48 hours or more to remove pollutants.

- Effective pollutant removal of a *flow-through control* requires that the WQV be transformed into a design hydrograph. Sizing the stormwater control to treat up to the design flowrate calculated in this manner is intended to provide effective treatment of the same volume of water that is treated by a stormwater control sized with a volume criterion.

Drawdown times, release rates, and flow hydrographs are established for the controls to achieve the appropriate volume, peak, concentration, and pollutant load exceedance frequencies necessary to meet objectives. A watershed-wide study using continuous simulation models can be conducted to define these performance criteria (e.g., establishing a TMDL). More commonly, technology-based criteria are established that presume compliance with water quality objectives.

1.2.3   Channel Protection

Stream erosion is part of a natural geomorphic process that balances tractive forces and sediment transport within the stream system. Chapter 2 provides an overview of geomorphologic principles associated with stream channel processes and the effects of stormwater controls.

The objective of channel protection is to minimize erosion of a stream channel that can occur with development if the increase in runoff is not mitigated. These criteria are intended to protect streamside property, infrastructure parallel to or crossing the stream, geomorphic features of the stream such as access to the floodplain, and aquatic habitat elements such as woody debris. This criterion is also intended to protect the integrity and composition of the channel bed. The bed substrate is important to aquatic organisms, which either deposit eggs in the bed in the winter or over-winter in the bed. The criterion involves managing the shear stress of channel flow by capturing a channel protection volume (CPV) based on precipitation and runoff statistics; removing a portion of the CPV through infiltration, evapotranspiration, or rainwater harvesting; and releasing the remainder at a non-erosive velocity. Release rates are often less than those for a target set of flow condition (e.g., predevelopment peak flows) to mitigate increased runoff volumes associated with development or match a reference flow duration curve. Historically, the CPV and release rate have been based on the predevelopment runoff frequency at which the water elevation in the stream reaches "bankfull," commonly specified as the 1-year event or some fraction of the 2-year event. Bankfull elevation generally refers to the bank elevation of the lower edge of perennial vegetation but geomorphologists use several additional indicators to ascertain bankfull elevations. Research indicates that effective designs must account for the frequency distribution of sub-bankfull flows, the capacity to transport heterogeneous bed and bank materials, and potential shifts in inflowing sediment loads (Bledsoe, 2002). Continuous simulation and flow and duration analyses of shear stresses to the streambed and streambanks are alternative methods to define channel protection volumes and performance effectiveness more reliably.

1.2.4   Overbank Flood Protection

Flooding is a natural phenomenon accommodated within natural drainage systems. During rainfall events of small to moderate size, stormwater runoff is contained within the banks, or the bankfull channel, of streams. During larger, less frequent storms, runoff overflows the channel banks into the surrounding floodplain (see Figure 3.3).

As watersheds are developed, storm sewers are installed to collect and convey runoff from small to moderate storms. Properly designed developments use streets or swales to convey runoff from larger, less frequent storms to the open-channel drainage system. Building, property, or street flooding may occur if an appropriate surface drainage system is not provided.

Effective drainage design depends on how frequently the capacity of the "low-flow" system should be exceeded, and how severe the effect of flooding would be within the "high-flow" system. Frequency is typically expressed as a recurrence interval. An example of a recurrence interval is the 10-year design storm event, defined as a storm with a 10% probability of occurrence in any given year. Severity is quantified through hydraulic modeling to determine specific characteristics such as length of roadway flooded, number of structures where flooding reaches the foundation, and depth of flooding at structures. These frequency and severity considerations drive the establishment of overbank flood criteria by local jurisdictions for design of drainage systems, stream crossings, and quantity stormwater controls.

The overbank flood protection criterion is intended to protect property and infrastructure near the waterbody from relatively infrequent events that inundate the immediate floodplain. It is also applied to size storm drainage systems and stream crossings. The overbank flood volume (OFV) to be captured varies by jurisdiction,

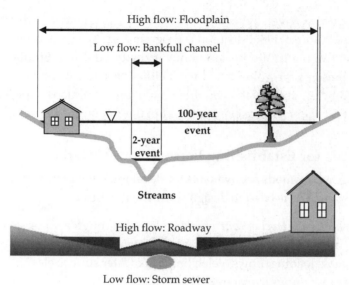

FIGURE 3.3 Illustration of stormwater objectives for low-flow and high-flow conveyance systems

ranging from a 5- to 25-year flood event. The same event frequency may be used across a jurisdiction or it may differ with land use. For example, residential properties frequently are provided a lower level of protection than commercial properties or properties that serve a critical function such as hospitals. Similar to CPV, OFV represents the volume that must be detained or removed by the stormwater control to maintain the peak flow of a specified event or achieve a certain water surface elevation within the conveyance system.

1.2.5 Extreme Flood Protection

Extreme flood protection criteria address the infrequent, highest magnitude events. Their intent as commonly given in manuals is to (1) prevent flood damage from large storm events, (2) maintain the 100-year floodplain boundaries delineated by the Federal Emergency Management Agency or the municipality, and (3) protect the physical integrity of stormwater controls in the watershed. The extreme flood volume (EFV) is commonly based on the 100-year event for existing conditions, although jurisdictions may specify other return periods such as the 25- or 50-year event. The EFV criteria are typically driven by federal and state floodplain management regulations, for instance the National Flood Insurance Program and state dam safety regulations.

As with OFV, the EFV criterion may vary with land use. Similar to CPV and OFV, EFV represents the volume that must either be safely passed or, where necessary, detained by the stormwater control to maintain the peak of a specified event or achieve a certain water surface elevation within the conveyance system.

1.3   Methods for Establishing Performance Criteria

The following two methods are available for developing the performance criteria and quantitative standards needed to design stormwater controls:

- *Watershed-based level of control* is developed through a watershed study that selects and sizes the controls necessary to achieve desired instream concentrations, mass loading, flows, velocities, peak water surface elevations, and shear stresses for various storm frequencies; and

- *Technology-based level of control* presumes that a set of properly selected controls, working at their maximum efficiency, will achieve stormwater management goals, for example, the "maximum extent practicable" performance standards in the 1987 Water Quality Act, or the "maximum extent technically feasible" performance standard of Section 438 of the Energy Independence and Security Act.

General recommendations for establishing watershed-based performance criteria are described in Section 2.0 of this chapter. Section 3.0 provides an approach for establishing technology-based criteria.

2.0   METHODS FOR ESTABLISHING WATERSHED-BASED PERFORMANCE CRITERIA

By definition, watershed-based criteria require more effort to develop. Comprehensive monitoring and modeling of a watershed conducted according to the guidelines presented in Chapters 13 and 14 of this MOP are needed, but yield greater confidence that performance will be consistent with management objectives.

With increased attention to the TMDL program under the CWA, states, U.S. EPA, and citizen groups now increasingly seek to impose numeric flow, volume, concentration, or mass limits on municipal stormwater discharges, especially discharges to impaired waters. During the past decade, U.S. EPA has continued to advance the National Pollutant Discharge Elimination System (NPDES) program as an important part of an integrated watershed approach. Integrating NPDES permits and TMDLs into a watershed approach means developing a watershed-based analysis as part of the permitting process and using that analysis to identify a range of implementation options to achieve ambient water quality goals (e.g., driven by TMDLs). The primary difference between a watershed-based approach and the more common technology-based approach is that the watershed-based approach explicitly considers the effect of multiple flow, volume, and pollutant sources and stressors, including non-point-source contributions. For water quality, disaggregating the effect of pollutant loads between dry weather and wet weather on ambient water quality is often technically challenging.

Watershed-based criteria are more effective than a management program based on uniform technology-based controls because they may more specifically consider upstream and downstream effects and the flow, volume, and pollutant loads from all stressors. A watershed-based approach can assist stormwater dischargers who wish to set priorities for potential solutions, for example, focusing on priority pollutants and sources first to achieve the greatest water quality improvements. The result is implementation of strategies and approaches that could generate cost savings and improved environmental conditions. If developed, watershed-based criteria developed through comprehensive studies would be applied to determine recharge and evapotranspiration volume, WQV, CPV, OFV, and EFV.

A watershed study can also shed light on the effectiveness of control strategies, for example the application of green infrastructure applied on a watershed basis. Medina et al. (2011) examined the effects of green infrastructure on the extent of flooding for a 100-km² (39-sq mi), 39% impervious watershed in the Southeastern United States. Hydrologic and hydraulic modeling using HEC-HMS and HEC-RAS was conducted to determine the extent of inundated areas for various flood-inducing events. Figure 3.4a shows the variation of the areal extent of the floodplain as a function of the return period for the predevelopment forested condition, the postdevelopment condition, and for a stormwater management approach in which green infrastructure controls distributed on the watershed capture the first 30 mm (1.2 in.) of runoff. The watershed consists mostly of B-type soils, which provide good infiltration. Figure 3.4a shows that green infrastructure has a minimal effect on the extent of the 100-year floodplain but is effective at reducing the inundation areas of lesser flooding events. The figure shows that the 2-year condition with green infrastructure

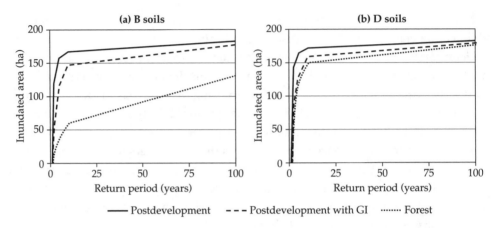

FIGURE 3.4 Effect of green infrastructure application on the extent of flooding.

approaches the forested watershed but is unable to match it. Figure 3.4b shows the results assuming that the watershed has D-type soils, which have much less infiltration capacity. Green infrastructure controls are less able to infiltrate water in soils with low hydraulic conductivity but, in this analysis, it is assumed that the controls are designed to capture the same 30 mm of runoff as in the case of the more pervious soils, which means that they must be larger to maintain the same performance. Therefore, the lesser reduction in the extent of the floodplains is not caused by reduced performance of the green infrastructure controls but because the watershed generates more runoff, and the fraction handled by the green infrastructure controls is proportionately less in the impervious watershed than it was in the original case with more pervious soils. On the other hand, impervious soils are closer to pavement than pervious ones; therefore, development causes a smaller relative increase in runoff generation in this case. The proximity of the curves in Figure 3.4b illustrates this effect. In this case, green infrastructure has proportionately better success in closing the gap between the developed condition and the forest condition but is more difficult to implement because of the soil properties. This type of analysis can test the feasibility of stormwater management strategies, bracket their effectiveness, and identify geographic variability that can assist in the placement of stormwater controls where they can provide the most benefits. A watershed-based approach can also support cost-effectiveness evaluations; the study in Medina et al., (2011) showed that implementation of green infrastructure can avoid flood losses ranging from $63,000 to $66,000/ha of floodplain ($25,000 to \$27,000/ac) for the 5-year event, and from \$17,000 to \$23,000/ha of floodplain (\$7000 to \$9000/ac) for the 100-year event.

One method of determining watershed-based control criteria is a flow-duration analysis to define the percent of time flow exceeds a specific control level. Analysis conducted by Booth and Jackson (1997) showed that there is a range of stream flows from approximately one-half of the 2-year flood to the 50-year flood that produces the majority of erosion in western Washington streams. This approach has been adopted by the Washington State Department of Ecology (2005) in its *Stormwater Management Manual for Western Washington*. The design criteria use the entire predevelopment and postdevelopment runoff record from a hydrologic simulation to estimate flow duration, which is computed by counting the number of flow values that exceed a specified level. Flow-duration analyses in other regions may yield different criteria, depending on hydrologic conditions. The criteria from western Washington are as follows:

- If postdevelopment flow-duration values exceed any of the predevelopment flow levels between 50 and 100% of the 2-year predevelopment peak flow values (100% threshold), then the flow-duration requirement has not been met;

- If postdevelopment flow-duration values exceed any of the predevelopment flow levels between 100% of the 2-year and 100% of the 50-year predevelopment peak flow values more than 10% of the time (110% threshold), then the flow-duration requirement has not been met; and

- If more than 50% of the flow-duration levels exceed the 100% threshold then the flow-duration requirement has not been met.

To facilitate the needed flow-duration analysis, the Washington State Department of Ecology developed a continuous simulation model based on Hydrological Simulation Program-Fortran (HSPF). This software became the Western Washington Hydrology Model (WWHM), an interactive tool to optimally size stormwater control facilities for both water quantity and quality. The model can also be used to review development plans for compliance with stormwater regulations, promote sustainable development practices, and educate the engineering community and public on the effects of land-use changes. This is an example of a tool developed for a specific geographic location to facilitate compliance with local standards. While the specific choice of tool will vary, other jurisdictions may find that development of a location-specific approach can be the best approach to implementation of standards.

More recently, the California Regional Water Quality Control Boards required municipal stormwater permittees to prepare Hydromodification Management Plans (HMPs) that establish criteria-limiting increases in runoff flow and volume that increase the erosion potential of receiving streams. Permittees used a combination of continuous simulation models and stream geomorphic analyses to define the critical recurrence periods for controlling increases in flow peaks and durations, which range between a low flow threshold where erosion begins (typically a fraction of the peak 2-year predevelopment design flow) through a high flow threshold that occurs so infrequently that further erosion control is not cost-effective (typically the peak flow under the 10-year predevelopment design storm). The goal of these HMPs is to maintain peak flows and durations at their predevelopment levels throughout this range, either through limiting increases in directly connected impervious areas or installing stormwater controls designed to meet these criteria. In some cases, site designers may use in-stream controls to better mitigate projected flow and duration increases.

Low flow thresholds are based on the flowrate at which average boundary shear stress exceeds a critical shear stress for the channel and its bed and bank material. The average boundary shear stress is the force that flowing water exerts on channel materials. As explained in Chapter 2, calculations spanning the depth of the bankfull channel produce a rating curve for boundary shear stress as a function of flow. The low flow threshold equals the flow where actual shear stress exceeds the critical shear stress of the channel, and continuous hydrologic simulation of runoff from the catchment associates the low flow threshold with a recurrence interval (e.g., design storm). As mentioned earlier in this section, the critical shear stress determined according to this method was found to be one-half of the peak 2-year design storms ($0.5Q_2$) for undeveloped watersheds in western Washington. In San Diego County, California, however, the critical shear stress was found to range between $0.1Q_2$ and $0.5Q_2$, depending on the receiving channel material and dimensions (County of San Diego, 2011). These evaluations demonstrate that channel stability criteria are most appropriately determined through an assessment of receiving stream morphology coupled with continuous simulations using local climatic data.

Some California HMPs use this methodology to define recommended design parameters for stormwater controls suitable for preventing stream hydromodification, for example, the Santa Clara Valley Urban Runoff Pollution Prevention Program (2005) and the Contra Costa Clean Water Program (2005). Contra Costa County performed continuous simulations to establish hydromodification control sizing factors for a suite of stormwater controls in the county's design manual. These sizing factors define the ratio of the stormwater control surface area to the directly connected impervious area of the tributary catchment that, when coupled with dimensions of the stormwater control in the manual, prevent postdevelopment flows and durations from exceeding predevelopment values. Sizing factors for each type of stormwater control vary with soil conditions of the tributary catchment. This methodology can be applied in other locations with local climatic and geomorphic data to develop performance goals for specific watersheds, in lieu of the technology-based methods described in the next section.

In summary, watershed-based-criteria developed from detailed studies that comprehensively analyze water quantity and quality data, complemented with modeling, provide a defensible foundation for identification of performance criteria. Whenever possible, performance criteria should be derived from watershed studies.

3.0 METHODS FOR ESTABLISHING TECHNOLOGY-BASED PERFORMANCE CRITERIA

Technology-based criteria can be developed in the absence of detailed watershed studies or when geographically uniform criteria are desired. This section lays out the following four-step process for establishing technology-based performance goals for each of the control objectives illustrated in Figure 3.2:

- Step 1: Establish goals;
- Step 2: Quantify desired level of control;
- Step 3: Select design precipitation;
- Step 4: Define capture volumes and release rates.

3.1 Step 1: Establish Goals

The objectives discussed in Section 1.2 can be collectively considered as having the purpose of maintaining a set of watershed functions that provide desirable environmental and societal values. Goals for maintenance of groundwater quantity and quality, surface water quality improvement, stream channel protection, and flood protection are needed to address the effects of impervious surfaces described in Chapter 2. The relative importance of these goals is a function of numerous site-specific factors, including the following, to name a few:

- Climatic variables: rainfall and evapotranspiration;
- Geology and soils;
- Groundwater characteristics;
- Designated use and sensitivity of receiving streams;
- Size of the receiving streams;
- Existing natural resources and ecosystem restoration objectives;
- Future development plans for the watershed;
- Condition of the receiving streams;
- Stormwater and instream pollutants;
- Flood and erosion hazards;
- Site constraints;
- Public health, safety, and welfare;
- Recreational and aesthetic value to the community; and
- Financial resources available.

Ideally, management goals should be consistent with the unique conditions of the project and its location in the watershed. For example, a project involving a bridge over a large stream may not need controls that provide extreme flow protection because the flooding characteristics of the site are dictated by the hydrology of the entire watershed upstream from the bridge. Controlling the peak flow from the roadway over the bridge is unlikely to make a difference in the peak flow in the stream. On the other hand, controls may be needed to remove the pollutants associated with runoff generated by small, frequent storms falling over the bridge's paved areas. If a project is located where easily dissolved bedrock (e.g., limestone or dolomite) is near the ground surface, groundwater recharge goals and pollutant removal goals need to work together to address the potential formation of sinkholes and deliver treated runoff to potentially fast-moving water flowing in underground dissolution pathways. As another example, water quality goals may be the most important for nutrient sensitive estuaries and lakes. Therefore, even though streams are not that sensitive to nitrogen and phosphorus loads, water quality goals may need to be applied to them because they discharge to a sensitive waterbody. In places where public or private property are exposed to flooding hazards and stormwater controls have a role in significantly reducing the overall flood risk, control of extreme events should be considered.

It is the responsibility of state and municipal environmental agencies to collect and evaluate scientific data on receiving bodies to develop location-specific suitable management goals and assign the appropriate importance. Some jurisdictions have stormwater criteria targeted to specific areas. For example, Delaware has peak flow control requirements for sets of two or three single-storm events, depending on the location in the state but, for six specific watersheds, the state requires control of any increases in runoff volume. On the other hand, water quality control criteria are uniform across the state (State of Delaware, 2010).

In summary, designers typically must abide by design standards in stormwater regulations. These standards are developed by regulators and should support a set of stormwater management goals judiciously weighted to reflect geographic differences, the specific characteristics of receiving water bodies, and the nature of the development project.

3.2   Step 2: Define the Desired Level of Control

Each goal established in Step 1 should be supported by specific numeric criteria for the receiving water or control technology that quantify the desired level of management. Technology-based standards are commonly used because of a desire to apply criteria uniformly throughout a jurisdiction or region. This type of standard is also easier to implement because the focus is on setting design criteria for a specific facility that, once developed, are often applied in a variety of settings. Effluent limits, pollutant load reduction percents, runoff volume reductions, and peak flow attenuation criteria are common level-of-control measures for stormwater control technologies.

3.2.1   Groundwater Recharge and Evapotranspiration Level of Control

The recharge and evapotranspiration volume is intended to preserve evapotranspiration, groundwater recharge, interflow, and baseflow in areas undergoing development. It is based on recharge and evapotranspiration rates derived from hydrologic relationships between rainfall and stream flow (e.g., using actual measurements of soil infiltration properties throughout the development site), water well withdrawal rates, or other appropriate methods. Recharge and evapotranspiration volume is typically quantified as a percent of average annual precipitation or runoff volume or through analytical methods and modeling based on site conditions.

3.2.2   Water Quality Level of Control

A common approach in many municipalities is to use the following two parameters to design a technology-based level of control for stormwater quality:

- A stormwater quality volume (WQV) able to capture a large percent of the average annual runoff; and

- A drawdown time of WQV into the atmosphere or the soil (based on evapotranspiration and soil infiltration properties) or to the downstream conveyance system (based on the outlet structure design) that is governed by treatment effectiveness of the unit processes occurring in the stormwater control and other criteria based on public health and safety concerns.

To illustrate how to determine WQV and its drawdown time, long-term simulations of runoff were examined by Roesner et al. (1991) in six U.S. cities: Butte, Montana; Chattanooga, Tennessee; Cincinnati, Ohio; Detroit, Michigan; San Francisco, California; and Tucson, Arizona. Hourly precipitation records of 40 to 60 years were processed for a variety of WQV control sizes for the typical urban developments in the six cities. Table 3.3 lists the average annual rainfall and the area-weighted runoff coefficient at

TABLE 3.3   Hydrologic parameters and maximized storage volumes evaluated at six watersheds.

City	Average annual rainfall, mm (in.)	Runoff coefficient of study watershed	Maximized WQV	
			Watershed mm (in.)	m³/ha (ac-ft/ac)
Butte, Montana	371 (14.6)	0.44	6.4 (0.25)	63.5 (0.021)
Chattanooga, Tennessee	749 (29.5)	0.63	12.7 (0.50)	127 (0.042)
Cincinnati, Ohio	1 013 (39.9)	0.50	10.2 (0.40)	102 (0.033)
Detroit, Michigan	889 (35.0)	0.47	7.6 (0.30)	76.2 (0.025)
San Francisco, California	490 (19.3)	0.65	20.3 (0.80)	203 (0.067)
Tucson, Arizona	295 (11.6)	0.50	7.6 (0.30)	76.2 (0.025)

each of the study watersheds. Runoff capture efficiencies of basins were tested using an outflow discharge rate that emptied the WQV in 24 hours. This drawdown time was based on field study findings by Grizzard et al. (1986) in the Washington, D.C., area. The authors determined that a basin had to be designed to empty a volume equal to the average runoff event's volume in no less than 24 hours to be an effective storm-water quality enhancement facility. Drawdown times for other types of stormwater controls are based on their unit processes, which relate pollutant removal to draw-down time or a related parameter (e.g., retention time, biouptake rates, evapotranspi-ration rates, soil infiltration properties, etc.). A maximum drawdown time may need to be established based on the statistics of the duration between storm events so that the stormwater control has capacity available when a new storm arrives.

If a watershed-based level of control is desired (e.g., to meet a targeted load reduction or concentration to achieve a specific water quality condition in the receiv-ing water), continuous simulation may be used to determine the percent capture of average annual runoff and its release rate to meet the load reduction limit. In con-trast, if a technology-based level of control is desired, it may be defined by a specific capture goal for the average annual runoff volume. One way to define a cost-effective WQV is to maximize capture efficiency. Urbonas et al. (1990) defined this maximum efficiency in terms of the "optimized" WQV and reported on a sensitivity study they performed relative to this volume for the Denver, Colorado area. Figure 3.5a shows

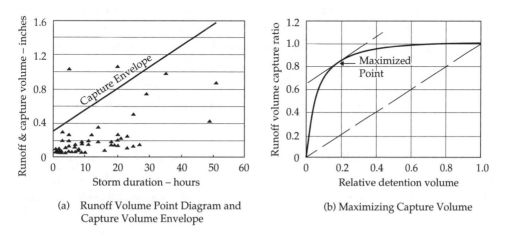

(a) Runoff Volume Point Diagram and   (b) Maximizing Capture Volume
     Capture Volume Envelope

FIGURE 3.5 Methodology for optimizing capture volume (Urbonas, et. al., 1990) (Reprinted with permission from ASCE).

that all but two runoff events are captured by relatively small WQVs, defined in this example as the "capture envelope" of a detention facility in Denver with a "brim-full" volume of 7.6 watershed-mm (0.3 watershed-in.) and a drawdown time of 12 hours.

Figure 3.5b shows the cumulative distribution of runoff volumes. The relative detention volume is each event's runoff and capture volume divided by the volume of runoff from the 99.9% probability storm, which in Denver is 77.2 mm (3.04 in.) of precipitation. The runoff volume capture ratio represents the percent of the total runoff that can be captured by a WQV equal to the relative detention volume. The optimum is determined as the point where the tangent to the cumulative distribution curve is 1:1. In this example, a relative detention volume of 18% of the 99.9% probability storm, equaling a WQV of 13.9 watershed-mm (0.55 watershed-in.), is able to capture approximately 83% of the average annual runoff volume. Later, Urbonas and Stahre (1993) redefined this optimal point as the "maximized" WQV because it is the point at which rapidly diminishing returns in the number of runoff events captured begin to occur. For each of the six study watersheds previously described, the maximized WQV values are listed in Table 3.3. This methodology is appropriate for defining maximized control volumes for other regions and types of controls based on local climatic and site conditions and appropriate drawdown times for each unit process (e.g., soil infiltration rates, hydraulic conductivity of various filter media, evapotranspiration potential, and retention times for biouptake).

The sensitivity investigation by Urbonas et al., (1990) also estimated the average annual stormwater removal rates of total suspended solids using the maximized WQV as the surcharge storage above a permanent pool of a wet pond. Estimates of total suspended solid removals were performed using the procedure reported by Driscoll (1983). Table 3.4 shows that a facility with a WQV twice as large as the maximized WQV (i.e., a ratio of 200%) provides an additional 9% increase in the total annual runoff volume captured and an insignificant 2% increase in the average

TABLE 3.4   Sensitivity of the stormwater control WQVs in Denver, Colorado.

WQV to maximized WQV ratio	Annual runoff volume captured, %	Number of storms completely captured	Average annual total suspended sediments removed, %
0.7	75	27	86
1.0	85	30	88
2.0	94	33	90

annual removal of total suspended solids. If a facility with a WQV 70% as large as the maximized WQV is used, only a 10% decrease occurs in the volume of runoff captured and an insignificant 2% decrease occurs in the annual total suspended solid load removed. Based on these findings, the Denver municipal area adopted a WQV for the sizing of stormwater controls equal to 95% of the maximized WQV, which captures the 80th-percentile runoff event (i.e., captures 80% of the annual runoff volume). This 80th-percentile runoff event is considered by the municipalities in this semiarid region of the United States as cost-effective for stormwater quality management and is viewed as the design event that achieves CWA's definition of *maximum extent practicable*. The "optimized" WQV is an example of a technology-based criterion for water quality that can be adapted to other regions.

3.2.3   Channel Protection Level of Control

There have been many technology-based design criteria proposed to protect downstream channels from erosive flows from uncontrolled runoff. To date, monitoring data have not been collected for a sufficient period to determine if the approaches are effective over the long term. Channel protection is a complex issue and the subject of active research to understand and improve approach and design criteria. Most of the knowledge gap is in collecting reliable data over a sufficiently long period and analyzing it to detect trends in channel integrity. Newly devised strategies have not been sufficiently evaluated because it takes a long time for them to move into practice. The economic factors and needs for timely permitting processes associated with land development create a preference for continuing to issue permits under outdated criteria. Ecoregional variability adds to the challenge. For instance, streams in semiarid and arid climates can be more susceptible to urbanization effects because of a prevalence of sand stream beds, weak streambank reinforcement because of sparse vegetation, and highly dynamic water and sediment regimes (Coleman et al., 2005; Hawley and Bledsoe, 2011).

Nevertheless, criteria based on engineering and geomorphic principles show strong promise. As mentioned in Chapter 2, continuous simulation and flow duration analyses using the tractive shear force method (Lane, 1955), excess shear stress methods (Pomeroy et al., 2008), or evaluation of stream power (Watson et al., 2001) are alternative methods able to define channel protection volumes and performance effectiveness more accurately than single-event hydrologic and hydraulic modeling of streams. This research has shown that changes in channel morphology caused by hydromodification are the result of many interrelated variables, including runoff volume; sediment loads and transport; frequency and duration of erosive flows;

magnitude and duration of base flows; and overall statistics of the full spectrum of flow patterns. Also important are properties of the watershed and receiving stream such as channel slope, stream bed and bank composition, geology, watershed physiography, channel cross section and plan form, vegetation, and existing stormwater infrastructure. In view of these complexities, great flexibility will be needed to take advantage of these new concepts and ensure that they can adapt as new lessons are learned.

Hydromodification is best addressed with a suite of strategies that attempt to maintain a watershed's hydrologic functions, including native soil and vegetation protection, hydrologically sensitive site design and landscaping, spatially distributed on-site controls, and restoration of degraded stream systems. End-of-pipe alternatives where runoff is accumulated in a central location and instream controls that create a barrier in natural channels are less effective at providing stream channel protection, as explained in Chapter 2.

For the purposes of this MOP, the current practice has generally been based on single-event hydrologic and hydraulic modeling of streams, even though, as stated earlier in this section, this approach has not been fully demonstrated to stabilize urban streams over the full range of sub-bankfull flows, geomorphic conditions, and sediment characteristics. The following are the two most common approaches:

- Two-year control—this option was the earliest form of detention for channel protection and was based on studies showing that the 2-year flood was considered to be the channel-forming event. The criteria were selected assuming that, if the postdevelopment peak flow for this event could be reduced to the same level as the predevelopment peak, the erosive potential from runoff would be minimized (McCuen and Moglen, 1988). Subsequent studies showed that, without reduction in runoff volume, the duration of the 2-year peak was extended and streams were exposed to channel-forming flows for a longer time (MacCrae, 1997). This criterion is not recommended for channel protection purposes unless it is supported by watershed-specific studies.

- One-year, 24-hour extended detention—several states, primarily on the East Coast, have adopted a requirement to provide a CPV corresponding to a 1-year storm and release it over an extended detention period of 24-hours. The reasoning is that the CPV will be stored and released so gradually that erosive velocities will rarely be exceeded during bankfull and near-bankfull events. Flows from larger, less frequent events are intended to flow over the streambanks into the floodplain, where velocities will be dissipated. Modeling based on several sites in Maryland demonstrated significant reduction in erosive flows. Long-term modeling was included as a permit requirement in Maryland's MS4 NPDES permits and has been underway for several years. Other states, mainly in humid climates, have adopted this criterion, for example, Iowa, Georgia, Missouri, Minnesota, and New York. However, broad applicability of these criteria over a wide range of climatic and geomorphologic conditions has not been fully demonstrated.

The remainder of this MOP assumes that channel protection is accomplished through capture and release of a specified volume, which could be the result of applying rigorous geomorphic analyses and watershed studies.

3.2.4 Level of Control for Large, Infrequent Storms

Several methods are used to establish level-of-control criteria for OFV and EFV. The simplest criterion is to release OFV or EFV from a developed drainage area at the peak predevelopment runoff rate for the same storm recurrence interval. The "predevelopment equals postdevelopment" criteria would seem to establish a reasonable level of flood control, but do not account for downstream effects of increased runoff volume associated with development. These effects are illustrated in Figure 3.6, in which hydrographs from three subareas result in a combined hydrograph at a point

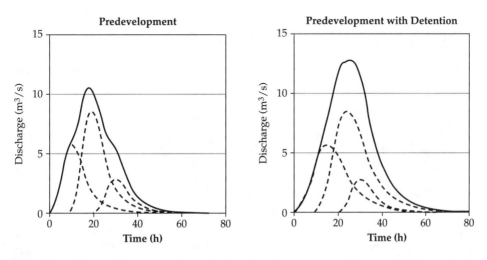

FIGURE 3.6 Effect of superposition of postdevelopment peak flows with detention.

of interest. The detention strategy is successful in maintaining individual peak flows at the predevelopment levels; however, the increased runoff volume and longer duration of high flows result in a combined peak flow greater than the predevelopment condition. This outcome of superposition of attenuated peak flows has been known for a long time (Leopold and Maddock, 1954) but goes unheeded in many municipal regulations. Therefore, criteria that require uniform geographic application of a peak attenuation condition over a watershed need to be supported by a defensible watershed study.

Increased stream flows associated with increases in runoff volume can be addressed through controls that promote infiltration and evapotranspiration of the increased runoff volume or that release runoff at less than the predevelopment peak flow to compensate for the increased volume. Figure 3.7 illustrates that in principle, "overcontrol" could prevent increased flows and water surface elevations throughout the watershed. The challenge in developing "postdevelopment-less-than-predevelopment" criteria is determining how much less the release rate should be. Some jurisdictions establish the peak of a more frequently occurring design storm through "conventional wisdom"; for example, release the postdevelopment peak flow from the 100-year design storm at the predevelopment peak flow from the 2-year design storm (City of Fort Collins, 1997). Others define rules for establishing the release rate based on drainage area or other parameters proportional to the increased volume.

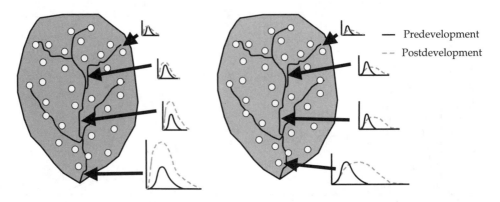

(a) Downstream effects of releasing detention volumes at peak predevelopment flowrates

(b) Effect of releasing detention volumes at less than predevelopment flowrates

FIGURE 3.7   Expected downstream effect of overcontrolling peak flows.

Another approach is to conduct a downstream analysis to ascertain at what point the effects of a development dissipate with respect to the overall response of the upstream watershed. This analysis can be used to determine a threshold ratio of the development's area to the upstream drainage area, at which changes in peak flows need to be checked to verify that no adverse effect is caused. For example, from studies in Greenville, South Carolina, and Raleigh, North Carolina, Debo and Reese (2002) determined that downstream effects of a development project and its stormwater controls need to be analyzed to a point downstream where the project area is 10% of the total watershed draining to that point. For other locations, watershed-specific studies need to be conducted to support this type of determinations.

As another example, the Critical Storm Method is used for sizing OFV-control facilities in Ohio (Mid-Ohio Regional Planning Commission, 1977). Under this methodology, the "critical storm event" is selected from Table 3.5 based on the percent increase in postdevelopment runoff volume from a site during a 1-year storm event. Runoff from storm events less than or equal to the critical storm event are released from the stormwater control at a rate no greater than the peak runoff during a 1-year storm event under predeveloped conditions. Runoff from storms larger than the critical storm event is released at the peak predevelopment runoff rate for that storm. For example, if the predevelopment 1-year, 24-hour runoff volume from a site is 120 000 m³ (100 ac-ft) and the corresponding postdevelopment volume is 300 000 m³ (250 ac-ft), then the percent increase in runoff volume is 180 000 m³ (150 ac-ft) divided by 120 000 m³ (100 ac-ft) or 150%; therefore, the critical storm is the 25-year, 24-hour

TABLE 3.5   Critical storm determination for central Ohio.

If the percent increase in runoff volume is		The peak flow shall be limited to that of the storm with return period
equal to or greater than	and less than	
—	10	1-year
10	20	2-year
20	50	5-year
50	100	10-year
100	250	25-year
250	500	50-year
500	—	100-year

design storm. In this instance, the OFV control is designed to release the postdevelopment 25-year, 24-hour design storm volume at the predevelopment 1-year, 24-hour design storm peak flow and the postdevelopment 50- and 100-year storm volumes at the predevelopment 50- and 100-year design storm peak flows, respectively.

As discussed in Section 2, the most reliable foundation for this type of rule is a modeling study of the watershed that supports determination of overcontrol requirements (e.g., Borton-Lawson, 2010). These studies can be replicated in other jurisdictions using watershed hydrologic models to simulate scenarios resulting from existing and planned development. Continuous simulation is preferable to single event modeling. Both the magnitude of superimposed peak flows and the duration of these combined peak flows must be considered when evaluating possible performance requirements for stormwater controls.

3.3   Step 3: Select Design Precipitation

This step identifies commonly used information and evaluations for determining design precipitation conditions for the large, infrequent storms that govern OFV and EFV and the smaller storms used to establish recharge and evapotranspiration volume, WQV, and CPV.

3.3.1   Large, Infrequent Storms

Traditionally, hydrologists have focused on evaluating the effects of and developing methods to control infrequent events such as larger storms for drainage and flood protection and drought periods for water supply development. Because large storms occur infrequently and flow monitoring data are somewhat limited, the design of many flood control measures is based on selecting a design rainfall volume to generate a runoff volume using a suitable rainfall–runoff relationship or numerical model. This section discusses methods to derive these design storms. However, it is important to note that the statistical properties of rainfall are different from those of peak flows. For example, there could be many storms of such small magnitude that they do not generate runoff; therefore, these events would be included in the rainfall statistics but not in the flow statistics. Because rainfall data are more readily available than flow data, it is common to assign the frequency properties of individual events from rainfall to runoff (e.g., the 50-year storm is assumed to produce the 50-year peak flow).

Intensity–duration–frequency (IDF) curves are a commonly used approach because of their straightforward application. Intensity–duration–frequency curves similar to the one from Columbus, Ohio, shown in Figure 3.8 are available for most locations in the United States through the National Weather Service (Bonnin et al., 2004). Peak flows can be derived through standard hydrologic methods by selecting the rainfall volume from the IDF curve for a particular recurrence interval and time of concentration. Alternatively, the IDF curve can be used to define the total rainfall volume for a particular recurrence interval and duration.

A design hyetograph can then be created using the design rainfall volume and a theoretical distribution such as those developed by the USDA NRCS. Details on how to apply this methodology are provided in USDA (1986) and the process has been automated in several public domain computer programs, such as HEC-HMS, TR-20, and TR-55. A more robust method is to develop hyetographs using municipality-specific rainfall data, which is possible using the datasets maintained by the National Oceanic and Atmospheric Administration (NOAA). The highest reliability will be achieved through the use of continuous simulation using a long term rainfall record, which allows understanding the response of the watershed or development site to the full spectrum of recorded rainfall.

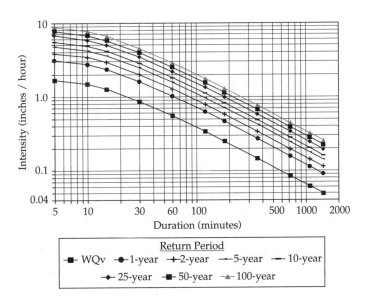

FIGURE 3.8   Intensity–duration–frequency curves, central Ohio (Section 05) (1 in. = 25.4 mm) (adapted from Huff and Angel, 1992).

3.3.2   Small, Frequent Storms

Infrequent events commonly represent only a small fraction of long-term rainfall–runoff volume. Examination of the statistics of precipitation suggests that capturing runoff from "smaller" storms allows treatment of a large fraction of the runoff events and runoff volume that occur from the urban landscape. In addition, addressing small storms also helps channel protection by managing the majority of the cumulative shear stresses, as discussed in Chapter 2.

Determination of an appropriate design storm that leads to capturing the majority of the annual runoff volume relies on some type of statistical evaluation of precipitation records. The following two methods are presented for defining a design precipitation depth: cumulative probability distributions and mean annual runoff-producing rainfall.

3.3.2.1   Cumulative Probability Distributions

This method can be applied when a long-term historic record of rainfall is available. NOAA maintains comprehensive rainfall datasets that can be used to apply this method, thereby facilitating its applicability.

To construct a cumulative probability distribution, the historic precipitation record for a particular time increment (e.g., hourly) is sorted according to rainfall volume. Alternatively, the record can be subdivided into individual storms separated by a specified period of no rain. Events with a large rainfall volume are infrequent and have a low probability of being exceeded; conversely, a small storm occurs more frequently and its volume has a high probability of being exceeded. Such distributions are used to define the design precipitation volume as a percentile, that is, the fraction of events that are equal to or smaller than a particular precipitation volume. For example, Roesner et al., (1991) analyzed the cumulative probability distribution of daily precipitation data from Orlando, Florida, and Cincinnati, Ohio, for 40 years (Figure 3.9), screening the data to include only runoff-producing precipitation events that were 2.5 mm (0.1 in.) or greater in Cincinnati and 1.5 mm (0.06 in.) or greater in Orlando. Most of the daily values were found to be less than 25 mm (1 in.) in total depth. In Orlando, which averages 1270 mm (52 in.) of rainfall per year, 90% of these events produce less than 36 mm (1.4 in.) of rainfall. In Cincinnati, which has 1020 mm (40 in.) per year of precipitation, 90% of the events produce less than 20 mm (0.8 in.) of rainfall. The 90% cumulative probability typically represents a point of diminishing returns in establishing WQV because even

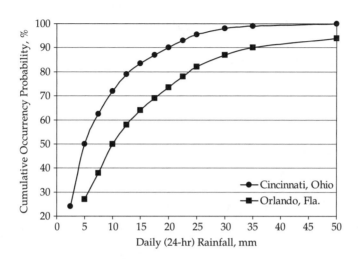

FIGURE 3.9   Cumulative probability distribution of daily precipitation for two cities in the United States (Roesner et al., 1991).

significant increases in facility size only achieve marginal increases in treatment performance.

Similar work was performed in the 1980s to determine the design precipitation event appropriate for defining WQV in the Chesapeake Bay region. Schueler (1987) studied hourly rainfall data from Washington, D.C., and determined that capture of the 3-month frequency storm (32 mm [1.25 in.]) would treat approximately 90% of the annual rainfall. Rainfall records from three other locations, Norfolk, Virginia; Frederick, Maryland; and Harrisburg, Pennsylvania, were subsequently evaluated to determine if capture of the 25-mm (1-in.) event would be an effective measure. The average capture percent using this criterion for the four locations ranged from 85 to 91%; the 1-in. capture criterion was subsequently adopted in stormwater design criteria by the State of Maryland.

As in the case of large storms, the statistical properties of rainfall are different from those of the runoff volumes, although it is common practice to assume that they follow the same statistical distributions. Some jurisdictions may choose to select capture percentiles based on runoff volume rather than rainfall depth.

The cumulative probability distribution method is recommended for estimating the rainfall depth producing the WQV because it is based on site-specific data covering the variability of rainfall patterns.

3.3.2.2 Mean Annual Runoff-Producing Rainfall

In the absence of rainfall statistics, the following method, proposed by Urbonas et al., (1990), provides an alternative for calculating a design precipitation volume P appropriate for determining the maximized WQV:

$$P = a\,P_{avg} \tag{3.1}$$

where

P_{avg} = the mean annual storm-producing rainfall and

a = the event capture ratio.

Figure 3.10 shows a map of the contiguous 48 states of the United States with the mean annual runoff-producing rainfall depths superimposed (Driscoll et al., 1989). These mean depths are based on a selected number of rain gauges, a 6-hour inter-event time to define a new storm event and a minimum depth of 2.5 mm (0.10 in.) of precipitation for a storm to produce incipient runoff. Figure 3.10 may be supplemented with local data.

After an analysis of long-term data from seven precipitation gauging sites located in different meteorological regions of the United States, Guo and Urbonas (1995) defined the event capture ratio a through regression equations that relate the mean precipitation depth P_{avg} to the maximized WQV. This method recognizes that a subsequent storm often occurs before the volume captured from the previous storm has been fully infiltrated, evapotranspired, or discharged from the stormwater control, requiring the maximized WQV to be larger as drawdown times increase. Table 3.6 lists the event capture ratios a that were defined through this analysis over a range of drawdown times for maximized WQVs. The determination coefficient r^2 ranges between 0.80 and 0.97. The event capture ratio was deemed important to receiving waters because it is the frequency of the shock loads that has the greatest negative effect on aquatic life in the receiving streams (Urbonas et al., 1990).

As stated earlier, the cumulative probability method is preferable but the event capture ratio method is suitable for calculating WQV at any given site where a sufficiently long rainfall record is not available to perform the statistical analysis described in the previous subsection.

3.4   Step 4: Define Capture Volumes and Release Rates

This step provides the information necessary to define the capture volumes and release rates to meet one or more control objectives described in Step 1, while

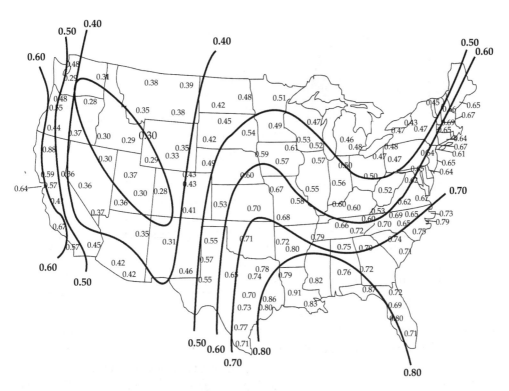

FIGURE 3.10 Mean storm precipitation depth in the continental United States in inches (1 in. = 25.4 mm).

TABLE 3.6 Event capture ratio *a* relating the mean annual runoff-producing rainfall to the optimized WQV (Guo and Urbanas, 1995).

	Draw-down time of WQV*		
	12 hours	**24 hours**	**48 hours**
a =	1.109	1.299	1.545

*Selected as approximately the 85th-percentile runoff event (range 82 to 88%)

applying the desired level of control in Step 2 and the design precipitation events in Step 3. The control strategy differs between large storms and small storms, as illustrated in Figure 3.11. This figure shows that OFV and EFV controls use a peak flow attenuation approach that only controls those flows that exceed downstream pipe or channel capacity, allowing flows from smaller storms to pass through virtually unimpeded.

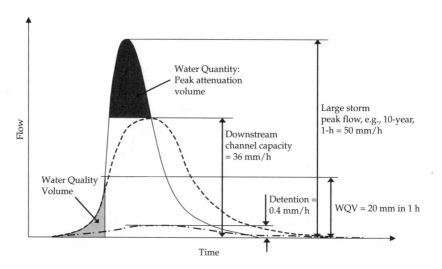

FIGURE 3.11   Illustration of large and small storm control strategies.

Conversely, recharge and evapotranspiration volume, WQV, and CPV controls use an approach that captures at least a fraction of runoff from every storm event, infiltrating, evapotranspiring, and discharging it over a long time to achieve the desired stormwater control objectives. In this example, the flow attenuation release rate (36 mm/h) is nearly two orders of magnitude larger than the water WQV drawdown rate (0.4 mm/h), which presents challenges in designing a multi-objective stormwater control.

The relationship between rainfall and runoff varies widely depending on the amount and type of impervious surfaces in the watershed, the degree to which the impervious surfaces are directly connected to the drainage system, infiltration properties of the soils, the size of the precipitation event, antecedent soil moisture conditions leading up to the rainfall event, length and slope of overland flow paths, the type and density of vegetation, and seasonal evapotranspiration. Chapter 14 presents models formulated to take into account this level of complexity. For technology-based goals, some of the hydrologic and hydraulic models in Chapter 14 are used for large storm events, whereas simpler representations of rainfall–runoff relationships are used for small storms.

3.4.1   Large, Infrequent Storms

These extreme events are typically managed through peak attenuation in stormwater controls. Standard hydrologic methods, e.g., *Urban Hydrology for Small Watersheds*

(USDA, 1986), U.S. EPA's Stormwater Management Model (SWMM), U.S. Army Corps of Engineers' HEC-HMS software, and others discussed in Chapter 14, are widely used to support design of OFV and EFV control facilities. The TR-55 methodology is a commonly used approach that uses a general rainfall–runoff model to generate runoff volumes, peak flows, and hydrographs given a precipitation depth and watershed characteristics. TR-55 is based on the concept of the runoff curve number (USDA, 1986) and uses synthetic dimensionless storm distributions to transform rainfall depth into a storm hyetograph. The long-standing methodologies for routing floods associated with OFV and EFV through a storage facility should be familiar to most readers of this MOP. Details of these computational techniques can be found in numerous manuals and textbooks, for instance, U.S. Department of Transportation (2002), Maidment (1993), and Bedient et al. (2008). ASCE and WEF (1992) provide in-depth discussion on this subject as well and on the design of stormwater conveyance systems. The reader is referred to these and similar publications for additional information.

Application of these methods results in runoff volumes, peak flows, and outflow hydrographs that can be used to design and evaluate performance of detention-based stormwater controls and develop peak attenuation strategies. The OFV and EFV cannot be calculated directly; instead, an iterative approach is used in which trial values of OFV and EFV are selected and tested until the desired peak flow reduction is attained. The postdevelopment hydrograph of an appropriate storm defined in Step 3 is routed through an assumed basin and outlet structure. The resulting release rates are evaluated against the levels of control defined in Step 2, and the basin's OFV and EFV are adjusted in subsequent iterations until a suitable design is achieved.

As an example, the overbank flood control criterion for a municipality requires that the 10-year peak flow from a 9.31-ha (23-ac) drainage area be maintained at 75% of predevelopment levels. The design rainfall depth is 112 mm (4.4 in.). The predevelopment curve number is 60 and the time of concentration is 1.25 hours. After development, the curve number increases to 70 and the time of concentration decreases to 1 hour. The WinTR-55 software (USDA, 2009) was used to estimate the flows resulting from these watershed properties. The predevelopment runoff volume is 30 mm (1.2 in.) and the corresponding peak flow is 0.32 m^3/s (11.3 cfs). After development, the runoff increases to 48 mm (1.9 in.) and the peak flow increases to 0.64 m^3/s (22.6 cfs).

For a basin, the first iteration to obtain the volume required for peak attenuation starts with a value estimated from (USDA, 1986):

$$R_s = \frac{\forall}{Q_{post}} = C_0 + C_1\alpha + C_2\alpha^2 + C_3\alpha^3 \qquad (3.2)$$

where

$\forall$ = peak attenuation volume (OFV in this case), watershed-mm (watershed-in.);

Q_{post} = postdevelopment runoff volume, watershed-mm (watershed-in.);

$\alpha = q_{out}/q_{post}$ is the peak attenuation desired from the stormwater control; q_{out} is the peak flow leaving the basin, and q_{post} the postdevelopment peak flow. In this case, q_{out} is 75% of the peak predevelopment flow.

C_0, C_1, and C_2, and C_3 are regression coefficients that depend on the type of synthetic rainfall distribution (see USDA, 1986). For this example, a Type II applies and C_0 = 0.682, $C_1 = -1.43$, $C_2 = 1.64$, and $C_3 = -0.804$.

The peak flow attenuation ratio α is (0.75)(0.32 m³/s)/0.64 m³/s = 0.375 and eq 3.2 yields R_s = 0.682 −1.43(0.375) + 1.64(0.375)² − 0.804(0.375)³ = 0.334.

The OFV is computed from

$$OFV = R_s Q_{post} A \qquad (3.3)$$

where A is the total drainage area. Therefore,

OFV = 0.334(48 mm)(9.31 ha) = 1492 m³ (1.2 ac-ft)

This initial value would be used to begin the iterative process that requires knowledge of the stage-volume relationship for the controls as well as the configuration and stage-discharge relationship for the outlet works. Additional details can be found in ASCE and WEF (1992).

3.4.2 Small, Frequent Storms

The size of the runoff event to be recharged or evapotranspired (recharge and evapotranspiration volume), captured and treated (WQV), and released at non-erosive rates (CPV) is a critical factor in the effectiveness of stormwater controls. Controls that are "too small" are ineffective because too many storms will exceed the capacity of the facility. Controls that are "too large" may also be ineffective if they do not provide sufficient hydraulic retention time for the small, frequent events. As noted in Step 3, most runoff-producing events occur from the predominant population of smaller storms, namely, those less than 13 to 25 mm (0.5 to 1.0 in.). To be effective, stormwater controls should be designed based on these smaller events.

Figure 3.12 illustrates the control strategy used to achieve recharge and evapotranspiration volume, WQV, and CPV control. The first part of this strategy is to maximize infiltration and evapotranspiration, to the extent allowable by site conditions, development patterns, and climate and soil characteristics. Excess runoff is discharged at release rates defined during Step 2, which may be suitable to provide pollutant removal, or matching predevelopment peak flows to deliver non-erosive velocities to the stream. The release rate could be less than the predevelopment rate to compensate for increased runoff volume and to enhance water quality treatment.

3.4.2.1 Water Quality Volume Calculation
The WQV can be estimated from the design precipitation depth P using

$$WQV = Rv\,P \qquad (3.4)$$

where

WQV = stormwater control size, watershed-mm (watershed-in.);

Rv = watershed runoff coefficient; and

P = design storm precipitation volume (from Step 3), watershed-mm (watershed-in.).

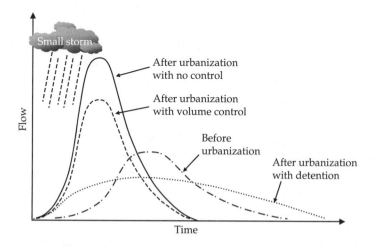

FIGURE 3.12 Illustration of strategy for achieving recharge and evapotranspiration volume, WQV, and CPV control.

Rv may be derived from one of the three methods described subsequently.

Because stormwater controls to manage recharge and evapotranspiration volume, WQV, and CPV are designed to handle the majority of storm events, the variability in the rainfall–runoff relationship becomes a significant design issue. The best way to address this variability is through continuous hydrologic simulation. Because many designs focus on a single property or control rather than an entire watershed, designers opt for simpler, albeit less accurate ways to estimate runoff volumes. Clar et al. (2004) describe three approaches to developing WQV for a particular area, with rainfall–runoff relationships varying in complexity: optimization of water quality capture volume, the Simple Method, and the small storm hydrology method. In addition, the NRCS TR-55 methodology (USDA, 2006 and 2009) can be used to estimate WQV based on a given precipitation event.

The basic procedure for "Optimization of Water Quality Capture Volume" (Urbonas et al., 1990) derived *Rv* through regression using data from more than 60 urban watersheds (U.S. EPA, 1983). The data were collected nationwide over a 2-year period and the method is considered to have broad applicability for small storm events in the United States. *Rv* is defined as

$$Rv = 0.858i^3 - 0.78i^2 + 0.774i + 0.04 \qquad (3.5)$$

where

Rv = runoff coefficient and

  i = watershed imperviousness fraction.

The Simple Method was proposed by Schueler (1987) as a linear regression from data collected during the Nationwide Urban Runoff Program study. As originally derived, in this method, eq 3.4 uses a volumetric runoff coefficient *Rv* times the annual precipitation volume to obtain annual runoff volume. Based on calculations of *Rv* for more than 50 sites, an analysis by Driscoll (1983) found that most of the variation could be explained by the level of urbanization and site imperviousness. The findings of this study also showed that *Rv* was only weakly correlated with variables from individual storms, such as volume, intensity, or duration. The regression equation developed from the data is

$$Rv = 0.05 + 0.9i \qquad (3.6)$$

Equation 3.6 generates somewhat higher runoff coefficients and consequently yields greater WQVs than eq 3.5.

The Small Storm Hydrology Method (SSHM) was derived from work by Pitt (1994) and Pitt and Voorhees (1989) upon realization that many commonly used models typically underpredict runoff flows from impervious surfaces during small rain events. The method is also based on a volumetric runoff coefficient, but one that is computed from the characteristics of both pervious and impervious surfaces in the drainage area. The SSHM involves computing a weighed Rv for the entire site based on the following information:

- The Rv for land surfaces present on the subject site are selected for a given rainfall depth using Table 3.7; and

- If a portion of the site has disconnected impervious surfaces, the reduction factors shown in Table 3.8 are multiplied by the Rv for disconnected impervious areas to obtain the corrected value.

TABLE 3.7 Volumetric runoff coefficient, Rv, for urban runoff for directly connected impervious area.

	Precipitation (mm)			
Impervious area	19	25	32	38
Flat roofs and large unpaved parking lots	0.82	0.84	0.86	0.88
Pitched roofs and large impervious areas (large parking lots)	0.97	0.97	0.98	0.98
Small impervious areas and narrow streets	0.66	0.70	0.74	0.77
Sandy soils (HSG-A)	0.02	0.02	0.03	0.05
Silty soils (HSG-B)	0.11	0.11	0.13	0.15
Clayey soils (HSG-C and HSG-D)	0.20	0.21	0.22	0.24

TABLE 3.8 Reduction factors to volumetric runoff coefficients, Rv, for disconnected impervious surfaces.

	Precipitation (mm)			
Impervious surface	19	25	32	38
Strip commercial shopping center	0.99	0.99	0.99	0.99
Medium to high-density residential with paved alleys	0.27	0.38	0.48	0.59
Medium to high residential without alleys	0.21	0.22	0.22	0.24
Low-density residential	0.20	0.21	0.22	0.24

The SSHM has the advantage of evaluating the precise elements of a particular site and can be used for most design applications to estimate more accurate runoff volumes. The method requires somewhat more effort to identify the specific land surface area ratios and to assess the disconnection of impervious areas. To use the reduction factors for disconnected impervious surfaces, the impervious area upstream of the pervious surface area should be less than one-half of the receiving pervious surface and the flow path through the pervious area should be at least twice the impervious surface flow path.

The TR-55 methodology is commonly used in practice because of the familiarity of designers with curve numbers and the availability of software (USDA, 2009). For small storms, the TR-55 method should be applied with caution; the synthetic storms tend to overestimate peak flows and, as pointed out by Pitt (1994), the curve number approach underestimates runoff volumes.

The drawdown times for different types of stormwater controls listed in Table 3.9 are used in the design calculations presented in Chapters 6 through 10. An examination of Table 3.4 in Step 2 indicates that the use of larger detention volumes does not significantly improve the average annual removal of total suspended solids. A stormwater control sized to capture the WQV will also capture the leading edge of the runoff hydrograph resulting from larger storms. Runoff volumes that exceed the design WQV either bypass the facility or receive less efficient treatment than do the smaller volume storms. Generally, this lower efficiency for larger events has a minimal net effect on quality and channel protection performance. If higher treatment efficiencies for large events are required, it is necessary to both increase WQV and the drawdown time; however, oversizing the control can cause small events to receive less treatment than that provided by properly designed smaller controls.

As an example, estimate the maximized WQV for a wetland basin serving a 22.3-ha (55-ac) watershed that has 40% of its area covered by impervious surfaces. Assume that this site is located in Houston, Texas. According to Table 3.9, the wetland basin needs to be sized to drain its WQV in no fewer than 24 hours to achieve optimal treatment efficiencies. Substituting a value of 0.40 for the variable i in eq 3.3 yields a runoff coefficient Rv equal to 0.28. Using Figure 3.10, the mean storm precipitation depth in Houston is $P_{avg} = 20$ mm (0.8 in.). Table 3.6, yields $a = 1.299$ for the 24-hour drawdown time. Thus, the maximized WQV is

$$WQV = 1.299 \, P_{avg} \, Rv = 7.3 \text{ mm } (0.29 \text{ in.}) \qquad (3.7)$$

TABLE 3.9   Draw-down times for determining maximized WQV of stormwater controls.

Type of control	Recommended draw-down time (hours)	Event capture ratio *a* (from Table 3.5)
Basins		
– Dry basin	48	1.545
– Wet basin (settling design)	12	1.109
– Wetland	24	1.299
Swales and Strips	12*	1.109
Filters	40	1.464
Infiltrators	24	1.299
Gross pollutant traps and mechanical operations	12*	1.109

* Used to calculate WQT, not as a drawdown time.

The volume of a wetland basin for this 22.3-ha (55-ac) watershed needs to be 1620 m^3 (1.31 ac-ft), which is equal to the WQV value from eq 3.7 multiplied by the total area of the watershed. It is recommended that this volume be increased by at least 20% to account for the loss in volume from sediment accumulation. The final design can then show a total volume for the basin of 1950 m^3 (1.6 ac-ft), with an outlet designed to empty 1620 m^3 (1.31 ac-ft) in approximately 24 hours.

3.4.2.2 Water Quality Treatment Rate

Some stormwater control systems (e.g., swales and strips, filters, and gross pollutant traps) are designed for a peak design water quality treatment (WQT) using a design hydrograph or a method specified by local design criteria. Many jurisdictions use some variation of the CN methodology, with rainfall distributed over a specified period such as 24 hours.

One method to transform WQV requirements into flow requirements was proposed by Lenhart and Battiata (2000), who used the Santa Barbara Unit Hydrograph model, a variant of the TR-55 methodology that better represents the flashiness of urban hydrographs, to determine the peak flows associated with a given WQV.

Another methodology for calculating WQT based on the maximized WQV defined earlier in this section is the following:

- Use eq 3.1 to calculate the rainfall volume of the maximized storm, assuming that $Rv = 1.0$ (i.e., complete runoff and no infiltration or evapotranspiration) and the event capture ratio *a* for a 12-hour drain time;

- Develop an IDF curve by assuming that the rainfall volume of the maximized WQV occurs over 1 to 2 hours and completing the curve by paralleling local IDF curves for other frequencies;

- Determine the time of concentration for the area draining into the stormwater control using standard hydrologic methods; and

- Use the Rational Method, the time of concentration for the catchment, its run-off coefficient Rv, and the IDF curve for the WQV to determine the peak flow through the stormwater control WQT.

As an example, the WQT needs to be estimated for a stormwater control in a site in Columbus, Ohio, with a drainage area of 0.81 ha (2 ac), an impervious fraction of 0.5, and a time of concentration of 40 minutes. From Step 3, the mean precipitation depth P_{avg} equals 13 mm (0.5 in.) and the event capture ratio is $a = 1.109$ from Table 3.6, yielding a WQV of 14 mm (0.55 in.) for $Rv = 1.0$. The actual Rv for the watershed as computed from eq 3.3 is 0.34. The 1-hour (60-minute) point on the IDF curve for the water quality event is 14 mm/h (0.55 in./hr), the 2-hour (120-minute) point is 14 mm/2 h = 7 mm/h (0.55 in./2 hr = 0.28 in./hr), and the remainder of the IDF curve was constructed parallel to the remaining family of IDF curves in Figure 3.8. This curve is labeled "WQV" in the figure and yields an intensity of 18 mm/h (0.7 in./hr) for a storm duration equal to the time of concentration of 40 minutes. Therefore, the WQT is

$$\text{WQT} = Rv\,I\,A = (0.34)(18 \text{ mm/h})(0.81 \text{ ha}) = 0.014 \text{ m}^3/\text{s} \ (0.48 \text{ cfs}) \tag{3.6}$$

4.0 A NOTE ABOUT WATER QUALITY TREATMENT EFFECTIVENESS

The aforementioned technology-based methods are presumed to yield stormwater controls able to maximize water quality treatment effectiveness. However, assessments of treatment effectiveness are limited because of the variability in performance data and often incomplete information about design criteria accompanying performance data. Chapter 13 provides recommendations for assessing the effectiveness of stormwater controls. At least two states, Washington and New Jersey, have developed testing protocols. Washington's Technology Assessment Protocol-Ecology and the New Jersey Corporation for Advanced Technology (NJCAT) set forth procedures for ascertaining the effectiveness of stormwater controls. To alleviate this deficiency, Barrett

(2008) explored the performance and relative pollutant removal of several common stormwater quality controls using data contained in the International Stormwater Best Management Practices Database (www.bmpdatabase.org). These controls include wet basins, dry basins, swales, and sand filters. Although the database contains numerous studies with varying amounts of detail, this comparison was based on the performance of only those sites with reported basic design characteristics and water quality data in the form of event mean concentrations (EMCs) so that constituent concentrations can be determined and related to the design of the individual control.

Historically, pollutant removal performance of stormwater quality controls was characterized by the percent reduction in concentration or mass load observed across the system. This method has been recognized as flawed (e.g., Strecker et al., 2001) as the percent removal is dependent on the influent concentration and other factors. Consequently, the analysis presented by Barrett (2008) focuses on effluent quality that can be achieved by these facilities. The effluent quality is then related primarily to influent concentrations. Barrett developed the plots shown in Figure 3.13 to illustrate the range of effectiveness at controlling six typical stormwater pollutants with the four types of stormwater controls evaluated. Each point on the figure represents the average influent and effluent event mean concentration (EMC) for a single control. For each control type, an ellipse is drawn on the plot to indicate the likely performance of a well-designed control. This ellipse does not necessarily encompass every single point contained in the database and presented on the plot, as some outliers may have been produced by inadequately maintained or designed controls or may have resulted from some measurement error during the monitoring period. Ellipses that are more horizontal indicate that the discharge concentration is relatively constant and independent of the influent concentration rises. Conversely, a steep slope means that the discharge concentration is sensitive to the influent value. Wet basins and filters produce the lowest discharge concentrations for most pollutants evaluated, with dry basins being somewhat less effective, and the effectiveness of swales being relatively sensitive to influent concentrations. It should be noted that analyses need to be conducted to incorporate the significance of many green infrastructure sites that rarely overflow. The pollutant removal values in the database are only for storms that produce effluent.

Additional data continue to be incorporated to the International Best Management Practices Database, especially from performance of green infrastructure stormwater controls (Clary et al., 2011). A summary of recent findings is published by the Water Environment Research Foundation (2011). Other relevant references can be found in www.bmpdatabase.org.

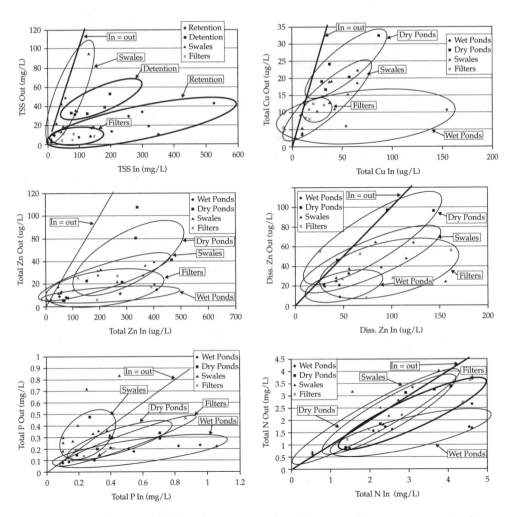

FIGURE 3.13   Influent and effluent concentrations for typical stormwater controls and pollutants (Barrett, 2008).

5.0   CONCLUDING REMARKS

Stormwater management in the 21st century needs to meet multiple objectives in groundwater recharge, pollutant removal, channel protection, flood hazard reduction, and aquatic ecosystem protection, while protecting the public's health, safety, and welfare in a cost-effective manner and consistent with regulations. Development of performance criteria for stormwater controls that address the various combinations of these objectives is challenging because of the complexities and linkages in geomorphologic processes, pollutant loads and concentrations, indicators of impacts and effects, ecosystem endpoints, and stakeholder priorities. The diversity of climate, geology, watershed physiography, land use and land cover, and demographics adds another dimension to the intricacy of the problem.

Performance criteria should be as geographically specific as practicable and account for the ecoregional variability of streams. Criteria should be based on an understanding of the vulnerability of streams to stormwater effects; the resources that must be protected such as, habitat, biota, infrastructure, and property; and the desired target condition to be attained if the stormwater management approach is successful. This approach is scientifically defensible and feasible but seldom implemented as it requires watershed-specific studies, field data verification, stakeholder consensus to select management goals, continuous simulation, and suitable analysis tools to support the development of the standards that support those goals. Some states, such as California, have undertaken efforts to develop this type of understanding about their streams (Bledsoe et al., 2010a, b), and some jurisdictions have implemented performance criteria based on a watershed approach (e.g., Santa Clara Valley Urban Runoff Pollution Prevention Program, 2005; Borton-Lawson, 2010).

Despite the ability of a watershed approach to result in better performance criteria, simpler standards are commonly in use. Some are supported by site-specific studies and exported to other locales. These standards are typically based on sets of single storm events, for which runoff volumes to capture and release rates are specified. Their simplicity and uniform applicability across all types of development sites allows cost-effective use by designers and plan evaluation by regulators. However, their effectiveness in meeting stormwater objectives such as channel protection has not been demonstrated.

In general, regardless of the origin and foundation of existing performance criteria, reliable, long-term monitoring data are not available to determine if they are effective in achieving stormwater management objectives. The ability of a dry basin to attenuate peak flows is well understood and the combination of all peak-attenuation controls in a watershed can be analyzed with existing tools, although it is rarely done. In contrast, little is known about whether releasing the 1-year storm over a 24-hour period is an effective channel protection criterion on a watershed-wide basis. Therefore, there is a knowledge gap in linking the standards to their receiving endpoints and desired outcomes. Research findings take a long time to move into practice, a fact exacerbated by hesitation to try new approaches because of cost concerns and fears of not securing development permits in time.

In summary, a successful process to arrive at appropriate performance goals relies on thorough understanding of the scientific and engineering information available. Failure to do so could result in overly simplistic and unfounded criteria. On the other hand, imperfect information should not lead to inaction and unwillingness to try new approaches based on the existing body of knowledge. Comprehensive monitoring should accompany implementation to gain additional knowledge that can be used to verify progress toward goals, adjust the criteria, and improve designs. Cost factors are important but the cost of developing defensible goals pales against that of having to mitigate the potential future effects of using improper criteria. Finally, harmonization of planning and zoning, robust regulations, and development of tools to facilitate plan approval processes are needed to give standards a chance to make a positive effect.

6.0   REFERENCES

American Society of Civil Engineers; Water Environment Federation (1992) *Design and Construction of Urban Stormwater Management Systems*; ASCE Manuals and Reports of Engineering Practice No. 77; WEF Manual of Practice No. FD-20; American Society of Civil Engineers: New York.

Anderson, D. L.; Janicki, A. (2010) *Linking Receiving Water Impacts to Sources and to Water Quality Management Decisions: Using Nutrients as an Initial Case Study*, Water Environment Research Foundation Report WERF 3C10; Water Environment Research Foundation: Alexandria, Virginia.

Barrett, M. E. (2008) Comparison of BMP Performance Using the International BMP Database. *J. Irrig. Drainage Eng.*, **134** (5), 556–561.

Bedient P. B.; Huber, W. C.; Vieux, B. E. (2008) *Hydrology and Floodplain Analysis*; Prentice Hall: New York, 816 pp.

Bledsoe, B. P. (2002), "Stream Erosion Potential and Stormwater Management Strategies." *J. Water Resour. Plann. Manage.*, **128** (6), 451–455.

Bledsoe, B. P.; Hawley, R. J.; Stein, E. D.; Booth, D. B. (2010a) *Hydromodification Screening Tools: Technical Basis for Development of a Field Screening Tool for Assessing Channel Susceptibility to Hydromodification*, Southern California Coastal Water Research Project (SCCWRP), Technical Report 607, Costa Mesa, California, 42 pp.

Bledsoe, B. P.; Hawley, R. J.; Stein, E. D.; Booth, D. B. (2010b) *Hydromodification Screening Tools: Field Manual for Assessing Channel Susceptibility.* Southern California Coastal Water Research Project (SCCWRP), Technical Report 606, Costa Mesa, California, March, 30 pp.

Bonnin, G. M.; Martin, D.; Lin, B.; Parzybok, T.; Yekta, M.; Riley, D. (2004) *Precipitation-Frequency Atlas of the United States, NOAA Atlas 14, Volume 2, Version 3;* National Oceanographic and Atmospheric Administration's National Weather Service: Silver Spring, Maryland. Data available interactively through the Precipitation Frequency Data Server, Hydrometeorological Design Studies Center, http://hdsc.nws.noaa.gov/hdsc/pfds/index.html (accessed November 2011).

Borton-Lawson (2010) *Appoquinimink River Watershed Stormwater Management Plan, New Castle County, Delaware,* Dover, Delaware, May.

Booth, D. B.; Jackson, C. R. (1997) Urbanization of Aquatic Systems: Degradation Thresholds, Stormwater Detection, and the Limits of Mitigation. *Water Resour. Bull.,* **33,** 1077.

California Regional Water Quality Control Board, San Francisco Bay Region (2009) *Municipal Regional Stormwater Permit, NPDES No. CA612008, Order No. R2–2009-0074, Provision C.3,* San Francisco, California.

City of Fort Collins (1997) *Stormwater Drainage Design Criteria and Construction Standards,* Fort Collins, Colorado.

Clar, M. L.; Barfield, B. J.; O'Connor, T. P. (2004) *Stormwater Best Management Practice Design Guide;* EPA—600/R-04-121; U.S. Environmental Protection Agency, Office of Research and Development: Cincinnati, Ohio.

Clary, J.; Quigley, M.; Poresky, A.; Earles, A.; Strecker, E.; Leisenring, M.; Jones, J. (2011) Integration of Low-Impact Development into the International Stormwater BMP Database. *J. Irrig. Drainage Eng., Special Issue: Urban Storm-Water Management in the 21st Century,* 137 (3), 190–198.

Coleman, D.; MacRae, C.; Stein, E. D. (2005) *Effect of Increases in Peak Flows and Imperviousness on the Morphology of Southern California Streams,* Stormwater Monitoring Coalition, Southern California Coastal Water Research Project, Westminster, California.

Contra Costa Clean Water Program (2005) *Hydrograph Modification Management Plan,* Martinez, California.

County of San Diego, California (2011) *Hydromodification Management Plan*, San Diego, California.

Debo, T. N.; Reese, A. J. (2002) *Municipal Stormwater Management*, 2nd ed.; CRC Press: Boca Raton, Florida, 1176 pp.

Driscoll, E. D. (1983) Performance of Detention Basins for Control of Urban Runoff Quality. *Proceedings of the International Symposium on Urban Hydrology, Hydraulics, and Sediment Control*; University of Kentucky: Lexington, Kentucky.

Driscoll, E. D.; Palhegyi, G. E.; Strecker, E. W.; Shelley, P. E. (1989) *Analysis of Storm Events Characteristics for Selected Rainfall Gauges Throughout the United States*; U.S. Environmental Protection Agency: Washington, D.C.

Grizzard, T. J.; Randall, C. W.; Weand, B. L.; Ellis, K. L. (1986) Effectiveness of Extended Detention Ponds. In *Urban Runoff Quality—Impact and Quality Enhancement Technology*; American Society of Civil Engineers: New York.

Guo, C. Y.; Urbonas, B. R. (1995) *Peat-Sand Filters: A Proposed Stormwater Management Practice for Urban Areas*; Metropolitan Washington Council of Governments: Washington, D.C.

Hanlon, J.; Keehner, D. (2010) *Revisions to the November 22, 2002 Memorandum Entitled "Establishing Total Maximum Daily Load (TMDL) Wasteload Allocations (WLAs) for Storm Water Sources and NPDES Permit Requirements Based on Those WLAs."* U.S. Environmental Protection Agency: Washington D.C., November 12. http://www.epa.gov/npdes/pubs/establishingtmdlwla_revision.pdf (accessed November 2011).

Hawley, R. J.; Bledsoe, B.P. (2011) How Do Flow Peaks and Durations Change in Suburbanizing Semi-Arid Watersheds? A Southern California Case Study. *J. Hydrol.*, **405** (1—2), 69–82.

Huff, F.A; Angel, J.R. (1992) *Rainfall Frequency Atlas of the Midwest*, Bulletin 71 (MCC Research Report 92–03), Midwestern Climate Center, Climate Analysis Center, National Weather Service, National Oceanic and Atmospheric Administration and Illinois State Water Survey, A Division of the Illinois Department of Energy and Natural Resources.

Lane, E. W. (1955) Stable Channel Design. *Trans. Am. Soc. Civ. Eng.*

Lenhart, J. H.; Battiata J. (2000) *Development of a Methodology for Sizing Flow-Based Stormwater Quality Treatment Facilities for the Commonwealth of Virginia.* StormCon—The North American Surface Water Quality Conference and Exposition. Santa Barbara, California.

Leopold, L. B.; Maddock, T. (1954) *The Flood Control Controversy*; The Ronald Press Corp., New York.

MacRae, C. R. (1997) Experience from Morphological Research on Canadian Streams: Is the Control of the Two-Year Frequency Runoff Event the Best Basis for Stream Channel Protection? In *Effects of Watershed Development and Management of Aquatic Ecosystems*, L. A. Roesner, Ed.; American Society of Civil Engineers: Reston, Virginia, 144–162.

Maidment, D. (Ed.) (1993) *Handbook of Hydrology*; McGraw-Hill: New York.

McCuen, R. H.; Moglen, G. E. (1988) Multicriterion Stormwater Management Methods. *J. Water Resour. Plann. Manage.*, **114** (4), 414.

Medina, D. E.; Monfils, J.; Baccala, Z. (2011) Quantifying the Benefits of Green Infrastructure for Floodplain Management. *Proceedings of 2011 EWRI World Water and Environmental Resources Congress*, Palm Springs, California, May.

Mid-Ohio Regional Planning Commission (1977) Stormwater Design Manual; Mid-Ohio Regional Planning Commission: Columbus, Ohio.

Minnesota Pollution Control Agency (2005) *Minnesota Stormwater Manual*; Minnesota Pollution Control Agency: St. Paul, Minnesota.

National Research Council (2008) *Urban Stormwater Management in the United States*; The National Academies Press: Washington, D.C.

Pitt, R. (1994) *Small Storm Hydrology*. University of Alabama–Birmingham. Paper presented at Design of Stormwater Quality Management Practices; Madison, Wisconsin; May 17–19.

Pitt, R.; Voorhees, N. (1989) *Source Load and Management Model—An Urban Nonpoint Source Water Quality Model*; v. I-III, PUBL-WR-218–89; Wisconsin Department of Natural Resources: Madison, Wisconsin.

Pomeroy, C. A.; Roesner, L. A.; Coleman, J. C.; Rankin, E. (2008) Protocols for Evaluating Wet Weather Practices and Urbanization Patterns; Final Report No. 03-WSM-3; Water Environment Research Foundation: Alexandria, Virginia.

Roesner, L. A.; Burgess, E. H.; Aldrich, J. A. (1991) Hydrology of Urban Runoff Quality Management." *Proceedings of the 18th National Conference Water Resources Planning and Management Symposium on Urban Water Resources*, New Orleans, Louisiana, May 20–22; American Society of Civil Engineers: New York.

Santa Clara Valley Urban Runoff Pollution Prevention Program (2005), *Hydromodification Management Plan Final Report*, Sunnyvale, California.

Schueler, T. R. (1987) *Controlling Urban Runoff: A Practical Manual for Planning and Designing Urban BMPs;* Metropolitan Washington Council of Governments: Washington, D.C.

State of Delaware (2010) 5101 Sediment and Stormwater Regulations, in *Title 7 Natural Resources and Environmental Control, 5000 Division of Soil and Water Conservation*, Dover, Delaware.

Strecker, E. W.; Quigley, M. M.; Urbonas, B. R.; Jones, J. E.; Clary, J. K. (2001) Determining Urban Storm Water BMP Effectiveness. *J. Water Resour. Plann. Manage.*, **127** (3), 144–149.

Urban Drainage and Flood Control District (2010) *Urban Storm Drainage Criteria Manual, Volume 3 – Best Management Practices;* Urban Drainage and Flood Control District: Denver, Colorado.

Urbonas, B. R.; Guo, J. C. Y.; Tucker, L. S. (1990) "Optimization of Stormwater Quality Capture Volume," in *Urban Stormwater Quality Enhancement: Source Control, Retrofitting and Combined Sewer Technology;* American Society of Civil Engineers: Reston, Virginia.

Urbonas, B. R.; Stahre, P. (1993) *Stormwater: Best Management Practices and Detention for Water Quality, Drainage, and CSO Management;* Prentice Hall: Englewood Cliffs, New Jersey.

U.S. Department of Agriculture (1986) *Urban Hydrology for Small Watersheds; Technical Release 55;* Natural Resources Conservation Service, Conservation Engineering Division: Washington, D.C.

U.S. Department of Agriculture (2009) *Small Watershed Hydrology: WinTR–55 User Guide;* Natural Resource Conservation Service, Washington, D.C.

U.S. Department of Transportation (2002) *Highway Hydrology*, Hydraulic Design Series No. 2, 2nd ed., Federal Highway Administration, National Highway Institute, FHWA-NHI-02–001, Washington, D.C, October.

U.S. Environmental Protection Agency (1983) *Results of the Nationwide Urban Runoff Program*, Volume I; Final Report; U.S. Environmental Protection Agency, Water Planning Division: Washington, D.C.

U.S. Environmental Protection Agency (2009) *Technical Guidance on Implementing the Stormwater Runoff Requirements for Federal Projects Under Section 435 of the Energy Independence Security Act;* EPA-841/B-09–001; U.S. Environmental Protection Agency, Office of Water: Washington, D.C.

U.S. Environmental Protection Agency (2011) *Storm Water Drainage Wells.* http://water.epa.gov/type/groundwater/uic/class5/types_stormwater.cfm (accessed November 2011).

Washington State Department of Ecology (2005) *Stormwater Management Manual for Western Washington;* Washington State Department of Ecology, Water Quality Program: Olympia, Washington. Watson, C. C.; Bledsoe, B. P.; Biedenharn, D. S. (2001) Specific Stream Power and a Risk-Based Design Approach. *Proceedings of the American Society of Civil Engineers Wetlands Engineering and River Restoration Conference;* Reno, Nevada; Aug 27–31; American Society of Civil Engineers: Reston, Virginia.

Water Environment Research Foundation (2011) *Research Digest: International Stormwater Best Management Practices (BMP) Database Pollutant Category Technical Summaries.* Prepared by Wright Water Engineers and Geosyntec Consultants for Water Environment Research Foundation, Federal Highway Administration, Environmental and Water Resources Institute of the American Society of Civil Engineers. July.

Chapter 4

Unit Processes and Operations for Stormwater Control

(continued)

1.0   INTRODUCTION

This chapter serves two purposes. The first is to present the concept of unit processes and unit operations as they apply to stormwater management. Very often the selection of a stormwater control proceeds from cookbook-style handbooks and does not consider the physical, chemical, and biological processes that take place within the control and the way that they may address the quantity and quality characteristics of the influent stormwater. The practice is now shifting to an approach similar to the unit processes and unit operations in the wastewater industry and this chapter provides a framework for selecting stormwater controls based on the quantity and quality parameters of concern and the way that they are addressed by the processes that take place in the control. The intent of this chapter is that it will serve as a rational guide for stormwater designers to select controls that suit the stormwater problem to address and match quantity and quality goals.

The second purpose of this chapter is to provide a simplified framework to facilitate communication between stormwater management professionals and promote consistency in design procedures and criteria. Different names have been proposed for the same stormwater control and the same name has been used for different devices. This chapter proposes a framework to add clarity, while showing the relationship to terms and names commonly used today.

2.0 APPLICATION OF UNIT PROCESSES AND OPERATIONS CONCEPTS

A concept frequently used in wastewater engineering is unit operations and processes (UOPs). However, the application of the concept put forth in this MOP is different. First, the concept is applied to both stormwater quantity and quality control, given that these two management objectives are frequently achieved in one facility (e.g., an infiltration basin provides volume reduction, peak attenuation, sedimentation, and filtration). Second, the terms *unit processes* and *unit operations* are defined differently for stormwater control from their historic definition in wastewater practice.

In wastewater treatment and related fields, *unit processes* refer to quantity pollutant removal mechanisms that are generally chemical or biological in nature, such as coagulation and nitrification, respectively. *Unit operations* refer to pollutant removal mechanisms, such as sedimentation, that are physical in nature (Metcalf and Eddy, 2003). The early distinction between process and operation appears arbitrary. Rich (1961), who first fully applied the distinction to wastewater treatment, neither explained nor established its purpose or benefit. In fact, later, Rich (1963) defined unit operations as physical processes and identified some physical processes as unit processes rather than operations because of their chemical dependence. An earlier text in wastewater engineering defined all pollutant removal mechanisms as unit operations (Fair and Geyer, 1954). In this MOP, a structure more applicable to stormwater management is presented. Here, *processes* refer to stormwater quantity (peak flow or volume) reduction mechanisms and pollutant removal mechanisms. *Operations* are the "boxes" in which treatment occurs. The concept of unit processes and operations was discussed in a Water Environment Research Foundation report entitled *Critical Assessment of Stormwater Treatment and Control Selection Issues* (Strecker et al., 2005) and is becoming more widely recommended in stormwater management manuals. Additionally, the concept has been applied in practice to stormwater control, for example in the design of stormwater detention facilities to achieve desired settling rates of sediment.

2.1 Unit Processes

As stated above, this MOP refers to *unit processes* as all mechanisms that reduce flow-rates, runoff volumes, pollutant loads, or thermal loads. Examples of stormwater unit processes are peak attenuation, evaporation, sedimentation, adsorption, and precipitation. Defining the unit process in complex stormwater treatment facilities is not always clear. Some pollutant removal mechanisms are a combination of adsorption and precipitation, for example. Some chemical mechanisms are enhanced by an intermediate biological process.

The rationale for the integration of quantity and quality control processes is a recent recognition of their relatedness. For example, infiltration can be used for either quantity or quality control or for both concurrently in the same facility.

Table 4.1 shows the primary unit processes and their suitability to address stormwater quantity and quality issues. Details on the mechanisms for each unit process are provided in Sections 3 and 4 of this chapter.

2.2 Unit Operations

In this MOP, a *unit operation* is defined as the stormwater control in which one or more unit processes occur (Rich, 1961; Casey, 1997). The term "unit operation" and "stormwater control" are used interchangeably in this MOP. Examples of unit operations are bioretention filters, swirl concentrators, landscaped roofs, and flood control basins. The perspective regarding what specifically is a unique unit operation is not always clear. For example, is a forebay upstream of a wet basin considered a unit operation, separate from the main basin? The distinction is reasonable because the function of the forebay differs from the larger basin. The forebay reduces the cost of maintenance by retaining coarse solids, such as sand, in a more accessible location. Recognizing the forebay as a separate unit operation leads the designer to consider alternatives such as a swirl concentrator. The manufactured unit may be more expensive than a forebay, but requires less space and may be more easily maintained than a larger forebay. Another example applies to dry basins. To improve the quality of discharge, a filter is used as the outlet rather than an orifice. The filter is considered a separate unit operation, given that it differs significantly from the dry basin with respect to its unit process (i.e., filtration rather than sedimentation).

TABLE 4.1 Suitability of unit processes to address stormwater quantity and quality.

	Unit process	Excess runoff volume	High peak flows	Total suspended solids	Total dissolved solids	Total nitrogen
Quantity control	Peak flow attenuation		×			
	Infiltration	×	×			
	Dispersion	×	×			
	Evapotranspiration	×	×			
	Runoff collection and usage	×	×			
Pollutant control	Sedimentation			×		×
	Flotation			×		
	Laminar separation			×		
	Swirl concentration			×		
	Sorption				×	
	Precipitation			×	×	
	Coagulation			×	×	
	Filtration			×		×
Biological	Plant metabolism				×	×
	Nitrification/ denitrification					×
	Sulfate reduction				×	
	Organic compound degradation					
	Pathogen dieoff					
Other	Temperature reduction					
	Disinfection					
	Screening					

Total phosphorus	Dissolved phosphorus	Biological oxygen demand	Chloride	Metals	Hydro-carbons	Pathogens	Trash	Thermal enrichment
								×
								×
								×
								×
×		×		×		×	×	
					×		×	
					×			
							×	
	×			×	×			
	×	×		×		×		
	×	×		×				
×		×		×	×	×	×	
×	×			×				
		×			×			
						×		
								×
						×		
		×					×	

To be designated as such, a unit operation requires a design distinctly different from others (e.g., a filter in comparison to a basin). For a given unit operation, a separate designation because of a physical change (e.g., vegetation or shape) should occur only if the change results in a significant difference in performance. For example, sand filters come in several shapes or configurations. However, if changes in the shape of the structure do not affect performance, these different configurations are variants, not separate unit operations.

There is typically more than one unit process occurring in a unit operation. For example, a filter provides both filtration and sedimentation. Although several unit operations may have the same unit process, their significance with respect to quantity and quality may vary. The effectiveness of each of the unit processes in Table 4.1 depends on the design, size, and maintenance of the particular unit operation. Some unit processes can continue essentially unaided by maintenance such as nitrification and denitrification or degradation of organic compounds. Most unit processes, however, require that the unit operation be properly maintained to be effective to the extent intended (see Chapter 11).

2.3   Systems

A *system* is defined as one or more unit operations in series. The concept is illustrated in Figure 4.1, which shows two examples of systems each with two unit operations. The first system is composed of a wet vault and a sand filter. The wet vault pretreats the stormwater, reducing the maintenance frequency of the filter. Within the wet vault, the unit processes of sedimentation and flotation occur; some peak flow attenuation may take place also. Within the filter, unit processes of sedimentation and filtration occur in addition to sorption and precipitation, depending on the media. The second example shows a landscaped roof that discharges to an infiltration trench. The landscaped roof provides runoff volume reduction by storing water in the pore space of the media. The infiltration trench provides additional volume reduction for the excess water that leaves the landscaped roof. Two unit operations in a series may remove the same pollutant with the same unit process but serve two different functions. For example, unit operations in the forebay in a wet basin or wetland remove suspended solids. However, the function of the forebay in this instance is to reduce maintenance costs by easing access for this activity. In summary, a *unit process* is how quantity or quality control occurs in the device called a *unit operation*, with one or more unit operations in a series being a *system*.

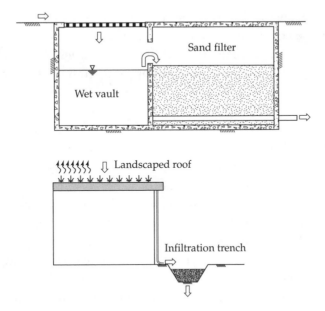

FIGURE 4.1   Example of a system with two unit operations.

A common term applied to a series of unit operations is *treatment train*. An example of a treatment train is a swale followed by a wet basin followed by a wet-land. This MOP proposes the term *system* for several reasons. First, the term *treatment train* has not been applied consistently. Rather, it is commonly applied to a series of unit operations placed in separate structures as in the second example in Figure 4.1. However, when two or more unit operations are placed in one structure, as in the first example in Figure 4.1, the term does not commonly apply. The sand filter in Figure 4.1 has two unit operations, the wet vault and the filter itself. In contrast, if a grass swale preceded the filter, with the swale providing pretreatment instead of the vault, the facility would be called a *treatment train*. On the other side of the spectrum, the informal rule is violated with the multi-chambered treatment train (MCTT) (Pitt et al., 1999), a system within one structure consisting of several unit operations, including a filter. *Treatment train* is more aptly applied to the combination of source control practices and stormwater controls. An example is cleaning of catch-basin sumps and sweeping combined with a treatment facility at an industrial site.

Source control should not be neglected because of the presence of a stormwater system. Source control is presented in Chapter 5 as a cost-effective approach that reduces maintenance frequency and improves effluent quality. In general, as explained in Chapter 3, the lower the influent concentration, the lower the effluent concentration.

2.4   Taxonomy of Stormwater Controls

Use of the concept of unit processes composing unit operations, which in turn compose systems, provides the foundation for a framework to classify the many stormwater controls available and discern the myriad of names currently in use in the industry. This paradigm may clarify discussions among professionals involved in stormwater management and offer consistency in design procedures. To further this objective, this section of the MOP proposes a taxonomy for stormwater controls framed on the concepts of unit processes and unit operations and based on a classification proposed by Minton (2007). The taxonomy addresses inadequacies of the terminology used in the field that tend to cause confusion. For example, there are several names that are used for essentially the same stormwater control, different controls with the same name, and instances of misapplication of words in names.

Swales are an example of controls with many names, some of which are grassy swales, vegetated swales, grass channels, landscaped swales, wetland swales, bioretention swales, dry and wet swales, and enhanced dry and wet swales. The critical issue for a designer is that some of these are sized based on the peak flow of a design event, while others are sized based on the volume of the design event. The latter type of design applies to a basin or a filter. Therefore, in this MOP, swales are considered flow-through stormwater controls sized to handle a given peak flow.

Some stormwater controls are the same but have different names. The organic filter presented in some municipal manuals and the bioretention filter are essentially the same. They both have filter media with an organic component, a vegetative cover that can be grass or other plant material, and an underdrain. They both provide the same unit processes of sedimentation, filtration, and sorption but, whereas the organic filter is sized as a filter using Darcy's law, the bioretention filter is often sized as an infiltration system even when it has underdrains.

Hydrodynamic separation is an example of misapplication of a term. The term *hydrodynamic separator* for stormwater treatment was first applied to devices that create a swirling motion but is now sometimes incorrectly applied to all manufactured vaults, including those that do not induce a rotational water motion. Oil–water separators have also been incorrectly categorized as hydrodynamic separators. The broadest definition, used in medicine and mining engineering, is the removal of particles from a moving fluid as a result of density differences between the particles and fluid. With this definition, the term would apply to any stormwater control, including wet basins, wetlands, dry basins, filters, and all devices that cause sedimentation or flotation. A narrower definition in chemical engineering is the removal of particles by an abrupt change in fluid direction. A device is configured such that the rapidly moving fluid undergoes an abrupt and substantial change in direction of 90 to 180 deg. Particles continue in a relatively straight direction and are removed by striking a wall in the device. However, this mechanism is not generally used in stormwater controls. In summary, the term "hydrodynamic" is meaningless in relation to stormwater controls.

The taxonomy proposed in this MOP seeks to eliminate most of the confusion resulting from vagueness in nomenclature by proposing names for unit operations that most adequately portray their characteristics and the processes they provide. Stormwater controls with common characteristics are grouped in the following five general categories:

1. Basins,
2. Swales and strips,
3. Filters,
4. Infiltrators, and
5. Gross pollutant traps.

Table 4.2 lists the most common unit operations within these categories and associates them with the corresponding unit processes. The subsequent paragraphs describe the distinct characteristics of each general category and highlight the rationale behind some of the name choices. For descriptions of the unit operations within each category, see Chapters 6 through 10, which also present detailed design procedures.

Basins are unit operations in which water is detained for a period that varies with the type of basin and the design requirements. Treated stormwater discharges to surface water via a weir or orifice to a pipe or channel. Some infiltration may take place through the bottom of the basin, but the volume infiltrated is much less than the discharge to surface waters. In general, basins provide peak flow attenuation and sedimentation and are generally sized based on a design volume, although small manufactured vaults are sized for a design peak flow.

TABLE 4.2 Unit operations and the unit processes present in them.

		Quantity control					
		Peak flow attenuation	Runoff volume reduction	Infiltration	Dispersion	Evapotranspiration	Runoff collection and usage
Basins	Wet basins	×	×			×	×
	Wetlands	×	×			×	×
	Dry basins	×	×	×			
	Vaults and swirl concentrators	×					
	Oil/water separators						
	Forebays						
	Cisterns			×			
Swales and strips	Swales				×	×	
	Strips				×	×	
Filters	Sand filters	×					
	Bioretention	×	×	×		×	×
	Landscaped roofs	×			×	×	
	Drain inlet inserts						
	Manufactured filters						
Infiltrators	Basins	×	×	×			
	Vaults	×	×	×			
	Trenches	×	×	×			
	Dry Wells	×	×	×			
	Permeable pavement	×	×	×			
Gross pollutant traps	Screens, nets, baskets, racks						
	Hoods						

	Pollutant control								Biological				Other			
	Sedimentation	Flotation	Laminar separation	Swirl concentration	Sorption	Precipitation	Coagulation	Filtration	Plant metabolism	Nitrification/ denitrification	Sulfate reduction	Organic compound degradation	Pathogen dieoff	Temperature reduction	Disinfection	Screening
	×	×			×				×	×	×	×	×		×	
	×	×			×				×	×	×	×	×		×	
	×															
	×	×		×												
	×	×	×													
	×	×														
	×															
									×					×		
	×								×					×		
	×	×						×		×					×	
	×	×			×	×	×	×	×	×		×		×	×	
					×				×					×		
	×							×								
	×				×											
	×	×			×	×	×			×		×	×	×	×	
	×				×	×	×			×		×	×	×	×	×
	×				×	×	×			×		×	×	×	×	
	×				×	×	×			×		×	×	×	×	
					×	×	×					×	×	×	×	
																×
		×														

The terms "wet basin" and "dry basin" are proposed as the best descriptors of the characteristics for these unit operations. Dry basins drain completely after each storm, as opposed to wet basins that maintain an open water pool. The term "pond" is not used because the word implies the constant presence of water, which is not the case with dry basins. The popular "detention" and "retention" terms are not used either because water is held back (detained) whether the basin is wet or dry. The only difference is how long water is detained and how it leaves the facility.

Vaults and swirl concentrators, whether proprietary or in the public domain, are grouped under this category because they are essentially basins with internal elements that improve hydraulic efficiency and inhibit resuspension of sediments. Oil–water separators (OWS) are vaults that enhance the removal of hydrocarbons lighter than water.

Wetlands are differentiated because of the extensive vegetation coverage but they behave hydraulically as dry basins that may include shallow pools. The various types of wetlands used for stormwater control are presented in Chapter 6. Subsurface flow wetlands are not included in the basin category because they are designed to behave like filters. This unit operation differs from other wetlands in that it has a gravel substrate that allows the stormwater to flow horizontally and be filtered through the root system.

A forebay is a small basin considered in this MOP as a separate unit operation because of the reasons presented in Section 2.2.

Swales and strips are unit operations with the distinct purpose of conveying stormwater from one point to another at very shallow water depths. Stormwater flows as shallow concentrated flow along the length of *swales* and as sheet flow across the width of *strips*. As with basins, infiltration may occur, but most of the water is discharged to a surface water body. All swales and strips have some kind of vegetation as bare soil is susceptible to erosion; therefore, the term "vegetated" is superfluous. The vegetative cover can be grasses, wetland plants, or a mix of grass, shrubs, and trees. Swales and strips are designed using open channel flow principles.

Swales and strips provide sedimentation as the vegetation slows down the flow of water. Some peak flow attenuation occurs in a swale of considerable length. Swales that store water, for instance behind check dams, are essentially very shallow and long basins sized based on a design volume rather than a peak flow. Therefore, they belong in the basin family. Similarly, a swale that infiltrates water and discharges it through an underdrain is not included in this category, but rather with the filters, as filtration is the dominant unit process. Finally, a swale that infiltrates water to the underlying soil is placed in the infiltrator category.

Filters are unit operations where stormwater flows through an engineered porous medium and into an underdrain, and the majority of the treated stormwater discharges to a surface water body, with only a minimal amount infiltrated to the underlying native soil and aquifers. Types of porous media include sand, metal oxide coated sand, organic mixes, peat, perlite, zeolite, or other commercial materials. The unit may have only one medium or a mix of media, arranged in one or several layers. Depending on the media, filters provide sedimentation and filtration, sorption, and precipitation. Peak flow attenuation takes place because of storage in and above the filter bed and slow flow through the porous medium. Filters are designed using Darcy's law for flow through saturated porous media.

Infiltrators are unit operations in which a design volume is infiltrated to the native soil to recharge aquifers. Infiltrators reduce runoff volume and remove pollutants as the water flows through the native soil. Infiltrators are generally designed using equations for flow in unsaturated soils. The most relevant configurations are described in Chapter 8. Permeable pavement as a unit operation falls in this category. The term "permeable" is used in this MOP to specify that the pavement has a high permeability. The word "porous" often used with this unit operation is not used in this manual because high porosity is not always conducive to high permeability: clay is 50% porous, whereas the porosity of sand is approximately 30%.

Gross pollutant traps (GPTs) consist of unit operations with large openings for the primary purpose of removing large solids such as litter, leaves, and plastics. Racks, nets, and baskets remove a variety of gross pollutants, whereas hoods are designed to remove floating particles. Almost all of the unit operations within the first four categories also remove gross solids but are not primarily designed to do so. Nonetheless, some may perform as well as some devices found in the GPT category. The majority of GPTs are manufactured and often integrated as elements in unit operations in the other categories, which often makes it difficult to categorize some of these manufactured products. For example, a swirl concentrator may have a screen to remove large solids and a device to exclude floating pollutants.

No classification system is perfect and adjustments need to be made for practicality and to facilitate communication. Some inconsistencies in the terminology are unavoidable. For example, "infiltration basins" and "infiltration vaults" are classified as infiltrators, not as basins. Some leeway had to be allowed for the use of the term "bioretention." The name implies that biological organisms play a role in pollutant removal. Indeed, plants remove nutrients and metals for growth and bacteria transform ammonia into nitrogen gas; however, thus defined, bioretention takes place in wet basins and wetlands as well. Therefore, the term bioretention would better describe a general mechanism of pollutant removal, that is, a unit process as defined earlier in Section 2.2. Nevertheless, the term adequately portrays the general biological processes and its usage in the industry is so significant that it makes practical sense to retain it to describe a unit operation.

Another inconsistency is that systems and unit operations may share the same name. For example, as a unit operation, a sand filter is only the filter bed and its container. As a system, the sand filter is composed of the pretreatment unit (e.g., a vault) and the filter bed, whether they are in the same container or separate containers.

The intent of this taxonomy is not that it become the industry standard, but that it can help designers make sense of the multitude of terms that pervade the industry. The classification shows that most stormwater controls fall under a small number of categories logically aligned with the dominant unit processes that occur within them. The framework adds needed clarity to assist designers in the selection of unit operations and systems to address a given set of stormwater management objectives. Equally important, the classification system serves to guide the proper sizing procedure by helping the designer recognize the general category in which a stormwater control belongs.

3.0   UNIT PROCESSES FOR QUANTITY CONTROL

As noted in Chapter 2, the most immediate effect of urbanization is the increase in volume and peak flows associated with precipitation events. Stormwater management began with quantity control given its effects on flooding, bank erosion, and associated economic losses; the water quality treatment of stormwater has become more important in recent years. This section presents unit processes that control runoff volumes and peak flows.

3.1   Peak Flow Attenuation

As presented in Chapter 2, increased peak flows result from larger runoff volumes, reduced natural storage in the watershed, and shorter travel times associated with flow over paved surfaces and pipes. Peak flow attenuation has traditionally been the single focus of stormwater management, as described in Chapter 1, with an emphasis on building storage facilities sized to reduce the peak flows to a given target specified through several approaches described in Chapter 3. In fact, attenuation is more effectively achieved by addressing also reducing the runoff volume and lengthening the travel time. These two elements are discussed in the following subsection, whereas this subsection focuses on storage attenuation attained through detention of runoff and on hydrodynamic attenuation that occurs as water flows through conveyances.

3.1.1 Storage Attenuation

The principles of storage attenuation are well known and thoroughly documented in classic textbooks (e.g., Bedient et al., 2008) and handbooks (e.g., Maidment, 1993). Attenuation is governed by the continuity equation, which balances inflows, outflow, and storage increases in a facility. The outflow from the facility is independent of the inflow and depends solely on the relationship between storage and outflow, typically known as a rating curve.

The computation of an outflow hydrograph resulting from the passage of an inflow hydrograph through a storage facility is known as storage routing. The most common computational technique is the *storage indication method,* also known as the *Puls method*. This method is discussed in detail in the references above and its application to stormwater management is presented in *Design and Construction of Urban Stormwater Management Systems* (ASCE and WEF, 1992). The method is incorporated to virtually all hydrologic modeling software (Chapter 14).

3.1.2 Hydrodynamic Attenuation

Peak flows are also attenuated as water flows through a variety of conveyances, natural or artificial and as a result of storage and frictional effects that take place in the channel or pipe. Green infrastructure approaches take advantage of this mechanism by replacing fast conveyances such as gutters and pipes with swales and other conveyances that slow down the flow of water and increase the travel time and the storage of runoff within the conveyance system. Flow velocities can be decreased by using wide channels, mild slopes, and high-roughness vegetation. The last component is still the subject of ongoing research (see Chapter 7).

In hydrodynamic attenuation the outflow from a channel reach depends on both the inflow and the storage in the reach. This highly complex process is governed by the unsteady momentum and continuity equations for open channel flow. These partial differential equations are known as the one-dimensional St. Venant equations and are solved by numerical methods commonly implemented in hydraulic models. In many cases, a simplified version of the equations known as *kinematic wave routing* that uses Manning's formula as an approximation to the momentum equation can be applied. Several computational methods to calculate the outflow hydrograph from a channel reach of given properties are described in various textbooks (e.g., Ponce, 1994; Bedient et al., 2008). The most common techniques are the *Muskingum, Kinematic Wave, Muskingum-Cunge,* and *Modified Att-Kin* methods and are summarized by the Federal Highway Administration (2002).

3.2   Runoff Volume Reduction

The relative recent concept of green infrastructure has emerged to "manage rain" and thus reduce the amount of runoff through practices that minimize the volume of runoff generated as well as infiltration and evapotranspiration to reduce the direct runoff that reaches receiving waters. As explained in Chapter 3, most of the annual rainfall depth takes place in the form of small storms. Also, in some regions of the United States much of the precipitation occurs as snow in winter. Effective volume control starts with site design that includes preservation of natural resources that maximize retention of rain water on site, for instance, forest stands that provide interception and well-drained native soils that provide storage of water in the pore space (see Chapter 5 for additional details). Soils that are unavoidably compacted by construction activities can be amended to restore its storage capacity and permeability. Infiltration performance in disturbed soils is improved by means of deep tillage and compost amendments (Pitt et al., 2002) as well as plantings with deep-rooted native species (Rachman et al., 2004). Excess runoff is further reduced by capturing it close to the point where it is generated, typically using green infrastructure controls that are distributed throughout the site. This water is either infiltrated to the native soil or evapotranspired by the vegetation in the controls.

3.2.1   Infiltration

Infiltration is the process of water entering soils from rainfall, snowmelt, or irrigation. Rates of infiltration are controlled by rates of soil water movement below the surface; this soil water movement also controls the supply of water for plant uptake and for evaporation at the soil surface. Infiltration and soil water movement directly affect surface runoff, groundwater recharge, evapotranspiration, soil erosion, and transport of chemicals in surface and subsurface waters. Soil properties affecting soil water movement are hydraulic conductivity and water retention characteristics that describe the ability of the soil to store and release water (Rawls et al., 1993). Hydraulic conductivity is a measure of the soil's ability to transmit water that is dependent on the geometric properties of the soil and the fluid's viscosity, which is a function of temperature (Klute and Dirkson, 1986). Seasonal and annual temperature variations significantly affect the performance of infiltration-based stormwater controls (Emerson and Traver, 2008).

Infiltration is a means of achieving quantity control, both volume and peak flow attenuation, but is also recognized as a means of pollutant control because, by reducing volume and filtering pollutants, it reduces the total load of pollutants to surface waters. Infiltration occurs not only in stormwater controls whose primary intent is infiltration (i.e., permeable pavement), but also in many other unit operations such as swales, wet basins, wetlands, underground recharge galleries (vaults), and unlined filters. Given the importance of minimizing groundwater contamination, the intervening soil should have a good capacity to remove pollutants, with sufficient separation between the bottom of the treatment facility and groundwater. Special consideration may need to be given to excessively well-drained soils, fractured geology, and karst terrain.

The soil moisture content and field capacity determine the volume of stormwater retained through infiltration. Field capacity is the water content held in soil after excess water has drained by gravity. Runoff volumes and thus flow rates are reduced by storage of water in the soil pore space. Retained water leaves the soil through evapotranspiration or deep percolation. Numerous methods are commonly used for calculating soil infiltration rates, including the Horton (1940) infiltration equation, Green and Ampt (1911) infiltration equation, and methods based on the curve number (USDA, 1986). Guidance regarding the calculation of soil infiltration rates using these and other methods is provided in Chapter 5, "Infiltration and Soil Water Movement," of the *Handbook of Hydrology* (Rawls et al., 1993). These computational methods are common in many computer models; however, recent research indicates that infiltration is a complex phenomenon dependent not just on soil properties but also on rainfall characteristics. Yu et al. (1997) observed that infiltration rates from bare plots increased with rainfall intensity and were independent of accumulated rainfall. Yu (1999) found the infiltration response to rainfall to be the opposite of what would be expected, in that infiltration rates were low in the beginning of the event and increased with intensity, even late in the event when the Green-Ampt model would project considerably lower rates.

However, even with these caveats, discrete infiltration approaches have considerable utility, especially when the watershed is disaggregated enough to separate each soil type and land cover. This discretization ability is the reason why models based upon Horton and Green-Ampt formulations are widely used.

3.2.2 *Dispersion*

Engineered dispersion attempts to minimize hydrologic change by moving stormwater from impervious surfaces to pervious areas, for example landscapes original to the site before development or soils that have been amended to restore storage and infiltration properties. The most common approaches are collectively known as imperviousness disconnection. In essence, disconnection is implemented to facilitate infiltration but also has the additional effect of slowing the flow of water and lengthening travel times. A common application is the dispersion of stormwater into vegetated buffers such as forests and grasslands abutting an adjacent waterbody, stream, lake, or wetlands.

The benefits of dispersion are often summarized as a reduction of the *effective impervious area* (EIA), which is the portion of the *total impervious area* (TIA) that discharges directly to receiving waterbodies. The term "directly connected impervious area" (DCIA) is also used interchangeably with EIA. Imperviousness disconnection is most applicable to residential development by conveying runoff generated by impervious surfaces such as rooftops, driveways, parking lots, and streets to vegetated areas. Disconnection of the large parking lots and rooftops for commercial areas yields much more modest reductions in runoff because of the large ratio of impervious to pervious area in these land uses. The amount of reduction is a function of the pervious area flow path, the ratio of impervious area to the receiving pervious areas, and the infiltration capacity of the pervious areas. For hydrologic soil types A and B, significant reductions in runoff are possible for most land uses when impervious surfaces drain to these very permeable soils. The less permeable type C and D soils allow lesser reductions and for relatively low-density land uses that have low impervious-to-pervious area ratios (Clar et al., 2004).

Imperviousness disconnection can be analyzed with computer programs that use the curve number method (USDA, 1986), for example, HEC-HMS, WinTR-55, and WinTR-20. The formulation computes a reduced curve number that results from the disconnection. The Small Storm Hydrology Method (SSHM) derived from work by Pitt (1994) and implemented in the WinSLAMM model (Pitt and Voorhees, 1989) accounts explicitly for disconnected impervious areas. Other models that allow detailed discretization of drainage areas in watersheds such as the EPA SWMM model can be used to simulate an impervious area discharging to a pervious area (Rossman, 2004).

3.2.3 Evapotranspiration

Evapotranspiration is the process by which water returns to the atmosphere by evaporation from water and soil surfaces and by transpiration as plants release water vapor through their leaves as part of their metabolic processes. Hanson (1991) found that evapotranspiration ranges from 40% of the annual precipitation in the Northeast and Northwestern United States, to approximately 70% in the Southeast and nearly 100% in the Southwest. Almost all of the precipitation may leave as evapotranspiration in semiarid regions on sites of relatively tight soils, such as welded tuff. During urbanization, pavement replaces native vegetation; in addition, plants brought to the site for landscaping are typically not mature, are more sparsely planted, and have less dense foliage than the native vegetation; therefore, less water returns to the atmosphere through evapotranspiration and the volume of runoff increases.

Evapotranspiration is a function of climatic factors such as air temperature, wind speed, relative humidity, and solar radiation and of evapotranspiring surface conditions, water temperature, roughness, density and type of vegetative cover, root depth, water availability, and albedo, which is the fraction of reflected incident sunlight. Plant physiology is highly complex as stomata openings in plant leaves allow the movement of water vapor and other gases. These functions vary with plant type and respond to water stress and other factors.

Actual evapotranspiration (AET) is the moisture released from the soil/plant complex. Potential evapotranspiration (PET) is the maximum evapotranspiration expected under the climatic conditions at a given location, assuming that water is always present in the soil with complete plant cover. Given PET, AET represents the fraction of PET that actually evaporates. While AET is a relatively minor aspect of the water balance of stormwater controls during runoff events, it is very important between storms. Actual evapotranspiration both determines and is determined by the soil moisture content, which in turn controls the infiltration rate. Methods to reliably compute AET from the soil profile and the ensuing infiltration response are thus perhaps more important than computation of the volume of runoff that is lost to the atmosphere (Lucas and Medina, 2011).

PET largely depends upon the energy available for the phase change of soil moisture to vapor, primarily by solar radiation. The distribution of solar energy and exposure factors such as albedo and vegetation affect this process. Because AET is limited by soil moisture available to meet this demand, irrigated areas have AET losses that approach PET demand. In extended droughts, vegetation is subject to moisture stress and AET declines. Because they capture substantial quantities of runoff, albeit irregularly, a similar behavior applies to vegetated stormwater controls.

Surprisingly, given the potential importance of evapotranspiration in the overall water budget, many computational approaches oversimplify root zone transpiration mechanisms, while focusing on less important PET mechanisms such as sensible heat loss and the effect of wind. The discussion below briefly presents the mechanisms involved in PET and AET.

3.2.3.1 Evaporation from Interception

As rainfall falls upon vegetated surfaces, some of it is intercepted by leaves and blades, of which some evaporates back into the atmosphere during and immediately after the storm, whereas the rest flows along the trunk as stemflow. This phenomenon is readily observed in small storm events, where interception can represent a substantial portion of total rainfall. In dense forests in the humid mid-Atlantic, annual rainfall losses caused by interception approach 30% (Dunne and Leopold, 1968). Interception is a component of the water cycle that is often poorly quantified.

3.2.3.2 Evaporation from Depression Storage

Evaporation also occurs from depression storage from puddles and other temporarily ponded areas in the landscape. Depression storage decreases with slope and increases with terrain roughness. Typical values of depression storage depth range from 1 mm (0.05 in.) in sloped roofs to 15 mm (0.6 in.) in woods and fields (UFCD, 2001). These mechanisms have substantial effects on runoff response, where such losses are typically addressed as the concept of "initial abstraction" and are subtracted from rainfall that is infiltrated or runs off.

3.2.3.3 Surface Evaporation

Evaporation from the soil surface is part of AET and is affected by interactions between soil characteristics and environmental factors. Energy demand and water availability dominate the processes involved. Soil evaporation is different from that from depression storage at the surface because water from deeper in the soil profile must move toward the surface to replace moisture lost to the demand of climatic energy. As such, this movement encounters variations in flow resistance because of moisture and temperature gradients (Philip and De Vries, 1957).

Soil water evaporation occurs within a thin (10- to 25-mm, 0.4- to 1-in.) upper boundary layer of the soil profile in which all moisture is readily evaporated and limited only by PET. The process consists of three drying stages: In the first stage, this upper boundary layer evaporation is limited only by the PET; in the second stage, upward movement and evaporation from a wet soil occurs at a decreasing rate with drying; while in the third stage, evaporation from a relatively dry soil becomes very restricted.

Evaporation from the soil surface can be a significant component of evapotranspiration. In an experiment comparing evaporation from containers, Blight (2002) reported that evaporation from a soil-filled container was approximately 30% greater than evaporation from one filled with water and only slightly less than that from a vegetated container. Another interesting finding of this study was that wind increased evapotranspiration only at low velocities.

When the canopy is sparse, some of the radiation energy on the soil surface is not used for water evaporation, instead heating the soil, adjacent air and canopy, from which it is then reflected, or absorbed and reradiated. This sensible energy represents the heat component of PET, as sensible energy transfer from vegetation is minimal (Blight, 2002). This is a second component of PET in addition to the directly intercepted energy. When the canopy value reaches 60%, all unused soil surface energy is recaptured by the canopy and it becomes a part of the PET (Saxton, 2005).

3.2.3.4 Plant Transpiration

Plants extract soil water by creating suction across their root hair membranes resulting in water uptake. Plants control transpiration losses by means of physiological processes within their vascular system and stomata. The literature on processes underlying soil water uptake and biological response is still sparse and conflicting; therefore, it is difficult to present a process-based approach for projecting the response of vegetation to water stress. The following discussion draws upon the concepts presented in Saxton (2005).

When soils are at or close to field capacity, active vegetation will transpire at rates approaching the rate demanded by PET. However, as soil moisture content declines, physical and biological processes begin to inhibit the rate of transpiration. With further moisture decline, transpiration drops to near zero, causing plant death if the decline persists. Plant transpiration is thus a function of both PET and the water in the soil available to plants.

The rate of transpiration is equal to PET at the wet endpoint and is zero at the dry end. However, there is considerable variability in published AET rates at intermediate moisture contents (Saxton, 2005). The variation is not well defined, particularly as to the moisture content when transpiration starts to decline (Denmead and Shaw, 1962).

Quantification of evapotranspiration rates is challenging because of the many factors involved. The methods available include mass transfer, energy budget, Penman, Penman-Monteith, McIlroy-Slatyer, Thornthwaite, Blaney-Criddle, root zone, and the pan evaporation and lysimeter approaches. A summary of these methods is provided in Lucas and Medina (2011). The American Society of Civil Engineers developed a standardized equation based on the Penman-Monteith method to provide a common process to calculate evapotranspiration and a basis for transferring crop coefficients from reference crops (short grass and alfalfa) to other agricultural and landscape uses (EWRI, 2005).

The most obvious means of promoting evapotranspiration is to retain as much of the site vegetation as possible, incorporating landscaping to the maximum extent practicable. Landscaped roofs are one method of evapotranspiring precipitation that would otherwise be converted to runoff. Permeable pavement may also be viewed as an evaporation device, especially when the water level in the gravel reservoir is close to the pavement layer. The base reservoir can be designed to provide sufficient volume to retain the complete design storm or spring snowmelt in cold climates, with subsequent evaporation to empty the reservoir.

Recent research has been aimed at understanding the role of evapotranspiration on various unit operations such as bioretention filters, landscaped roofs, and wetlands (Feller et al., 2010; Hickman et al., 2011; Schneider et al., 2011). The results reveal that the effect of evapotranspiration should be considered more formally in the design and performance analysis of stormwater controls. Better quantification of evapotranspiration can result in smaller footprints and more efficient design of stormwater controls.

3.2.4   Runoff Collection and Usage

In a world of increasing demands for limited water resources, use of collected stormwater runoff is gaining popularity. The trend began in semiarid regions but is rapidly spreading to wetter climates. The focus of this unit process is storage and use for landscape irrigation, nonpotable consumption such as toilet flushing, industrial processes, and potable use with additional treatment. Water is typically collected from rooftops. By capturing runoff for beneficial purposes, water is either completely removed from direct runoff or its flow to receiving waters is delayed. Harvesting rainwater is also effective in reducing stormwater pollution by preventing rain to come in contact with pollutants from pavement and bare soil.

The means of storage varies from small cisterns and rain barrels for individual residences to large water tanks and ponds akin to small lakes with pumps and other mechanical and electrical equipment. Several manufactured systems integrate the application equipment with the storage. Storage may be provided above the ground surface or below. A form of the latter is *aquifer storage and recovery* (ASR) in which water is injected to an aquifer for later pumping and use. The most common application involves injection of treated potable water (Pyne, 1995) but the concept can be expanded to treated wastewater, stormwater, or river water taken during high-flow periods, provided there is adequate treatment that protects groundwater resources.

The effectiveness of rainwater harvesting in reducing runoff volume depends on the demand for the collected water. Irrigation is seldom needed soon after a storm; therefore, in humid climates where storms occur relatively often, the facility must be emptied at least partially to provide storage for the next storm. In such situations, rainwater harvesting behaves like a basin. Additional demand such as toilet flushing increases the effectiveness of rainwater harvesting as water is moved from the stormwater drainage system to the wastewater collection system. Water rights in some states in the Western United States may limit the capture of rainwater.

Several states have published rainwater harvesting manuals to encourage better use of urban water resources. Examples are Georgia (Van Giesen and Carpenter, 2009), Hawaii (Macomber, 2001), Texas (Texas Water Development Board, 2005), and Virginia (Cabell Brand Center, 2007). Procedures for evaluation and sizing of rainwater harvesting systems are presented in Argue (2004).

4.0 UNIT PROCESSES FOR QUALITY CONTROL

Stormwater quality is a significant urban environmental issue because of the effects described in Chapter 2. The sources of pollutants, generation of runoff, and temporal and spatial distribution of stormwater require an approach to management based on unit process that target dissolved and particulate fractions for various pollutants as well as thermal loads. This science-based approach is the foundation for effective design of unit operations.

4.1 Sedimentation

Sedimentation is gravity separation by the downward movement of particles under quiescent conditions. It occurs in all commonly used unit operations, including filters. Although four types of particle settling are typically defined in water and wastewater treatment, only two are relevant to stormwater: discrete settling and flocculent settling (Minton, 2011). *Discrete* means that each particle settles separately from the others and does not attach when coming into contact with other particles. Small particles in water tend to stick together when coming into contact and form a *flocculent suspension*. Sand, defined as particles greater than approximately 75 µm, and larger particles in the silt range settle discretely. Finer silts and clays tend to flocculate after a few hours of quiescence.

4.1.1   Stokes's Law

Stokes's law describes settling velocities of particles falling or rising under laminar flow in the vicinity of the particle surface. The laminar condition is in reference to the fluid mechanics at the surface of the particle, not within the waterbody itself. Inorganic particles with a specific gravity of approximately 2.65 retain this condition to a diameter of approximately 100 µm, increasing as the specific gravity or density of the particle decreases. The fall velocity of larger particles creates a turbulent boundary condition in which instance Stokes's law does not apply and adjustments are required (Graf, 1984; Cheng, 1997). Laminar conditions are governed by viscosity rather than gravity. Stokes's law is defined as

$$V_p = \frac{g(\rho_s - \rho)d^2}{18\mu} \tag{4.1}$$

where
V_p = settling velocity of a particle (m/s or ft/s);
g = gravity constant (m/s² or ft/s²);
ρ_s = density of particle (kg/m³ or slugs/cu ft);
ρ = density of water (kg/m³ or slugs/cu ft);
d = particle diameter (m or ft); and
μ = dynamic viscosity of the water (m²/s or sq ft/s).

Salinity from deicing salt increases the viscosity of stormwater. Seawater, for example, has a viscosity that is 6, 9, and 34% greater than fresh water at 0, 20, and 40 °C, respectively. Viscosity also increases with decreasing temperature. Hence, particles settle more slowly in cold water (approximately 35% slower at 5 °C compared with 20 °C). The settling rate of particles in winter and spring melts has been observed to be approximately one half that during warmer periods in cold climate regions (Roseen et al., 2009).

It is frequently stated that particles in stormwater do not conform to Stokes's law. Equation 4.1 reasonably predicts settling velocities if the densities of the particles and the effect of their shape on the settling rate are known. The problem is that specific gravities of particles in stormwater are highly variable, from less than 1 to 2.7. In addition, the derivation of eq 4.1 assumes a spherical shape; however, shapes of stormwater particles vary widely. Variation in densities and shapes occurs between sites and between and within storms at a site. One study found the settling velocity of particles began to deviate from eq 4.1 at approximately 20 μm. The settling velocity of particles of 5 μm was only approximately 10% of that estimated by Stokes's law using the typical inputs (Bäckström, 2002).

To calculate settling velocities using eq 4.1, particle size is determined using sieves for larger silts and sand. Smaller sizes can be determined with the hydrometer method or with optical methods such as the Coulter counter. However, given the variability of stormwater particle characteristics noted previously, it is preferable to determine settling velocities directly as is done with the hydrometer method or with settling columns. Settling columns recognize that some fine particles begin to coagulate within a few hours, which has been observed with stormwater. Factors that inhibit coagulation are reduced with cold temperatures. For example, at temperatures less than 5 °C, clays have been found to coagulate quite rapidly (Lau, 1993). Stokes's law does not recognize that small particles coagulate given sufficient time or with reduced temperatures, thus making the use of eq 4.1 to describe the setting of stormwater problematic.

4.1.2 Hydraulic Loading Rate and Residence Time

When water is flowing into a basin during a storm, the determinant of performance is the hydraulic loading rate (HLR). The HLR is the rate of flow into the treatment system divided by the surface area of the basin:

$$\text{HLR} = \frac{Q}{LW} \qquad (4.2)$$

where
  HLR = hydraulic loading rate (m/s or ft/s);
    L = basin length (m or ft);
    W = basin width (m or ft); and
    Q = flow rate (m³/s or cfs)

Equation 4.2 does not contain the parameters of basin volume or depth or hydraulic residence time. Consider two basins having the same volume and residence time. One is shallower and covers a larger area than the second basin. The shallow basin will perform better during a storm given its lower hydraulic loading rate, assuming both basins have the same hydraulic efficiency, a factor discussed in the next section.

Where water is retained between storm events, as with wet basins and wetlands, performance is also a function of volume; that is, the greater the volume relative to the storms being treated, the more effective the performance between storm events (Chapter 3). Greater volume gives more time for small silts and clays to settle before the resident water is pushed out by a subsequent storm. Hydraulic residence time (HRT), therefore, matters for the removal of small particles. However, it is the average residence time between storms, rather than during the storm, that is relevant.

Use of either HLR or HRT to size a basin depends on the treatment objective, the coarseness of particle suspension, and whether the removal of dissolved pollutants is an objective. If the objective is the removal of sands, the sedimentation process is dominated by HLR. Most manufactured vaults are relatively small and thus selection of the appropriate device is based on the peak rate of flow of the design event, synonymous with HLR.

Where the objective includes removal of fine particles, small silts, and clay-sized particles, sizing is based on basin volume and, in effect, is related to HRT. The finer the particle suspension, the more important settling between storms becomes and hence, the more important volume and HRT become for performance. In summary, sizing of small basins relative to their drainage area should be based on HLR; sizing of large basins should be based on HRT.

Application of HRT to semiarid regions is problematic. The result is a basin volume that is too small because the annual runoff is much less than that for humid and temperate climates. As such, the basin does not operate as well as needed during each event because too much fresh, relatively dirty stormwater reaches the outlet during the storm, decreasing performance. Therefore, the method for sizing wet basins is the ratio of volume of the basin to the volume of the mean annual runoff event, as described in Chapter 3.

Residence or drawdown time is a common design criterion for dry basins, suggesting that time is relevant during storms for this unit operation. However, an important design criterion to note is the drawdown rate, which is akin to the HLR of a wet basin. Time is relevant to the extent that the suspension is flocculent, that is, the suspension has some particles that come in contact and form larger particles. Clays and perhaps fine silts begin to coagulate within a few hours with gentle mixing by wind and a significant residence time occurs in the basin even with the smallest storms. It should be noted that there is a potential for resuspension in dry basins.

4.1.3 Hydraulic Efficiency

Ideal settling conditions do not exist in basins. Dead zones, short-circuiting, turbulence, and uneven distribution of the stormwater entering and leaving the basin cause deviations from the ideal conditions. The effect of a hydraulic condition that is less than ideal is to increase the HLR above the minimum theoretical value (the peak flow divided by the basin surface area as described previously) while also decreasing the residence time below the maximum theoretical value.

Dead zones are areas in the basin in which relatively clean water present from previous storms is not replaced effectively by incoming influent during the current storm. Incoming water flows too quickly through the basin, reducing performance. Dead zones are caused for various reasons, including inlets and outlets that are small in comparison to the width of the basin, irregular basin geometry, wind, and differential vegetation densities. For example, cattails along the sides of the basin length, perhaps growing on safety benches, provide a higher resistance to flow than the open water in the center of the basin. The area of cattails is often a dead zone, significantly reducing the effective treatment portion of the basin. Conversely, vegetation placed on shelves that are placed across the basin at appropriate intervals improves hydraulic efficiency because they help distribute the flow more evenly.

A horizontal dead zone, called *water layering,* can also exist in which the density at the bottom of a wet basin is sufficiently greater than at the surface to create two distinct layers between which there is little water movement. Pollutants and dissolved oxygen move slowly between the two layers. Two causes for this condition are temperature and salinity. During summers, thermal stratification can occur in a wet basin as it occurs in lakes. Thermal stratification has been observed in basins as shallow as 1 m (3 ft). Salinity stratification has been observed where deicing salt is used. If the basin is too deep, summer storms may not be able to push out the salinity, resulting in year-round stratification. Hydraulic efficiency is reduced significantly as stormwater passes along the surface, unless the inlet discharges at the bottom of the basin. Horizontal stratification can also adversely affect beneficial chemical and biological reactions in the bottom of the basin (see Section 4.9).

Short-circuiting is the direct movement of incoming water from the inlet to the outlet. It is caused by differences in density between incoming stormwater and water present in the basin. These differences are a result of differing temperatures or solids concentrations. Short-circuiting also occurs if the distance between the inlet and outlet is small, as is the case with small, round, wet vaults without baffles.

Hydraulic efficiency is also affected by turbulence. The influent is turbulent and turbulence may continue into the basin for some distance. The area near the outlet is possibly turbulent, as flow velocities are higher than in the center of the basin. Density currents and wind also create turbulence. Even mild turbulence may reduce efficiency by preventing the settling of finer silt and clay-sized particles. Conversely, gentle turbulence likely accelerates the coagulation of clays, thereby enhancing their settling. Turbulence can be beneficial because it can eliminate thermal or saline stratification. The effect of wind on residence time can be beneficial (McFarlane et al., 2006) or adverse (McCorquodale et al., 2005), depending on its direction and magnitude and the depth of water.

4.2   Flotation

In stormwater treatment, flotation is relevant to material with a specific gravity less than water. This includes petroleum hydrocarbons and light gross solids such as paper, cigarette butts, and plastic bags, which are neutrally buoyant. Stokes's law (eq 4.1) is applicable to flotation. As the specific gravity for these materials is less than water, the settling rate of the oil droplet or light gross particle is negative and is called the *rise rate*.

4.3   Laminar Separation

Even mild turbulence inhibits removal of oil droplets and small silt and clay-size particles, although it assists coalescence and coagulation of these particles. Laminar separation of particles from liquids minimizes if not eliminates this turbulence. The term *laminar*, in this instance, refers to the hydraulic condition of the water in the stormwater control. Laminar conditions are created by the use of plates or tubes. The configuration calms the water as it passes through and provides protection from inlet turbulence and wind in the case of open basins.

There is a second, important benefit of these configurations. Envision the bottom of a large basin cut into a large number of small plates of equal size. The plates are stacked with little separation and are placed at an angle to the bottom. Accumulated sediment slides downward and light material moves upward. The configuration exploits the previous observation that depth and volume are not relevant to settling during a storm (eq 4.2). HLR is important in this instance and the laminar configuration provides a significant increase in surface area per unit volume of basin, leading to a decrease in the size of the basin for the same design event. The effect is to achieve equivalent removal efficiency during each storm, but with a smaller basin.

Coalescing oil and water separators are a widely recognized application of laminar separation. Coalescence is the formation of large oil droplets from the collision of smaller droplets. Collisions occur as the droplets rise to the underside of each plate. The concept is used in some small manufactured vaults to enhance the removal of fine sediments as well. However, care must be taken with the use of laminar separation for settling sediments. As previously noted, volume is a significant parameter for these particles and it is unlikely that fine silts and clays are removed unless the vault has a relatively large unit volume, irrespective of the presence of laminar devices. The larger the unit volume (cubic meter per hectare served), the less incremental benefit provided by laminar devices.

4.4   Swirl Concentration

A swirling motion of fluid around a common center (Sullivan et al., 1982) is used in some cylindrical vaults to enhance separation of particles, hence the alternative name of *vortex separation*. The expectation is that the motion produces an inertial force that adds to the gravitational force found with normal sedimentation. The swirling motion may initiate at a peak flow of 10 to 20% of the control's rated flow capacity. The effect is better performance with all other factors being equal such as basin size and hydraulic efficiency. However, it has not been established that the swirling motion in products called *vortex separators* adds significantly to performance. It is possible that observed improvement in performance over a nonswirl vault is a result of improved hydraulic efficiency, more closely approaching the ideal hydraulic loading rate rather than the effect of swirling motion per se.

There is a second attribute of swirling motion that may assist performance, which is the minimization of resuspension. The swirling motion results in what is called *secondary flow,* or movement of water toward the center axis, as illustrated in Figure 4.2. Larger deposition, particularly of small particles, occurs at the center of the unit where they are less susceptible to resuspension at high flows. This effect may be negated if a strong vortex occurs that may resuspend the accumulated particles.

4.5   Sorption

4.5.1   *Types of Sorption*

There are three types of sorption; these are adsorption, absorption, and ion exchange. Ion exchange is not strictly a sorptive process but it is placed here for convenience. As implied by its name, ion exchange involves replacement of ions of

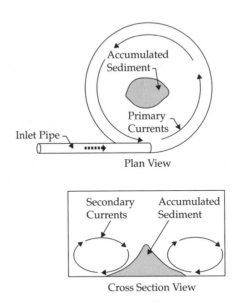

Plan View

Cross Section View

FIGURE 4.2   Vortex secondary motion (Minton, 2011).

less "interest" with ions in incoming stormwater that are of greater interest to the media. Heavy metal removal by zeolite is an example of ion exchange. Ion exchange can be cationic or anionic. Most media have a cationic exchange, which means that the media has the ability to exchange lighter positively charged metals such as calcium, magnesium, and sodium, for heavier metals such as copper, zinc, and lead. The exchange capacity can be measured in a laboratory to determine the useful life of the media.

With adsorption and absorption, there is no exchange of ions. Rather, sorption is brought about by physical van der Waals forces and binding between chemical complexes of stormwater pollutants on the surface of the media. The difference between adsorption and absorption is the degree of homogeneity between the pollutant and the media. With adsorption, there is no homogeneity. Attachment occurs at the media surface, either its immediate exterior surface or interior surfaces within the porous medium. With absorption, the pollutant penetrates to the molecular level of the media. The pollutant and media become homogenous in structure, although no chemical transformation occurs. With both unit processes, media attachment occurs without alteration of the media's chemical structure. The distinction between adsorption and absorption is relevant to stormwater treatment. With absorption, the pollutant will not desorb from the media once bonded. This is not the case for adsorption, which is the dominant sorption process in soils and filter media. The sorbed pollutant can desorb because attachment is related to conditions of chemical equilibrium, which can change. For example, desorption of pollutants from wet basin soils during periods of dry weather flow has been observed.

Adsorption occurs as runoff flows into stormwater controls. With few exceptions, all pollutants in stormwater are hydrophobic to some degree, including bacteria and viruses. Notable exceptions are ethylene glycol (antifreeze) and chloride, which are highly soluble. Absorption does not occur naturally in wet basins or filters. It occurs with solid polymers used in drain-inlet inserts to absorb free oils.

The distinction between adsorption and precipitation (see Section 4.6) is the nature of the bond that forms between the pollutant and media. With sorption, surface attraction between the pollutant and the media causes the pollutant to leave the aqueous solution and adhere to the media. With precipitation, a new chemical forms by the joining of two elements, such as a metal with sulfide. With some pollutant removal reactions in stormwater controls, particularly soils, the distinction between adsorption and precipitation is neither distinct nor fully understood. In some instances, it appears that sorption is followed by precipitation in the same process.

With respect to engineered filter media, removal of pesticides, petroleum hydrocarbons, and metals by activated carbon, compost, and other organic media is by adsorption and sometimes followed by biological degradation. In soils, organic matter, known as *humic substances*, is naturally created from the degradation of dead vegetation.

Phosphorus and metals removal by inorganic media, such as a metal oxide on sand or in soils, is likely a sorption and precipitation complex. The initial reaction appears to be adsorption, with slow alteration of the complex to a precipitate. The metal oxides of interest are iron, aluminum, and manganese. As the precipitate forms, sorption sites reopen, resulting in continued sorption during subsequent storms. Removal of phosphorus by calcium complexes such as calcium carbonate may be a combination of sorption and precipitation, whereas direct removal by calcium takes place by precipitation only. These unit processes also occur in soils.

Ammonia sorbs to clay in infiltrators, sand filters, and bioretention filters. Specialized bacteria subsequently change the ammonia to nitrate (see Section 4.9.3). Nitrate is leached from clay during a subsequent storm, rejuvenating sorptive sites for incoming ammonia. Nitrate is lost from the system unless used by plants for growth or converted to nitrogen gas by another specialized group of bacteria.

As mentioned earlier in this section, pollutants removed by adsorption may subsequently desorb due to a change in the chemistry of the water in the stormwater control. Significant shifts in any one of the following chemical conditions may cause the reentry of the pollutant to aqueous solution: pH, background concentration of the pollutant, dissolved oxygen concentration, and salinity. A reduction in pH to below 6 may cause the release of metals sorbed to oxides. Calcium formations are enhanced by high pH, which can occur in wet basins and wetlands. Similarly, an increase in dissolved phosphorus and metals has been observed in basins and wetlands during dry weather flow. It is likely that dry weather flow has a lower concentration of pollutants than typically occur in stormwater, causing a shift in chemical equilibrium and release of the pollutant into aqueous solution.

Some pollutant removal mechanisms are reversed by anaerobic conditions, whereas others are promoted. Iron phosphate formation requires aerobic conditions; metal sulfide precipitation requires anaerobic conditions. Anaerobic conditions are preferable, although not necessary for the sorption of toxic organic compounds and dissolved metals to organic matter, which is resistant to degradation in the absence of dissolved oxygen. Adsorption and precipitation to aluminum oxide and calcium or calcium carbonate is unaffected by the oxygen condition. Adsorption and precipitation of dissolved phosphorus with ferric and ferric oxide can only occur in an aerobic environment. The complex dissolves under anaerobic conditions. Another consideration is that anaerobic conditions lower the pH, with a subsequent dissolution of metal complexes resulting in metals being discharged by the control in a subsequent storm. A final consideration is the potential adverse effect of the discharge of low dissolved oxygen stormwater on receiving streams resulting from the development of anaerobic conditions.

4.5.2   Sorption Capacity

Performance and capacity are the two main characteristics of sorptive unit processes. *Performance* refers to the efficiency of the process and the pollutant concentration in the effluent. *Capacity* refers to how much of the pollutant can be removed before the filter media or soil must be replaced. It is important that both be defined.

There are three different capacities: total saturation capacity, total capacity, and operating capacity. The *total saturation capacity* represents the amount of pollutant removed if all of the sorption sites in the media are used. With the types of media of interest to treatment, this condition only occurs at concentrations higher than those commonly experienced in stormwater. This is because capacity is not independent of pollutant concentration, that is, the higher the concentration the greater the total saturation capacity. *Total capacity* refers to the mass of pollutant removed as the concentration present in solution. Both total saturation capacity and total capacity are determined in the laboratory with a standard test under ideal conditions.

The *operating capacity* determines the needed volume of media. Using the total saturation capacity to size the media volume significantly underestimates the needed volume to avoid frequent replacement. The operating capacity is typically less than the total saturation capacity; therefore, tests to estimate capacity must be conducted at influent concentrations common to stormwater.

Operating capacity can be understood with the use of Figure 4.3, which shows a granular filter. The media should be of a gradation and depth under consideration for the prototype filter. The operating capacity is determined by passing stormwater through the column. With time, the front of the pollutant-saturated media moves progressively down the column as represented by the dark area. The water used in the tests may be real or synthetic stormwater. However, real stormwater is preferred, even if adjusted, because the effect of the complex chemistry of stormwater on sorptive filtration is not well understood. Synthetic stormwater made by adding chemicals and salts of interest to potable water may not possess the necessary complexity.

The effluent concentration is determined several times, represented by the curve at the bottom of Figure 4.3. The curve is prepared by dividing the effluent concentration

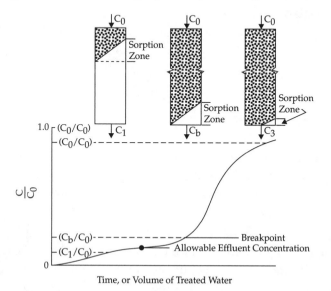

FIGURE 4.3   Breakthrough curve for a sorption column.

by the influent concentration to normalize the data. Eventually, the ratio reaches a value of one, when the influent and effluent concentrations are the same. However, the media need to be replaced sooner, when the allowable concentration in the effluent is reached as established by permits or local regulations.

Also illustrated in Figure 4.3 is the breakpoint, which occurs when the effluent concentration begins to rapidly increase, reflecting the approach of the front of saturated media to the filter outlet. The curve of effluent concentration in Figure 4.3 is called the *breakthrough curve.*

Other terms to describe the operating capacity are *bed volume* and *pore volume,* which are related to the volume of water passed through the column divided by the volume of the column before the allowable effluent concentration is reached. The volume occupied by the media is ignored with bed volume, as this typically does not vary between media types. However, the media volume is subtracted when basing capacity on the saturated pore volume. Either ratio facilitates upsizing from the laboratory or pilot scale to the prototype. The operating capacity of a column is described as a certain number of bed volumes (for instance, 5000 bed volumes). The term allows for a quick calculation of the media volume needed given the desired operating cycle and peak flow. These capacity concepts also apply to soils in wet basins and infiltration devices.

4.6   Precipitation

Precipitation is a unit process in which a settleable or filterable particulate is formed by joining two inorganic dissolved species with the objective of removing one of them. Precipitation occurs naturally without the aid of chemicals or can be induced by a chemical. Both of these processes are presented in this section.

4.6.1   Natural Precipitation

Natural precipitation refers to reactions that occur without the purposeful addition of chemicals to a stormwater control. Natural precipitation occurs in the soils of infiltrators, wet basins and wetlands, and filter media. It also occurs with incidental infiltration to soils from the bottoms of swales and dry basins. Precipitation may occur in the standing water of wet basins or infiltration basins (Kadlec and Knight, 1996).

Calcium phosphates may form in wet basins if the stormwater has sufficient calcium and alkalinity. Algae may enhance the process. Dissolved phosphorus may be removed by aluminum, iron, and manganese in the water column and in the soil of wet basins and infiltration basins, or in sand filters if the sand contains these metals. Removal may take place directly with the metal or its oxide. As mentioned previously in this chapter, metals such as zinc and copper precipitate with sulfide, an important sequestering process in wet basins and wetlands.

As noted in Section 4.5, the distinction between adsorption and precipitation is not always clear with some of the removal processes in nature, particularly in soils. In some instances, both appear to occur with the dissolved pollutant initially removed by adsorption into a complex that slowly changes to a precipitate.

Precipitates may undergo dissolution similar to desorption if water chemistry changes significantly, as noted previously with adsorption. The precipitates primarily affected are metal sulfides and ferric phosphate. The former dissolve in aerobic conditions and the latter in anaerobic.

4.6.2 Chemical Precipitation

Chemical precipitation is induced by the two general methods: modifying the surface of a filter media, or adding the chemical as a liquid or solid to stormwater. These chemicals can be liquid or solid and induce precipitation by altering water chemistry. Effective precipitation is achieved with rapid and complete mixing at the point of chemical addition, followed by gentle stirring to flocculate the precipitate. The flocculent is removed by sedimentation or filtration.

Alum and sodium aluminate are used to precipitate phosphorus in stormwater to reduce eutrophication in small lakes. The appropriate dosage of chemical enters directly into the storm drain upstream of the discharge point and the turbulence in the flow mixes the chemical. Flocculated precipitates settle in the lake. Reductions of total and dissolved phosphorus of approximately 90% are achieved at dosages of 5 mg/L of alum to give a phosphorus concentration to approximately 0.025 mg/L. There may not always be sufficient alkalinity in the stormwater to avoid an excessive drop of the pH to toxic levels; the occurrence of this condition varies with the site. The process produces both metal-phosphate and metal-hydroxide precipitates. The latter flocculates the former, producing a settleable floc. Other precipitants include poly aluminum chloride and ferric sulfate and chloride.

Dissolved metals sorb to metal-hydroxide flocs. The addition of aluminum and iron salts is, therefore, one means of removing dissolved metals. Bacteria are also removed by metal-hydroxide flocs, either by sorption to the floc or by being swept into the floc as colloids.

Limitations to the practical application of precipitation in stormwater treatment are the highly variable nature of flows and dissolved pollutant concentrations, the need to manage chemical sludges, and the added complexity of operating and maintaining mechanical systems. If the system operates in real time, the dosage may have to vary correspondingly with the highly fluctuating flow. An equalization basin can dampen peak flows and allow the precipitation unit to operate at a lower, less variable peak flow.

4.7   Coagulation

Coagulation is the agglomeration of small particles into larger particles that typically have a more rapid settling rate. With the aid of chemicals, it may occur in conjunction with precipitation or to solely remove clay and fine silts that do not otherwise settle within a given timeframe needed for adequate performance of stormwater controls (i.e., from a few hours to several days). Coagulation is becoming more common in stormwater treatment, particularly at construction sites. The same constraints noted for precipitation with liquid chemicals apply to coagulation.

Coagulation consists of the following two steps: destabilization and flocculation. Unanimity does not exist in related engineering fields on the terminology of coagulation. Some consider coagulation to be the destabilization step, with flocculation as a separate process. Others define coagulation as it is presented in this MOP.

Suspensions of small particles, including bacteria, are stable because they resist aggregation into larger particles as they repel each other because of a negative surface charge. Destabilization with chemicals allows aggregation of these small particles into large, denser flocs. The rate of aggregation is a function of collision frequency and how many of the collisions result in floc growth. If the flocs grow too large or the energy input is excessive, hydrodynamic shearing forces break the flocs. The combined processes of floc formation and breakup reach a steady state after a period of mixing. The final condition of the floc depends on the original characteristics of the solids, the coagulant, and the mixing conditions. Some coagulants create a floc that sweeps small particles.

Successful flocculation occurs as transport processes bring particles together. Transport occurs by natural means, such as wind in a wet basin, or by artificial mixing with pumps, paddles, and fountains.

4.7.1   Natural Coagulation

Because coagulation occurs naturally in lakes and estuaries, it likely occurs in stormwater basins without the aid of chemicals. The significance of its role on performance of stormwater controls has not been defined, although it has been observed in untreated stormwater under ideal conditions in the laboratory. Under quiescent conditions, coagulation begins within approximately 6 hours. Coagulation likely begins in only 1 to 2 hours if the basin is stirred (Lick, 1993).

With residence times of months to years, colloids have time to flocculate in natural waters with the aid of natural polymers extruded by bacteria. Of interest is whether the conditions in wet basins are conducive to flocculation with or without artificial mixing. One study of wet basins found relatively large, light, floc-like material on the order of 40 μm during the winter that was larger in the summer when algae were present. The flocs appeared to be agglomerations of clay and bacteria and free-floating algae. These flocs were light and, therefore, settled slowly if at all (Dugan, 1975).

4.7.2 *Chemical Coagulation*

A variety of coagulants are used in water and wastewater treatment to address the wide range of characteristics of these waters. Optimum efficiency is often obtained with a primary chemical, the coagulant, and a lesser quantity of a second coagulant, called a *coagulant aid*. Coagulants are divided into the following groups: inorganic salts, organic polymers, and inorganic polymers. As noted previously, inorganic salts used in stormwater treatment such as aluminum sulfate (alum), aluminum chloride, ferric chloride, and ferric sulfate produce a metal-hydroxide that causes coagulation. Most coagulants are available as a liquid, powder, and solid log or block. Organic polymers are often used at construction sites.

4.8   Filtration

Filtration may be characterized as physical or sorptive. Sorptive unit processes related to filters were presented in Section 4.5. Physical filtration is the subject of this section and is defined as a unit process in which filter media remove particles and attached pollutants by straining and sedimentation on and within the media. Particles smaller than the openings of the media are retained in niches or held against the media by the force of the water. In practice, particles as small as 10 to 15% of the nominal void diameter are removed, although at decreasing efficiencies (Sherard et al., 1984). This process is enhanced in porous media such as perlite whose porous structure traps fine particles, likely increasing the sediment retention capacity over nonporous media.

Electrostatic and related forces cause clays and fine silts to attach to sand, with the effect varying with the relative differences in electric surface charges between the sand and incoming particles (Collins, 1985; Stenkamp, 1992). It has not been established whether this mechanism occurs with other types of media.

4.9   Biological Processes

There are a multitude of biological processes, making it somewhat unclear as to which should be defined as unit processes. It is reasonable to consider a biological process as a unit process if it can be controlled in some manner by design. The application of this criterion to the various known processes determines their inclusion in Tables 4.1 and 4.2.

Plants and other biological forms present in stormwater controls are viewed as removers of many pollutants of interest, which, to the plants, can be building blocks of their metabolism; for example, nitrogen and phosphorus nutrients, and various metals are micronutrients. However, their metabolic requirements are modest relative to the mass of each pollutant available in stormwater. Without removal of the biological mass by maintenance, a stormwater control reaches a steady-state condition in which the mass of pollutants (nutrients) used by new growth is offset by the loss from death and decaying organic matter. Positive removal likely occurs in the first few years of a stormwater control as the biological mass increases. Steady state is reached when growth is balanced by death and decay.

Studies of biological systems conflict with respect to the removal of nutrients, particularly nitrogen and phosphorus. Most of these studies are of small laboratory-scale units called *mesocosms*. The tests are frequently of immature systems. Positive removal in short-term tests also may occur because of the ability of many plant and bacteria species to accumulate nutrients in excess of their immediate metabolic needs when exposed to higher-than-normal concentrations. Known as *bioaccumulation,* the metabolic process is an evolutionary response to scarcity in the natural environment. Algae and some plants are capable of substantial bioaccumulation, as are several terrestrial species.

The seasonal variation in growth, dormancy, and death may benefit the receiving water even if net removal (pollutant uptake from growth minus loss from death) is essentially zero on an annual basis. In temperate climates, removal of nutrients including metals in the spring and early summer may benefit a creek during the most sensitive time in its ecological cycle. The loss of the previously removed nutrients in the fall and winter may be of little consequence to the receiving water depending on specific factors in the aquatic environment.

Biological unit processes are also important in infiltrators and filters, including bioretention filters and, potentially, sand filters. The sediment that accumulates on the surface of sand filters includes bacteria and other small organisms that degrade petroleum hydrocarbons and pesticides and prey on pathogens. In addition, the bacteria degrade incoming leaves, providing sorption sites for dissolved metals.

Plants provide substantial benefits indirectly. For example, foliage retains sediments and protects or at least minimizes clogging of filters and infiltration basins. The roots of plants maintain the infiltration rates of well drained soil and likely increase the rates of tight soils. With their deeper roots, prairie grasses have been observed to provide greater enhancement than turf grasses. Decaying organic matter provides sorption sites for dissolved metals, pesticides, and other toxic organics. The presence of plants results in a more complex ecosystem conducive to bacteria and other small organisms, which accelerate the degradation of toxins and the death of pathogenic bacteria and viruses. Plants use nutrients that have sorbed to clay during stormwater treatment, making those sites available again for sorption. Vegetation increases evapotranspiration, accelerating the removal of pollutants in wet basins and wetlands and restoring void space in filters and infiltrators to store water from the next storm.

An important point to recognize, particularly with vegetated stormwater controls, is that nitrogen, phosphorus, and metals present in the effluent during a storm are not necessarily coming directly from the influent runoff. Nutrients cycle through the treatment system, whether it is a wet basin or bioretention filter with plant uptake and decay, chemical sorption and precipitation, and desorption and dissolution. Depending on the circumstances, pollutant releases may take place from lake-type stormwater controls. Lakes with anoxic hypolimnia (anoxic lakes) have significantly lower values for phosphorus retention than do lakes with aerobic hypolimnia (oxic lakes) (Nürnberg, 1984). This type of potential release after a storm is one reason that percent pollutant removal efficiency is a poor indicator of the performance of a stormwater control, as presented in Chapter 3.

Not all biological unit processes are beneficial. The mat of bacteria and algae on a filter or infiltrator may contribute to clogging. Biological unit processes may require a lower limit on effluent concentration because of nutrient cycling and loss from decaying vegetation. The lower limit for nitrogen appears to be in the range of 1 to 2 mg/L. Studies have shown an increase in some nitrogen forms as stormwater passes through a wetland. In addition, organic suspended sediments may result from algal production within a lake-like stormwater control, followed by the accumulation of phytoplankton biomass. This internally generated organic sediment adds to the incoming sediment load from stormwater and could significantly reduce the storage capacity of the control.

4.9.1   Biological Forms

4.9.1.1 Aquatic Plants

Vegetation in wet basins and wetlands can be placed in the following general groups: rooted-emergent, rooted-floating, rooted-submerged, and free-floating. *Emergent* refers to plants whose foliage extends above the water surface, such as cattails. The leaves of *rooted-floating* plants, such as water lilies, rest on the water surface. Those with foliage below the water surface, such as milfoil, are placed in the *rooted-submerged* group. *Free-floating* plants such as duckweed obtain nutrients directly from the wet pool.

Biofilms of bacteria and algae grow on plant foliage, which remove pollutants. Also, large quantities of metals have been found attached to plant roots, differing between species. The likely mechanism is sorption of zinc, copper, and other metals to iron-oxide plaques that form on plant roots. The plaque sorption is a defense mechanism that prevents excessive intake by the plants of zinc and copper, which are toxic in high concentrations. This process illustrates the symbiotic relationship between chemical and biological unit processes and the gray line between the two. Although the metals are removed by sorption, it is reasonable to consider it a biological process, given the key role of the plants.

As mentioned earlier, once rooted vegetation in a wetland is well established, use of nutrients by fresh growth is offset by death and decay. A small fraction is essentially permanently sequestered in a portion of the organic matter resistant to degradation, particularly in the anaerobic soils of wet basins. Although information on the time to full vegetation infill is lacking, it is likely only a few years.

Aquatic plants provide substantial benefits indirectly, as noted previously. With the exception of small colloidal matter, which sorbs to the biofilm, foliage retains but does not filter sediments in surface wet basins. The shading effect of plants combined with evapotranspiration cools the stored stormwater.

Aquatic plants significantly affect the dissolved oxygen conditions of wet basins and wetlands because they pump dissolved oxygen into the root zone, a survival mechanism in saturated soils, thereby increasing the area of oxygen-enriched conditions conducive to biological and chemical unit processes in the soil that require oxygen. The dissolved oxygen in the overlying water is affected, particularly in basins dominated by wetland plants. The dissolved oxygen concentration rises substantially during the afternoon and may create a supersaturated condition. However, in turn, respiration during the night significantly decreases the dissolved oxygen concentration, possibly to near zero. This aspect suggests a possible concern over the discharge from wetlands during dry weather.

4.9.1.2 Terrestrial Plants

Although plants are an inherent component of bioretention filters, they should be specified for all surface treatment systems to the extent limited by climate and from species native to the area. Even sparse native vegetation in semiarid regions may enhance performance. Shrubs and trees provide the particular benefit of growing many years to reach maturity, on the order of a decade or more. Turf grass requires frequent mowing; clippings must be removed in the vicinity of the stormwater control if nutrients are a concern. This removal is not necessary with woody plants, although annual pruning likely increases net productivity. Information on net productivity in stormwater controls and nutrient content is lacking. Studies of agricultural crops indicate that approximately 1 to 2 g/m^2 of phosphorus is used per year. Uptake by trees in temperate climates is on the order of 1 $g/m^2 \cdot yr$. The rate of nitrogen removal should be on the order of 10 times the phosphorus rate because plants use approximately 10 times more nitrogen than phosphorus. These rates are considerably less than the rate of loading to vegetated stormwater controls sized to current design criteria, assuming that the control is properly maintained to remove dead vegetation.

4.9.1.3 Bacteria

Specialized bacteria likely are primarily responsible for the removal of nitrogen in wet basins and bioretention filters. They transform ammonia to nitrate in infiltrators and sand filters, but the nitrate is highly mobile and can flow out through underdrains. Specialized bacteria produce sulfide from sulfate, which binds metals in the soils of wet basins. Bacteria degrade pesticides, petroleum compounds, and other anthropogenic organics removed from stormwater by soils and filter media. Bacteria break down plant matter into more useful forms for the sorption of dissolved metals and pesticides. If nutrient deficient, bacteria can remove phosphorus in excess of their metabolic needs when exposed to higher-than-normal concentrations.

While bacteria generally play a positive role, their growth may contribute to the clogging of filters and infiltration devices. Periodic drying of these unit operations restores infiltration and filtration rates.

4.9.1.4 Algae

Algae are found free-floating and attached in unit operations with wet pools. Their effects are potentially both beneficial and adverse. Attached algae process nutrients. However, free-floating algae, sometimes in the form of algal mats, escape wet pool systems, carrying nutrients and metals. Algae may clog filters and infiltrators if the water drains too slowly, although some studies have found that algal mats improve performance where a standing water level is maintained (Rice, 1974). Gas produced by the mats causes them to rise, removing sediments from the surface. Biofilms of algae and bacteria form on wetland foliage and soils, improving performance. Algae can amass metals concentrations far in excess of their metabolic needs (Vymazal, 1994), although this has not been documented in stormwater systems.

There is a diurnal pH cycle in natural wetlands, which likely occurs in stormwater wetlands as well. Through the consumption of carbon dioxide, algae and plants cause the pH to rise above 9 in the afternoon. If there is sufficient calcium in the water, precipitation of calcium phosphate occurs. The likely precipitate is hydroxyapatite, a calcium phosphate complex.

4.9.2   Plant Metabolism

Plant metabolism is considered a unit process inasmuch as a design specifies the presence and density of plants in a stormwater control. Through photosynthesis, plants use energy from the sun to transform carbon dioxide and water into starches and sugars, which are the source of energy for plants. By way of metabolic activity, pollutants useful to growth by plants, algae, and some bacteria are removed from stormwater in the process of making biomass. The general equation is

$$CO_2 + H_2O + \text{Sunlight} + \text{Nutrients} = \text{Biomass} \qquad (4.3)$$

Phosphorus and nitrogen are considered macronutrients, given the proportionally greater metabolic need for these two elements. The general composition of algae is $C_{106}H_{263}O_{110}N_{16}P\text{-}M$, where M refers to the micronutrients that in total represent approximately 2% of the biomass. The relationship indicates the following fractions for the macronutrients: oxygen, 48.6%; carbon, 35%; hydrogen, 7.2%; nitrogen, 6.2%; and phosphorus, 0.9%. Zinc, the most used metal, is approximately 0.1%. Other metals in trace amounts are manganese, iron, copper, molybdenum, and cobalt. It is likely that, in stormwater controls with wet pools, metals and other toxic pollutants cause a shift in plant and algal species tolerant of such conditions. Examination of plant and algal biomass indicates a wider range in the fractions of nitrogen, phosphorus, and metals than suggested by the aforementioned simple relationship for algae (Vymazal, 1994).

The phosphorus cycle is presented in Figure 4.4 and consists of both biological and chemical unit processes. Plant metabolism is the primary biological process by which phosphorus is removed in stormwater controls. Phosphorus in stormwater is mostly in the particulate form and is removed by settling. Generally, one-fourth to one-third of incoming phosphorus is in aqueous solution as free orthophosphate

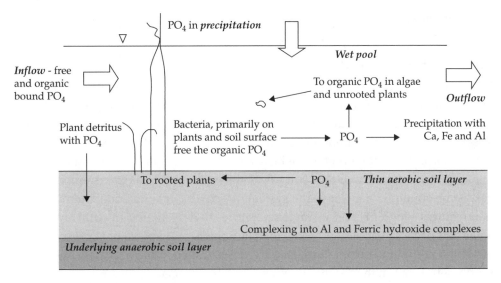

FIGURE 4.4   Phosphorus cycle (Minton, 2011).

or bound to aqueous organics. Although stormwater manuals focus on the removal of total phosphorus, stormwater control design should address phosphorus that is biologically available and present as dissolved and on surfaces of fine sediments. Controls such as vaults may be effective at reducing total phosphorus, but may only modestly affect what is potentially biologically available.

The potential for particulate phosphorus to dissolve or be released by bacterial activity is not well understood. It is known that some of the phosphorus bound to fine silts and clays becomes biologically available, most likely by desorption. Some of the phosphorus present in organic matter in incoming stormwater may be released as degradation by bacteria occurs. This fraction is likely site specific and highly variable among storms at each site.

As mentioned earlier, once vegetation fills in a surface stormwater control, the uptake of phosphorus, nitrogen, and metals is offset by their loss from decaying vegetation. Loss also occurs as plants enter a stage of senescence in the fall. A small portion of the phosphorus is essentially permanently sequestered in a portion of dead organic matter that is resistant to degradation by bacteria, particularly in the anaerobic soils of wet basins and wetlands. This portion has been estimated to be approximately 0.5 to 1 g/m² per year in natural wetlands, which may serve as the basis for design (Richardson, 1985). Phosphorus can be removed by harvesting vegetation;

however, the effectiveness of foliage harvesting depends on design; that is, the larger the unit surface area, the greater the role harvesting can play.

4.9.3   Nitrification and Denitrification

Figure 4.5 illustrates the aquatic nitrogen cycle. Nitrogen exists in the following forms: bound within organic matter, ammonium and ammonia, nitrite, nitrate, and nitrogen gas. Nitrogen in untreated stormwater is primarily organically bound, with lesser concentrations of ammonium, ammonia, and nitrate. Nitrogen does not precipitate or sorb, except for ammonia, which sorbs to clay in soils. Ammonium (NH_4^+) is the ionic form of ammonia (NH_3) in solution in water, whereas free ammonia is as a gas. Some ammonia may leave the system directly by volatilization, but this condition requires a high pH and warm temperatures to be a significant pathway. Certain algae and bacteria species and some wetland plants are capable of altering nitrogen gas to ammonium to obtain nitrogen for growth. Called *nitrogen fixation*, this process is only significant in the absence of other forms of nitrogen.

It is likely that most of the nitrogen removal in vegetated systems is performed by bacteria through nitrification and denitrification (Tanner, 2001; Minton, 2011).

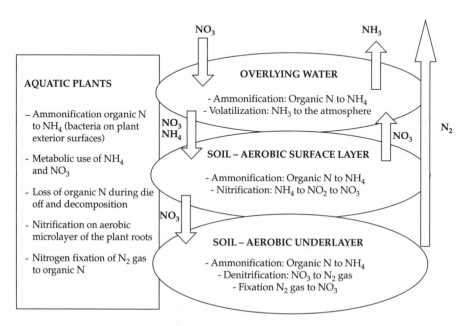

FIGURE 4.5   Nitrogen cycle (Minton, 2011).

Like phosphorus, some is sequestered in organic matter resistant to degradation, particularly in the anaerobic soils present in wet basins and wetlands. Transformation by bacteria ultimately causes nitrogen release to the atmosphere as a gas. Bacterial activity occurs primarily in the soil and on biofilms, where the density of bacteria is greatest, rather than in the wet pool. The transformation is described as

$$\text{Organic-bound nitrogen} \rightarrow NH_4^+/NH_3 + O_2 \rightarrow NO_2 + NO_3 \rightarrow N_2 \uparrow \qquad (4.4)$$

$$\textit{ammonification} \qquad \textit{nitrification} \quad \textit{denitrification}$$

While many bacteria species carry out the first step in eq 4.4, nitrification and denitrification depend on a few species. Nitrification proceeds from ammonium to nitrite and then from nitrite to nitrate. Each step is conducted by two different groups of bacteria, *Nitrosomonas* and *Nitrobacters*, respectively. Nitrite is changed relatively quickly to nitrate; little persists unless the temperature is low. For denitrification, the genera *Bacillus, Micrococcus,* and *Pseudomonas* are the most significant in soils; the genera *Pseudomonas, Aerininasm,* and *Vibrio* are the most significant in aquatic environments. A little ammonia is lost by direct volatilization. A group of bacteria capable of transforming ammonia directly to nitrogen gas without the intermediate step of nitrification may also be present in wet basins (Strous et al., 1997).

Nitrification and denitrification are sensitive to dissolved oxygen and temperature. Process rates decrease significantly below 15 °C. Nitrification only occurs in the presence of dissolved oxygen. Denitrification occurs when dissolved oxygen is nearly absent and takes place completely only when dissolved oxygen is zero. Because nitrification and denitrification occur in separate areas, ammonia and nitrate ions must move to aerobic and anaerobic areas, respectively, by slow diffusion. Process rates have been found to differ substantially among natural wetlands because of differences in soils, particularly pH and organic matter. Therefore, this is possibly the case for stormwater wetlands as well. In a filter, nitrification and denitrification may not occur to a significant degree if the residence time of the stormwater through the filter is for only a few hours rather than days.

The terrestrial nitrogen cycle differs to the extent that the soils are generally aerobic because of the lack of standing water. Nitrification occurs readily in infiltrators and sand and bioretention filters, and may occur as stormwater is passing through. More likely, ammonium and ammonia sorb to clays during each storm, with transformation to nitrate occurring later. This nitrate desorbs from clay during each storm, giving the impression that nitrification is occurring. Denitrification in filters and infiltrators is not likely to be significant. Bacterial degradation of organic matter, if present in the media, may create micro sites with low dissolved oxygen, leading to some denitrification. While these treatment systems may become temporarily anaerobic during storms, the time period is insufficient to promote effective denitrification. However, bioretention filters can be designed to maintain an anaerobic internal water storage (IWS) zone, where denitrification can occur between storms (Chapter 8). Denitrification may also be limited by low concentrations of dissolved carbon.

As nitrification and denitrification are likely the two most important processes for the ultimate removal of nitrogen from a stormwater unit operation, they are identified as unit processes because they can be directly enhanced by design. As with phosphorus, design of stormwater controls should focus on the bioavailable fraction of nitrogen, not the total nitrogen load.

4.9.4   Other Biological Unit Processes

Tables 4.1 and 4.2 list other biological processes whose significance depends on the conditions inherent to the unit operation. For example, sulfate reduction requires extreme anaerobic conditions and time for the specialized bacteria to process sulfate. Hence, while it occurs in the saturated soils of wet basins and wetlands, it is not likely to occur to a significant degree in a unit operation that may only occasionally experience anaerobic conditions, such as an infiltration basin or a sand filter. In stormwater wetlands, unit processes may be assisted by the diurnal shift in dissolved oxygen induced by plant activity from high dissolved oxygen in the afternoon to anaerobic conditions in the early morning. However, bacteria do not necessarily shift into operation for such a short period of time given the energy needed.

The rate of removal of anthropogenic compounds such as pesticides varies widely, from days to centuries, depending on the particular compound. Bacteria require time to adjust to the presence of these organics and, therefore, may not be fully effective where a particular compound enters the system sporadically. However, these compounds likely sorb to organic matter in the facility, providing time for gradual degradation. Some compounds break down more readily in anaerobic environments.

Fecal coliform and related bacteria define receiving water standards, serving as surrogates for pathogenic organisms that are not readily determined by analytical procedures. It is generally believed that pathogenic organisms die more quickly than indicator bacteria. Hence, low counts of indicator bacteria imply low counts of pathogenic organisms. However, this presumption has been proved to be problematic for fecal coliform bacteria. Many states have shifted to Escherichia coli as the surrogate. Determination of the performance of particular stormwater controls regarding the removal of indicator organisms is confounded by the prescribed protocol of only taking grab samples, uncertainty in laboratory procedures, growth of the bacteria in the stormwater control, and its introduction directly into basins and wetlands from sources such as wildlife and pets.

4.10   Temperature Reduction

Thermal enrichment is of particular concern for streams with cold water fish species such as trout and salmon. Warm pavement heats runoff. Groundwater that enters surface basins increases in temperature as it passes through the basins. Because there are means to reduce the temperature of stormwater before discharge, temperature reduction can be considered a unit process. Design measures to minimize thermal enrichment or to cool water once it has been heated by pavement include avoidance of low-flow channels in dry basins, shading of wet basins and wetlands, use of vaults rather than surface basins, deployment of rock gallery outlets from basin, and use of bioretention (Jones and Hunt, 2009).

4.11   Disinfection

While pathogens naturally die in stormwater controls, disinfection can be more directly controlled by mechanical methods. Spraying or recirculating water in a basin enhances death by ultraviolet (UV) radiation; field studies in this process, however, are lacking. Ozonation and UV radiation systems are being used to treat dry weather and stormwater at modest peak flows. Some manufacturers of stormwater products have modified the surface of filter media with specific chemical complexes such as amines that kill bacteria on contact.

4.12   Screening

Screening removes gross pollutants, including litter, debris, very coarse sediment, and vegetation by straining them through devices with large openings. Gross pollutants can impair aquatic habitat, injure aquatic life, degrade aesthetic conditions, and cause clogging of drainage infrastructure. In addition, they may undergo a variety of transformations that may cause additional stormwater pollution. Gross pollutants have gained importance as a water quality concern and, in recent years, trash total maximum daily loads (TMDLs) have been added to municipal stormwater permits; for example in the cities of Los Angeles and Washington D.C.

The size threshold for gross pollutant varies across various studies. In the Los Angeles TMDLs the minimum size is 5 mm (0.2 in.) (LARWQCB, 2001). Sansalone and Kim (2008) proposed the limit between fine sands and silt per ASTM D422, which is 75 μm (0.0030 in.). The ASCE Task Committee on Gross Solids formalized a classification following a study by Roesner et al. (2007) that resulted in Figure 4.6. The ASCE proposed scheme (England and Rushton, 2007) includes the following classes:

- Litter–anthropogenic trash or rubbish, such as paper, plastic, polystyrene products, metal and glass greater than 4.75 mm (0.19 in.) or No. 4 U.S. standard sieve size;

- Organic debris–for example, leaves, branches, seeds, twigs, and grass clippings greater than 4.75 mm (0.19 in.); and

- Coarse sediments–organics or inorganics that can be derived from soils, pavement, building materials, litter or other materials greater than 75 μm (0.003 in.) or No. 200 U.S. standard sieve size.

Currently, only a handful of gross solids studies sought to classify the various types of litter and debris that make up gross pollutants. Sartor and Boyd (1972) originated much of the research in an early U.S. EPA study that defined the knowledge of street-surface pollution. This study found a high variability in loading rates based on samples from eight cities in the United States. A South African study found that litter wash-off rates varied from 0.53 to 96 kg/ha/yr (0.47 to 86 lb/ac/yr) for residential areas (Armitage et al., 1998). A series of Australian studies found similar variability (Allison, 1998a, 1998b). Caltrans performed a litter management pilot study and found that freeway surfaces generated 97.6 L/ha (893 cu ft/sq mi) (Caltrans, 2000). There is no consistent relationship between litter volume and mass because litter is generated in such a variety of sizes and shapes and can change with time and degradation (URS Corp., 2004). A summary of these studies is presented in Table 4.3. Another study

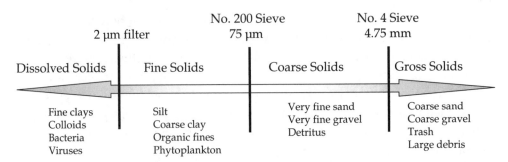

FIGURE 4.6 Solids size classification scheme used to define gross pollutants (after Roesner et al., 2007).

TABLE 4.3 Summary of litter load studies.

Source	Land use	Loading rate
Ballona Creek and Wetland Trash TMDL (LARWQCB, 2001)	General	9.3 L/ha (640 gal/sq mi), or 0.009 m³/ha (85.6 cu ft/sq mi) Based on uncompressed litter
Ballona Creek and Wetland Trash TMDL (LARWQCB, 2001)	Freeways	13.1 kg/ha (7479.4 lb/sq mi), or 0.1 m³/ha (892.6 cu ft/sq mi)
South Africa (Armitage et al., 1998)	Residential	0.53 kg/ha/yr (0.47 lb/ac/yr), minimum residential value 96 kg/ha/yr (86 lb/ac/yr), maximum residential value
Australia (Allison et al. (1998b)	Urban	30 dry kg/ha/yr (27 lb/ac/yr)
Australia (Allison et al. (1998a)	Commercial/residential/light industrial mix	81 and 236 g/ha per storm (46 and 135 lb/sq mi per storm) - Noted for individual storms
Sartor and Boyd (1972) Residential	Low density/old/single-family	310 kg/km (1100 +/- lb/curb mi)
	Medium density/new/single-family	140 kg/curb km (500 lb/curb mi)
	Low density/old/multifamily	280 kg/ curb km (1000 lb/curb mi)
	Medium density/old/multifamily	340 kg/curb km (1200 lb/curb mi)
Sartor and Boyd (1972) Industrial	Light	650 kg/curb km (2300 lb/curb mi)
	Medium	540 kg/curb km (1900 lb/curb mi)
	Heavy	1130 kg/curb km (4000 lb/curb mi)
Sartor and Boyd (1972) Commercial	Shopping center	113 kg/curb km (400 lb/curb mi)
	Central business district	85 kg/curb km (300 lb/curb mi)

TABLE 4.4 Types of floatable litter found on the streets of New York City (HydroQual, 2005).

Category	Fraction by number of Items (%)	Fraction by weight of Items (%)	Density, g/L (lb/cu ft)
Plastics	57.2	44.3	44.9 (2.8)
Metals	18.9	12	60.9 (3.8)
Paper	5.9	4	32.0 (2.0)
Wood	5.9	5.3	123 (7.7)
Polystyrene	5.4	1.3	11.2 (0.7)
Cloth/fabric	2.5	12.5	133 (8.3)
Glass	0.4	15.6	221 (13.8)
Other	3.8	5	157 (9.8)

performed by the City of New York (HydroQual, Inc., 1995) found that 2.3 floatable litter items were discharged through storm drain inlets per day per 30 m (100 ft) of curb, and the total litter load was two times this floatables quantity. The New York City study also characterized the types of litter collected as listed in Table 4.4.

Almost every type of stormwater control will remove gross pollutants to some degree; for example, the vegetation in bioretention filters and wetlands traps plastic bags and other floating items. Most manufactured vaults are designed to remove large pollutants. The most effective means of litter removal is direct screening with devices known as gross pollutant traps (GTPs). Gross pollutant traps that remove pollutants primarily by screening include screens, nets, baskets, and racks, whereas hoods exclude large floating solids from the flow (Chapter 10). The effectiveness of both processes is heavily dependent on maintenance activities that remove the material collected. When screens are perpendicular to the flow path, they can clog easily as material becomes lodged in the openings, which requires taking the unit out of operation for cleaning. An arrangement in which the flow meets the screen at an angle provides more effective screening because it allows self cleaning.

5.0 CONCLUDING REMARKS

This chapter presents a series of concepts to help the designer understand the mechanisms in unit processes for stormwater management and to align them with unit operations that are effective in addressing water quantity and quality management goals. A framework to classify stormwater controls is proposed to simplify terminology currently used to describe stormwater controls and thus facilitate communication among stormwater professionals. The framework strives to use descriptors that are as explicit as possible to portray the essence of a stormwater control. The system allows identification of variants and grouping them under a common descriptor thus leading to consistent design procedures.

6.0 REFERENCES

Allison, R. A.; Chiew, F. H. S.; McMahon, T. A. (1998a) *A Decision-Support-System for Determining Effective Trapping Strategies for Gross Pollutants.* Cooperative Research Centre for Catchment Hydrology, Victoria, Australia, April.

Allison, R. A.; Walker, T. A., Chiew, F. H. S.; O'Neil, I. C.; McMahon, T. A. (1998b) *From Roads to Rivers Gross Pollutant Removal from Urban Waterways.* Cooperative Research Centre for Catchment Hydrology, Victoria, Australia, May.

American Society of Civil Engineers; Water Environment Federation (1992) *Design and Construction of Urban Stormwater Management Systems*; ASCE Manuals and Reports of Engineering Practice No. 77; WEF Manual of Practice No. FD-20; American Society of Civil Engineers: New York.

Argue, J. R. (Ed.) (2004) *Water Sensitive Urban Design: Basic Procedures for "Source Control" of Stormwater: A Handbook of Australian Practice.* University of South Australia, Adelaide, South Australia, 246 pp.

Armitage, N.; Rooseboom, A.; Nel, C.; Townshend, P. (1998) *The Removal of Urban Litter from Stormwater Conduits and Streams*, WRC Report No. TT 95/98, July.

Bäckström, M. (2002) Sediment Transport in Grassed Swales During Simulated Runoff Events. *Water Sci. Technol.*, **45** (7), 41–49.

Bedient, P. B.; Huber, W. C.; and Vieux, B. E. (2008) *Hydrology and Floodplain Analysis*, Prentice Hall: New York, 816 pp.

Blight, G. E. (2002) Measuring Evaporation from Soil Surfaces for Environmental and Geotechnical Purposes. *Water SA*, **28** (4), 381–394.

Cabell Brand Center (2007) *Virginia Rainwater Harvesting Manual.* Salem, Virginia.

California Department of Transportation (2000) *California Department of Transportation District 7 Litter Management Pilot Study;* Caltrans Document No. CT-SW-RT-00-013, June.

Casey, T. J. (1997) *Unit Treatment Processes in Water and Wastewater;* Wiley and Sons: New York.

Cheng, N. S. (1997) A Simplified Settling Velocity Formula for Sediment Particles. *J. Hydrau. Eng.,* **123** (2), 149.

Clar, M. L.; Barfield, B. J.; O'Connor, T. P. (2004) *Stormwater Best Management Practice Design Guide;* EPA-600/R-04-121; U.S. Environmental Protection Agency, Office of Research and Development: Cincinnati, Ohio.

Collins, A. G. (1985) Reduction of Turbidity by a Cola-Aluminum Filter. *J. Am. Water Works Assoc.,* **77** (6), 88.

Denmead, O. T.; Shaw, R. H. (1962) Availability of Soil Water to Plants as Affected by Soil Moisture Content and Meteorological Conditions. *Agron. J.,* **54,** 385–390.

Dugan, P. R. (1975) Bioflocculation and the Accumulation of Chemicals by Floc-Forming Organisms; EPA-600/2-75-032; U.S. Environmental Protection Agency: Washington, D.C.

Dunne, T. H.; Leopold, L. (1968) *Water in Environmental Planning;* W.H. Freeman and Company: New York.

Emerson, C.; Traver, R. (2008) Multiyear and Seasonal Variation of Infiltration from Storm-Water Best Management Practices. *J. Irrig. Drain. Eng.,* **134** (5), 598–605.

England, G.; Rushton B. (2007) *ASCE Guideline for Monitoring Stormwater Gross Solids.* Report of the Task Committee on Gross Solids; Environmental and Water Resources Institute/American Society of Civil Engineers: Reston, Virginia.

Environmental and Water Resources Institute (2005) *The ASCE Standardized Reference Evapotranspiration Equation.* American Society of Civil Engineers: Reston, Virginia, January, 70 pp.

Fair, G. M.; Geyer, J. C. (1954) Water Supply and Wastewater Disposal; Wiley & Sons: New York.

Federal Highway Administration (2002) *Hydraulic Design Series No. 2: Highway Hydrology.* FHWA-NHI-02-00; National Highway Institute: Arlington, Virginia.

Feller, M.; Traver, R.; Wadzuk, B. (2010) Estimation of Green Roof Evapotranspi-ration—Experimental Results. Proceedings of the 2010 International Low Impact Development Conference, San Francisco, California, April.

Graf, W. H. (1984) *Hydraulics of Sediment Transport*; Water Resources Publications: Littleton, Colorado.

Green, W. H.; Ampt, G. A. (1911) Studies on Soil Physics: 1. Flow of Air and Water through Soils. *J. Agric. Sci.*, 4, 1.

Hanson, R. L. (1991) Evapotranspiration and Droughts. In *National Water Summary 1988-89—Hydrologic Events and Floods and Droughts: U.S. Geological Survey Water-Supply Paper 2375*; Paulson, R. W., Chase, E. B., Roberts, R. S., Moody, D. W., Compilers; U.S. Geological Survey: Reston, Virginia; pp 99–104.

Hickman, J.; Wadzuk, B; Traver, R. (2011) Evaluating the Role of Evapotranspiration in the Hydrology of a Bioinfiltration Basin Using a Weighing Lysimeter. *Proceedings of 2011 EWRI World Water and Environmental Resources Congress*, Palm Springs, California, May.

Horton, R. E. (1940) An Approach Toward a Physical Interpretation of Infiltration-Capacity. *Soil Sci. Soc. Am. J.*, 5, 399.

HydroQual, Inc. (1995) *Floatables Pilot Program Final Report: Evaluation of Non-Structural Methods to Control Combined and Storm Sewer Floatable Materials*; New York Department of Environmental Protection, Division of Water Quality Improvement: New York, Dec.

Jones, M. P.; Hunt, W. F. (2009) Bioretention Impact on Runoff Temperature in Trout Sensitive Waters. *J. Environ. Eng.*, 135 (8), 577–585.

Kadlec, R. H.; Knight, R. L. (1996) *Treatment Wetlands*; Lewis Publishers: Boca Raton, Florida.

Klute, A.; Dirkson, C. (1986) "Hydraulic Conductivity and Diffusivity—Laboratory Methods." In *Methods of Soil Analysis, Part I—Physical and Mineralogical Methods*, Soil Science Society of America Book Series No. 5, Soil Science Society of America, Madison, Wisconsin; pp 687–734.

Lau, Y. L. (1993) "Temperature Effect on Settling Velocity and Deposition of Cohesive Sediments." *J. Hydraul. Res.*, 32 (1), 41.

Lick, W. (1993) The Flocculation, Deposition, and Resuspension of Fine-grained Sediments. In *Transport and Transformation of Contaminants Near the Sediment-Water Interface*; DePinton, J. V; Lick, W.; Paul, J.; Eds.; Lewis Publishers: Boca Raton, Florida.

Los Angeles Regional Water Quality Control Board (2001) *Trash Total Maximum Daily Loads for the Los Angeles River Watershed*, September 19, Los Angeles, California.

Lucas, W.; Medina, D. E. (2011) *Back to the Basics: Computational Methods in Low Impact Development Stormwater Controls - Part 1: Hydrology and Hydraulics.* Report of the LID Computational Methods Task Committee, Environmental and Water Resources Institute/American Society of Civil Engineers: Reston, Virginia.

Macomber, P. S. H. (2001) *Guidelines for Rainwater Catchment Systems for Hawaii.* College of Tropical Agriculture and Human Resources, University of Hawaii, Manoa, Hawaii.

Maidment, D. (1993) *Handbook of Hydrology*; McGraw-Hill: New York.

McCorquodale, A.; Zhou, S.; Richardson, J. (2005) Mathematical Modeling of Secondary Settling Tanks. *Proceedings of the Water Environment Federation*, (11), 4467–4480.

McFarlane, A.; Bremmell, K.; Addai-Mensah, J. (2006) Improved Dewatering Behavior of Clay Minerals Dispersions Via Interfacial Chemistry and Particle Interactions Optimization. *J. Colloid Interface Sci.*, **293** (1), 116–127.

Metcalf and Eddy, Inc. (2003) *Wastewater Engineering: Treatment Disposal and Reuse*; McGraw-Hill: New York.

Minton, G. (2007) A Tower of Babel: A Proposed Framework for Stormwater Treatment Terminology. *Stormwater*, March–April.

Minton, G. (2011) *Stormwater Treatment: Biological, Chemical, and Engineering Principles*, 3rd ed.; RPA Press: Seattle, Washington.

Nürnberg, G. K. (1984) The Prediction of Internal Phosphorus Load in Lakes with Anoxic Hypolimnia. *Limnol. Oceanogr.*, **29**, 111–124.

Philip, J. R.; De Vries, D. A. (1957) Moisture Movement in Porous Materials Under Temperature Gradients, *Trans. Am. Geophys. Union*, **38** (2), 222–228.

Pitt, R. (1994) *Small Storm Hydrology*. University of Alabama–Birmingham. Paper presented at Design of Stormwater Quality Management Practices; Madison, Wisconsin; May 17–19.

Pitt, R.; Voorhees, N. (1989) *Source Load and Management Model—An Urban Nonpoint Source Water Quality Model*; v. I-III, PUBL-WR-218-89; Wisconsin Department of Natural Resources: Madison, Wisconsin.

Pitt, R.; Robertson, B.; Barron, P.; Ayyoubi, A.; Clark, S. (1999) *Stormwater Treatment at Critical Areas: The Multi-Chambered Treatment Train (MCTT)*. U.S. Environmental Protection Agency, Wet Weather Flow Management Program, National Risk Management Research Laboratory, EPA-600/R-99/017; U.S. Environmental Protection Agency: Cincinnati, Ohio, 505 pp.

Pitt, R.; Chen, S.-E.; Clark, S. (2002) Compacted Urban Soil Effects on Infiltration and Bioretention Stormwater Control Designs. *Proceedings of the Ninth International Conference on Urban Drainage*, Portland, Oregon.

Ponce, V. M. (1994) *Engineering Hydrology: Principles and Practices*; Prentice Hall: New York.

Pyne, R. D. G. (1995) *Groundwater Recharge and Wells: A Guide to Aquifer Storage Recovery*; CRC Press: Boca Raton, Florida.

Rachman, A.; Anderson, S. H.; Gantzer, C. J.; Alberts, E. E. (2004) Soil Hydraulic Properties Influenced by Stiff-Stemmed Grass Hedge Systems. *Soil Sci. Soc. Am. J.*, **68**, 1386–1393.

Rawls, W. J.; Ahuja, L. R.; Brakensiek, D. L.; Shirmohammadi, A. (1993) Infiltration and Soil Water Movement. In *Handbook of Hydrology*; Maidment, D. R., Ed.; McGraw-Hill: New York.

Rice, R. (1974) Soil Clogging During Infiltration of Secondary Effluent. *J.—Water Pollut. Control Fed.*, **46**, 708.

Rich, L. (1961) *Unit Operations of Sanitary Engineering*; McGraw-Hill: New York.

Rich, L. (1963) *Unit Processes of Sanitary Engineering*; McGraw Hill: New York.

Richardson, C. J. (1985) Mechanisms Controlling Phosphorus Retention Capacity of Freshwater Wetlands. *Science*, **228**, 1424.

Roesner, L. A.; Pruden, A.; Kidder, E. M. (2007) *Improved Protocol for Classification and Analysis of Stormwater-Borne Solids*, WERF 04-SW-4; Water Environment Research Foundation: Alexandria, Virginia.

Roseen, R. M.; Ballestero, T. P.; Houle, J. J.; Avellaneda, P.; Briggs, J.; Fowler, G.; Wildey, R. (2009) Seasonal Performance Variations for Storm-Water Management Systems in Cold Climate Conditions. *J. Environ. Eng.*, **135** (3), 128–137.

Rossman, L. (2004) *Storm Water Management Model: User's Manual, Version 5.0;* Environmental Protection Agency, National Risk Management Research Laboratory, Cincinnati, Ohio.

Sansalone, J.; Kim, J. Y. (2008) Transport of Particulate Matter Fractions in Urban Source Area Pavement Surface Runoff. *J. Environ. Qual.,* **37** (5), 1883–1893.

Sartor, J. D.; Boyd, G. B. (1972) *Water Pollution Aspects of Street Surface Contaminants,* EPA-R2-72-081, U.S. Environmental Protection Agency, Office of Research and Monitoring, U.S. Environmental Protection Agency: Washington, D.C.

Saxton, K. E. (2005) *SPAW: Soil-Plant-Atmosphere-Water Field & Pond Hydrology.* http://hydrolab.arsusda.gov/SPAW/Index.htm (accessed Aug 2011).

Schneider, D.; Wadzuk, B. M.; Traver, R. G. (2011) Using a Weighing Lysimeter to Determine a Crop Coefficient for a Green Roof to Predict Evapotranspiration with the FAO Standardized Penman-Monteith Equation. *Proceedings of the 2011 World Environmental and Water Resources Congress,* Palm Springs, California, May.

Sherard, J. L.; Lorn, P. D.; Talbot, J. R. (1984) Basic Properties of Sand and Gravel Filters. *J. Geotechnol. Eng.,* **110** (6), 684.

Stenkamp, V. S. (1992) The Effects of an Iron Oxide Coating on the Filtration Properties of Sand. Masters Thesis, University of Washington, Seattle, Washington.

Strecker, E.; Huber, W.; Heaney, J.; Bodine, D.; Sansalone, J.; Quigley, M.; Leisenring, M.; Pankani, D.; Thayumanavan, A. (2005) *Critical Assessment of Stormwater Treatment and Control Selection Issues;* Final Report 02-SW-1; Water Environment Research Foundation: Alexandria, Virginia.

Strous, M.; Gerven, E.; Kuenen, J.; Jetten, M. (1997) Effects of Aerobic and Microaerobic Conditions on Anaerobic Ammonium-Oxidizing (Anammox) Sludge. *Appl. Environ. Microbiol.,* **63**, 6, 2446.

Sullivan, R. H.; Ure, J. E.; Parkinson, F.; Zielinski, P. (1982) *Design Manual: Swirl and Helical Bend Pollution Control Devices;* EPA-600/8-82-013; U.S. Environmental Protection Agency, Office of Research and Development, Municipal Environmental Research Laboratory: Cincinnati, Ohio.

Tanner, C. (2001) Plants as Ecosystem Engineers in Subsurface-Flow Treatment Wetland. *Water Sci. Technol.,* **44** (11–12), 9–17.

Texas Water Development Board (2005) *The Texas Manual on Rainwater Harvesting,* 3rd ed.; Austin, Texas.

Urban Flood Control District (2001) *Urban Storm Drainage Criteria Manual Volume 1.* Denver, Colorado.

URS Corp. (2004) *Draft Enginering Report: Solid Waste Prevention Investigation – Chollas Creek and Paleta Creek.* February.

U.S. Department of Agriculture (1986) *Urban Hydrology for Small Watersheds;* Technical Release 55; U.S. Department of Agriculture, Natural Resources Conservation Service, Conservation Engineering Division: Washington, D.C.

Van Giesen, E.; Carpenter, F. (2009) *Georgia Rainwater Harvesting Guidelines.* Georgia Department of Community Affairs.

Vymazal, J. (1994) *Algae and Element Cycling in Wetlands;* Lewis Publishers: Boca Raton, Florida.

Yu, B. (1999) A Comparison of the Green-Ampt and a Spatially Variable Infiltration Model for Natural Storm Events. *Trans. ASAE,* **42** (1), 89–97.

Yu, B.; Rose, C. W.; Coughlan, K. J.; Fentie, B. (1997) Plot-Scale Rainfall-Runoff Characteristics and Modeling at Six Sites in Australia and Southeast Asia. *Trans. ASAE,* **40** (5),1295–1303.

7.0 SUGGESTED READINGS

American Water Works Association (1990) *Water Quality and Treatment;* Pontius, F. W., Ed.; McGraw-Hill: New York.

California Department of Transportation (2004) BMP Retrofit Pilot Program, Final Report; Report ID CTSW – RT – 01 – 050; California Department of Transportation: Sacramento, California.

Caraco, D.; Claytor, R. (1997) *Stormwater BMP Design Supplement for Cold Climates;* Center for Watershed Protection: Ellicott City, Maryland.

DB Environmental Inc. (2005) Quantifying the Effect of a Vegetated Littoral Zone on Wet Detention Pond Pollutant Loading. Report for the Florida Department of Environmental Protection, Tallahassee, Florida

Dietz, M.; Clausen, J. (2006) Saturation to Improve Pollutant Retention in a Rain Garden. *Environ. Sci. Technol.,* **40,** 1335.

Ferguson, B. (2005) *Porous Pavements*; CRC Press: Boca Raton, Florida.

Guo, J. C.; Urbonas, B. (1996) Maximized Detention Volume Determined by Runoff Capture Ratio. *J. Water Resour. Plann. Manage.*, **122**, 1, 33.

Heasom, W.; Traver, R.; Walker, A. (2006) Hydrologic Modeling of a Bioinfiltration Best Management Practice. *J. Am. Water Resour. Assoc.*, **42**, 5, 1329.

Hunt, W.; Jarrett, A.; Smith, J.; Sharkey, L. (2006) Evaluating Bioretention Hydrology and Nutrient Removal at Three Field Sites in North Carolina. *J. Irrigation Drainage Eng.*, **132**, 6, 600.

Kadlec, R. H. (2007) The Effects of Deep Zones on Wetland Nitrogen Processing. *Water Sci. Technol.*, **56**, 3, 101.

Minnesota Pollution Control Agency (2005) *Minnesota Stormwater Manual*; Minnesota Pollution Control Agency: St. Paul, Minnesota.

Nielson, A. H. (1994) *Organic Chemicals in the Aquatic Environment*; Lewis Publishers: Boca Raton, Florida.

Novotny, V.; Smith, D.; Kuemmel, D.; Mastriano, J.; Bartosova, A. (1999) *Urban and Highway Snowmelt, Minimizing the Impact on Receiving Water*; WERF Project 94-IRM-2; Water Environment Research Foundation: Alexandria, Virginia.

Persson, J.; Somes, N. L.; Wong, T. H. (1999) Hydraulic Efficiency of Constructed Wetlands and Ponds. *Water Sci. Technol.*, **40** (3), 291.

Pitt, R.; Robertson, B.; Barron, P.; Ayyoubi, A.; Clark, S. (1999) *Stormwater Treatment at Critical Areas: The Multi-Chambered Treatment Train (MCTT)*; EPA-600/R-99-017; U.S. Environmental Protection Agency, Wet Weather Flow Management Program, National Risk Management Research Laboratory: Cincinnati, Ohio.

Pond, R. (1993) *South Base Pond Report: The Response of Wetland Plants to Stormwater Runoff from a Transit Base*. Municipal King County Department of Metropolitan Services, Seattle, Washington.

Reuter, J. E.; Djohan, T.; Goldman, C. R. (1992) "The Use of Wetlands for Nutrient Removal from Surface Runoff in a Cold Climate Region of California—Results from a Newly Constructed Wetland at Lake Tahoe." *J. Environ. Manage.*, **36**, 35.

Roseen, R.; Ballestero, T. P.; Houle, J. J.; Avelleneda, P.; Wildey, R.; Briggs, J. (2006) Water Quality and Flow Performance-Based Assessments of Stormwater

Control Strategies During Cold Weather Months; *Proceedings of the North American Surface Water Quality Conference and Exposition*; Denver, Colorado; July 24–27; Forester Communications: Santa Barbara, California.

State of Maine (2006) Stormwater Management for Maine; No. DEPLWO738; Maine Department of Environmental Protection: Augusta, Maine.

Thullen, J. S.; Sartoris, J. J.; Walton, W. E. (2002) Effects of Vegetation Management in Constructed Wetland Treatment Cells on Water Quality and Mosquito Production. *Ecol. Eng.,* **18,** 441.

Washington State Department of Ecology (2005) *Stormwater Management Manual for Eastern Washington;* Washington State Department of Ecology, Water Quality Program: Olympia, Washington.

Water Environment Federation (2006) *Membrane Systems for Wastewater Treatment;* Water Environment Federation: Alexandria, Virginia.

Chapter 5

Selection Criteria and Design Considerations

(continued)

1.0   INTRODUCTION

The stormwater management master plan for a development or re-development project must be consistent with the management goals and objectives for runoff quantity and quality and with applicable standards. Chapter 2 presented a summary of the effects of urbanization on water quantity, water quality, channel form, and aquatic biota. Chapter 3 explained how management goals and objectives to address these effects should be formulated at the watershed level and translated to design criteria applicable to individual sites. Chapter 4 presented stormwater controls and their capabilities to address stormwater effects. This chapter presents a framework to develop a stormwater management strategy at the site level that serves as a blueprint for the design process.

Stormwater is just one component of urban hydrology and is so intricately related to the other components to the point that the management strategy should start with managing rain. Stormwater is linked to wastewater, not only in combined sewer communities but also through "leaky" infrastructure. Stormwater is related to water supply for various residential, commercial, and industrial uses, especially in dry climates. There is also an energy nexus as rain harvesting can reduce the energy needed to supply water.

Successful stormwater management strategies follow a landscape-based and water-centric approach to site planning that evaluates resource, land use, and design decisions with respect to their potential effects on watershed health, protection of people and property, economic growth, and infrastructure sustainability. This strategy that integrates water, land use, people, and buildings, has parallel applications at four different scales.

1. At the watershed level, it leads to science-based, stakeholder-supported, realistic stormwater management goals and policies as explained in Chapter 3.
2. At the municipality level, the strategy adapts the watershed findings to sound design standards and regulations that support community growth and adequate infrastructure maintenance.
3. At the site level, it enables mitigation of development effects through a holistic view of water and its relation with site assets and problems; a sustainable, cost-effective stormwater management plan is devised in which the sources of problems are reduced to the extent feasible and the residual effects are mitigated through science-based selection of stormwater controls (Chapter 4).
4. At the lot level, it guides the placement and configuration of buildings, waterscape, hardscape, and landscape to meet the site's objectives.

This chapter addresses concepts to implement the third and fourth scales, that is, the scale for site design. The presentation assumes that the first and second scales have provided management goals and design criteria that are applicable to the geographic location of the site. Nonetheless, some aspects of these two larger scales are discussed in the chapter as they related to general points that need to be considered in the design process. The development of the stormwater management plan for a site consists of the following five steps:

- Understanding of goals and design criteria;
- Understanding and protecting the site's resources;
- Identification of source controls;
- Selection of stormwater controls;
- Implementation and performance monitoring.

The remainder of the chapter expands these steps. Detailed design of stormwater controls is the topic of Chapters 6 through 10.

2.0   UNDERSTANDING GOALS AND DESIGN CRITERIA

Chapter 3 presents a detailed discussion on the development of performance goals for stormwater controls. The basis for these goals stems from regulations that direct agencies to establish the water quantity and quality issues of concern and the level of treatment needed to achieve the goals. These findings are used to develop municipal codes and design criteria for designers, typically in the form of a design manual.

2.1   Planning Considerations

As stated in Chapter 3, management goals and design criteria should be derived from watershed studies based on the best available data and science-based understanding. Watershed plans can cover a wide variety of geographic scales, from small tributaries of 5 to 10 km^2 (2 to 4 sq mi) to regional-scale watersheds for major rivers, lakes, or estuaries. Watershed plans can be developed for a variety of purposes, such as flood mitigation, water supply, or protection of fisheries or habitat. Depending on the purpose, stormwater may be the only focus or one of several water resource issues discussed.

Some local jurisdictions or state agencies may have completed a watershed management plan for the area where the site is located. Chapter 3 provides additional details on development of management goals with and without the benefit of watershed management plans.

2.2   Goals for Stormwater Management

Chapter 3 summarized performance goals for stormwater management in the following categories:

- Groundwater recharge and evapotranspiration;
- Water quality protection;
- Channel protection;
- Overbank flow protection; and
- Extreme flow protection.

The remainder of this section briefly summarizes how these goals are addressed by federal and local regulations.

2.2.1   Federal Regulations

Chapter 3 summarizes the most relevant federal requirements related to stormwater management. These requirements are typically delegated to the states, although not in all states. For example, the U.S. Environmental Protection Agency (U.S. EPA) Underground Injection Control Program may regulate stormwater infiltration controls, either through a state agency or one of U.S. EPA's regional offices (U.S. EPA, 2010b). In addition, it is possible that local recharge or wellhead protection plans may have been established to protect the groundwater resources in the area.

Total maximum daily loads (TMDLs) are a regulatory process to ensure protection of beneficial uses required by the Clean Water Act (CWA) for water bodies listed under Section 303(d) as being impaired by pollutants. Development of each TMDL requires determination of the maximum amount of pollutant that an impaired water body can receive and an allocation of that amount to the point and non-point sources within the watershed. For point source dischargers with CWA-based National Pollutant Discharge Elimination System (NPDES) permits, such TMDL allocations ultimately result in discharge limitations that may present significant compliance challenges. TMDLs are numeric limits on pollutant loads that are estimated at a watershed level. Although the program was established by the CWA in 1972, it only became prominent as a water pollution control measure in the 1990s (U.S. EPA, 2010a). For each waterbody listed as impaired in a state's 303(d) list, and for each pollutant causing the impairment, a TMDL should be established to achieve water quality standards by

- Determining the maximum daily load that can be introduced into the waterbody without causing impairment;

- Determining all the sources of the pollutant, both point source and nonpoint source, along with the annual loading from each source;

- Estimating a margin of safety that accounts for lack of knowledge concerning the relationship between effluent limitations and water quality; and

- Allocating the total allowable pollutant load among sources.

After determination, TMDLs are incorporated to stormwater permits, which often results in modifications to operations and facilities for stormwater, wastewater, and industrial NPDES permittees to meet TMDL requirements. A TMDL implementation plan must be developed to meet the requirements of the TMDL. The plan needs to be closely coordinated with existing watershed management plans and results in a series of actions to control sources of pollution, install stormwater controls, and implement wastewater treatment options. Watershed pollutant trading is a useful mechanism to coordinate among multiple dischargers in watersheds to cost-effectively address impairments. Total maximum daily load implementation can be modified by site-specific objectives or use attainability analyses (UAA) that adjust goals based on additional information at a finer scale. Additional information on UAAs can be found in a publication by the Water Environment Research Foundation (WERF) and the National Association of Clean Water Agencies (NACWA) (2004).

Total maximum daily loads are most frequently derived for sediment, nutrients (nitrogen and phosphorus), pathogens, and metals, but others for benthic impairment, trash, and even stream flow are increasingly more common. U.S. EPA prepared a summary of several TMDLs developed across the United States for a variety of pollutants from stormwater sources (U.S. EPA. 2007a).

To date, TMDLs have not been completed for all of the thousands of waters listed for impairments from stormwater sources. Where they exist, however, the amount allocated to a particular source can be used as a guideline for determining treatment goals. For urbanized areas, the allocation will typically be included with the waste load allocation for a Municipal Separate Storm Sewer System (MS4), which is regulated as a point-source discharge through the National Pollutant Discharge Elimination System program.

If a TMDL implementation plan exists for the watershed where the project takes place, during and after the development process, the pollutant loads leaving the site need to be consistent with the load allocations assigned. Depending on the focus of the TMDL, Tables 4.1 and 4.2 can be used to guide the designer in the identification of unit processes that address the issues of concern and the unit operations that provide those processes.

Because TMDLs involve a comprehensive analysis of all the sources of impairment, it is important to emphasize that stormwater needs to be viewed as one component of the urban water environment and recognize its interrelatedness with wastewater treatment, irrigation, drinking water supply, recreation waters, environmental flows, and industrial supply systems.

2.2.2 Municipal Regulations

In recent decades, criteria for the design of stormwater controls have been established by states and local governments as the significance of problems of uncontrolled stormwater have been realized. The first ordinances were designed to address concerns about downstream drainage capacity or flooding, typically by setting postdevelopment peak flow release rates to be equal or less than predevelopment conditions for a particular design storm such as the 10- or 100-year event. Beginning in the 1960s and continuing to the present, research has shown that urban runoff is a significant source of degradation of receiving waters (APWA, 1969; U.S. EPA, 1983; 2007b). As summarized in Chapter 3, the criteria have been expanded to include groundwater recharge, water quality protection, and channel protection. The body of knowledge continues to expand to support the evolution of design criteria.

Municipalities issue stormwater design manuals to provide designers with a set of geographically specific parameters to address the issues of concern. Most handbooks include information and accepted methodologies to develop design volumes and peak flows, and a "cookbook" style set of acceptable stormwater controls. Unfortunately, most jurisdictions rely on uniform application of the design criteria that do not consider differences in watershed physiography, location of the project in the watershed, or specific conditions of the receiving waters. In addition, few jurisdictions benefit from trading programs that would allow off-site mitigation.

2.3 Enforcement

Inadequate enforcement will render ineffectual even the most comprehensive and best coordinated stormwater management program. Enforcement typically lags regulations while the process of information dissemination takes root. Legally defensible methods are needed to elicit corrective actions by contractors and citizens. Consistency of enforcement action is also essential to avoid confusion, delays, and differences of opinion over jurisdictions and financial responsibility for actions.

Permits issued to operators of municipal separate storm sewer systems (MS4s) under the National Pollutant Discharge Elimination System (NPDES) assign legal authority to enforce construction and post-construction stormwater regulations. There are numerous types of regulatory actions that can be applied as a result of violations. Verbal warnings or notices of violations are official communications to spell out potential enforcement actions and penalties. Minor violations may receive notices to comply with specific statutes. Violators may be ordered to clean or correct a deficiency within a given period, or issue a cease-and-desist order when there are more serious transgressions. Monetary fines and referrals for criminal action are the highest level of escalation, usually reserved for chronic problems or willful violations.

Enforcement is an essential component of stormwater management but it is often hampered by financial limitations of municipal agencies, difficulty in learning about violations, and slow enforcement response.

3.0 UNDERSTANDING AND PROTECTING SITE RESOURCES

At the conclusion of the previous step, the designer should be fully aware of all the requirements that need to be met at the site. The next step is to understand the resources available at the site, how they need to be protected, and what advantages they present for stormwater management.

If a site is a new development, critical areas where natural hydrologic processes are at work should be identified and not disturbed as much as possible. These include ephemeral and perennial streams, riparian buffers, forests, soils with high recharge potential, and wetlands. Preservation of natural conditions, to the extent possible, also provides natural water quality control processes, including sedimentation, filtration, sorption, biological uptake, degradation of organic compounds with subsequent nitrification and denitrification, and pathogen die-off. Natural conditions are also the most effective means of controlling thermal effects.

Redevelopment of older developed areas brings an opportunity to restore natural conditions. *Daylighting*, or reconstructing a stream that had been buried in a storm drain, may be feasible if there is sufficient area to restore it to a stable pattern and profile. Restoration of riparian buffers along an existing stream is a potential restoration measure if the new development is sited to provide the area needed. Opportunities may also exist to remove imperviousness from permeable soils to restore infiltration or wetlands in hydric soils that have been drained.

The goal of resource protection is to keep hydrologic and water quality characteristics of an undeveloped site unchanged as much as possible. Preservation of sensitive areas reduces effects from development. The existing ecology also provides benefits that are difficult or impossible to restore with runoff controls. The following sections discuss resources that are among the most important to protect.

3.1 Headwater Streams

A large fraction of streams in a watershed are first- or second-order streams generally termed headwaters. Leopold et al., (1964) estimated that in many watersheds headwater streams account for more than 90% of the streams network. These areas contain springs, marshes, and intermittent streams that provide much of the baseflow for larger channels. Headwater streams house dynamic biological processes and thus provide more opportunity for natural processes to improve water quality and biological diversity precisely because of their smaller size. A smaller ratio between the cross-sectional area and wetted perimeter means there is more contact between the water and the stream-bed, where nutrients can be recycled and biota established. In contrast, higher-order streams provide mostly conveyance. Unfortunately, many headwater streams have been replaced with pipes and ditches in urban environments. From the point of view of stream network topology, it can also be argued that streets, parking lots, and other directly connected imperviousness are the de facto headwaters in urban areas. Under this viewpoint, not only are these headwaters devoid of biological activity but also accumulate and transport a variety of pollutants, excessive flows, and thermal loads.

Headwater streams are best protected by impervious disconnection and preservation and enhancement of the native riparian vegetation. The riparian zone controls temperatures and sunlight, supplies food sources and habitat for aquatic biota, supports diverse ecosystems, stabilizes streambanks, and removes pollutants.

3.2 Wetlands

Wetlands are one of the most important aquatic ecosystems, providing habitat for plants and wildlife that cannot survive elsewhere and spawning habitat for a number of species. From a stormwater perspective, wetlands provide storage, peak attenuation, runoff-volume reduction, and pollutant removal through sedimentation and biological processes.

Wetlands are protected by avoiding disturbance and placing buffers between sources of high flows and pollution between them. These measures are required for virtually every site development as explained in Section 6. Another important aspect of wetlands protection is appropriate vegetation management to minimize invasive species and maintain biodiversity to preserve wetlands functionality. For example, cattails are native species in many locations but can outcompete other aquatic plants; a cattail monoculture encourages mosquito breeding (Hunt and Lord, 2006).

3.3 Floodplains

Floodplains serve a critical hydrologic function by providing non-erosive conveyance for infrequent high flows. They also provide temporary storage for runoff, attenuate peaks, and reduce volume through infiltration and evapotranspiration. Without access to a floodplain that slows down flow velocities, a stream channel will degrade much more quickly, first by incising and then by widening. Floodplains can reduce runoff volume through depression storage and infiltration. Floodplain vegetation also provides filtering for sediment and solid-phase pollutants.

3.4 Riparian Buffers

Riparian buffers provide multiple benefits for stream systems. Vegetation and root masses help to armor streambanks against high flows and reduce erosion. Shading is one of the most significant methods of controlling temperature in the stream. In addition, leaf litter and other vegetation provide the basis of the food web for all aquatic life within the stream. Shading also reduces algae production, improving the diversity of macroinvertebrates and overall species diversity. Buffers are also effective filters of stormwater flowing from adjacent land uses to the stream.

Buffer width is considered the critical factor for effectiveness in reducing pollutants and protecting stream health. Too narrow of a buffer may not afford sufficient streambank protection and shading. Determination of buffer width involves site specific factors such as topography, hydrology, geology, and land use. However, often decisions about buffer widths must strike a balance between environmental goals and socioeconomic factors. To reach a consensus, the former need to be supported by scientific data that establish the value of the natural resources associated with the stream. High-value resources may warrant wider buffers.

The U.S. Forest Service proposed a three-zone model for buffers (Welsch, 1991). The zone closest to the stream extends a minimum of 5 m (15 ft) and contains native shrubs and trees that must be left undisturbed. The middle zone extends a minimum of 20 m (60 ft) from the edge of the first zone. The vegetation is the same as in the first zone but can be removed provided that it is replaced. The outer zone extends for a minimum width of 6 m (20 ft) from the edge of the middle zone and contains mix of vegetation that can be grazed but mostly chosen to slow down stormwater and remove pollutants through filtering and biological processes.

3.5 Existing Forests and Vegetation

The amount of forest cover has a significant effect on water quality. Forested areas provide hydrologic benefits through depression storage, infiltration, and evapotranspiration in addition to pollutant control through filtration and biological processes. Native vegetation typically has deeper root systems allowing better reduction of stormwater effects and protection of the soil. The organic litter layer in a forest is a critical element in the benefits provided.

3.6 Native Soil Structure

Native soils have been formed through weathering and chemical and biological processes to contain a complex structure of macropores providing the capacity for infiltration both horizontally and vertically. Construction activity can greatly change the characteristics of the native soils on-site. Compaction from construction equipment will result in decreased permeability, which will change runoff characteristics from those used to design stormwater treatment and conveyance systems. Disturbance of highly erodible soils can also cause problems. Areas of a site that are vital for groundwater recharge or where soils are erodible should be off limits to construction activity.

3.7 Steep Slopes

Steep slopes are much more susceptible to erosion when cleared, leading to high rates of runoff, loss of soil, and stream sedimentation. Cuts into steep slopes can also intercept seasonal water tables or interrupt interflow.

4.0 IDENTIFICATION OF SOURCE CONTROLS

After the previous step, the designer knows the resources that need to be protected and how they influence the hydrology of the site. In this step, the site is evaluated to identify potential options for minimization of runoff volume and pollutants.

Land should be developed to incorporate source controls that maintain or restore interception, infiltration, and evapotranspiration to reduce runoff volume. With less runoff, there is also less wash-off of pollutants from impervious surfaces, fewer high flow events to damage aquatic systems downstream, and fewer thermal effects.

4.1 Runoff Source Controls

4.1.1 Elimination or Disconnection of Impervious Surfaces

Reducing effective imperviousness is one of the most successful ways of reducing runoff volumes. Increasing the vegetated area of a site incorporates all of the quantity control processes. Directing runoff onto vegetation allows the biological processes to reduce pollutants. This is also an effective method of preventing temperature increases in runoff. Rooftop disconnection must be done in such a way that positive drainage around the foundation is maintained. This source control is more effective with permeable soils that allow infiltration, but it is useful for all soil types. Care must be taken in the grading design to ensure that flow is not reconcentrated resulting in erosive velocities and that infiltration does not destabilize any slopes.

4.1.2 Pervious Area Management

This source control refers to practices that improve soil conditions on the pervious area of the site by reducing soil compaction, aerating soils, and applying organic amendments. It is effective at improving infiltration and dispersion of runoff, which, in turn, helps to reduce peak flows and runoff volume. Soil restoration can also help establish vegetation, which further improves infiltration and evapotranspiration.

4.1.3   Vegetation Management

Restoration of native vegetation and replacement of deforested areas help reduce runoff volume through increased evapotranspiration. Biological processes would be enhanced for pollutant removal. If restoration is performed in an area accessible to the public, it can be made into an educational opportunity with appropriate trails and signs. This practice can function as a primary treatment for pervious areas or as a tertiary treatment to improve biological processes if applied on a primary treatment system such as a wetland, wet pond, or bioretention system.

4.1.4   Rainwater Harvesting

Rainwater harvesting is the collection and storage of rainwater for landscape irrigation, aquifer recharge, nonpotable domestic uses, and even drinking water. Runoff reduction can be another use by itself or an incidental benefit derived from other uses (Crowley, 2005). Rainwater harvesting systems range from rain barrels for household garden irrigation to large cisterns serving complex domestic potable systems or industrial water supply systems. Large catchment surfaces such as commercial building roofs offer the potential to collect volumes of rain that are significant both for runoff reduction and for other beneficial uses such as landscape irrigation and toilet flushing.

The essential caveat for a stormwater management approach based on rainwater harvesting is that storage must be empty prior to the arrival of the next storm, which can be challenging depending on the primary use of the system. For example, in humid climates, the water is not needed for irrigation right after a storm and perhaps not at all during the rainy season. Consequently, the reliability of a rainwater harvesting system for stormwater management purposes must be clearly documented.

4.2   Pollutant Source Control

4.2.1   Segregation

Segregation refers to the practice of covering or removing potential pollutants so they are not washed off by rainfall. Examples include salt storage areas for highways, manure storage on farms, or excavated soil from construction sites.

4.2.2   Material and Waste Management

These source controls consist of education and follow-up for proper use, storage, and disposal of potentially polluting materials. One example would be better management of pesticide use by maintenance staff or using integrated pest management to reduce or eliminate use of the polluting material. Use of materials developed through green chemistry principles can help reduce toxicity both during manufacture and in application. Materials for winter deicing should also be managed to reduce application, apply alternate deicers, adjust the timing of application, and implement good housekeeping in storage.

4.2.3   Cleanup

Cleanup refers to periodic maintenance to remove potential pollutants from the environment before they are washed into storm drains and streams. Typical cleanup activities include catch-basin cleaning, spill control, or site maintenance and cleaning.

4.2.4   Street Sweeping

Street sweeping refers to cleaning of roads, gutters, and parking lots to remove street dust, dirt, traction sand, and road salt before it is washed into storm drains and streams. Street sweeping can be used as primary treatment or pretreatment for pollutants that cannot be entirely removed from the environment through other source control methods. Periodic sweeping reduces maintenance costs of stormwater controls.

There are numerous publications that describe source control practices in detail, for example, California Stormwater Quality Association (2003a, b, c), U.S. EPA (2005), and Washington State Department of Ecology (2005). The reader is encouraged to consult this literature and related publications.

4.3   Runoff Conveyance and Diversions

Conveyance systems range from conventional curbs, gutters, and storm drains to grass channels and rip-rap channels. They are designed to collect and convey runoff from developed areas to a stormwater control or stream. They are also used to protect against erosion, dissipate erosive velocities, and to protect steep slopes. If designed to provide hydrologic or water quality treatment through the unit processes of flow attenuation, sedimentation, or filtration, they are included in the category of swales. If designed to provide temporary storage in the conveyance system, they can act as a type of basin and may provide the unit processes of evapotranspiration or sedimentation. Many runoff and conveyance features also provide some level of infiltration.

Outfall protection is a form of conveyance that may also provide treatment. Traditionally rip-rap channels have been used to dissipate the energy of flows coming from storm drains. Some jurisdictions in the mid-Atlantic are adopting an alternative design known as *step pool storm conveyance* (SPSC), which consists of a series of shallow pools, riffles, and cascades formed by large-rock weirs, native vegetation, and an underlying amended sand filter bed. These SPSC designs are naturalized conveyances that also provide water quality and ecosystem benefits as they convey storm flows to the receiving stream (Flores et al., 2009).

Site slopes and topography constrain the design of a conveyance system. They also may have environmental effects on instream flows and stream temperature by concentrating flow, reducing the time of concentration, heating runoff as it flows over impervious surfaces.

5.0 SELECTION OF STRUCTURAL CONTROLS

At the conclusion of the previous step, the designer would have minimized effects as much as practicable and should have a clear understanding of the residual effects that the site will have on receiving waters and other natural resources. This step entails selection and design of stormwater controls that address those effects.

When selecting and designing structural controls, it is preferable to work from upstream to downstream whenever possible. Controls that treat precipitation, sheet flow, or runoff before it becomes concentrated flow are preferred. If these are not feasible, controls at the head of stream systems are preferred over instream controls further downstream. Headwater controls protect more of the stream system. Smaller systems that work together onsite should be designed. The controls should begin to work at the point that precipitation reaches the ground, before stormwater becomes concentrated. Once runoff is concentrated, it becomes more difficult to effectively restore the hydrologic processes.

Unit processes that are effective at reducing runoff volume, attenuating peak flows, and removing given pollutants should be identified. Table 4.1 shows a matrix of unit processes and the pollutants they address should be used for this purpose. For example, there are six processes that can reduce phosphorus loading. Sedimentation and filtration reduce phosphorus bound to solids and sorption, precipitation, coagulation, and plant metabolism reduce dissolved phosphorus. Selection of the unit processes to be used for treatment is based on maximizing the removal of pollutants of concern. While each unit process may have a different degree of effectiveness at pollutant removal, in practice, selection will be governed more by the constraints on design of a particular type of control incorporating the unit process.

After the necessary unit processes are identified, unit operations that provide the required treatment can be identified. Table 4.2 displays stormwater controls with the unit processes that take place in them. As explained in Chapter 3, these controls can be arranged in a system with two or more controls in series to effectively address the pollutant of concern.

It is important to recall that several of the controls combine more than one unit process in a single facility. Wet basins, wetlands, and bioretention filters, in particular, are multiprocess devices. They can provide sedimentation to remove solid-phase pollutants and biological processes to remove dissolved-phase pollutants. Whenever possible, controls should be designed so that unit processes are provided in the order of physical and then biological treatment. Gross pollutants such as trash and debris are removed first, followed by coarse sediment, fine sediment, colloids, microbes, and dissolved pollutants.

Lastly, the designer should identify site constraints and select controls that are most appropriate to the site.

5.1   System Configuration Principles

Stormwater control systems are composed of one or more unit operations able to effectively remove pollutants and control the flow as necessary to meet receiving water goals. To be effective, each stormwater control system should consist of the components discussed in the following sections.

5.1.1   Pretreatment

Many stormwater controls require some form of pretreatment to improve their function, reduce maintenance, or extend their useful life. Pretreatment can minimize the amount of pollutants captured by the primary unit operation to facilitate maintenance and thereby reduce maintenance costs of the entire facility. An example is a forebay at the inlet to a wet basin. Pretreatment is also used to protect downstream unit operations as is the case with filters and infiltrators, which are prone to clogging. Performance of these controls is enhanced by reducing the sediment load of large particles from runoff to be treated before it reaches the control. Table 4.1 shows that sedimentation and filtration are two processes for controlling suspended solids (TSS).

According to Table 4.2, sedimentation is provided by swales, basins, vaults, and swirl concentrators, which can be installed as a pretreatment unit operation upstream of filters. Gross pollutant traps may be the single unit operation needed if the water quality objective is limited to these pollutants, or it may serve as a pretreatment element of a facility with multiple pollutant-removal or multiuse objectives. Similarly, swales and strips may provide adequate pollutant control when sized to capture and treat the 90th-percentile storm or they may be used as pretreatment for filters or infiltrators.

5.1.2 Storage and Flow Control

In most parts of North America, a range of rainfall intensities, particularly during extreme events, creates runoff rates that exceed the specified treatment capacity of the selected unit operation. The result can be release of previously retained pollutants. In addition, stormwater systems often are designed to achieve downstream flooding and erosion control objectives. As a result, an effective stormwater control system incorporates flow equalization storage elements with outlets that achieve desired flow control levels, and spillways to safely bypass flows that exceed the design capacity. Storage and flow control are fundamental to the successful operation of all of the controls described in this section and, as such, are included in the description of those controls in Chapters 6 through 10. Other controls that are aimed primarily at pollutant removal (e.g., gross pollutant traps, swirl concentrators, and oil and water separators) must be coupled with storage units to achieve desired downstream flow control objectives.

5.1.3 Pollutant Removal

All the unit operations described in this section reduce pollutant loads either by reducing total runoff volume or reducing pollutant concentrations, or both. Under most situations, the stormwater system will be required to meet some level of pollutant removal.

5.2 Constraints

Site constraints often preclude the installation of certain stormwater controls. The designer should identify these constraints and evaluate the factors in Table 5.1 to find a set of controls that combine the required unit processes, work within the site constraints, and result the most effective and efficient design. The entries in Table 5.1 are neither negative nor positive factors but aspects that need to be considered in relation to a particular stormwater control. In some cases they flag a potential hindrance; for example, depth to bedrock may make infiltrator deployment infeasible. In other cases, the factor is something that needs to be evaluated in detail. For example, karst

TABLE 5.1 Factors to consider during selection of stormwater controls.

					Physical					
		Drainage area	Land area requirements	Topography	Site slope	Geology (karst)	Depth to bedrock	Water table	Soils	Climate
Basins	Wet basins	×	×			×	×	×	×	×
	Wetlands	×	×			×	×	×	×	×
	Dry basins		×			×	×	×	×	×
	Vaults and swirl concentrators									×
	Oil/water separators									×
	Forebays					×	×	×	×	×
	Cisterns									×
Swales and strips	Swales	×		×	×			×		×
	Strips			×	×					×
Filters	Sand filters				×		×	×		×
	Bioretention filters				×		×	×		×
	Landscaped roofs						×			××
	Drain inlet inserts						×			
	Manufactured filters						×			
Infiltrators	Basins	×	×			×	×	×	×	×
	Vaults	×				×	×	×	×	×
	Trenches	×				×	×	×	×	×
	Dry wells	×				×	×	×	×	×
	Permeable pavement					×	×	×	×	×
Gross pollutant traps	Screens, nets, baskets, racks, hoods									

Construction and maintenance				Environmental factors and permitting									Social				
Complexity	Maintenance requirements	Construction access	Utility and road conflicts	Forests	Wetlands	Instream flows	Discharge temperature	Beaches and shellfish beds	Reservoirs	Floodplains	Aquifers	Urban habitat modification	Land ownership	Health and safety	Aesthetics and amenity usage	Impacts to adjacent land use	Education/stewardship opportunities
	×	×		×	×	×	×	×	×	×		×	×	×	×	×	×
×	×	×		×	×	×	×	×	×	×		×	×	×	×	×	×
	×	×		×	×		×		×	×		×	×		×	×	×
	×	×	×						×				×	×			
×	×	×	×						×				×				
	×	×					×		×			×	×		×		
	×	×	×						×			×	×		×		
	×	×	×					×	×			×	×		×	×	
	×	×							×			×	×		×		
	×	×				×			×	×			×				
×	×	×				×			×	×		×	×		×	×	×
×	×	×	×						×			×	×		×		
	×	×							×				×				
	×	×							×				×				
	×	×		×		×			×	×	×	×	×		×	×	×
	×	×							×	×	×		×				
	×	×							×	×	×		×				
	×	×	×						×	×	×		×				
×	×	×	×			×			×	×	×	×	×		×		×
	×	×											×	×	×	×	×

terrain does not preclude infiltration but the stormwater must be treated by a suitable unit process before infiltration. As another example, a wet basin may need proximity to the water table to maintain a permanent pool but, for an infiltrator, a high water table is a negative factor. Some factors apply to all controls; for example, land ownership needs to be evaluated for all cases and the presence of a reservoir should trigger additional evaluation of the effluent quality and consequences of system failure.

5.2.1   Physical Constraints

5.2.1.1   Drainage Area

The contributing drainage area to a stormwater control constrains the type of system that can be installed. Typically, smaller controls such as swales, filters, or infiltrators have an upper limit on the amount of area that each can treat. Conversely, any system that requires a permanent pool has a lower limit on the drainage area that can provide sufficient flow to sustain the pool through dry weather unless the pool level is set to the level of groundwater or lower.

5.2.1.2   Land Area Requirements

The amount of surface area required varies widely among stormwater controls. Retrofits in developed areas are constrained by limitations on the amount of land available. If stormwater controls reduce the land available for parking or buildings in new developments and redevelopments, the project may not be economically viable. Landscaped roofs and permeable pavement offer viable options in space-constrained redevelopment projects; however, not all buildings can support a landscaped roof and utility conflicts common in urban areas present challenges to underground installation of controls. Whereas in new development the cost of stormwater treatment is directly related to the amount of land that may need to be acquired, in redevelopment projects utility conflicts and road realignment are the largest components of stormwater retrofits. A more difficult challenge is the lack of sufficient hydraulic grade in many redevelopment situations.

Manufactured vaults and swirl concentrators offer smaller footprints than many other stormwater controls and, therefore, are especially attractive in ultra-urban areas. In some situations, a manufactured device may be the only option given space constraints. The concepts presented in Chapter 4 and Chapter 6 need to be considered in the evaluation of manufactured controls. They can be effective at removing gross pollutants but are often too small to provide settling beyond the coarsest fraction of particles. The compact nature that is attractive in space-constrained areas can be an operational drawback because they may be overlooked during maintenance activities.

Operational failure may go unnoticed because the flows bypass the device without any visible indication. There is also a potential for particle resuspension, especially if the units are not properly maintained. Manufactured filters can be tailored to remove specific pollutants, provided that sufficient hydraulic head is available and the filter bed is inspected regularly to determine when it needs replacement.

In summary, manufactured devices can be very useful provided that a full analysis of advantages and disadvantages, including whole life costs and feasibility of effective operation and maintenance, is conducted during the alternative selection process.

5.2.1.3 Topography

Flow direction, drainage area, and the hydraulic head required for gravity operation are all factors of the site topography, which governs the type of system that can be designed. Some controls, particularly manufactured devices, have specific head requirements and may not work in flat terrain.

5.2.1.4 Site Slope

Steep slopes can restrict the use of infiltration or filtering systems, most of which require some amount of residence time to perform correctly. Conveyance systems such as swales require enough of a slope to convey the flow, but not so much as to cause erosive conditions.

5.2.1.5 Geology (Karst)

Runoff treated where there is Karst and other carbonaceous rock is capable of rapidly contaminating groundwater supplies. Any ponding or filtering systems may be required to have a clay liner to make the bottom impermeable. Infiltration may be prohibited entirely; therefore, geotechnical testing is strongly recommended (Chesapeake Stormwater Network, 2009).

5.2.1.6 Depth to Bedrock

A layer of bedrock within 1.5 m (5 ft) of the bottom of a proposed facility constrains drainage ability and thus limits the design of filtration and infiltration systems. In arid lands, the same limitation arises from hardened carbonate layers called caliche. Bedrock can limit the size of larger storage facilities such as ponds if it lies in the area that must be excavated to provide storage.

5.2.1.7 Water Table

High water tables, either seasonal or permanent, affect the performance of infiltrators. One effect is the change from unsaturated vertical flow to saturated horizontal groundwater flow. Whereas under unsaturated conditions the water percolates downwards under a hydraulic gradient equal to one, in saturated conditions the hydraulic gradient is dictated by the shallow aquifers and is typically much smaller. Therefore, the infiltrator drains more slowly. Another performance issue is that the soil under the infiltrator is expected to provide water quality treatment before run-off reaches the water table. This treatment capacity is reduced if the water table is too close to the bottom of the infiltrator, which raises concerns about groundwater contamination (see Chapter 9). Wet basins and wetlands may be able to be sited in smaller drainage areas if the water table is high enough to create permanent pool storage.

5.2.1.8 Soils

Hydraulic conductivity is the most critical factor for infiltrators. The soils must be able to infiltrate the water quickly enough to be feasible, but slowly enough to provide filtering treatment. Soils with low permeability require special consideration when designing infiltration facilities because of long drain times. Conversely, soils with too high of an infiltration rate can make it difficult to sustain a permanent pool in a basin or wetland control without a liner.

Hydraulic conductivity is a function of soil structure and the viscosity of the water, which depends on temperature and salinity. Soil structure depends not only on the geometry of grains and pores but also macrofeatures such as fissures and fractures that create preferential pathways. While a soil survey may be sufficient for a planning-level analysis, geotechnical tests are required for design, particularly in areas where soils have been disturbed. The inherent heterogeneity of soils complicated by compaction (Pitt et al., 1999) introduces a large degree of uncertainty in estimates of hydraulic conductivity. Often, measurements vary over orders of magnitude in relatively short distances across the bottom of an infiltrator. In addition, in unsaturated flow, hydraulic conductivity is a function of soil saturation; therefore, infiltration does not proceed as a uniform wetting front but the water may flow preferentially in zones of higher water content. The observed result is that point measurements of hydraulic conductivity often underestimate the areal hydraulic conductivity of clayey soils and overestimate it in sandy soils (Argue, 2004). Chapter 9 presents additional information on infiltration rates.

5.2.1.9 Climate

Most of the stormwater controls presented in this MOP can be adapted to wet, cold, semi-arid, and arid regions. However, design procedures across the United States use the same design parameters, disregarding the effect of climatic differences. Effective design must recognize that these climates can alter the performance of different stormwater controls seasonally (Minton, 2011).

5.2.1.9.1   Humid Climates

The primary characteristic of humid climates is many storms with less time between events. This frequency must be taken into consideration in the sizing of unit operations and their outlet works so that there is adequate capacity available when the next storm arrives. In some cases, the storage capacity is designed to contain a portion of runoff from the previous storm event. The volume must be increased if the volume performance goal is to be achieved.

The design of filters and infiltrators needs to consider whether there may be insufficient drying between events. Growth of bacteria and algae that can clog filters and infiltrators may be exacerbated in very wet climates. Vegetated stormwater controls are less susceptible to these effects.

5.2.1.9.2   Cold Climates

Aspects to consider for design of stormwater controls in cold climates include hydrology of rain on snow and snowmelt; temperature-dependent changes in aquatic chemistry; water density and viscosity; ion-exchange capacity of filter media, deicers, snow dumping, and hauling (Pierstorff and Bishop, 1980); and accumulation of pollutants in rain-on-snow storage volumes during winter runoff events (Sansalone and Glenn, 2002). Sizing of controls may be dictated by the runoff volume generated during spring snowmelt and rain-on-snow events (Barr Engineering Company, 2001; Washington State Department of Ecology, 2005). The volume of water released during snowmelt is the water equivalent of the annual snow fall minus sublimation (evaporation from ice) losses, winter melt, and snow hauled to other locations. Practically all of the rain from rain-on-snow events and rain immediately following the spring melt becomes runoff (Bengtsson, 1990). A comprehensive summary of snow flow calculations was compiled by the Ontario Ministry of Natural Resources (1989).

The performance of green infrastructure stormwater controls during winter is a concern because of frozen filter media and dormant biological functions (Oberst, 2003). However, Roseen et al. (2009) demonstrated that cold weather affects sedimentation-based controls more than infiltration- or filtration-based controls. Sedimentation depends on the viscosity of water, which increases with salinity and decreasing temperatures, thereby increasing the settling time for particles. The study shows that frozen filter media do not reduce performance either in hydraulic efficiency or pollutant removal of filters and infiltrators, including permeable pavement, bioretention filters, and subsurface flow wetlands. In contrast, wet basins, swirl concentrators, and swales exhibit large variations in seasonal performance. Decreases in settling velocities of approximately 50% indicate that sedimentation-based controls may need to be oversized to compensate (Jokela and Bacon, 2000).

Cold climates can affect operational aspects of stormwater controls. Examples of situations that may develop include freezing pipes, ice formation on open-water controls, scour at basin entrances when runoff occurs beneath the ice, salinity stratification of wet basins, short growing season for plants, vegetation kill as a result of salt application, and chloride contamination of groundwater. Many of these concerns can be addressed by design modifications (Center for Watershed Protection, 1997). The risk of frozen pipes can be mitigated by increasing minimum pipe diameter to compensate for ice buildup, increasing the pipe slope to increase flow velocities, and burying pipes below the frost line. In extreme cold, pipes can be insulated, albeit at a high cost. Ice formation reduces the capacity of wet basins and wetlands in winter; therefore, it may be necessary to increase the areal extent of this type of stormwater control to compensate for the expected volume of ice and snow in the basin. Multiple basins in series can be used to provide redundancy if water tends to flow over the ice. Basins should be deepest at the outlet to reduce potential scouring as water flows from under the ice at the outlet (Oberts, 1994). The effects of chlorides can be reduced by source control through deicing management; however, salt-tolerant vegetation tends to develop in vegetated stormwater controls, especially wetlands, thus reducing diversity and lessening functional value. Wet basins may have high salinity and low oxygen zones at the end of winter; therefore, they should not be drained as discharges may negatively affect aquatic ecosystems downstream. The growing season for vegetation in cold climates can be only a few months, which reduces the window of time for plant establishment and also the time in which plants are metabolically active. This limitation can be mitigated by choosing appropriate native, salt-tolerant plants and maintaining the vegetation.

Stormwater controls bring additional benefits in cold climates. For example, landscaped roofs reduce heat flow, thus lowering a building's heating and cooling energy demand (Liu and Baskaram, 2005). A study by the University of New Hampshire Stormwater Center compared performance of pervious and conventional asphalt, including salt application rates, snow and ice cover, and the friction factor. Research findings showed that, with 25% of the salt required by conventional asphalt, the snow and ice cover on the pervious asphalt was the same. Without salt application, pervious asphalt showed higher frictional resistance than dense-mix asphalt (Houle, 2008; Roseen et al., in press). To retain performance, pervious pavement should be maintained regularly, including in winter, and application of granular material that may clog the surface should be avoided.

5.2.1.9.3   Arid and Semiarid Climates

The southeastern United States and the interior areas between the west coast mountain ranges and the Rocky Mountains are semiarid to arid. These areas exhibit sparse vegetation, steep topography, complex soils, unique geology, and highly dynamic stream channels. Climate characteristics involve high potential evapotranspiration rates, intense precipitation events, long periods between storms, and smaller annual rainfall volumes. Sparse vegetation, rapid urbanization, and geology combine to yield a high runoff generation potential (Osterkamp and Friedman, 2000). In Colorado, conversion of rangeland to single family development increases the number of runoff-producing events from less than 1 to more than 29, an effect that is readily manifested in erosion of gulches and stream channel (Urbonas, 2003).

Development has introduced green landscaping that requires irrigation and constitutes a very high fraction of total water usage in dry regions. Western Resources Advocates (2003) estimated this fraction to range from 58% in Boulder, Colorado, to 72% in Scottsdale, Arizona. Excess flows from irrigation have transformed ephemeral streams into perennial ones, for example the Las Vegas Wash, Nevada. Dry-weather flows can cause channel erosion and raise shallow water tables (Gautam et al., 2010). These return flows are also laden with fertilizers and cause water quality problems, which has led to the terms "urban slobber" and "nuisance flows" to refer to them. For example, the Santa Monica Urban Runoff Recycling Facility (SMURFF) in California was built to capture and treat dry-weather flows (irrigation, spills, construction site water, pool drainage, water from car washing, and wash water from paved areas) to remove this source of pollution from Santa Monica Bay. The facility has a capacity to treat nearly 1900 m^3 (500 000 gal) per day.

The unique characteristics of arid and semiarid climates require modifications to stormwater controls that are typically used in humid climates. Controls should be designed based on the vegetation, soil type, and geology of these regions and their needs for sustainable water use and land use management. Infiltration should not degrade groundwater; for example, infiltrators should not be used in some areas whose geology naturally contains selenium. The high potential evapotranspiration value can be used in design for runoff reduction more effectively than in a humid region. On the other hand, the sparser coverage of native vegetation may reduce the effectiveness of some controls. For example, native grasses in the Southwestern United State are bunchgrasses and do not form the turf mat found in swales in humid climates; therefore, microfeatures such as meandering and rock dams may need to be added to further slow down the flow of water and facilitate sedimentation. Wetlands are little used because of the lack of water to maintain vegetation. Wet basins are viable if the total loss of water through infiltration and evaporation is low enough to maintain a permanent pool. The large areas of exposed soil require additional provisions so that filters and infiltrators are protected against clogging. Cacti, yuccas, and agave can be planted in bioretention filters. These plants require very little water, and can be used in areas that receive minimal runoff but they need to be planted above the ponding level. Organic mulch or rock can be used as cover in stormwater controls. Organic mulch reduces evaporation and controls weeds; it should be used in areas where low flow velocities are expected. Rock should be used where velocities may lead to scouring. Organic soils amendments are of limited benefit to drought-tolerant plants; however, the infiltration properties of soils can be improved with the addition of these amendments (MacAdam, 2010).

The scarcity of water in these regions insinuates that water conservation measures such as xeriscaping, and rainwater harvesting should play an essential role in stormwater management. Trees pose conflicting points of view in these regions. They are attractive to the public as part of the urban landscape and provide many environmental benefits such as shading and habitat; on the other hand, nonnative species are often imported that require irrigation and more maintenance. The U.S. Forest Service (2011) has developed tools to assist in the analysis of structure, function, and value of urban trees in various regions of the United States, including arid and semiarid climates. To be sustainable and cost-effective, stormwater controls should require minimal irrigation beyond initial establishment of vegetation. The establishment period for some species could be 2 to 3 years and irrigation may be needed during the driest months. A successful strategy to vegetation selection and placement in stormwater controls is to opt for native species and to develop a water budget to verify that the additional runoff collected in the controls is sufficient to maintain plant health.

Rainwater harvesting has to contend with water rights in some Western States; however, many communities are supporting the concept and developing guidelines and incentives. For example, Arizona offers tax credits to homeowners for costs of installing a water conservation system that collects rainwater or graywater. A corporate tax credit is also available for installation of systems that separates all graywater sources from the regular plumbing (Arizona Department of Revenue, 2008).

Most stormwater controls have been developed for humid regions or have been well documented in those climatic regions of the country. Research is needed to refine design procedures suitable for arid and semiarid regions.

5.2.2   Construction and Maintenance Constraints

5.2.2.1 Complexity

Most of the stormwater controls described in this MOP can be designed and maintained as individual unit operations. A higher level of complexity is introduced with controls that function with more than one unit process. Controls that rely on biological processes, in particular, require more care in selection and siting to ensure that the conditions to ensure of the health of vegetation or other biota are met. Additional care is also needed when controls are constructed in a series to provide additional treatment or reduce maintenance efforts. Examples would include swales or forebays to reduce coarse sediment loads upstream of ponds or infiltrators.

5.2.2.2 Maintenance Requirements

Routine and nonroutine maintenance requirements are described in Chapter 11. All controls need some level of routine maintenance to preserve their effectiveness. Common issues to verify include construction deficiencies, drawdown rates, sedimentation and erosion, structural integrity, vegetation health, and vectors. Some controls, such as swales, may be maintained as easily as normal roadside right-of-way activities. Vegetated controls will need more attention paid to vegetation to ensure it is healthy and functioning as part of the control. Access to these controls may be an issue for the stormwater management agency; easements may not always be obtainable and maintenance by homeowners may be unreliable (Donofrio and Trackett, 2008). A single, large control treating a wide area may be easier to maintain. However, many large stormwater controls are unmaintained for numerous reasons. Some belong to homeowner associations that do not know that they have maintenance responsibilities or ignore those responsibilities. With thousands of stormwater controls in existence in many counties, it is common that many are missing from municipal records and, therefore, do not receive any maintenance. In some controls performance issues are apparent; for instance, clogged permeable pavement. In others problems may remain unseen, for example an underground swirl concentrator may be bypassing all flows after filling with debris without any indication at the surface. Many basins are hidden from view in commercial or industrial sites and performance problems are visible but go unnoticed for lack of inspections. Therefore, ease of maintenance needs to be weighed against performance effectiveness and maintenance requirements of a suite of distributed controls. Determination of the ability of the owner to maintain the control is an important step in selecting the most effective control for a site. A control that operates at a lower level of performance but requires less maintenance may be the most effective for long-term operations in a given situation. It is also essential to provide redundancy in the stormwater management plan so that failure of some components of the system will not compromise overall performance.

Inspection and preventive maintenance require planning but are more cost-effective than reactive activities as a result of an emergency. Preventive maintenance includes activities such as vacuum sweeping for permeable pavement, landscaping of swales, correction of minor erosion, testing of mechanical components, and tree removal from basin embankments. Scheduled on a regular basis, preventive activities reduce the overall maintenance burden. Major repairs are often caused by construction deficiencies and can trigger emergency repairs. For example, errors in construction sequencing that cause clogging of an underdrain may need total reconstruction of a bioretention filter. However, some significant activities are part of routine maintenance, for example, dredging of wet basins.

In conclusion, an effective stormwater management strategy for a site needs to include provisions for a maintenance plan.

5.2.2.3 Construction Access

The ability to move construction equipment to the site and to perform the work safely is an important factor in selection. Access constraints include physical factors such as steep slopes and soft ground, environmental effects that outweigh the benefits of the treatment system, or legal or property issues.

5.2.2.4 Utility and Road Conflicts

Utilities, which include water and sewer lines, gas lines, and electric or communications cables, and existing roads may present challenges for construction of any of the proposed controls if they are located on or adjacent to the site. These conflicts, however, may not necessarily prevent the use of a particular control. In many instances, they can be relocated as part of the project, but at an additional cost to design, coordination, and construction.

5.2.3 Environmental Factors and Permitting

5.2.3.1 Forests

Natural wooded areas provide a significant amount of interception, evapotranspiration, and filtration, reducing runoff volume and improving stormwater quality. For this reason, stormwater controls that require tree removal for construction may be creating effects that counteract the goal of the control. In addition, many jurisdictions have developed forest conservation or tree replacement ordinances that limit the amount of clearing allowed for construction.

5.2.3.2 Wetlands

Tidal and nontidal wetlands and buffers are highly sensitive areas that already filter runoff and provide critical habitat. Wetland permits are required for any construction in these areas and, in many instances, the requirement to avoid disturbance of existing wetlands may make some controls unbuildable.

Activities that may result in the disturbance of natural wetlands are regulated by the CWA. Two sections of the CWA are relevant. Section 404 enables the U.S. Army Corps of Engineers (USACE) to issue permits for certain activities within waterways and wetlands. Construction affecting wetlands in any state requires a 404 permit. Section 401 of the CWA confers the U.S. EPA authority to prohibit activities, including construction, that can degrade water quality or have deleterious environmental consequences. Most often, this is an authority that U.S. EPA delegates to state environmental agencies. These two regulatory provisions are administered through use of a joint application form.

5.2.3.3 Instream Flows

Change in flow regimes downstream of urbanized watersheds can jeopardize the health and population of aquatic life. Depending on the site, different types of controls can mitigate these effects. Infiltration controls can help recharge groundwater and limit the loss of baseflow. Basins and wetlands can be built to treat stormwater offline and return the discharges at levels approaching baseflow; however, as presented in Chapter 3, storage modifies the entire range of flows and can have undesirable results such as increased erosion. Instream impoundments should be avoided because they become a barrier to fish passage. The permitting process is very complex and protracted for these structures.

5.2.3.4 Discharge Temperature

Cold and cool water streams have habitat qualities capable of supporting trout, salmon and other sensitive aquatic species. Warm water releases can cause thermal shock to aquatic life in cold water streams. Stormwater controls in these areas should be capable of discharging water at the desired temperature of the receiving stream by reducing runoff at the source, use of subsurface storage and vegetated surface controls, or shading through re-establishment of forest canopy. Features can be designed to meet this objective, for example, an outlet that draws cooler water from the lower layers of wetlands, provided that the water has sufficient dissolved oxygen.

A study by the University of New Hampshire (2011) evaluated several stormwater controls for their ability to modify the temperature of runoff and found that it is directly related to its exposure to solar radiation, exposure to the air, and the depth of the control. Overall, the larger the control is, the greater the capability it has to exacerbate or moderate the temperatures. The study found that, during the summer, controls with large surface area, such as wet and dry basins, increase stormwater temperatures. Wet basins can increase temperatures beyond the lethal levels for aquatic biota. In contrast, infiltrators and filters moderate runoff temperatures by thermal exchange with the cooler subsurface. Deeper controls have greater capability to buffer temperatures, and controls with a large subsurface footprint best moderate runoff temperatures. These controls cool summer runoff and warm winter runoff so that the effluent temperature approaches the average groundwater temperature.

5.2.3.5 Beaches and Shellfish Beds

Runoff that drains to beaches or shellfish beds may require a different level of treatment than other watersheds to prevent closings caused by bacterial contamination. Controls that are designed for pathogen removal should be required.

5.2.3.6 Reservoirs

Runoff in watersheds that drain to a water supply reservoir may require higher levels of pollutant removal for pathogens, metals, nutrients, or sediment. Controls that treat runoff with potential toxic pollutants, in particular, should be reviewed carefully.

5.2.3.7 Floodplains

The 100-year floodplain, as determined from Federal Emergency Management Agency maps, is frequently left undeveloped to preserve a riparian greenway and prevent properties from flooding. In many jurisdictions, design criteria prohibit construction of stormwater treatment systems in floodplains. Otherwise, controls can be subject to periodic flooding; the design should take this into account.

5.2.3.8 Aquifers

Areas that recharge existing public water supply wells are also constrained in the types of controls that can be applied. To prevent contamination of groundwater, infiltration of hotspot runoff from gas stations, waste management, or other similar areas should be avoided. Basins may need a clay liner if highly pervious soils are present. As discussed earlier, karst terrain provides little treatment in the native soil formations and stormwater must be treated before discharge in this type of geology.

5.2.3.9 Urban Habitat Modification

Stormwater systems can be designed to create terrestrial or wetland habitat in urbanized areas that are otherwise uninviting to wildlife. Wetlands and wet basins attract waterfowl, marsh birds, and other wildlife. Strips deployed as riparian buffers represent another type of control that can be designed to create terrestrial wildlife habitat. Size, water features, wetland features, and vegetative cover can all be designed with the goal of improving habitat.

Some habitat modification may not be beneficial. For instance, wet basins, wetlands, and other types of controls may be a significant source of noxious weed seed and serve as a habitat for undesirable wildlife. As described in the following section, in some areas, there may be safety issues associated with wildlife that begin to inhabit areas adjacent to housing developments. Specifically related to water quality, overpopulation of birds around wet basins has caused concerns over nutrients, pathogens, and aesthetics.

5.2.4   Social

5.2.4.1 Land Ownership

Land ownership may prevent construction of a control system in a site where all other factors are optimal. It is typically easier to obtain land or easements from areas in public ownership than for privately held property. The number of property owners that need to agree to the project should also be assessed. All things being equal, a site that requires fewer agreements is a better choice.

5.2.4.2 Health and Safety

As with any component of civil infrastructure, safeguarding the health and safety of the public is a critical requirement for planning, designing, constructing, and operating stormwater controls. Open-water basins pose significant threats, especially when located near a park, playground, trail, or other recreational spaces. There are many elements in the stormwater management system of a site that could pose safety threats:

- Stormwater controls with a permanent pool of water, in particular wet basins, present drowning hazards. In cold climates, ice on the surface may compound the danger.

- Some controls can create mosquito-breeding conditions. Wet basin and wetlands designed to have permanent pools are examples but clogged infiltrators and filters can cause ponding that becomes mosquito habitat.

- Noxious wildlife, including snakes and alligators, can be attracted to open water controls.

- The water in wet basins is most often not suitable for public contact because of the presence of pathogens. In industrial areas, it is possible that stormwater controls concentrate heavy metals like chromium or lead and organic chemicals. Some wet basins receiving excessive nutrients may develop toxic algae blooms that can threat people, pets, and wildlife. Consumption of fish caught in these facilities may pose health dangers.

- Open channels may present high velocities during storms.

- Embankments and channel side slopes may present falling hazards. If the slope is too steep or the surfaces do not offer solid footing, exiting the facility to safe ground may be impossible.

- Flow near outlet works from wet basins may drag people, pets or wildlife into the drop structure and barrel. Unprotected pipe inlets present similar hazards. Racks that may reduce this danger typically trap debris that may injure victims.

- Underground vaults may present drowning and asphyxiation hazards in case of unauthorized access by individuals or if entered by personnel without proper training in confined-space access.

- Dams of wet basins may breach.

The basic approach to reduce safety risk consists of four elements:

- Plan and design stormwater controls to reduce the hazard to the extent practicable;

- Place barriers between the public and potential hazards;

- Provide rescue features in case of an accident; and

- Inspect facilities to identify safety concerns.

Designers need to consider risk from the conceptualization of the stormwater management plan for a site. For example, children and teenagers are attracted to open water and may purposefully break access restrictions. Design that emphasizes runoff minimization and deployment of controls that do not impound significant amounts of water significantly contribute to risk reduction. Spatially distributed infiltrators and filters, are examples of such controls. High velocity flows can be reduced with the deployment of wide shallow swales instead of deeper channels. Controls that are sited in places of high visibility are safer because deficiencies can be noticed and reported by the public and, in case of accidents, help can be summoned quickly. At the same time, careful attention must be placed to siting open-water stormwater controls within easy access to children, the elderly, and people with disabilities. Vertical walls in open-water should be minimized and preferably avoided. Outlets where high velocities may occur should be planned away from potential access by the public.

Mosquitoes can be controlled by natural predators such as dragonflies and mosquitofish. Properly operating infiltrators and filters drain in 12 to 48 hours and offer little opportunity for mosquito breeding, which typically requires at least 72 hours.

The dams of wet basins need to be designed with applicable dam safety requirements. The emergency spillway and downstream conveyance need to have sufficient capacity to safely pass the design event. At the same time, the facility should be analyzed for more severe events to understand the nature of the risk, even if it is small.

Some issues entail straightforward security solutions; for example, entry points to underground vaults should be properly locked. However, as discussed in the next section, wet basins are often deployed as site amenities and some level of public access is encouraged. When they are not planned as amenities, the public may still view them as such rather than a device that could contain polluted water. In this situation, a primary objective of siting and design should be to discourage people, pets, and wildlife from coming in contact with water in the facility. Barriers can be used but their deployment entails a careful compromise between aesthetics and safety that requires close collaboration between engineers and landscape architects. Examples of barriers that limit or deter access include fencing and planting dense vegetation around the perimeter of basins. The choice of vegetation and type of fencing must consider aesthetics and functionality of the site. Fencing can hinder unauthorized entry but can also obstruct access in case of an emergency, hamper maintenance activities, and serve as an enticement for children to gain access to the basin.

Access by the public is one of the first considerations in the design of landscaped roofs. If the landscaped roof is to become a public amenity, railings and other features that reduce the risk of falls are integrated as part of the overall architectural design of building safety. If public access is not allowed, entrance to the roof needs to be locked to prevent unauthorized entry.

In case of accidents, features are needed that allow self rescue or enable rescue by safety staff. Design criteria for wet basins have been revised to provide safety benches, shallow side slopes, safety racks, and safer riser configurations to mitigate some of the dangers. In case of a fall along an embankment or side slope, foot and hand holds should be available to regain solid ground. These holds can be ladders or vegetation that the victim can grab. Soft soils and slippery geosynthetic liners exposed by erosion can prevent a person or animal from reaching high ground after a fall.

Sloping racks should be installed to protect inlets to risers and pipes. The size of the openings needs to be small enough to keep victims from getting swept into the conduit. The bars of racks need to be rounded to minimize injury should a person come in contact with them. The racks should be positioned at a distance upstream from the opening so that flow velocity will not pin victims against the rack. Additional information on the deployment of racks in culverts can be found in Urban Drainage and Flood Control District (2001).

Regular inspection and maintenance of stormwater controls and ancillary infrastructure are an essential component of safety. Inspection can reveal deterioration in safety features such as racks, damaged fences, eroding emergency spillways, or underperforming infiltrators that may be ponding water.

While careful planning, design, and construction by experienced professionals can minimize risks, it is impossible to eliminate completely all hazards that open-water stormwater controls can pose to the public. Education for the community, operators of the stormwater management system, and public officials is essential to further reduce the risk. Appropriate signage can explain the purpose of the facility and provide warning of dangers. Education about hazards should include school children and teachers as well as homeowner associations. Members of the public are often the first to identify safety hazards that require maintenance. Integration into the landscape and site amenities improves the commitment of the public to remain alert and report safety issues. A hotline should be provided for citizens who observe damage or performance problems. Emergency response plans need to be in place for exposed areas downstream of wet basins in which the volume of the impoundment or the height of the dam pose a significant risk in case of a breach.

This summary of safety issues is not intended to be an exhaustive treatment. The subject of safety, particularly around wet basins, is part of numerous municipal guidelines. The reader is urged to consult these sources for additional information.

5.2.4.3 Aesthetics and Amenity Usage

Stormwater controls should be completely integrated to a site so that they become part of the landscape and an amenity to the community. Some stormwater controls, particularly those with a significant component of vegetation, can improve site landscaping or provide beneficial habitat. Bioretention filters are designed for vegetative uptake and can be an improvement over conventional parking islands, for example. If properly landscaped, wetlands, marshes, and buffers can provide passive recreation opportunities, particularly if combined with bike paths, picnic areas, or playgrounds. Close and early collaboration between engineers, landscape architects, owners, and regulators is required to develop a functional design that adds value to the community. Responsibility and effectiveness of maintenance activities should also be considered; even the most pleasing stormwater controls become an eyesore for lack of maintenance.

Not only is trash buildup an aesthetic problem, but it is a source of mosquito habitat that can affect every type of stormwater control because most are designed to remove floatables along with other pollutants. The key to managing trash is regular maintenance.

Aesthetics is often a matter of personal opinion and must be tempered with the environmental goals for the site. For example, some people insist on mowing grass to the edge of the water and even apply herbicides and fertilizers in areas close to wet basins. Knowledge legacy is another issue. The first owner of a house may know well the purpose of the bioretention filter in the yard and how to maintain it; however, the information may not be transmitted to subsequent homeowners who may elect to replace the native plants with more appealing, high maintenance vegetation. Public education about the purpose of stormwater controls is essential to maintain a functional system.

5.2.4.4 Effects on Adjacent Land Use
Although effects to adjacent land owners are variable, to a large extent they depend on how successfully the stormwater control is designed into the site and the aesthetic value of its landscaping. As mentioned in the previous section, wet basins should be used to create a waterfront effect in residential developments and, that improves the value of adjacent property.

5.2.4.5 Education and Stewardship Opportunities
Education and stewardship fall into the category of opportunities rather than constraints. Encouraging awareness of how behaviors affect the watershed and educating residents on more environmentally sensitive behavior are goals of an outreach program. Several of the treatment options can be sited and designed to improve public access and can be highlighted with signs and outreach materials that educate visitors about the benefits of the stormwater management system.

6.0 IMPLEMENTATION AND PERFORMANCE MONITORING

After the previous step, all elements of the stormwater controls system, including the stormwater controls and ancillary infrastructure, can be sized and design drawings prepared. After the appropriate permits are secured, the construction phase can begin. Permitting and construction activities are beyond the scope of this MOP. However, construction sequencing and inspection, and performance monitoring are discussed herein.

6.1 Construction Sequencing and Inspection

Proper design and construction sequencing of stormwater systems is vital to their long-term sustainability. For example, if erosion control during construction is not rigorously practiced, the facility will be rendered inoperative in a short time. This is the case for filters, infiltrators, and forebays, in particular. Without effective source erosion controls, investment in structural facilities will be lost and expensive rehabilitative maintenance or reconstruction of these facilities will then be needed to return them to a working condition. Regardless, facilities must be inspected upon completion to ensure that the facility has been built according to plans and specifications and verified by the site inspector with as-builts. Examples of potential contractor errors include

- Discrepancies between design drawings and the actual configuration of stormwater controls;
- Inadequate infiltration in filters and infiltrators;
- Improper stabilization of disturbed soils;
- Inadequate planting and irrigation on completed slopes;
- Deficient rock slope protection;
- Outlets with insufficient protection to dissipate velocities;
- Improper connections to the storm drain system; and
- Insufficient vegetation coverage in swales and bioretention filters.

6.2 Monitoring

Monitoring of constructed stormwater controls or systems is rarely done, unless it is required by regulations or as part of a research program. The need for reliable performance data was highlighted in Chapter 3 but it is worth repeating it here. This section presents a brief discussion on activities to identify performance issues with installed stormwater controls.

6.2.1 Pollutant Removal

Pollutant removal benefits are one of the key factors in selecting stormwater controls. There are a number of methods for estimating effectiveness. The most common is the percent of pollutant removed, based on monitoring studies (Winer, 2000). With this method, each family of controls has a different degree of effectiveness in reducing a particular pollutant. This method assumes that the removal rate can remain constant despite variations in site characteristics, design and construction of stormwater control, storm events, monitoring procedures, and inflow concentrations. Two other issues that are not addressed with this method are

- How much pollutant load was avoided through runoff reduction and
- How much of the runoff that occurs is treated or bypassed.

As explained in Chapters 3 and 13, pollutant removal has been dismissed as unacceptable to measure water quality control effectiveness. A thorough review of pollutant removal performance estimating methods is provided by Strecker et al. (2002) using data in the International Stormwater Best Management Practices Database (www.bmpdatabase.org), which was developed under a cooperative agreement between the American Society of Civil Engineers and U.S. EPA. Several methods are discussed that have been used historically for evaluation of pollutant removal. All provide single number for the removal rate but do not give any statistical information on the differences between inflow and outflow. The authors recommend the Effluent Probability Method, which performs a more rigorous statistical analysis of the monitoring data, first determining if the influent and effluent concentrations are statistically different then plotting the data as a log-normal distribution. This approach shows if there is consistent removal regardless of influent concentration or if there is a level at which no removal occurs. Up-to-date results of monitoring efforts and analysis are available at www.bmpdatabase.org. A commentary on influent and effluent concentrations is presented in Chapter 3. Detailed information on performance assessment of stormwater controls is given in Chapter 13.

6.2.2 Quantity Control

Two types of quantity control are of concern in runoff management. Peak-discharge control is designed to limit the rate of flow from development and volume control is designed to limit the amount of runoff volume. Surface water aspects of monitoring performance for quantity control are straightforward. Precipitation and stream flows can be measured with good accuracy; runoff volumes can be estimated with water balance calculations, albeit with additional uncertainty. Measurement of infiltration, interflow, and groundwater flow are more complex and introduce a larger margin of error. However, surface or subsurface measurements are seldom performed in stormwater controls, except for research purposes. Indirect observations are the most common approach to determining whether a stormwater control is performing adequately; for example, evidence of erosion downstream of a wet basin, ponding of water on the surface of permeable pavement, or exceedingly long drain times in bioretention filters. Examples related to wetlands and wet basins are high pool levels and activation of the high-flow bypass running during small storm events, which may indicate a clogged low-flow orifice, and unusually low pool levels that may indicate a leak through the embankment (Center for Watershed Protection, 2004). These types of observations may be better indicators of performance issues.

Effectiveness of stormwater controls for channel protection has not been fully demonstrated and is the subject of active research. Chapter 3 presents additional information on this subject.

7.0 REFERENCES

American Public Works Association (1969) *Water Pollution Aspects of Urban Runoff. Final Report on the Causes and Remedies of Water Pollution from Surface Drainage of Urban Areas;* Research Project No. 120; U.S. Department of the Interior, Federal Water Pollution Control Administration: Washington, D.C.

Argue, J. R. (Ed.) (2004) *Water Sensitive Urban Design: Basic Procedures for 'Source Control' of Stormwater–A Handbook for Australian Practice;* Urban Water Resources Centre, University of South Australia, Adelaide, South Australia, in collaboration with Stormwater Industry Association and Australian Water Association.

Arizona Department of Revenue (2008) *Water Conservation Systems (Individual Income Tax Credit) and Plumbing Stub Outs (Corporate Income Tax Credit);* Publication 565, Phoenix, Arizona.

Barr Engineering Company (2001) *Minnesota Urban Small Sites BMP Manual. Stormwater Best Management Practices for Cold Climates;* Metropolitan Council Environmental Services: St. Paul, Minnesota.

Bengtsson, L. (1990) *Urban Snow Hydrology. Proceedings of an International Conference on Urban Hydrology Under Wintry Conditions,* Narvik, Norway.

California Stormwater Quality Association (2003a) *Stormwater Best Management Practice (BMP) Handbooks: Industrial and Commercial,* Menlo Park, California.

California Stormwater Quality Association (2003b) *Stormwater Best Management Practice (BMP) Handbooks: Municipal,* Menlo Park, California.

California Stormwater Quality Association (2003c) *Stormwater Best Management Practice (BMP) Handbooks: New Development and Redevelopment,* Menlo Park, California.

Center for Watershed Protection (1997) *Stormwater BMP Design Supplement for Cold Climates*, Ellicott City, Maryland, 141 pp.

Center for Watershed Protection (2004) *Stormwater Pond & Wetland Maintenance Gudebook*, Ellicott City, Maryland, 75 pp.

Chesapeake Stormwater Network (2009) *Stormwater Design Guidelines for Karst Terrain in the Chesapeake Bay Watershed: Version 2.0*, June, 31 pp.

Crowley, B. J. (2005) Neighborhood Level Analysis of Rainwater Catchment in Portland, OR. In *Geography*; Portland State University: Portland, Oregon.

Flores, H.; Markusic, J.; Victoria, C.; Bowen, R.; Ellis, G. (2009) Implementing Regenerative Storm Conveyance Restoration Techniques in Anne Arundel County: An Innovative Approach to Stormwater Management. *Water Resour. Impact,* **11** (5).

Gautam, M. R.; Acharya, K.; Stone, M. (2010) Best Management Practices for Stormwater Management in the Desert Southwest. *J. Contemporary Water Res. Educ.,* Issue 146, December, 39–49.

Houle; K. M. (2008) *Winter Performance of Permeable Pavements: A Comparative Study of Porous Asphalt, Pervious Concrete, and Conventional Asphalt in a Northern Climate*. Master's Thesis, University of New Hampshire, Department of Civil Engineering, Durham, New Hampshire.

Hunt, W. F.; Lord, W. G. (2006) *Maintenance of Stormwater Wetlands and Wet Ponds*, North Carolina State University, AGW-588-07. http://www.bae.ncsu.edu/stormwater/PublicationFiles/WetlandMaintenance2006.pdf (accessed Sept 2011).

Jokela, J. B.; Bacon, T. R. (1990) Design of Urban Sediment Basins in Anchorage. *Proceedings of Cold Regions Hydrology and Hydraulics, American Society of Civil Engineers*, Technical Council on Cold Region Engineering, New York, 761–789.

Leopold, L. B.; Wolman, M. G.; Miller, J. P. (1964) *Fluvial Processes in Geomorphology;* W. H. Freeman and Company: San Francisco, California.

Liu, K.; Baskaran, B. (2005) *Thermal Performance of Extensive Green Roofs in Cold Climates*, National Research Council Canada, NRCC-48202.

Lowrance, R.; Leonard, R.; Sheridan J. (1985) Managing Riparian Ecosystems to Control Nonpoint Pollution. *J. Soil Water Conserv.,* **40,** 87–97.

MacAdam, J. (2010) *Green Infrastructure for Southwestern Neighborhoods;* Tucson, Arizona, 47 pp.

Maryland Department of the Environment (2000) *Maryland Stormwater Design Manual, Volumes I & II;* Maryland Department of the Environment, Water Management Administration: Baltimore, Maryland.

Minton, G. R. (2011) *Stormwater Treatment: Biological, Chemical, and Engineering Principles,* 3rd ed.; RPA Press: Seattle, Washington.

Oberts, G. L. (1994) Performance of Stormwater Ponds and Wetlands in Winter. *Watershed Protection Techniques,* **1** (2), 64–68.

Oberts, G. L. (2003) Cold Climate BMPs: Solving the Management Puzzle. *Water Sci. Technol.,* **48** (9), 21–32.

Ontario Ministry of Natural Resources (1989) *Snow Hydrology Guide,* Ministry of Natural Resources, Queen's Park, Ontario, Canada.

Osterkamp, W. R.; Friedman J. M. (2000) The Disparity Between Extreme Rainfall Events and Rare Floods—with Emphasis on the Semi-Arid American West. *Hydrol. Proc.,* **14,** 2817–2829.

Pierstorff, B. W.; Bishop, P. L. (1980) Water Pollution from Snow Removal Operations. *J. Environ. Eng. Div.,* **106** (2), 377–388.

Pitt, R.; Lantrip, J.; Harrison, R. (1999) *Infiltration through Disturbed Urban Soils and Compost-Amended Soil Effects on Runoff Quality and Quantity.* EPA/600/R-00/016; National Risk Management Research Laboratory; U.S. Environmental Protection Agency: Cincinnati, Ohio, 233 pp.

Roseen, R. M.; Ballestero; T. P.; Houle J. J.; Avellaneda, P; Briggs, J.; Fowler, G; Wildey, R. (2009) Seasonal Performance Variations for Storm-Water Management Systems in Cold Climate Conditions. *J. Environ. Eng.,* **135** (3), p. 128–137.

Roseen, R. M.; Ballestero; T. P.; Houle J. J.; Briggs, J.; Houle, K. M. (in press) Water Quality and Hydrologic Performance of a Porous Asphalt Pavement as a Stormwater Treatment Strategy in a Cold Climate. *J. Environ. Eng..*

Sansalone, J. J.; Glenn, D. W. (2002) Accretion of Pollutants in Snow Exposed to Urban Traffic and Winter Storm Maintenance Activities. I. *J. Environ. Eng.,* **128** (2), 151–166.

University of New Hampshire (2011) *Examination of Thermal Impacts from Stormwater Best Management Practices.* University of New Hampshire Stormwater Center, January, 148 pp.

Urban Drainage and Flood Control District (2001) *Urban Storm Drainage Criteria Manual, Volume 2*, Denver, Colorado.

Urbonas, B. R. (2003) Effectiveness of Urban Stormwater BMPs In Semi-Arid Climates. *Regional Conference on Experience with Best Management Practices in Colorado;* Colorado Association of Stormwater and Floodplain Managers Urban Drainage and Flood Control District, April 9, Denver, Colorado.

U.S. Environmental Protection Agency (1983) *Results of the Nationwide Urban Runoff Program. Volume I. Final Report;* U.S. Environmental Protection Agency, Water Planning Division: Washington, D.C.

U.S. Environmental Protection Agency; American Society of Civil Engineers (2002) *Urban Stormwater BMP Performance Monitoring: A Guidance Manual for Meeting the National Stormwater BMP Database Requirements;* EPA-821/B-02-001; U.S. Environmental Protection Agency: Washington, D.C.

U.S. Environmental Protection Agency (2005) *National Management Measures to Control Nonpoint Source Pollution from Urban Areas;* EPA-841-B-05-004; U.S. Environmental Protection Agency: Office of Water: Washington, D.C.

U.S. Environmental Protection Agency (2007a) *Total Maximum Daily Loads with Stormwater Sources: A Summary of 17 TMDLs;* EPA-841-R-07-002; U.S. Environmental Protection Agency, Office of Wetlands, Oceans and Watersheds: Washington, D.C.

U.S. Environmental Protection Agency (2007b) *Development Growth Outpacing Progress in Watershed Efforts to Restore the Chesapeake Bay;* Report No. 2007-P-00031; U.S. Environmental Protection Agency, Office of Inspector General: Washington, D.C.

U.S. Environmental Protection Agency (2010a) *Impaired Waters and Total Maximum Daily Loads.* http://water.epa.gov/lawsregs/lawsguidance/cwa/tmdl/index.cfm (accessed Oct 2010).

U.S. Environmental Protection Agency (2010b) *Underground Injection Control Program.* http://water.epa.gov/type/groundwater/uic/ (accessed Oct 2010).

U.S. Forest Service (2011) *I-Tree: Tools for Assessing and Managing Community Forests.* www.itreetools.org (accessed Sept 2011).

Washington State Department of Ecology (2005) *Stormwater Management Manual for Western Washington;* Washington State Department of Ecology, Water Quality Program: Olympia, Washington.

Water Environment Research Foundation; National Association of Clean Water Agencies (2004) Collaborative Water Quality Solutions: Exploring Use Attainability Analyses; Report No. 04-WEM-7; Water Enviroment Research Foundation: Alexandria, Virginia.

Welsch, D. J. (1991) *Riparian Forest Buffers: Function and Design for Protection and Enhancement of Water Resources;* NA-PR-07-91; U.S. Department of Agriculture Forest Service, Northeastern Area: Radnor, Pennsylvania.

Western Resources Advocates (2003) *Smart Water: A Comparative Study of Urban Water Use Efficiency Across the Southwest.* Boulder, Colorado.

Winer, R. (2000) *National Pollutant Removal Performance Database for Stormwater Treatment Practices: 2nd Edition;* Center for Watershed Protection: Ellicott City, Maryland.

8.0 SUGGESTED READINGS

Beyerlein, D. (2005) Flow-Duration Based Stormwater Mitigation Modeling. *Stormwater,* Forester Communications: Santa Barbara, California. May-June.

Booth, D. B.; Jackson, C. R. (1997) Urbanization of Aquatic Systems: Degradation Thresholds, Stormwater Detection, and The Limits of Mitigation. *Water Resour. Bull.,* **33,** 1077.

Cappuccitti, D. J.; Page, W. E. (2000) *Stream Response to Stormwater Management Best Management Practices in Maryland;* Maryland Department of the Environment, Water Management Administration: Baltimore, Maryland.

Caraco, D. (2000) Dynamics of Urban Stream Channel Enlargement, Article 19; In *The Practice of Watershed Protection;* Schueler, T. R., Holland, H. K.; Center for Watershed Protection: Ellicott City, Maryland.

Comstock, S. R.; Wallis, C. (2003) The Maryland Stormwater Management Program: A New Approach to Stormwater Design. *Proceedings of the National Conference on Urban Storm Water: Enhancing Programs at the Local Level;* EPA-625/R-03-003; U.S. Environmental Protection Agency: Chicago, Illinois.

Donofrio, D.; Trackett, T. (2008) Seattle Public Utilities' Natural Drainage System Operation and Maintenance. *Proceedings of the 2008 International Low Impact Development Conference*, Nov 16–19, Seattle, Washington; American Society of Civil Engineers: Reston, Virginia.

Donovan, T.; Lowndes, M. A.; McBrien, P.; Pfender, J. (2000) *Wisconsin Stormwater Manual. Technical Design Guidelines for Storm Water Management Practices;* Cooperative Extension of the University of Wisconsin: Madison, Wisconsin.

Heaney, J. P.; Huber, W.; Strecker, E. (2005) *Critical Assessment of Stormwater Treatment and Control Selection Issues;* Water Environment Research Federation: Alexandria, Virginia.

Hunt, W. F.; Apperson, C. S.; Kennedy, S. G.; Harrison, B. A.; Lord, W. G. (2006) Occurrence and Relative Abundance of Mosquitoes in Stormwater Retention Facilities in North Carolina, USA. *Water Sci. Technol.*, **54** (6–7), 315.

Li, H.; Davis, A. P. (2009) Water Quality Improvement through Reductions of Pollutant Loads using Bioretention. *J. Environ. Eng.*, **135** (8) 567–576.

Maryland Stormwater Consortium (2007) *Core Environmental Site Design Principles for the Implementation of the Maryland Stormwater Management Act of 2007.* http://www.stormwaterpartners.org/PDF/CorePrinciples2008.pdf (accessed Oct 2010).

Oregon State University; Geosyntec Consultants; University of Florida; The Low Impact Development Center, Inc. (2006) *Evaluation of Best Management Practices and Low Impact Development for Highway Runoff Control;* National Cooperative Highway Research Program (NCHRP) Report 565; Transportation Research Board: Washington, D.C.

Schueler, T. R. (1987) *Controlling Urban Runoff: A Practical Manual for Planning and Designing Urban BMPs;* Metropolitan Washington Council of Governments: Washington, D.C.

Shaver, E.; Horner, R.; Skupien, J.; May, C.; Ridley, G. (2007) *Fundamentals of Urban Runoff Management: Technical and Institutional Issues,* 2nd ed.; North American Lake Management Society: Madison, Wisconsin.

U.S. Environmental Protection Agency (2005) *National Management Measures to Control Nonpoint Source Pollution from Urban Areas;* EPA-841/B-05-004; U.S. Environmental Protection Agency, Office of Water: Washington, D.C.

Chapter 6

Basins

(continued)

(continued)

1.0 DESCRIPTION

The term *basins*, as used in this manual of practice (MOP), refers to controls that primarily store stormwater, reduce the magnitude of peak flows, provide water quality treatment mainly by sedimentation, and discharge stormwater to another stormwater control such as a filter or to a surface waterbody. This MOP focuses on basins deployed for postdevelopment stormwater management, not sedimentation basins used during construction.

The duration of detention varies from a few hours to several days, depending on the basin type, stormwater control objectives, and unit processes used. A fraction of the stormwater may be evaporated, transpired (if plants are present), or infiltrated through the bottom and sides of the basin. The basin may also receive baseflow during dry weather.

Basins are one of five categories of stormwater controls addressed in this MOP. The design capture volume (*Vd*) of a basin typically incorporates the following stormwater control functions: water quality volume (WQV), channel protection volume (CPV), and a peak attenuation volume necessary to achieve overbank flood protection (OFP) and extreme flood protection (EFP). The design capture volume may be determined using guidelines found in Chapter 3 or it may be defined in pertinent state or local design manuals. Selection criteria for determining whether basins are appropriate for a particular application are found in Chapter 5.

Basins are used for flood control, channel protection, and pollutant removal. These functions are "stacked" in the basin. The lowest portion of the basin defines the volume required for water quality treatment (WQV), the middle portion defines the volume required for channel protection (CPV), and the upper volume defines the volume required to provide OFP and EFP during events that occur infrequently, but may cause flooding damages downstream. The portion of basins designed to provide channel protection (CPV) and/or pollutant reductions (WQV) are commonly configured to provide detention (12 to 48 hours) for a design event.

Engineers typically use the term *detention* for dry basins designed to discharge all of the stored stormwater to a surface waterbody within a given period of time. Engineers frequently use the term *retention* for wet basins with a permanent pool, where some or all of the stormwater captured remains until the next storm occurs. Other practitioners limit the term *retention* to infiltration basins. This MOP refers to these stormwater controls simply as *basins* because the design process is the same regardless of how water leaves the facility. The designer should refer to Chapter 9 if the facility is intended to infiltrate runoff through the bottom. The terms *dry* and *wet* are recommended for general use because they are more explicit than *detention* and *retention*. "Live" volume is the portion of a basin that recovers its storage capacity through an outlet set at the elevation of the permanent pool for a wet basin and at the bottom of a dry basin. "Dead" storage is the portion of a basin that remains in the basin after the storm ends and can be removed only through evapotranspiration, infiltration to the soil, or rainwater harvesting. Dead storage provided below the invert of the outlet may be designed to provide water quality control through one or more unit processes, as discussed in Chapter 5, or for rainwater harvesting. Live storage provided above the invert of the outlet may be designed to enhance water quality control through sedimentation and provide peak-flow attenuation for channel or flood protection, with the outlet restricted as necessary to meet these design objectives. Aquatic vegetation is often provided within the dead storage volume of a wet basin, either floating on the surface (e.g., in an aquatic bench along the banks of the basin) or in constructed wetland areas with a relatively shallow permanent pool of water and expansive vegetation coverage.

Dry basins designed for water quality control, also commonly known as *dry extended detention ponds*, are best at removing suspended constituents. The detention times also promote infiltration of a portion of WQV into the soil, achieving a runoff volume reduction of nearly 30% in some dry basins (Strecker et al., 2004). Dry basins are not particularly effective in removing dissolved pollutants. Also, as discussed later in this chapter, wet basins tend to outperform dry basins in removal of solids, although enhanced design techniques are continually being developed to improve their performance.

This chapter also includes design guidelines for cisterns and rain barrels, vaults (including swirl concentrators), and oil and water separators. Cisterns and rain barrels are typically used to store runoff and reuse it for irrigation and other nonpotable uses. Swirl concentrators (particle separators) are flow-through structures that typically use the power of swirling water to separate floatables and coarse sediments and include a settling or separation unit to remove sediments and other pollutants. Oil and water separators are underground structures designed to remove oil, grease, trash, debris, and some amount of sediment from stormwater runoff.

Most basins remove pollutants primarily through sedimentation of solids that are controlled by the hydraulic loading rate (HLR) and residence time. Wet basins and wetlands also remove pollutants through physical and biochemical processes that occur in the permanent pool during dry weather periods that follow (see Chapter 4). Typically, wet basins and wetlands are more efficient than dry basins at removing typical suspended pollutants found in stormwater, although conditions within the basin (low dissolved oxygen, vegetation die-off, and thermal stratification) have been observed to affect unit processes and, in some instances, cause pollutant releases from basins.

Hydraulic efficiency is a consideration for basins (see Chapter 4), particularly wet basins without restricted outlets. The restricted outlet in dry basins enhances hydraulic efficiency by distributing the flow of stormwater to areas of the basin where it would not otherwise flow during frequent small storm events. Considerations for hydraulic efficiency, including methods for its enhancement, are presented with each type of basin.

As described in Chapter 3, effective treatment of stormwater is a function of the basin volume, the drain time of any live storage included in the basin, and the residence time in dead storage areas. Larger basins are required for unit processes that require longer drain times and residence times to achieve effective pollutant removal. This additional volume is provided to properly capture runoff from a sequence of storms and to achieve cumulative annual runoff capture targets. Consequently, the recommended WQV will differ depending on the unit process selected. For example, up to 48-hour drain times are typically recommended for dry basins to (1) allow sediment particles and associated pollutants to settle out, (2) maintain release velocities that do not resuspend the settled solids, and (3) provide storage for subsequent storms. As a result, the "maximized" WQV recommended in Chapter 3 for dry basins is approximately 40% larger than the recommended permanent pool volume of a wet basin. Effective basin designs typically include a forebay or another pretreatment device to remove the coarser suspended solids as they enter the basin by slowing incoming runoff.

2.0   DESIGN PRINCIPLES

2.1   Sediment Storage Considerations

Sediment accumulation within the basin will diminish its effectiveness until the sediment is removed. To avoid reduced treatment effectiveness and frequent maintenance, a sediment storage volume is typically incorporated into the basin design (see Chapter 11 for maintenance recommendations for sediment removal).

Much of the sediment storage volume is provided by the forebays or alternative pretreatment systems placed at basin inlets, which should trap approximately half the sediment load entering the basin if designed according to criteria in this chapter. The remaining finer sediment typically accumulates near the basin outlet, particularly if a two-stage design is provided, as described later in this chapter.

2.2   Basin Geometry

Where site conditions allow, the basin should gradually expand from the inlet and contract toward the outlet to reduce short-circuiting. A long flow path to the outlet is preferred to maximize treatment early in the storm and a length to width of 4:1

assists in this regard, as do interior features that spread flow and lengthen the flow path from the inlet to the outlet. Baffles and energy dissipaters at the inlet also help reduce short-circuiting.

2.3 Physical Site Suitability

Soils, depth to bedrock, and depth to the groundwater table should be evaluated before designing a basin. The basin depth may be limited by groundwater conditions and soils. Where bedrock is close to the surface, high excavation costs may also make construction infeasible. If bedrock or the water table is within 0.6 m (2 ft) of the bottom of a basin or the site soils are relatively impermeable, a dry basin may experience standing water unless the bottom of the basin is graded to promote positive drainage toward the outlet. If soils are permeable, a wet basin may drain completely during dry periods and a liner is needed to maintain the permanent pool.

To be effective, a basin should be located where it can intercept most of the runoff from a site, typically at the low point of a site. This is where wetlands are often found, and the effects of the basin on wetland resources should be examined. Altered wetland resources should be mitigated in accordance with local, state, and federal regulations. Depending on volume and depth, basin designs may be subject to state dam safety regulations.

3.0 CISTERNS AND RAIN BARRELS

Cisterns and rain barrels function as water conservation systems by harvesting stormwater to supplement nonpotable water uses such as irrigation. If deployment is substantial in a watershed, they provide runoff volume, peak attenuation, and pollutant removal depending on how quickly the storage volume is restored to capture subsequent storms. They typically capture stormwater that drains off rooftops, although they can also capture runoff from vegetated areas.

3.1 Typical Applications

3.1.1 Physical Site Suitability

Appropriate applications include residential, commercial, and industrial areas planned for development or redevelopment. Rooftops provide better water quality than ground surfaces.

3.1.2 Water Quantity Control

The stormwater management benefits of these controls depend on the volume provided and the rate of use of captured runoff. These controls can provide reductions in total annual runoff and associated peak-flow attenuation if designed to capture and reuse WQV and/or channel CPV determined according to the methodologies in Chapter 3 or pertinent state or local design manuals.

3.1.3 Water Quality Control

Pollutants captured by rain barrels and cisterns are removed by settling and, if the captured runoff is directed to landscaped areas, through filtering and vegetative uptake. Most rain harvesting systems have a "first flush" bypass and screens at the inlets to capture leaves and gross particulates from the roof. Larger systems often include upstream separators or filters. The outlets are frequently equipped with pumps, pressure filters, UV disinfection units, or other processes for pathogen control, which are necessary if people may come in contact with the water.

3.2 Limitations

Climate plays a large role in the design of cisterns. It is important to size cisterns to store runoff based on the amount of rainfall in the design location. In addition, they must be designed and maintained to reduce the potential of mosquito breeding. Large cisterns must be covered and locked to minimize accidents. A rain barrel or cistern is useful for stormwater management only if it is empty or only partly full at the beginning of a storm. Therefore, there are uncertainties in the reliability of these controls given that they are numerous and mostly operated by private citizens. The City of Philadelphia promotes the use of soaker hoses attached to rain barrels to provide a gradual draw-down of water from the barrel before the next storm.

3.3 Design Procedure and Criteria

3.3.1 Typical Configurations

A cistern is an above-ground or below-ground storage vessel with a pumping system, a manually operated valve, or a permanently open outlet. Roof runoff is temporarily stored and then released for irrigation or infiltration between storms. The cistern volume or number of rain barrels needed is a function of rooftop area, the precipitation in the design location, and the rate at which stored water is used.

For houses, two rain barrels with a minimum total storage capacity of 1000 L (256 gal) are recommended. If the average roof area is 315 m^2 (3400 ft^2), the rain barrels would be able to capture about 3 mm (0.12 in.) of runoff. A cistern should have an overflow outlet for times when flows exceed outlet capability or the tank is full.

Studies of larger commercial and industrial developments in New England have concluded that half of nonpotable water demand for irrigation can be supplied by stormwater reuse (Camp Dresser & McKee, 2007). Approximately 90% of storms in New England are comprised of 25 mm (1 in.) of rainfall or less. It was assumed that runoff from rooftops during all storms with 25 mm (1 in.) or less of precipitation would be collected in cisterns. The average cistern tank volume needed per 3.6 ha (9 ac) parcel for an 81-ha (200-ac) development of commercial and industrial property, of which 20 ha (50 ac) was proposed rooftops, was found to be approximately 150 m^3 (40 000 gal).

3.3.2   Pretreatment Unit

Runoff entering a cistern or rain barrel is typically screened to trap leaves and other debris before entering the device. For large installations, a first-flush diverter is typically used to avoid collecting the most polluted runoff.

3.3.3   Main Treatment Unit

Several types of rain barrels are commercially available. In addition, some barrels are designed with a bypass valve that filters out grit and other contaminants and routes overflow to an infiltration stormwater control.

Larger cisterns for commercial and industrial developments may be above-ground or below-ground tanks made of concrete, fiberglass, or other material. Cisterns have also been installed in the top stories of buildings.

3.3.4   Outlet Structure

If the cistern has an operable valve, the valve can be closed to store stormwater for irrigation and opened to allow irrigation between storms. This arrangement requires continual monitoring, but provides greater flexibility in water storage and metering. A control with a permanently open outlet releases water immediately after a storm at a time when plants do not need irrigation and the soil is saturated and more prone to generating runoff from additional water.

3.4   Aesthetic and Safety Considerations

Consideration must be given to selecting rain barrels and cisterns that are vector-proof and childproof. If a cistern is provided with an operable valve and water is stored inside for long periods of time, the cistern must be covered to prevent mosquitoes from breeding. Large cisterns must have the same safety precautions of any potable water storage tank.

3.5 Access and Maintenance Features

Screens used to trap larger debris before entering a rain barrel or cistern need to be cleaned periodically. Other maintenance activities can include changing filters; recharging disinfection elements; cleaning or changing UV bulbs; and inspection of pumps, fittings, and wiring. Access to larger systems should be considered confined space entry.

4.0 FOREBAYS

A *forebay* is a small basin designed to remove coarse sediment. They are typically used as pretreatment controls intended to extend the useful life of a downstream primary treatment control. Forebays are typically excavated pits or cast structures designed to slow incoming stormwater runoff and settle suspended solids. Forebays may be dry or wet and must be able to be dewatered.

4.1 Typical Applications

4.1.1 Physical Site Suitability

Forebays have the same physical constraints of geology, bedrock, water table, and soils as other basins. If the forebay is designed to infiltrate, the bottom of the forebay should be placed a minimum of 1.5 m (5 ft) above high groundwater or bedrock.

4.1.2 Water Quantity Control

Forebays provide some peak attenuation and can reduce runoff volume if infiltration can take place through the bottom.

4.1.3 Water Quality Control

The primary unit process for water quality is sedimentation. Sediment forebays should be designed with an HLR suitable for settling coarse sediment. Forebays should be designed to withstand anticipated velocities during 2- and 10-year storms without scouring to avoid resuspension of settled particles.

4.2 Limitations

Frequent maintenance is required to preserve storage volume and avoid resuspending and flushing of sediment.

4.3 Design Procedure and Criteria

4.3.1 Typical Configurations

Sediment forebay-sizing criteria may vary from state to state. For example, the *Massachusetts Stormwater Handbook* (MassDEP, 2008) recommends, at a minimum, sizing the volume of a sediment forebay to hold 2.5 mm (0.1 in.) of runoff per unit impervious area. If there are multiple inlets, forebays should be placed to capture the inflow from all of the inlets, except for those that convey runoff from only a small portion of the drainage area. To facilitate significant cleanout activities within the pool area of a basin, a sediment forebay with a hardened bottom should be constructed near the inlet to trap coarse sediment particles, defined as particles 0.075 mm (0.003 in.) or larger that are retained by a no. 200 sieve size according to the Unified Soil Classification System. If the combined design capture volume is equal to WQV plus an additional sediment storage volume, then the forebay is commonly sized to 15 to 25% of the design capture volume, with the remainder of the design capture volume placed within the primary control. Sediment storage volumes may be calculated as the difference in influent and effluent loading over the desired maintenance frequency, but is commonly approximated as 20% of the WQV. Vaults or swirl concentrators can be installed to achieve similar pretreatment levels, hence allowing for a reduction in the total footprint of the impoundment.

The inlet design should dissipate flow energy and diffuse the inflow plume where it enters the forebay or permanent pool. Examples of inlet designs include drop manholes, energy dissipaters at the bottom of a paved rundown, a lateral bench with wetland vegetation, and the placement of large rock deflectors.

4.3.2 Pretreatment Unit

Sediment forebays are pretreatment units compatible with an array of stormwater controls such as wet and dry basins and constructed wetlands. However, installation of deep-sump hooded catch basins and/or particle separators upstream of forebays will further enhance sediment and pollutant removal.

4.3.3 *Main Treatment Unit*

Forebays are typically inline units designed to slow stormwater runoff and settle out sediments. Generally, the depths of sediment forebays are between 1 and 2 m (3 and 6 ft). Side slopes should be no steeper than 3:1, with 4:1 being preferable. The channel geometry should be designed to prevent erosion during a 2-year storm peak discharge; flow velocities should be less than 1.2 m/s (4 fps).

4.3.4 **Outlet Structure**

The forebay can be separated from the primary control by one of the following means: a lateral sill with wetland vegetation, two basins in a series, differential pool depth, a retaining wall, or a horizontal rock filter or check dam placed laterally across the permanent pool.

4.4 Aesthetic and Safety Considerations

The size of the forebay and the lateral sill or spillway between the forebay and the primary control should be designed using accepted engineering practices to prevent the forebay from overflowing to adjacent property and to protect the basin's embankment. Side slopes of 4H:1V or less will facilitate maintenance such as mowing and reduce risks to the public of slipping and falling into the water. In addition, a littoral zone should be established around the perimeter of the forebay to promote the growth of emergent vegetation along the shoreline and deter individuals from wading.

4.5 Access and Maintenance Features

Hardened maintenance access must be deployed for access of mechanized equipment to facilitate sediment removal. Regular maintenance is essential for proper functioning of a sediment forebay. Frequently removing accumulated sediments will make it less likely that sediment will be resuspended. Ideally, forebays should be inspected often and cleaned several times a year, although annual inspections and cleanups are the most common practice allowed by municipal resource availability.

5.0 VAULTS AND SWIRL CONCENTRATORS

Vaults may be primary treatment or pretreatment controls, depending on size. A vault has a permanent water pool, generally 0.9- to 1.5-m (3- to 5-ft) deep. The vault may also have a constricted outlet that causes a temporary rise of the water level during each storm, draining within 12 to 48 hours after the end of each storm. Manufactured vaults vary considerably in terms of geometry, inclusion of radial baffles, and number of internal chambers.

Swirl concentrators (also called *particle separators*) are cylindrical vaults in which the water moves in a circular fashion before exiting. By having the water move in a circular fashion, rather than a straight line as is the case with a standard vault, it is possible to achieve removal of suspended sediments and attached pollutants with less space. Swirl concentrators were originally developed for combined sewer overflows and were primarily used to remove coarse inorganic solids. Swirl concentration has been adapted to stormwater treatment by several manufacturers.

Vaults may give better performance than standard catch basins, given the inclusion of design elements that are intended to minimize resuspension. Research conducted at the University of New Hampshire (UNH) Stormwater Center found relatively low removal efficiencies for swirl concentrators and concluded that they are most effective when used for pretreatment in areas where runoff is expected to contain sediment particles greater than 100 μm in diameter (UNH Stormwater Center, 2007). The state of New Jersey also has a verification program for manufactured devices conducted through the New Jersey Corporation for Advanced Technology (New Jersey Department of Environmental Protection, 2011). The state of Washington also implements a technology assessment protocol (Washington State Department of Ecology, 2011).

The UNH study and manufacturers differ in terms of performance claims, but a general statement is that the manufacturer's design flow rate for each model is based on and believed to achieve an aggregate reduction of 30% of all particles generally observed in stormwater. Laboratory tests of two products support this claim. Therefore, the stated performance expectation implies that a lesser removal efficiency is obtained with particles less than 100 μ (0.00394 in.) and the lighter, organic settleables. Removal efficiencies for manufactured units should be tested through verification programs such as New Jersey's Technology Acceptance and Reciprocity Partnership and Washington's Technology Assessment Protocol – Ecology.

5.1 Typical Applications

5.1.1 Physical Site Suitability

There are no unique siting criteria. The size of the drainage area that can be served by a manufactured vault is directly related to the capacities of the largest models.

Depending on the characteristics of the drainage area, this upper range of capacity limits the applicability of vaults. The type of vault should be chosen based on soils and bedrock information. If bedrock is close to the ground surface, a shallower model should be chosen to reduce the amount of rock removal required. Many vaults are deep structures by design, requiring excavation depths in the range of 6 m (20 ft); however, some models that provide more horizontal treatment through the system, and shallower excavation requirements, are available. If high groundwater is found at the site, buoyancy calculations should be performed to determine whether a concrete collar or other weighting system is required.

5.1.2   Water Quantity Control

Vaults are typically flow-through systems and do not provide peak-flow attenuation or volume reduction. However, vaults can be designed as storage tanks constructed underground with outflow controls such as weirs or orifices for hydraulic control and peak-flow attenuation unit processes.

5.1.3   Water Quality Control

Sedimentation and flotation are the primary water quality unit processes in vaults. They have the highest value, providing pretreatment for other controls or in constrained sites where space for stormwater management facilities is limited. They are useful for both sediment removal and floatables control.

5.2   Limitations

Limitations of vaults and separators include the following:

- There are concerns about mosquito breeding in standing water;
- Vaults can become a source of pollutants via resuspension if not properly maintained;
- Inspection and maintenance of smaller vaults may be neglected because they are often not visible;
- Entrance velocities and flowrates need to be properly evaluated to limit resuspension of sediment and pollutants;
- The area served is limited by the capacity of the largest models;
- Because the products come in standard sizes, facilities may be oversized in many instances relative to the design treatment storm, thereby increasing the cost;

- Vaults are ineffective at removing dissolved pollutants, fine particles, or other pollutants;

- Discharges of dissolved pollutants may occur as accumulated organic matter (e.g., leaves) decomposes in units that are not routinely cleaned; and

- Because of underground construction, there are potential utility conflicts in urban environments.

5.3 Design Procedure and Criteria

5.3.1 Typical Configurations

A vault is typically comprised of a rectangular box, pipe, or arched chamber. Pipes are manufactured in various diameters and lengths and using a variety of materials. Arched chambers are manufactured in segments, which are combined to give the necessary volume. The number of vaults will be determined by the capacity of the systems used. It is more effective to provide numerous vaults upstream within a watershed than to provide only a few at the downstream end of the system.

Manufactured vaults fall into two general configurations: segments or modules and complete units. With the first configuration, several segments are assembled to give a volume equal to the design capture volume most commonly set equal to WQV. Other products are single units, most with the appearance of a large, round manhole. In this MOP, they are referred as *single-unit vaults.* Two or more single-unit vaults can be placed in parallel to increase treatment as with the segment configuration, although this occurs infrequently.

It is preferable to place vaults off-line to reduce the potential for scouring, resuspension of separated particles, and sediment wash-out. For an inline facility, the design peak flow should be 4 times the peak of the design treatment event water quality treatment (WQT) rate; for an off-line facility, the design peak flow is equal to the peak of the WQT rate. Chapter 3 provides guidance for determining the WQT rate.

5.3.2 Pretreatment Unit

As noted previously, placing deep-sump hooded catch basins upstream of the vaults will increase the pollutant removal efficiency of the system and reduce the chance of clogging.

5.3.3 Main Treatment Unit

Vaults are typically sized based on the WQT rate as specified by regulations or calculated according to the methodology presented in Chapter 3. It is the HLR that drives the performance of vaults. Hydraulic efficiency is particularly important for the small, single-unit, manufactured vaults. Manufacturers strive to maximize hydraulic efficiency by controlling the direction of the flow at the inlet. The objective is to minimize short-circuiting and dead zones and to reach hydraulic loading rates close to the theoretical value. A secondary objective is to minimize resuspension during high-flow events. Designs vary significantly among products, suggesting wide variability for performance. Figure 6.1 illustrates several different concepts that are currently used.

The vault in Figure 6.1a consists of a single circular structure, typically a standard precast manhole although larger models in nonstandard sizes are available. Stormwater is diverted downward into the center well where settling occurs. Flows in excess of the treatment capacity are diverted directly across the top of the device to the outlet to minimize resuspension of settled solids. There is also some storage capacity for floatables immediately beneath the bypass structure. This type of vault typically requires relatively deep excavation. Some configurations combine two similar structures in a series. Stormwater enters the first manhole where coarse solids are removed. The stormwater flows out of the first manhole, carrying floatables to the second manhole where they are captured and retained. Additional sedimentation occurs in this second manhole. A bypass is also included for large flows.

Another type of vault is a concrete box that has various configurations of internal baffles affixed at different elevations to reduce the energy of the flow entering the unit, reduce resuspension of settled sediments and dense gross pollutants, and trap hydrocarbons and floating gross pollutants. These vaults may include both a permanent wet pool and live storage volume that is filled during each storm. Some systems are modular; standard units can be added to attain a desired performance.

The term originally used for devices using rotational flow is *swirl concentrator* (Sullivan et al., 1982); the swirling motion causes particles to concentrate toward the center of the unit. It has not been established that swirl concentration provides a sufficient boost to gravity separation to make the use of the term appropriate. Originally, the inlets of devices identified as swirl concentrators were placed off-center, thereby inducing rotational motion (see Figure 6.1b). However, the inlet in recently introduced products gives direct entry with a 90-deg elbow to induce rotational motion (see Figure 6.1c). Figures 6.1d and 6.1e show two additional variants. Although head loss differs by type of vault, it is generally on the order of 0.3 m (1 ft) or less in most instances.

For all types of vaults, manufacturers provide information on the total system water volume, design peak flow, sediment capacity, and floatable capacities. Manufacturers can typically modify the size of the vault to increase treatment capacity.

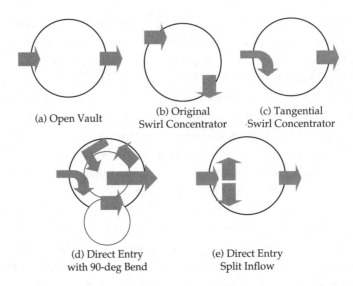

(a) Open Vault   (b) Original Swirl Concentrator   (c) Tangential Swirl Concentrator

(d) Direct Entry with 90-deg Bend   (e) Direct Entry Split Inflow

FIGURE 6.1   Flow direction for several single-unit vaults.

5.4   Aesthetic and Safety Considerations

As discussed previously, vaults are useful on constrained sites. They are below-grade structures that require relatively small footprints, and are safer for children and pedestrians than open controls such as wet basins.

5.5   Access and Maintenance Features

Access for maintenance is important in the design of vaults. Maintenance consists of the removal of accumulated material with an eductor truck. It may be necessary to remove and dispose the floatables separately because of the presence of petroleum product. Maintenance depends on climate and pollutant production in the watershed. Vaults should be inspected monthly during the wet season and cleaned several times a year. It is important to recognize that as storage of accumulated sediment occurs directly in the operating area of the vault, treatment efficiency will decline over time given the reduction in treatment volume. Whether this represents a significant decrease in performance depends on the design capacity.

Each manufacturer provides storage capacities with respect to sediments and floatables, with recommendations on the frequency of cleaning as a function of the fraction of the volume in the unit that has been filled by these materials. Although the recommended frequency of cleaning differs by manufacturer, it typically ranges from 1 to 2 years. It is prudent to inspect the unit monthly during the first wet season of operation and set the cleaning frequency accordingly. As a general rule, maintenance is recommended when approximately 25% of the storage is occupied by sediment and gross pollutants.

6.0   OIL AND WATER SEPARATORS

An oil and water separator is a specialized vault designed to maximize the removal of petroleum hydrocarbons, grease, sand, and grit. There are two types of oil and water separators: American Petroleum Institute (API) separators and coalescing plate separators. The API separator is a relatively large vault with a few baffles to enhance hydraulic efficiency. Vaults called *oil and grit separators* have the appearance of an API separator, but are considerably smaller. They are not effective at removing oil droplets or fine particles to which most of the sorbed oil associates. As such, they are more appropriately called *grit or sand separators* given that they primarily remove only larger particles.

The coalescing plate separator requires much less space than an API basin. Sediment and oil removal are achieved with a package of sloped plates or extruded tubes. The coalescing plate separator process is based on the concept that HLR determines performance during storms. *Coalescing* refers to the aggregation of oil droplets as they rise. The plate structure enables laminar flow over a large surface area. The plates are made from oleophilic polymers that attract small suspended droplets of oil, which attach to the plate surfaces. Eventually, the droplets coalesce until they form a droplet large enough to overcome the attraction of the plates and begin to rise to the surface. Stokes law is used to determine the size of the coalescing configuration.

6.1   Typical Applications

6.1.1   Physical Site Suitability

This control is applicable when the concentrations of oil-and grease-related compounds are high and source control does not provide effective control. Typical applications include gasoline stations, vehicle maintenance and washing enterprises, and other commercial and industrial facilities that generate high levels of oil products in runoff wastes. Public facilities for which separators may be considered include marine ports, airfields, fleet vehicle maintenance and washing facilities, and mass transit park-and-ride lots.

Similar to vaults, there are no unique siting criteria for oil and water separators. The size of the drainage area that can be served by an oil and water separator is directly related to the capacities of the largest models. If high groundwater is found at the site, buoyancy calculations should be performed to determine whether a concrete collar or other weighting system is required.

6.1.2   Water Quantity Control

Oil and water separators are typically flow-through systems and do not provide peak-flow attenuation or runoff volume reduction.

6.1.3   Water Quality Control

Oil and water separators are a form of vault designed to eliminate turbulence in runoff and allow small oil droplets to coalesce, rise to the surface, and sorb to material in the separator. Unit processes for water quality include flotation and sorption. Sedimentation removes suspended solids.

6.2   Limitations

Constraints for oil and water separators are similar to those for vaults. As an underground facility, there are potential utility conflicts in construction. Maintenance and cleanout are crucial to successful functioning, but may be neglected because oil and water that are separated are often not visible. As mentioned earlier in this chapter, the drainage area served is limited by the largest models. These controls are ineffective at removing dissolved pollutants, fine particles, or other pollutants.

6.3   Design Procedure and Criteria

6.3.1   Typical Configurations

The basic configurations of the API and coalescing plate separators are illustrated in Figure 6.2. With small installations, a conventional API gravity separator has the general appearance of a septic tank. Larger facilities have the appearance of a municipal wastewater primary sedimentation tank. The depth of flow in the separator varies between 1 and 2.5 m (3 and 8 ft). The width of the unit ranges between 2 and 6 m (6 and 20 ft), with a width-to-depth ratio ranging between 2 and 3. The coalescing plate separator contains closely spaced plates that enhance removal efficiency and, consequently, the separator requires less space than an API separator. The size depends on the flowrate to treat. The horizontal angle of the plates ranges from 0 to 60 deg, with 45 to 60 deg being typical. The perpendicular distance

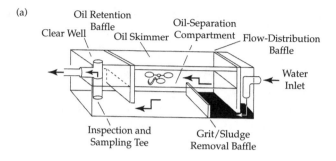

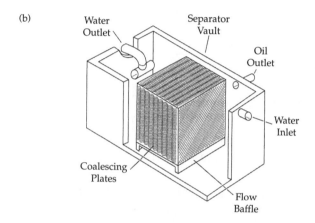

FIGURE 6.2   (a) Conventional API and (b) coalescing plate separators.

between the plates typically ranges from 20 to 25 mm (0.75 to 1.0 in.). Stormwater will flow either across the plates or down through the plates, depending on the plate configuration.

6.3.2   Pretreatment Unit

Oil and water separators are typically installed as pretreatment for other controls. Similar to vaults, installation of deep-sump hooded catch basins upstream of oil and water separators will enhance floatables, sediment, and oil and grease removal.

6.3.3   Main Treatment Unit

6.3.3.1 Sizing

American Petroleum Institute separators are capable of removing oil droplets with diameters greater than 150 μm. A coalescing plate separator should be used if smaller droplets must be removed. Oil and grease concentrations can be reduced to 10 mg/L or less if most droplets fall within this recommended range (Lettenmaier and Richey, 1985).

Separator sizing is based on the rise velocity of an oil droplet, using oil density and droplet size to calculate rise velocity or using direct measurement of rise velocities. The sizing of a separator varies by manufacturer. One method is based on the calculation of the rise velocity of the oil droplets using eq 6.1 modified from API (1990), as follows:

$$V_P = \frac{g(d_p - d_c)d^2}{18\mu} \tag{6.1}$$

where
V_p = oil-droplet rise velocity (m/s);
d_p = density of the oil (kg/m³);
d_c = density of the water (kg/m³);
d = diameter of the droplet to be removed (m);
m = absolute viscosity of the water (kg/m²); and
g = gravitational acceleration (9.81 m/s).

An appropriate water temperature value for selecting water density and viscosity is the expected temperature of the stormwater during the winter period. There is little data on the specific gravity of petroleum products in urban stormwater, although values between 0.85 and 0.95 typically are used. Also, distribution of droplet sizes must be estimated to select the appropriate droplet diameter for a stated efficiency goal. Distributions for oil-droplet size and volume for stormwater from a petroleum product storage facility is depicted in Figure 6.3. Because a design influent concentration must be assumed, there will be considerable uncertainty because it will vary widely among storms.

If the effluent goal is 20 mg/L and the design influent concentration is 50 mg/L, a removal efficiency of 60% is required. Using Figure 6.3, this efficiency can be achieved by removing all droplets with diameters 90 µm or larger. Using a water temperature of 10 °C (a water density of 0.999) and an oil density of 0.898, the rise velocity for a 90-µm droplet is 1.2 m/h (0.001 1 ft/sec).

It is commonly believed that conventional API separators are not effective at removing droplets smaller than 150 µm (API, 1990). Theoretically, a conventional API separator can be sized to remove a smaller droplet, but the resulting facility may be so large that a coalescing plate separator may be more cost-effective.

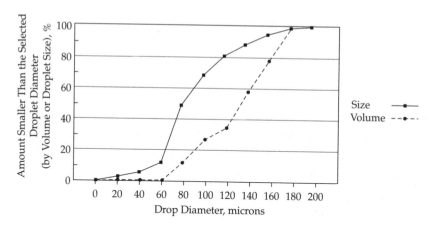

FIGURE 6.3 Oil droplet size distribution in stormwater from petroleum products storage facilities.

6.3.3.2 Sizing American Petroleum Institute Separators

To size an API, the depth should be computed first, as follows:

$$D = \sqrt{\frac{WQT}{2V}} \tag{6.2}$$

where

D = depth, which should be between 1 and 2.5 m (3 and 8 ft);

WQT = design flow rate, m³/s (cfs), determined according to the methodology in Chapter 3 or in state or local design manuals; and

V = allowable horizontal velocity, no more than 15 times the design oil rise rate but not greater than 55 m/h (0.05 ft/sec).

If the computed depth exceeds 2.5 m (8 ft), additional parallel units should be designed such that the maximum recommended depth of 2.5 m (8 ft) is not exceeded at the design flowrate WQT. Minimum depth is 1 m (3 ft). The next steps are as follows:

- Calculate length, $L = f\ (V/V_p)\ D$, where f is a short-circuiting factor ranging between 1.28 and 1.74 (API, 1990);

- Select width, W = 2 to 3 times the depth, but not to exceed 6 m (20 ft);

- Determined baffle height-to-depth ratio of 0.85 for top baffles and 0.15 for bottom baffles;

- Locate the distribution baffle at 0.10 L (0.03 gal) from the entrance;

- Add 0.3 m (1 ft) for freeboard; and
- Install an inlet flow control and a bypass for flows in excess of the WQT rate.

6.3.3.3 Sizing Coalescing Plate Separators

Manufacturers can provide packaged separator units for flows up to several cubic meters per second. For larger flows, the engineer must size the plate pack and design the vault. Given the variability of separator technology among manufacturers with respect to plate size, spacing, and inclination, it is recommended that the design engineer consult manufacturers for a plate package that will meet the engineer's criteria.

The engineer can size the facility using the following procedure. First, identify the expected plate angle (vertical above horizontal), H, in degrees, and calculate the total plate area required, A, in square meters (square feet), as follows:

$$A = \frac{Q}{V_p \cos H} \tag{6.3}$$

where the terms are the same as those defined in eqs 6.1 and 6.2.

Coalescing plate separators are not 100% hydraulically efficient; efficiency ranges from 0.35 to 0.95, depending on plate design. To incorporate this factor, the result from eq 6.3 should be divided by the selected efficiency. The following are the general sizing steps:

- Select spacing, S, between the plates, typically 20 to 40 mm (0.75 to 1.5 in.);
- Identify reasonable plate width W and length L;
- Number of plates $N = A/(W \cdot L)$;
- Calculate plate volume, P_V (m³), as follows:

$$P_V = W \cdot L \sin H \, [NS + L \cos H]; \tag{6.4}$$

- Add 0.3 m (1 ft) beneath the plates for sediment storage;
- Add 0.1 to 0.3 m (6 to 12 in.) above the plates for water clearance so that the oil accumulates above the plates;
- Add 0.3 m (12 in.) for freeboard;
- Add a forebay for floatables and distribution of flow if more than one plate unit is needed;

- Add an afterbay for collection of the effluent from the plate pack area; and

- For larger units, include a device to remove and store oil from the water surface.

Horizontal plates require the least plate volume to achieve a particular removal efficiency. Settleable solids will accumulate on the plates, complicating maintenance procedures. Experience shows that, even with slanted plates, some solids will stick to the plates because of the oil and grease. If debris is expected, such as sticks, plastics, and paper, then a larger plate separation distance should be selected. As an alternative, street sweeping should be conducted and/or a forebay, manufactured system, or a gross pollutant trap (Chapter 10) with smaller openings than the plate spacing should be installed. The plates may be damaged by the weight when removed for cleaning.

6.4   Aesthetic and Safety Considerations

Similar to vaults, oil and water separators are below-grade structures that require relatively small footprints and are safer for children and pedestrians than open controls such as wet basins. In cases where volatile compounds are being captured and concentrated, precautions should be taken with respect to explosions of accumulated vapors. In some cases, a buoyant mechanical valve is installed that senses a high level of accumulated hydrocarbons, shuts off the outlets, and triggers an alarm.

6.5   Access and Maintenance Features

Oil and water separators should be checked monthly during wet season and cleaned several times a year. They should always be cleaned before the start of the wet season, and the oil and other collected material should be properly disposed.

7.0   DRY BASINS

A dry basin temporarily detains all or a portion of stormwater from each storm event by placing a restricted outlet at the bottom of the basin (see Figure 6.4). The intent is to discharge all of the detained stormwater before the next storm arrives. The volume of the entire dry basin is commonly referred to as *live storage*.

Dry basins serve one or more of the control objectives previously identified in Figure 4.6. Basins intended to provide only overbank flood protection or extreme flood protection have a volume and outlet structure designed to detain and release infrequent extreme events. Water quality treatment and channel protection benefits

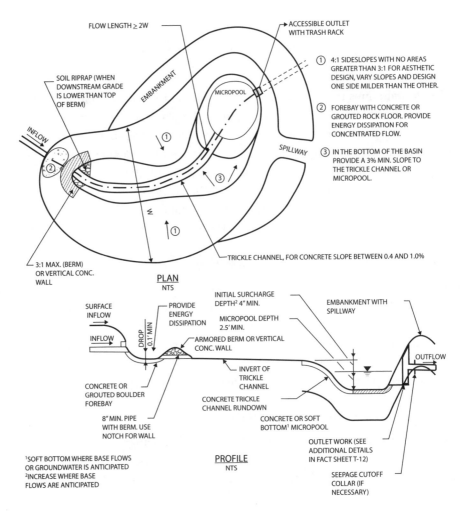

FLOW LENGTH ≥ 2W

ACCESSIBLE OUTLET
WITH TRASH RACK

SOIL RIPRAP (WHEN
DOWNSTREAM GRADE
IS LOWER THAN TOP
OF BERM)

EMBANKMENT

MICROPOOL

① 4:1 SIDESLOPES WITH NO AREAS
GREATER THAN 3:1 FOR AESTHETIC
DESIGN, VARY SLOPES AND DESIGN
ONE SIDE MILDER THAN THE OTHER.

② FOREBAY WITH CONCRETE OR
GROUTED ROCK FLOOR. PROVIDE
ENERGY DISSIPATION FOR
CONCENTRATED FLOW.

③ IN THE BOTTOM OF THE BASIN
PROVIDE A 3% MIN. SLOPE TO
THE TRICKLE CHANNEL OR
MICROPOOL.

INFLOW

SPILLWAY

3:1 MAX. (BERM)
OR VERTICAL CONC.
WALL

PLAN
NTS

TRICKLE CHANNEL, FOR CONCRETE SLOPE BETWEEN 0.4 AND 1.0%

INITIAL SURCHARGE
DEPTH[2] 4" MIN.

EMBANKMENT WITH
SPILLWAY

SURFACE
INFLOW

PROVIDE
ENERGY
DISSIPATION

MICROPOOL DEPTH
2.5′ MIN.

INFLOW

DROP
0.1′ MIN

ARMORED BERM OR VERTICAL
CONC. WALL

OUTFLOW

CONCRETE OR
GROUTED BOULDER
FOREBAY

INVERT OF
TRICKLE
CHANNEL

CONCRETE TRICKLE
CHANNEL RUNDOWN

8" MIN. PIPE
WITH BERM. USE
NOTCH FOR WALL

CONCRETE OR SOFT
BOTTOM[1] MICROPOOL

OUTLET WORK (SEE
ADDITIONAL DETAILS
IN FACT SHEET T-12)

[1]SOFT BOTTOM WHERE BASE FLOWS
OR GROUNDWATER IS ANTICIPATED
[2]INCREASE WHERE BASE
FLOWS ARE ANTICIPATED

PROFILE
NTS

SEEPAGE CUTOFF
COLLAR (IF
NECESSARY)

Figure 6.4   Schematic of a dry basin (1 ft = 0.3048 m; 1 in. = 25.4 mm) (UDFCD, 2010).

are provided by detaining and slowly releasing WQV and CPV to control the frequent small storms.

Dry basins designed to remove pollutants and control erosive velocities are commonly referred to as *dry extended-detention ponds*. The term *extended* refers to the ability of the basin to detain a WQV and CPV during small, frequent storm events and release the detained runoff over an extended period of time, typically 1 to 2 days. While the intent is for a dry basin to empty completely before the next storm arrives, this may not occur in wet climates with frequent storms. Failure to recognize the statistical probability of storm spacing and residual stormwater can lead to undersizing of basin volumes (Guo and Urbonas, 1996; Washington State Department of Ecology, 2005). Chapter 3 describes various methods for establishing the volume and release rate of a dry basin. Continuous simulation based on the historical rainfall record with due consideration to infiltration and evaporation is warranted in wet climatic regions.

7.1 Typical Applications

7.1.1 Physical Site Suitability

Dry basins have historically been used where soils are relatively impermeable and subsurface conditions (e.g., rock and high groundwater) do not extend into the basin footprint. Recent research, however, has found that up to 30% of the average annual runoff volume may infiltrate through the bottom or be used by vegetation within dry basins with drain times of 24 to 48 hours, contributing to runoff volume control (Strecker et al., 2004). Regional facilities often offer economies of scale and greater reliability in capturing stormwater, while on-site facilities offer institutional and fiscal advantages of implementation as the land is urbanized. When configuring a dry basin, the designer should consider fitting these facilities into the urban landscape and providing multiple uses, aesthetics, and safety features. Maintainability is also an important consideration. The individuality of each on-site or regional facility and its place within the urban community make it incumbent on the designer to seek out local input, identify site constraints, identify the community's concerns, and consider an array of possibilities during design.

Dry basins have several advantages compared to wet basins, presented in the next section. Advantages include avoidance of mosquito breeding, less thermal warming of stormwater or baseflow, and safety for people who may inadvertently enter the basin. However, unlike wet basins, dry basins require a drop in elevation from the inlet to the outlet, which may not be available, or, because of limited availability, may increase the space requirement.

7.1.2 Water Quantity Control

The main water quantity unit process in a dry basin is peak attenuation. Therefore, the performance of the basin is dictated by inflow, outlet structures, and the rate of infiltration through the bottom of the basin during storm events. Flood protection is achieved by attenuating increased flowrates from development during moderate to large, relatively infrequent storm events. Attenuation requires storage of a portion of the runoff, calculated as the difference in volume between the pre- and post-development hydrographs, as illustrated in Figure 6.5. Dry basins designed solely for OFV and EFV control typically are not effective at channel protection and stormwater pollution control.

7.1.3   Water Quality Control

Dry basins remove pollutants primarily through sedimentation. Removal of total suspended solids (TSS) and other constituents associated with sediments is effective if (1) the dry basin is designed with a 24- to 48-hour draw-down time for WQV, (2) a sediment forebay is provided at each inlet, (3) the basin is configured to minimize short-circuiting, and (4) the basin is designed to minimize resuspension of settled sediments during dewatering and storms larger than the WQV event. It should be noted that the total solids load is greater than what is defined as TSS. These solids contribute a large amount of mass and volume, for example, in areas where sand is used for deicing or where debris is captured. Vegetated dry basins may have greater pollutant removal than concrete basins. Concrete basins have been found to export pathogens, sediment and sediment-bound pollutants during various storms. Export is not as common in earthen basins, where the vegetation appears to stabilize the retained sediment.

The performance of dry basins in removing particles and attached pollutants is generally less than wet basins of the same volume; in addition, dry basins are generally ineffective for removal of dissolved pollutants because of the absence of

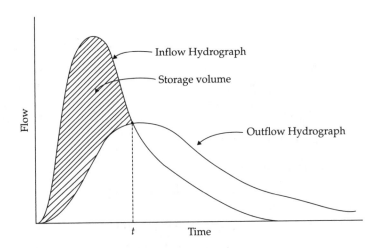

Figure 6.5   Peak-flow attenuation provided by dry basins.

a permanent pool. Possible reasons for this include resuspension of particles at the inlet with loss in the discharge, erosion in the vicinity of the inlet and/or outlet and the banks of the basin; decreased hydraulic efficiency of a single, narrow, discharge outlet; and poor performance early in each storm (Minton, 2011).

7.2 Limitations

Constraints for dry basins are similar to other basins. They are as follows:

- Land area required for the basin itself; forest clearing may be needed to create sufficient space for the basin;

- Sufficient depth to bedrock such that it does not affect grading;

- A deep water table so the basin stays dry; dry basins that do not drain completely because of poor maintenance create habitat for mosquitoes;

- Removal of only settleable pollutants and required draw-down times approaching 48-hours;

- Relative ineffectiveness at removing dissolved pollutants;

- Aesthetic concerns because of dry, bare, marshy areas and sediment and debris that accumulate at inlet and outlet structures;

- The proliferation of undesirable and invasive plants; and

- Attraction of waterfowl, and increases in pathogens and in the nutrient content in runoff.

7.3 Design Procedure and Criteria

7.3.1 Typical Configurations

Figure 6.4 shows the typical components of dry basins. Actual configurations of each on-site or regional facility and its place within the urban community make it incumbent on the designer to seek local input, identify site constraints, identify the community's concerns, and consider an array of possibilities during design.

7.3.2 Pretreatment Unit

Dry basin inlets often receive high-velocity flows that cause erosion. As velocities decrease, sediment deposition approaching 50% of the total sediment load in typical stormwater runoff occurs near the inlet of a dry basin. An ideal inflow structure will convey stormwater to the dry basin, prevent erosion of the dry basin's bottom and banks, reduce resuspension of previously deposited sediment, minimize favorable mosquito-breeding conditions, and facilitate deposition of the heaviest sediment near the inlet. Inflow structures can be flared end sections with rip-rap splash pads, drop manholes, chutes with an energy dissipater near the bottom, a baffled chute, a pipe with an impact basin, or one of numerous other types of diffusing devices.

Designs that encourage sediment deposition near the point of inflow and discourage resuspension help to focus dry basin maintenance near the inlet and extend the service life of the rest of the basin. One common method of encouraging sediment deposition is a forebay or vault designed for pretreatment, as described earlier in this chapter. The pretreatment device should be equipped with stabilized access and a concrete or soil cement-lined bottom to prevent mechanical equipment from sinking to the bottom and to make it easier to remove accumulated sediment. Resuspension and erosion in the vicinity of the inlet can also be minimized using a wet forebay. Although this potentially provides a mosquito breeding ground, the area is small and, therefore, may be acceptable. Alternatively, a manufactured vault can be used; vaults require less space and are typically easier to clean, although they may require confined space entry.

7.3.3 Main Treatment Unit

7.3.3.1 Determining Water Quality Volume

The detention volume of a dry basin should be sized for projected build-out conditions and discharged slowly to capture 80 to 90% of the average annual runoff volume and allow a "temporary" pool with relatively quiescent conditions to form in the basin during and after the precipitation event. The goal is to achieve a hydraulic retention time that maximizes settling while the basin is draining, most commonly found to be achieved with drain times of 24 to 48 hours for the full WQV. Chapter 3 presents appropriate methodologies for determining WQV, including state or locally mandated values, continuous simulation of a basin with a 24- to 48-hour draw-down time, and an approach provided for estimating the maximized WQV. Following this procedure yields a WQV that is 30 to 60% larger than the runoff volume generated by the mean precipitation event for a given area to account for back-to-back storms that influence performance over these long draw-down times.

Draw-down time is chosen by the designer or dictated by local authorities. Longer draw-down times produce somewhat better removal rates of suspended solids. However, longer drain times tend to produce less attractive facilities that have little or no vegetation on the bottom. Facilities with long draw-down times may have wet bottoms with marshy vegetation and can be difficult to maintain and clean unless a two-stage design and/or hybrid dry–wet basin is used, as described later in this section.

7.3.3.2 Hydrograph Routing

A reservoir routing method should be used to refine initial sizing estimates and verify the expected performance of the basin. The WQV has to first be converted to a design hyetograph to simulate a runoff hydrograph. How this is done will be dictated by the typical design storm temporal distribution in use within the region where the facility is located. General practice appropriate for most parts of the United States suggests that the maximized depth be redistributed into a 2-hour design storm hyetograph. The goal of reservoir routing is to balance inflow rates against outflow rates to find the needed volume, as illustrated in Figure 6.5. This is accomplished by solving eq 6.5 with numerical methods or using one of the many available computer programs written for this purpose (see Chapter 14). Equation 6.5 states that the needed storage volume is a time integral of the difference between inflow and outflow hydrographs from the beginning of storm runoff to the point in time where the outflow rate exceeds the inflow rate, as follows:

$$V_{max} = \int_0^t (Q_{in} - Q_{out})\, dt \qquad (6.5)$$

where

V_{max} = storage volume (m³);

t = time from beginning of runoff to a point of maximum storage(s);

Q_{in} = inflow rate (m³/s); and

Q_{out} = outflow rate (m³/s).

The most common computational method is the storage indication method that is described in numerous hydrology textbooks and handbooks such as the *Hydrology Handbook* (ASCE, 1996).

7.3.3.3 Two-Stage Design

Whenever feasible, two stages should be provided in a dry basin. The lower stage is placed near the outlet of the basin and fills during the most frequent storm events, reducing periods of standing water and sediment deposition in the remainder of the basin. The lower stage can be 0.5- to 1-m (1.5- to 3-ft) deep and should include the sediment storage volume not provided in the forebay plus 15 to 25% of the WQV. The top stage should be 0.6- to 2-m (2- to 6-ft) deep and large enough to contain the remainder of the WQV, with its bottom sloping at approximately 2% toward a low-flow channel.

As stated previously, dry basins generally do not achieve the level of pollutant removal of wet basins and wetlands. However, there are design elements that can be included within the dry basin to improve performance. These include placing a wet pool in the lower stage, thereby creating a hybrid dry–wet basin. This wet pool is typically much smaller than the permanent pool of a wet basin designed according to the criteria in the next section. The primary purpose of a small wet pool within the lower stage of a dry basin is to hide accumulating sediment and minimize resuspension. To a lesser degree, a hybrid dry–wet basin does have the disadvantages of the standard wet basin (i.e., thermal warming, mosquito habitat, and safety considerations).

7.3.3.4 Basin Side Slopes

Earthen basin side slopes need to be stable under saturated soil conditions. They also need to be sufficiently gentle to limit rill erosion, facilitate maintenance, and address the safety issue of people falling in the basin when it is full of water. Erosion can be reduced with a grass surface along the basin bottom and banks. Bank erosion may occur because of sloughing rather than direct erosion. This occurrence is minimized with grass and/or a gradual slope. A minimum slope of 3H:1V should be used, with 4H:1V being preferable. Erosion control may be enhanced by a rock toe.

7.3.3.5 Low-Flow Channel

Low-flow channels should be included in dry basins because they assist in drying of the basin bottom depending on the forebay and inlet configuration, type of outlet used, and flow path between the inlet and outlet. Some low-flow channel designs include meanders and/or other features that extend detention time to improve pollutant removal early in each storm and prevent resuspension during basin dewatering. Such designs may provide limited pollutant removal in dry basins designed solely for flood control, but are often not needed if the dry basin includes outlets that release WQV during a 24- to 48-hour period. Low-flow channels should not be lined with concrete or asphalt.

7.3.3.6 Basin Embankment

Basin embankments should be designed and built so that they will not fail. An emergency spillway should be provided or the embankment should be designed to withstand overtopping commensurate with the size of the embankment, the volume of water that can be stored behind it, and the potential of downstream damages or loss of life if the embankment fails. Emergency spillway designs vary widely with local regulations; generally, spillways should be designed to safely pass the extreme flow event, typically the 50- to 100-year storm peak flows, or larger if dam safety regulations apply. The designer should always consult the state's dam safety regulations to assess design criteria and permitting requirements relative to basin size and embankment height.

Embankment slopes should be no steeper than 3H:1V, preferably 4H:1V or less. The slopes also need to be planted with turf-forming grasses and maintained to deter tree growth and burrowing animals. Embankment soils should be compacted to 95% of their maximum density at optimum moisture.

7.3.3.7 Vegetation

A basin's vegetation provides erosion control and enhances sediment entrapment. The basin can be planted with water-tolerant native grasses or with irrigated turf, depending on local setting, basin design, and intended uses such as recreation. Sediment deposition and frequent, prolonged periods of inundation make it difficult to maintain healthy grass cover on the basin's bottom. Options for an alternative bottom liner include a marshy wetland bottom, bog, layer of gravel, riparian shrub, bare soil, low-weed meadow grass mix, or any type that can survive the conditions on the bottom of the basin.

7.3.4 Outlet Structure

A designer should use one or more outlets, as needed, to achieve the intended objectives of the dry basin (i.e., slowly releasing WQV and CPV over the design emptying time and properly routing extreme events as necessary to achieve downstream flood-control objectives). The outlet should be sized to empty less than 50% of WQV in the first one-third of the design drawdown period (e.g., 16 hours if the design drawdown time is 48 hours, with the remaining 50% of WQV requiring 32 hours to drain). This distribution improves removal of small suspended solids.

Numerous authors (ASCE, 1985; ASCE and WEF, 1992; DeGroot, 1982; Roesner et al., 1989; Schueler, 1987; Schueler et al., 1992; Urbonas and Roesner, Eds., 1986; and Urbonas and Stahre, 1993) reported several reasons for outlet problems, including clogging by trash and debris, sediment accumulation at the outlet, damage from vandalism, intentional plugging, and other factors that modify discharge characteristics of the outlet. Each outlet has to be designed with these factors in mind. Several types of outlets may be appropriate, depending on design objectives.

7.3.4.1 Single Orifice

The simplest form of outlet is a pipe or orifice sized to achieve the desired drain time. Because dry basins are designed to encourage sediment deposition and urban stormwater has substantial quantities of settleable and floating solids, single orifice outlets smaller than 300 mm (12 in.) in diameter are prone to being clogged, which can make the design of reliable outlet structures for dry basins difficult. A clogged outlet will invalidate the hydraulic function of even the best design. Generally, the minimum size single-orifice outlet from a dry basin should be 300 mm (12 in.), unless other means are provided to address clogging problems and sediment accumulation near the outlet such as a V-notch weir in front of a large-diameter pipe outlet or one of the alternative outlets described in the following sections.

7.3.4.2 Outlets for Hybrid Dry–Wet Basins

A catch basin-type hood or other submerged outlet can be beneficial in preventing floating materials from clogging the outlet in a two-stage basin with a small pool at the outlet when there is sufficient room below the invert of the outlet to fit the hood. Section 8.0 ("Wet Basins") provides design guidance for these types of outlets.

7.3.4.3 T-Weir Outlet

An alternative outlet, such as the T-weir outlet, can be used if a 300-mm (12-in.) diameter outlet does not sufficiently reduce peak rates of runoff and/or does not provide the desired draw-down time. T-weir structures are precast rectangular structures with a T-shaped opening controlling flow from the basin (see Figure 6.6). Such structures have been found to be effective at reducing peak rates of runoff for basins with relatively small tributary areas without clogging. Outlet clogging has not been a problem even for tee weirs with 100-mm (4-in.) openings at the bottom because, if sediment and debris accumulate at the bottom outlet, flow can still be released above the sediment through the T-shaped opening.

7.3.4.4 Perforated Riser

Another alternative outlet is a perforated riser, illustrated in Figure 6.7. In this outlet, the perforations in the pipe control the outflow. In cold climates, ice can clog the orifices and, as such, the minimum orifice diameter should be 15 mm (0.5 in.). Schueler et al. (1992) suggested a hooded perforated riser located in a small permanent pool if a two-stage basin design is used as described previously.

7.3.4.5 Skimmers

Other technologies such as skimmers are available that improve the capture of sediment, debris, oil, and grease.

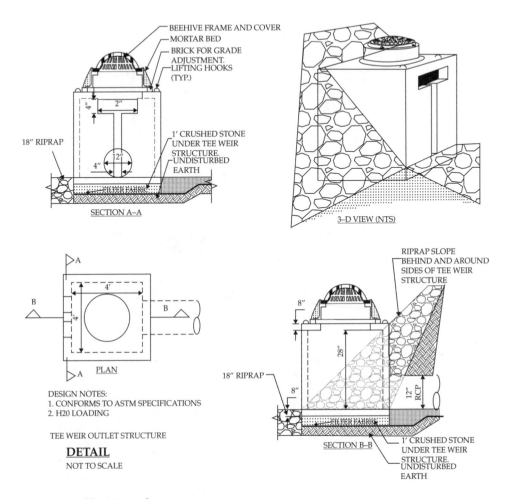

FIGURE 6.6   T-weir outlet.

7.3.4.6 *Sand and Bioretention Filters*

A horizontal sand filter, bioretention filter, or similar filtering system can be used (designed according to the principles outlined in Chapter 8) that will allow the basin to completely dry between storm events, presuming the filter is adequately maintained to address clogging. Filter sand or bioretention media can be placed in one or more trenches or rectangles positioned laterally or longitudinally in the basin. Alternatively, a sand filter can be configured as a rectangular or square bed placed

(a)

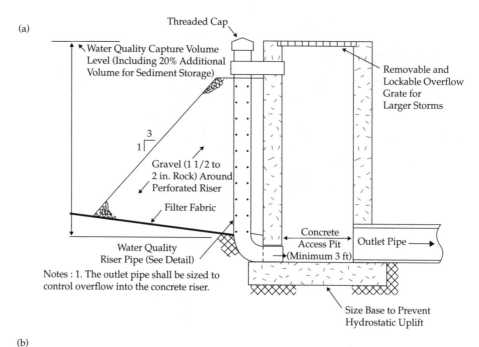

Threaded Cap

Water Quality Capture Volume Level (Including 20% Additional Volume for Sediment Storage)

Removable and Lockable Overflow Grate for Larger Storms

$\dfrac{3}{1}$

Gravel (1 1/2 to 2 in. Rock) Around Perforated Riser

Filter Fabric

Water Quality Riser Pipe (See Detail)

Concrete Access Pit (Minimum 3 ft)

Outlet Pipe →

Notes : 1. The outlet pipe shall be sized to control overflow into the concrete riser.

Size Base to Prevent Hydrostatic Uplift

(b)

Notes : 1. Minimum number of holes = 8.
       2. Minmum hole diameter = 1/8 in. diameter

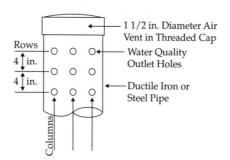

1 1/2 in. Diameter Air Vent in Threaded Cap

Rows

4 in.

Water Quality Outlet Holes

4 in.

Ductile Iron or Steel Pipe

Columns

Maximum Number of Perforated Columns				
Riser Diameter, in.	Hole Diameter, in.			
	1/4 in.	1/2 in.	3/4 in.	1in.
4	8	8	±	±
6	12	12	9	±
8	16	16	12	8
10	20	20	14	10
12	24	24	18	12
Hole Diameter, in.	Area of Hole, sq in.			
1/8	0.013			
1/4	0.049			
3/8	0.110			
1/2	0.196			
5/8	0.307			
3/4	0.442			
7/8	0.601			
1	0.785			

FIGURE 6.7   An example of a perforated riser outlet, (a) outlet works (not to scale) and (b) water quality riser pipe (not to scale) (1ft = 0.3048 m; 1 in = 25.4 mm) (UDFCD, 2010).

directly in the embankment at the outlet. The filter surface must be cleaned periodically. An additional potential opportunity for a filter is the removal of dissolved pollutants. Amendments such as zeolite, activated alumina, or compost can be mixed into the sand to enhance pollutant removal.

A variant of the aforementioned solution is to place the lowest orifice above the basin bottom (ca. 300 mm). A relatively small sand or bioretention filter is located at the outlet. The majority of the stormwater passes through the orifice, reducing the portion that passes through the filter with the pool and detaining the early volume of each storm. The purpose of the filter is to bleed residual water after a storm, thereby avoiding mosquito issues. A low-flow channel can also be used to reduce puddling as water that enters early in each storm is filtered.

7.3.4.7 Mechanical Outlets
Delayed discharge can also be accomplished mechanically. One manufacturer uses a bladder, where a rain sensor that detects the outset of a storm actuates an air pump that fills the bladder. The bladder plugs the outlet for an extended period, after which a timer actuates the air-release valve. A solar panel and battery can provide power.

7.3.4.8 Gross Solids Control
A trash rack or one of the other similar mechanisms described in Chapter 10 may be provided to prevent gross solids from entering a discharge pipe. A gravel pack, as shown in Figure 6.7, can be used to prevent sediment and debris deposits from clogging the outlet pipe. Wrapping a perforated outlet in a geotextile filter cloth often causes it to seal quickly and should be avoided unless another means (e.g., a wire mesh between the cloth and the outlet) is provided.

7.4 Aesthetic and Safety Considerations
Aesthetics are what the public uses to judge how "successful" a dry basin is within the community. Because aesthetics are important, new facilities should be tastefully integrated into the neighborhood in consultation with a landscape architect.

When the facility is in operation, safety concerns need to focus on flow velocities, water depths, and keeping the public from hazardous areas. Safety is enhanced by reducing the use of high vertical walls and steep side slopes. Outlets, inflow structures, and adjacent areas require special attention; the American Society of Civil Engineers (ASCE) (1985) suggests use of thorny shrubs and trash and safety racks at all outlet orifices, pipes, and weirs.

For large basins, the design should also address safety issues such as the structural integrity of the water-impounding embankment. As discussed earlier, the embankment should be protected from catastrophic failure. In the United States, dam failure is almost always judged as an absolute liability of its owner. A designer should always consider this principle of common law when designing facilities. A safety bench may be designed that provides a shallow area for people or animals that inadvertently enter the open water to exit the basin. Additional discussion of safety issues is presented in Chapter 5.

7.5   Access and Maintenance Features

Although dry basins provide treatment with no operational attention, continued successful performance will depend on good maintenance. A designer should always provide adequate maintenance access.

For large forebays requiring entry by maintenance equipment, vehicular maintenance access should be provided to the forebay and outlet with grades that do not exceed 8 to 10% and have a stable surface of gravel-stabilized turf, a layer of rock, open-type concrete pavers planted with low-maintenance grass, or concrete pavement.

7.6   Dry Basin Design Example

A dry basin is proposed to meet local and state requirements for a 10-ha (25-ac) drainage area composed of a single-family residential development at densities of 5 and 10 lots per hectare (2 and 4 lots per acre). The basin is designed to control the 25- and 100-year storms to minimize downstream flooding and for water quality treatment. The project is located in Massachusetts, where the required WQV equals 25 mm (1 in.) of precipitation times the total impervious area of the postdevelopment project site for a discharge to critical environmentally sensitive areas such as those defined as Outstanding Resource Waters under the Massachusetts Surface Water Quality Standards of 2007. Water quality volume equals 13 mm (0.5 in.) of precipitation times the total impervious area of the postdevelopment site for discharges to all other areas. Alternatively, a maximized WQV could be calculated from the procedures outlined in Chapter 3.

- At a minimum, the volume of the sediment forebay should be sized to hold 2.5 mm (0.1 in.) of runoff over 0.4 ha (1 ac) of impervious surface to provide pretreatment.

- Peak rates of runoff under postdevelopment conditions shall not exceed peak rates under existing conditions during 2-, 10-, and 100-year storm events.

7.6.1   Basic Site Data

The proposed development is depicted in Figure 6.8. The area is to be developed in two phases, with the proposed stormwater management facility intended to serve both phases of development. Key attributes of the site include the following:

- Site area equal to 10 ha (25 ac);

- The entire site currently drains to a single receiving stream located at the western side of the drainage area;

- Existing land cover consists of pasture considered to be in "good" hydrologic condition;

- Land use under postdevelopment conditions consists of 0.1-ha (0.25-ac) single-family residential lots in 8.3 ha (20.5 ac) and 0.2-ha (0.50-ac) single-family residential lots in the remaining 1.8 ha (4.5 ac); and

- Approximately 60% of the site consists of Hydrologic Soil Group C soils, while the remaining 40% of the site consists of Hydrologic Soil Group B soils based on the Natural Resources Conservation Service Soil Survey.

7.6.2   Define Hydrologic Characteristics of the Site for Flood Protection

7.6.2.1 Composite Curve Number Calculation

The composite curve number for determining OFV and EFV is calculated by choosing a runoff curve number for each soil type and land use combination and using the

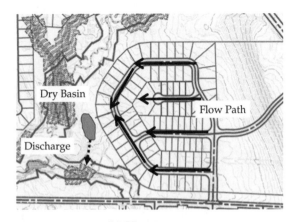

Figure 6.8   Development site layout (10 ha [25 ac]).

area of each combination to calculate an area-weighted curve number for the entire development site. A composite curve number is calculated for both predevelopment and postdevelopment land use conditions.

Table 6.1 presents the calculation of the area-weighted curve number and the drainage area characteristics for predevelopment and postdevelopment conditions within the development site. The site has a predevelopment runoff curve number of 69 and a postdevelopment curve number of 79.

7.6.2.2 Time of Concentration Calculation

Time of concentration (*Tc*) is defined as the time required for runoff to travel from the hydraulically most distant point in the drainage area to the design point. The hydraulic length of the drainage area (*L*) is the length from the design location to the most hydraulically distant location in the drainage area. The lag time (*TL*) is the time between the center of mass of effective rainfall and the inflection point of the recession (falling limb) of the direct runoff hydrograph. The *TL* is equal to 0.6 *Tc*, based on the Conservation Service (SCS) method.

Time of concentration is typically based on the slope of the watercourse and the type of surface cover. The U.S. Department of Agriculture Upland Method is applicable to small watersheds less than 800 ha (2000 ac) and the following types of flow: overland, through grassed waterways, over paved areas, through small

TABLE 6.1   Drainage area characteristics.

Drainage area description	Area ha (ac)	Soil type	CN*	Time of concentration (min)
Predevelopment conditions				
Pasture (good)	6 (15)	C	74	
Pasture (good)	4 (10)	B	61	
Total area	10 (25)		69	20
Postdevelopment conditions				
Residential 0.1 ha (0.25 ac)	6 (15)	C	83	
Residential 0.1 ha (0.25 ac)	2.2 (5.5)	B	75	
Residential 0.2 ha (0.50 ac)	1.8 (4.5)	B	70	
Total area	10 (25)		79	12

*Curve Number (USDA, 1986).

upland gullies, and along terrace channels (USDA, 1986). This method is used because the types of flow at this site are overland, through pasture, and over paved areas. Table 6.1 shows the times of concentration calculated for predevelopment and postdevelopment conditions. The site has a predevelopment time of concentration of 20 minutes and a postdevelopment time of concentration of 12 minutes.

7.6.2.3 Determine Feasibility of a Dry Basin

Soil borings found that the subsurface soils at the proposed location of the dry basin primarily consist of silty sand, silty clay, and clayey silts that are predominantly Hydrologic Soil Group C. Depth to groundwater ranges from 3 to 3.7 m (10 to 12 ft) below the ground surface. The Hydrologic Soil Group C soils are suitable to support a dry basin because these types of soils provide some infiltration.

In addition, topographic relief on the site is suitable for providing a positive gradient along the bottom of the basin. Therefore, use of a dry basin is feasible for this site.

7.6.3 Design Steps

7.6.3.1 Step 1: Find Rainfall Depth and Distribution Data for the Site

The 24-hour rainfall depth and distribution data for this site are taken from the *Atlas of Precipitation Extremes for the Northeastern United States and Southeastern Canada* (Wilks and Cember, 1993). The estimated precipitation depths during the 2-, 10-, 25- and 100-year 24-hour storms are 81 mm (3.2 in.), 124 mm (4.9 in.), 155 mm (6.1 in.), and 216 mm (8.5 in.), respectively. This site is located in the northeastern United States where Type III rainfall distribution applies (USDA, 1986).

7.6.3.2 Step 2: Compute Predevelopment and Postdevelopment Peak Rates of Runoff

A hydrologic modeling program such as the U.S. Army Corps of Engineers (USACE) Hydrologic Engineering Center-Hydrologic Modeling System (HEC-HMS) software, the rainfall depth and distribution determined in step 1, and the curve numbers and times of concentration in Table 6.1 can be used to determine predevelopment and postdevelopment peak rates of runoff. The peak rates of runoff are shown in Table 6.2.

7.6.3.3 Step 3: Compute Water Quality Volume

Because this site does not discharge to an environmentally sensitive area, the WQV equals 13 mm (0.5 in.) multiplied by the impervious area. The fraction of

TABLE 6.2   Peak flows.

Conditions	Peak rate of runoff m³/s (cfs)			
	2-year	10-year	25-year	100-year
Predevelopment conditions	0.2 (8.8)	0.7 (23.7)	1.0 (35.8)	1.8 (62.1)
Postdevelopment conditions	0.8 (28.9)	1.7 (59.4)	2.3 (82.1)	3.6 (128.2)

imperviousness of 0.1-ha (0.25-ac) residential lots is approximately 38 and 25% for 0.2-ha (0.50-ac) residential lots. This information is shown in standard curve number tables (USDA, 1986). Hence, the total proposed impervious area is 0.38 (8.3 ha) plus 0.25 (1.8 ha), equaling 3.6 ha (8.9 ac), and the WQV is 13 mm times 3.6 ha, equaling 45.7 ha-mm or 457 m³ (0.37 ac-ft).

If the maximized WQV sized according to methodology in Chapter 3 is used to size the detention volume, the design precipitation depth would be 17 mm (0.67 in.) times the event capture ratio of 1.463, or 25 mm (0.98 in.). The percent imperviousness is calculated as 3.6 ha (8.9 ac) impervious area divided by 10.1-ha (25-ac) total development site, or 0.36 ha. The water quality runoff coefficient, Rv, would be calculated using eq 3.3 ($0.05 + 0.9i$), or 0.37. This yields a maximized WQV of 26 mm (1.04 in.) times 0.37 times 10.1 ha (25 ac), equaling 97.2 ha-mm or 972 m³ (0.8 ac-ft), which is roughly double the local requirement.

Water quality volume should be increased by 20% to provide a sediment storage volume and reduce maintenance frequency. As a result, the sediment storage volume would equal 86 m³ (0.07 ac-ft) under Massachusetts WQV criteria, or 185 m³ (0.15 ac-ft) under the maximized WQV criteria in Chapter 3. In this example, the sediment storage volume is provided below the lowest elevation used for routing and partly within the forebay.

7.6.3.4 Step 4: Determine Preliminary Geometry and Sizing of the Dry Basin
Preliminary basin geometry is dependent on existing site topography. A minimum length to width of 2:1 is recommended using wedge-shaped basins that are narrow at the inlet and wide at the outlet.

Typically, basin sizing is done using a trial and error approach. A preliminary basin grading plan is established and then the WQV and design storms are routed through the basin to determine maximum water depths, peak release rates, and WQV drain time. Then, basin geometry or outlet sizes are adjusted to provide adequate storage to meet the design objectives. To perform routing calculations a preliminary outlet structure first needs to be designed to define a stage–storage–discharge table for the basin. Table 6.3 shows the elevation-area relationship for the preliminary basin geometry.

The actual grading plan for the basin will reflect the sediment storage volume below an elevation of 29.6 m (97 ft). This volume is not used in the routing calculations.

7.6.3.5 Step 5: Size the Outlet for Water Quality Volume

Using the relationship in Table 6.3, the maximum elevation of the WQV can be determined using linear interpolation. With a WQV of 456.4 m³ (0.37 ac-ft) and a basin bottom at 29.6 m (97 ft), the maximum elevation of the WQV is 29.7 m (97.6 ft). This is the starting water surface elevation to use when calculating WQV draw-down time.

Flood hydrograph routing software such as HEC-HMS should be used to determine the draw-down time of WQV. A HEC-HMS model was created without rainfall and using a starting water surface elevation within the basin of 29.7 m (97.6 ft). Next, an orifice outlet was modeled with an initial diameter of 100 mm (4 in.). The elevation within the basin was plotted for each time step of the simulation to estimate the drain time of WQV. Because the drain time using a 100-mm (4-in.) orifice was less than 24 hours (see Figure 6.9), then a 75-mm (3-in. orifice diameter was modeled. The 75-mm (3-in.) diameter orifice provided the 40-hour drain time as shown in Figure 6.9. The drain-time curves shown in Figure 6.9 trend toward different minimum elevation values because the equation for flow through an orifice is calculated using the elevation of the center of the orifice. If the orifice had been submerged, then the elevation difference would have been that between the upstream and downstream water surface elevations. When the water surface elevation reaches the center of the orifice opening, HEC-HMS calculates the flow through the orifice as 0.

In addition to providing the required drain time, the WQV outlet should also be sized to release less than 50% of WQV during the first one-third of drain time. To check

TABLE 6.3   Elevation-area relationship for preliminary pond geometry.

Elevation m (ft)	Area m² (ac)	Cumulative storage volume m³ (ac-ft)
29.6 (97)	1983 (0.5)	0 (0.0)
29.9 (98)	3521 (0.9)	839 (0.7)
30.2 (99)	5423 (1.3)	2196 (1.8)
30.5 (100)	8094 (2.0)	4194 (3.4)
30.8 (101)	10 360 (2.6)	6994 (5.7)

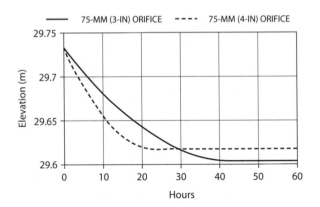

FIGURE 6.9   Drain time curves for 75-mm (3-in.) orifice and 100-mm (4-in.) orifice outlets.

that the 75-mm (3-in.) orifice meets this requirement, a plot of the fraction of WQV released and fraction of drain time was created. Figure 6.10 shows that the 75-mm (3-in.) orifice size will release only 40% of the WQV at one-third of the drain time (13.3 hours).

Because the selected orifice size is less than 300 mm (12 in.), design elements to prevent clogging need to be incorporated. Design elements can include both a micropool and forebay. The use of a micropool allows the outlet to be constructed with hooded intakes to reduce the potential for clogging.

Alternatively, a 45-deg angle V-notch weir can be used in front of a large-diameter pipe outlet to control draw-down of WQV. This type of weir would drain the WQV in this example in greater than 24 hours and is less susceptible to clogging than a small-diameter pipe outlet.

7.6.3.6 Step 6: Size the Flood Protection Outlets

To size the flood protection outlets, the designer should start with sizing the outlet to control the 2-year 24-hour storm event and then work through to the 100-year storm event. The designer should start by choosing an orifice diameter, weir length, or pipe size for the 2-year outlet. Flood hydrograph routing software should be used to route the 2-year 24-hour rainfall event through the preliminary basin geometry to determine the peak outflow rate for the 2-year event. At this point, the basin will be modeled with two outlets, the WQV orifice or weir and the 2-year outlet. The combined peak flow of these two outlets must meet the peak-flow requirements of the regulations that are to be met. The size of the 2-year outlet should be adjusted if the peak flow is too high or too low.

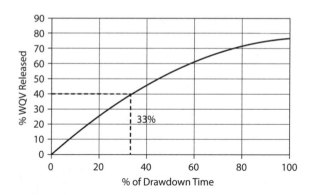

FIGURE 6.10   Fraction of WQV released over drain time for a 75-mm (3-in.) orifice.

For this example, a 45-deg angle V-notch weir was chosen to control WQV draw-down with a 900-mm (36-in.) diameter pipe outlet to control 2-year 24-hour storm peak rates of runoff. This type of weir in front of this size outlet provided a peak out-flow of 0.2 m³/s (8.3 cfs). The maximum elevation in the basin for the 2-year event was 30.0 m (98.4 ft).

Next, the 10-year storm was routed through the basin to determine the reduction in peak flow for the 10-year event with the combined weir and 900-mm pipe outlet. The results of the run showed that the peak flowrate for the 10-year event was slightly less than the predeveloped rate of 0.7 m³/s (23.7 cfs). Therefore, the V-notch weir and 900-mm pipe outlet meet requirements for controlling WQV, and 2- and 10-year storm events.

Similarly, the 25-year event was routed through the basin to determine the reduc-tion in peak flowrate using the proposed outlet structures. The peak outflow from the basin for the 25-year event is 0.9 m³/s (30.2 cfs), which is less than the 1.0 m³/s (35.8 cfs) predevelopment 25-year peak flowrate.

Finally, an emergency spillway sized to control 100-year, 24-hour peak rates of runoff is needed. A 6.1-m (20-ft) wide broad-crested weir at an elevation of 30.5 m (100 ft) is used for this purpose. The peak 100-year flowrate from the basin is 1.7 m³/s (58.7 cfs), which is less than the predevelopment peak flowrate of 1.8 m³/s (62.1 cfs). Table 6.4 presents a summary of outlet types used in the final design and the eleva-tions at which the outlets begin flow control.

Table 6.5 shows the results of reservoir routing through the proposed dry basin using HEC-HMS. The design requirements for all flood protection events were met using the staged outlet structure design.

TABLE 6.4   Summary of staged outlet structure.

Outlet type	Size	Invert elevation m (ft)
V-notch weir	45 deg	29.6 (97)
Pipe outlet	900 mm (36 in.)	29.6 (97)
Broad-crested weir	6.1 m (20 ft)	30.5 (100)

TABLE 6.5   Results of reservoir routing through the proposed dry pond.

	Peak flowrate m³/s (cfs)			
	2-year	10-year	25-year	100-year
Predevelopment conditions				
Total runoff from the site	0.2 (8.8)	0.7 (23.7)	1.0 (35.8)	1.8 (62.1)
Postdevelopment conditions				
Inflow to the basin from the site	0.8 (28.9)	1.7 (59.4)	2.3 (82.1)	3.6 (128.2)
Outflow from dry basin	0.2 (8.3)	0.6 (22.4)	0.9 (30.2)	1.7 (58.7)
Maximum elevation in basin	30.0 m (98.4 ft)	30.2 m (99.2 f)	30.4 m (99.7 ft)	30.6 m (100.3 ft)

7.6.3.7 Step 7: Size the Forebay

The local and state stormwater policy in this example requires that, at a minimum, the volume of the sediment forebay should be sized to hold 2.5 mm (0.1 in.) per unit of impervious area to pretreat WQV, which is equal to (2.5 mm) (3.6 ha), equaling 91.3 m³ (0.074 ac-ft). The designer should assume that approximately 50% of this volume will consist of a portion of the sediment storage volume of 86.3 m³ (0.07 ac-ft), and the rest will be provided as a portion of the WQV.

7.6.3.8 Step 8: Size the Micropool

The micropool at the outlet fills often and should be able to store 15 to 25% of WQV. Using 20%, the volume of the micropool is 91.3 m³ (0.07 ac-ft). The designer should assume that the remainder of the sediment storage volume 40.7 m³ (0.03 ac-ft) will settle in the micropool, but none of the WQV may be placed in the micropool.

8.0 WET BASINS

A wet basin is an artificial lake or pond designed to promote sedimentation of particulate matter and other pollutants associated with particulates (see Figure 6.11). Wet basins also provide peak attenuation for channel protection and flood control. Dissolved pollutants may also be controlled by increasing the hydraulic residence time (HRT) and incorporating a diverse aquatic ecosystem within the basin (e.g., by incorporating emergent wetland vegetation around the perimeter) or by chemical addition. This unit operation is also sometimes called a *wet detention pond*. This MOP, however, refers to it as a *wet basin* to distinguish it from the dry basin described in the previous section.

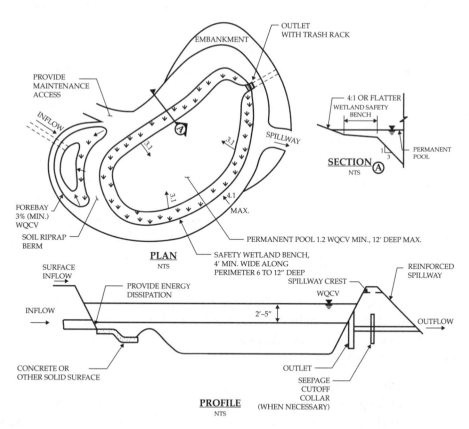

FIGURE 6.11 Schematic of a dry basin (1 in. = 25.4 mm) (UDFCD, 2010).

8.1 Typical Applications

8.1.1 Physical Site Suitability

Wet basins are commonly placed at locations able to maintain a permanent pool of water during part or all of the year, depending on climatic conditions. To maintain a permanent pool, the bottom of the basin needs to be underlain by relatively impervious soils and the drainage area should be large enough to provide sufficient inflow. In some instances, design guidelines call for installation of impermeable liners and supplemental sources of water, increasing both construction and operational costs and causing other environmental issues. Current experience suggests that these traditional siting and design criteria may be relaxed in some instances, yielding a facility design more suited to site conditions without sacrificing pollutant removal. Key site suitability considerations are outlined in the following sections.

8.1.1.1 Perennial and Seasonal Permanent Pools

Permanent pools are relatively easy to maintain year-round at sites in humid regions with large drainage areas or high groundwater conditions. Permanent pools are preferred in many developments for aesthetic reasons. Permanent pools are more difficult to maintain and may periodically dry up in arid climates and at sites with permeable soils. Such seasonal pools may promote infiltration and provide volume control in addition to pollutant removal. Anaerobic conditions in wet basins that dry up commonly return within hours to a few days, and any metals or phosphorus released during the refilling process are likely to rebind once fresh stormwater enters the basin. The designer should consider using an infiltration basin in areas with high evaporation or infiltration and where a seasonal permanent pool is difficult to maintain (see Chapter 9).

8.1.1.2 Drainage Area

It is common to specify a minimum drainage area to provide flow into the wet basin during dry weather to maintain its permanent pool. If a seasonal permanent pool is acceptable, these drainage area thresholds may be relaxed, allowing smaller wet basins with smaller drainage areas.

8.1.1.3 Receiving Water Quality Issues

Wet basins with longer retention times and aquatic vegetation are effective at removing dissolved pollutants. Wet basins can cause an increase in temperature by heating of the permanent pool because of solar radiation (Jones and Hunt, 2010) and should not be used upstream of receiving waters that are sensitive to increases in temperature (e.g., fish spawning or hatchery areas).

8.1.1.4 Groundwater

It is important to check with local regulatory authorities before excavating into the groundwater table. However, if the basin is not sited over a gravel or karst formation, it should not adversely affect groundwater quality, although such a possibility may exist in some instances. Most pollutants typically are removed from the infiltrating stormwater in the first 0.4 to 0.9 m (18 to 36 in.) of soil beneath the basin if loamy soil.

8.1.1.5 Baseflow Quality

Sources of baseflow into the wet basin include natural springs, groundwater seeps, and dry weather runoff from the developed drainage area (e.g., yard and landscape watering runoff). In some areas, baseflow into wet basins may contain concentrations of nutrients and other constituents higher than typical urban runoff (CASQA, 2003), leading to algae blooms and the need for nutrient control. While treatment achieved by the wet basin should significantly reduce these baseflow concentrations, basin effluent may be higher than expected. In addition, dry weather baseflows with low influent concentrations may desorb or dissolve pollutants captured in the basin.

8.1.1.6 Upstream Pollutant Sources

Increased risk of pollutant delivery exists where development will not be completed for an extended period of time or where the potential for a chemical spill is higher than normal. In such instances, adequate containment and pretreatment of flows should be provided. In developing watersheds, frequent maintenance of the forebay may be necessary.

8.1.1.7 Site Conditions

Existing wetlands at the site may restrict use of a permanent pool. Wet basins typically require a relatively large footprint, but can be designed to require little hydraulic head to operate. In flat terrain, wet basins can be excavated below ground surface, a practice common in Florida.

8.1.2 Water Quantity Control

Wet basins provide peak attenuation with overflow restricted to create a live pool that stores runoff. Volume control may also be provided in that infiltration may occur through the bottom of the basin and evapotranspiration occurs within the basin.

8.1.3 Water Quality Control

Wet basins remove pollutants through a variety of physical, chemical, and biological processes in the permanent pool. The primary water quality unit process is sedimentation. Biological processes include organic matter degradation, nitrification, denitrification, organic compound degradation, and pathogen die-off. Within wet basins, precipitation and sorption of key pollutants occurs in the bottom soils and in the water column. Important removal reactions are dissolved phosphorus with iron, aluminum, and manganese oxides and dissolved metals with sulfides and organic matter. Several of these removal mechanisms are affected by the dissolved oxygen concentration. The thin aerobic soil layer may become anaerobic if thermal or saline stratification occurs. Conversely, the lower soil area that is anaerobic may become aerobic if the basin dries seasonally or between events because of limited runoff, evaporation, and infiltration.

Photodegradation from light exposure breaks down organic compounds such as petroleum hydrocarbons, pesticides, and personal care products. Wet basins also host higher-order organisms such as amoebas and rotifers that will prey on pathogens.

8.2 Limitations

Wet basins have many more constraints than most controls. Physical constraints include the need for a large land area for the basin, a significant drainage area sufficient to provide baseflow for the basin or a high water table to maintain a year-round permanent pool, a susceptibility to failure in karst terrain, and difficult construction issues if bedrock is near the surface.

Environmental effects vary by site and may include effects on wetlands, floodplains, or instream flows if sited in or near a stream. Tree removal may be required at some sites. Wet basins may be viewed as open-water safety hazards or habitat for vectors such as mosquitoes. In some states, like Colorado, there must be legal availability to impound water.

Effects to adjacent land uses are considerable because of the size of a wet basin. The effects can be either positive, providing a community amenity, or negative, becoming an eyesore, depending on design, landscaping, and maintenance. Sediment, floating litter, and algae blooms can be difficult to remove or control. Wet basins attract wildlife and may increase loads of nutrients and pathogens leaving the basin. As mentioned earlier, wet basins increase water temperature.

Wet basins are not recommended as inline facilities built on natural stream channels. One potential constraint on the use of a wet basin or wetland as regional stormwater control is the USACE Section 404 permit program, restricting the filling of streams and wetland areas. Although wet basins typically are designed to enhance pollutant removal by incorporating wetland areas along the perimeter, regulatory agencies may restrict their use if a significant amount of native wetlands and/or streams will be submerged within the permanent pool. In addition, restorative maintenance of the created wetland areas, which includes removal of silt, may require a Section 404 permit.

Potential wetlands constraints must be addressed on a case-by-case basis during final design of each wet basin. If field inspections indicate that a significant wetland area will be affected at a particular site, the following options can be pursued during final design:

- Investigate moving the embankment and permanent pool upstream of the wetland area;

- If the aforementioned option is not feasible, a wetland mitigation plan can be developed as a part of the wet basin design; and

- If neither of the aforementioned options results in a design acceptable to regulatory agencies, the designer should consider using a dry basin or stormwater wetland instead. Eliminating the permanent pool can often reduce adverse effects on native wetlands, but their oversight by regulatory agencies may not be avoided.

8.3   Design Procedure and Criteria

8.3.1   Typical Configurations

Features of a wet basin are shown in Figure 6.11. The permanent pool provides a vessel for the settling of solids and the removal of nutrients and dissolved pollutants between storms. The wetland vegetation bench, called the *littoral zone,* provides aquatic habitat, enhances pollutant removal, and reduces the formation of floating algal mats. Wet basins often incorporate a forebay at each inlet to remove coarse sediments and facilitate maintenance. They may also incorporate a restricted outlet at the basin overflow, creating a live pool that can be designed for channel protection and flood control.

8.3.2   Pretreatment Unit

To reduce the frequency of significant cleanout activities within the pool area, a forebay with a hardened bottom should be constructed near the inlet to trap coarse sediment particles. Design criteria for sediment forebays are provided earlier in this chapter. Alternatively, a vault can be used in lieu of the forebay. These vaults require less space and are typically easier to clean.

Access for mechanized equipment should be provided to facilitate sediment removal. The forebay or vault can be separated from the remainder of the permanent pool by one of the following means: a lateral sill with wetland vegetation, two basins in a series, differential pool depth, a rock check dam, or a retaining wall placed laterally across the permanent pool. The inlet design should dissipate flow energy and diffuse the inflow plume where it enters the forebay or permanent pool. Examples of inlet designs include drop manholes, energy dissipaters at the bottom of a paved rundown, a lateral bench with wetland vegetation, rip-rap, and the placement of large rock deflectors.

8.3.3   Main Treatment Unit

8.3.3.1 Sizing for Water Quality Treatment

There are several methodologies to size wet basins according to unit processes for pollutant removal. The methodologies are divided in categories for sedimentation of suspended solids and treatment of dissolved pollutants (Minton, 2011).

The following methods are used for suspended solids:

- Specify a runoff volume to capture and treat;
- Specify HRT;
- Select the area of the basin as a fraction of either the total drainage area or the total impervious area;
- Specify a relative volume of the basin volume with respect to runoff volume; and
- Continuous simulation.

The following methods are available for dissolved pollutants:

- Select the area of the basin as a fraction of the total drainage area;
- Specify an HLR;
- Specify HRT; and
- Specify a pollutant loading rate per unit area.

These aforementioned sets of methodologies are also described by Minton (2011). This MOP presents the following methods for sizing the wet basin for water quality purposes, supplemented by recent design and performance experience:

- Solids-settling design method relies on the solids-settling theory and assumes that all pollutant removal is because of sedimentation (Driscoll, 1983; U.S. EPA, 1986). This method corresponds to the fourth bullet in the sedimentation-based design methodologies.

- Phosphorus removal design methods that rely on phosphorus removal kinetics (Hartigan, 1989; Minton, 2011; Walker, 1987). This method is based on the third bullet in the design methodologies based on dissolved-pollutant removal. Much of the body of knowledge for nutrient removal in stormwater has been adapted from the wastewater industry (Minton, 2011).

Removal of pollutants associated with particulates is achieved through a wet basin designed according to the solids-settling design method, where pollutant removal is controlled by the HRT of the basin and does not necessarily require the basin to incorporate any vegetation or other features to enhance pollutant removal. Removal of dissolved nutrients and other dissolved pollutants typically requires longer HRTs coupled with natural or artificial processes within the basin.

8.3.3.2 Solids-Settling Design Method

Settling of solids present in stormwater runoff occurs in wet basins both during storm events (dynamic conditions) and between storm events (quiescent conditions). The solids-settling method assumes that the wet basin is designed such that a plug flow of the influent storm volume displaces an equivalent volume of treated water within the basin, with "treatment" attributed to sediment settling during dynamic and quiescent conditions. Solids removal efficiency between storm events is largely dependent on the ratio of permanent pool volume, V_B, to the mean storm runoff volume, VR (Driscoll, 1983). Removal efficiency increases as the permanent pool volume and mean storm runoff volume increase.

Recent analysis based on data from ASCE and U.S. Environmental Protection Agency's International Stormwater Best Management Practices (BMP) Database (http://www.bmpdatabase.org) found that basins with a permanent pool volume smaller than the mean runoff volume lead to significantly higher effluent concentrations of TSS and other stormwater pollutants, but that the variability in effluent concentration diminishes as the permanent pool volume approaches 2 to 3 times the mean runoff volume. Furthermore, these data suggest that increasing the size of a wet basin or wetland beyond this does not result in significant improvement in the effluent concentration of TSS and other pollutants associated with settleable particulates. In other words, the plug flow of runoff from storms larger than the mean storm event displaces the entire volume of a permanent pool sized equal to the mean runoff volume, while this same plug flow displaces the entire volume of larger permanent pools less frequently, providing a more consistent effluent concentration. These findings suggest that the following factors should be considered during design to maximize pollutant removal:

- The effectiveness of settling and resuspension during quiescent periods between runoff events (e.g., wind, thermal stratification, mechanical mixing, baseflows, and constituents);

- The frequency at which the entire permanent pool is displaced, governed largely by the ratio of permanent pool volume to the mean storm runoff volume;

- The ability of the wet basin to maintain plug flow conditions (e.g., length-to-width ratios, flow-path lengths, and other measures that minimize short-circuiting); and

- The time it takes to displace the permanent pool volume during and immediately following a runoff event (e.g., longer displacement periods should allow more time for pollutants in the runoff volume entering the basin to settle).

The following wet basin design methods have emerged based on these findings:

- Permanent pool design—provide a permanent pool volume equal to the mean runoff volume, at a minimum, and potentially up to 2 to 3 times the size of the mean runoff volume depending on local climate, precipitation intensity, and basin design features; and

- Split permanent pool and "live" pool design—provide a permanent pool sized roughly equal to the mean runoff volume plus a detention volume ("live" volume) and regulate the discharge from the live storage to maximize pollutant removal.

The first method is grounded in solids-settling theory, but may result in a larger facility size. Large, intense runoff events may disrupt plug flow conditions on which this method is founded, thereby diminishing effectiveness for these events. Data from the International Stormwater BMP Database also indicate that effectiveness of wet basins is diminished in cold weather conditions, where the greater viscosity of water reduces particle-settling velocity by 50% and thermal stratification and deicing chemicals also negatively affect settling (Barrett, 2008).

The second method, recommended in design manuals from Denver's Urban Drainage and Flood Control District (2010) and the State of Georgia (Atlanta Regional Commission and Georgia Department of Natural Resources, 2001), results in roughly the same basin volume as the first method, but split between dead and live storage, often yielding a smaller basin footprint. This method recognizes that many WQV-generating events are accompanied by high rainfall intensity in many parts of North America, rapidly filling the basin and displacing its volume. The live pool also provides flow control benefits that contribute to effective channel erosion and flood control. However, definitive performance data are not available for basins with this design.

The maximized WQV calculated according to methodology provided in Chapter 3 is used to size both the permanent pool and a live detention pool. Equation 3.4 calculates the maximized WQV as the product of the runoff from the mean storm event and an event capture ratio for a 12-hour drain time (i.e., 1.109 from Table 3.6), yielding both a permanent pool and live detention volume approximately 10% larger than the volume of the mean annual precipitation event (or $V_B/V_R > 1.10$). The outlet is then designed to draw down, or empty, this live volume in 12 hours, contributing to channel erosion control. Additional live volume and outlet control structures may be added to fully meet channel erosion and flood control objectives.

Proper selection of a basin sizing methodology depends on water quality objectives established for the receiving water. The primary benefit of using larger basins is to promote sedimentation of fine silt and clay particles, which represent a small fraction of the total mass load of particles but are found in large numbers with significant surface area commonly associated with pollutants contributing to toxicity. Continuous simulation modeling may also provide insights into optimal pollutant removal and flow control levels for different types of urban catchments. Continued evaluation of wet basin performance is recommended to better define optimal design configurations.

8.3.3.3 Phosphorus Removal Design Method

There are several variants of the phosphorus removal design method, but they all assume that the phosphorus processes in a wet basin can be represented by empirical models used to evaluate lake eutrophication effects (Hartigan, 1989; Minton, 2011; Walker, 1987). Using this design method, a wet basin can be sized to achieve a given removal rate for phosphorus. The method is based on the average HRT, which is the volume of the basin divided by annual runoff. This method typically results in a basin design with a permanent pool volume to mean storm runoff volume ratio of 4 to 6, which results in designs larger than those for solids removal only. Recent studies based on data from the International Stormwater BMP Database indicate that such designs do produce somewhat lower phosphorous concentrations but do not significantly improve removal of TSS and other constituents compared to basins with a permanent pool volume to mean storm runoff volume ratio of 1 to 4. Accordingly, alternative methods may be able to achieve phosphorus control more cost-effectively.

The lake eutrophication design model is the phosphorus retention coefficient model developed by Walker (1985; 1987). Like most input and output lake eutrophication models, this model is an empirical approach that treats the permanent pool as a completely mixed system and assumes that it is not necessary to consider the temporal variability associated with individual storm events. Unlike the solids-settling model, which accounts for temporal variability of individual storms, the Walker model is based on annual flows and loadings.

The model is applied through the following two equations:

$$k = \frac{0.056\,\text{HLR}}{F(\text{HLR}+13)} \tag{6.6}$$

where

k = removal rate factor (m^3/mg/d);
HLR = hydraulic loading rate = Z/HRT the mean overflow rate (m/d);
Z = mean basin depth (m);
HRT = average hydraulic residence time (d);
F = fraction of dissolved phosphorus in the inflow = $C_{ortho\,P}/C_{TP}$;
$C_{ortho\,P}$ = inflow orthophosphorus concentration (µg/L); and
C_{TP} = inflow total phosphorus concentration (µg/L).

The phosphorus removal efficiency is

$$E = 1 + \frac{1 - \sqrt{1 + 4kC_{TP}\,\text{HRT}}}{2kC_{TP}\,\text{HRT}} \tag{6.7}$$

Equations 6.6 and 6.7 were developed from a database of 60 USACE reservoirs and were verified for 20 other reservoirs. Walker (1987) applied the model to 10 Nationwide Urban Runoff Program (NURP) sites and 14 other basins and small lakes. The goodness-of-fit test yielded $R^2 = 0.8$, indicating a good replication of monitored total phosphorus removals.

The permanent pool storage volume (V_B) is calculated for the desired average removal rate for P_T, which is a function of the average HRT. Field studies indicate that an optimum removal rate for T_P of approximately 50% occurs at HRT values of 2 to 3 weeks for pools with mean depths of 1.0 to 2.0 m (3 to 6 ft) (Hartigan, 1989). In the eastern United States, this optimum range for HRT values corresponds to permanent pool volume to mean storm runoff volume ratios of 4 to 6. Basins with values of HRT greater than 2 to 3 weeks have a greater risk of thermal stratification and anaerobic bottom waters, resulting in an increased risk of significant export of nutrients from bottom sediments.

8.3.3.4 Depth of Permanent Pool

Mean depth of the permanent pool is calculated by dividing the storage volume by the surface area. The mean depth should be shallow enough to promote aerobic conditions and reduce the risk of thermal stratification, but deep enough so that algal blooms are not excessive and reduce resuspension of settled pollutants during significant storm events. The minimum depth of the open water area should be greater than the depth of sunlight penetration to prevent emergent plant growth in this area, namely, on the order of 2 to 2.5 m (6 to 8 ft). However, safety precautions such as mild side slopes (discussed in Section 8.3.3.5), a fence around the basin, or a safety bench should be incorporated to the design to reduce the risk of drowning.

A mean depth of approximately 1 to 3 m (3 to 10 ft) should produce a basin with sufficient surface area to promote algae photosynthesis and should maintain an acceptable environment within the permanent pool for the average HRT recommended previously, although separate analyses should be performed for each locale. If the basin has more than 0.8 ha (2 ac) of water surface, mean depths of 2 m (6.5 ft) will protect it against wind-generated resuspension of sediments. The mean depths of the more effective wet basins monitored by the NURP study typically fall within this range. A water depth of approximately 1.8 m (6 ft) over the significant portion of the basin will also increase winter survival of fish (Schueler, 1987).

A maximum depth of 3 to 4 m (10 to 13 ft) should reduce the risk of thermal stratification (Mills et al., 1982). However, in the state of Florida, pools up to 10-m (30-ft) deep have been successful when excavated in high groundwater areas. This is probably because of improved circulation at the bottom of the basin as a result of groundwater moving through it.

8.3.3.5 Side Slopes along the Shoreline and Vegetation

Side slopes along the shoreline of the wet basin should be 4:1 or less to facilitate maintenance (such as mowing) and reduce risks to the public of slipping and falling in the water. In addition, a littoral zone should be established around the perimeter of the permanent pool to promote the growth of emergent vegetation along the shoreline and deter individuals from wading. The emergent vegetation around the perimeter serves several other functions, such as reducing erosion, enhancing removal of dissolved nutrients, potentially reducing the formation of floating algal mats, and providing habitat for aquatic and wetland wildlife. This bench for emergent wetland vegetation should be at least 3-m (10-ft) wide with a water depth of 15 to 30 cm (0.5 to 1 ft). The total area of the aquatic bench should be 25 to 50% of the permanent pool's water surface area. Local agricultural agencies, commercial nurseries, a landscape architect, or other specialists should be consulted about guidelines for using wetland vegetation within shallow sections of the permanent pool. Is it also possible to install floating wetlands in a wet basin.

8.3.3.6 Live Detention Zone above the Permanent Pool

A live detention zone may be added to the permanent pool to provide channel protection, overbank flood protection, and extreme flood protection. Design guidance was provided previously for the split permanent pool and live pool design. Storage in the live pool is released during a specified period through an outlet structure. The designer should use principles described in Section 7.0, Dry Basins, to design the live pool and outlet structure.

8.3.3.7 Minimum and Maximum Drainage Areas

The minimum drainage area should permit sufficient baseflow to prevent excessive residence times or severe draw-down of the permanent pool during dry seasons, unless the permanent pool is designed to dry up seasonally. Unless regional experience is available for determining the minimum drainage area required in a particular location, a water balance calculation should be performed using local runoff, evapotranspiration, exfiltration, and baseflow data to determine that the flow is adequate to keep the basin full during the dry season. In some locations, inflows may include excess lawn irrigation.

A maximum tributary catchment area may need to be set to reduce the exposure of upstream channels to erosive stormwater flows, reduce effects on perennial streams and wetlands, and reduce public safety hazards associated with dam height. Again, regional experience will be useful in providing guidelines. For example, in the southeastern United States, some stormwater master plans have restricted the maximum tributary catchments to 40 to 120 ha (100 to 300 ac) depending on the amount of imperviousness in the watershed, with highly impervious catchments restricted to the lower end of this range and vice versa. Conversely, experience in semiarid areas has shown that even a small area of new land development can cause downstream erosion and that drainage-way stabilization is needed between the new development and the basin for relatively small catchments.

8.3.3.8 Basin Geometry

Relatively large length-to-width ratios can help reduce short-circuiting, enhance sedimentation, and help prevent vertical stratification within the permanent pool. A minimum length to width of 2:1 (preferably 3:1) is recommended for the permanent pool. The permanent pool should expand gradually from the basin inlet and contract gradually toward the outlet, maximizing the travel time from the inlet to the outlet. Baffles or islands within the pool can increase the flow path length and reduce short-circuiting. These concepts should be incorporated in the geometry of basins while attempting to mimic a natural water feature that looks like it was shaped by water. For example, the banks of the basin should have an undulating outline rather than straight lines (UDFCD, 2010).

8.3.3.9 Soil Hydraulic Conductivity

Highly permeable soils may not be acceptable for wet basins because of excessive draw-down during dry periods. Where permeable soils are encountered and an infiltration basin is not a desired practice, exfiltration rates can be minimized by scarifying and compacting a 0.3-m (12-in.) layer of the bottom soil of the basin, incorporating clay to the soil, or providing an artificial liner. Excavating the pool into the groundwater table can also create a more permanent pool, although seasonal fluctuations in the groundwater table need to be taken into account.

8.3.4   Outlet Structure

An outlet for a wet basin typically consists of a riser with a hood or trash rack to prevent clogging and an adequate antivortex device for basins serving large drainage areas. Some typical outlet structures are illustrated in Figure 6.12. Anti-seep collars should be installed along outlet conduits passing through or under the dam embankment. If the basin is part of a larger basin designed for OFV or EFV control, the outlet should be designed for the desired flood control performance. An emergency spillway must be provided and designed using accepted engineering practices to protect the basin's embankment. Generally, the basin's principal and emergency spillways should be sized at a minimum to provide 0.3 m (1 ft) of freeboard during a 25-year, 24-hour event and to safely pass the 100-year, 24-hour storm peak rate of runoff. The designer should be certain that the basin embankment and spillway are designed in accordance with federal, state, and local dam safety criteria.

A trash rack or screen helps maintain the outlet unclogged. The rack should allow sufficient hydraulic capacity while the rack is partially clogged. Openings

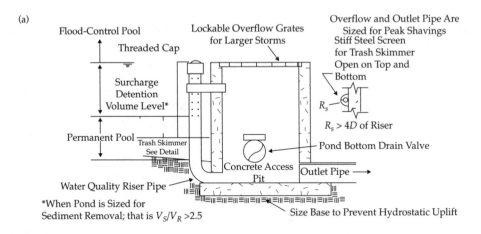

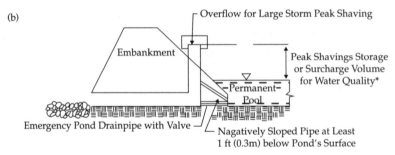

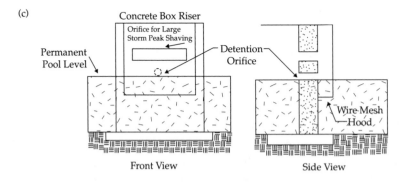

Figure 6.12   Typical outlet structures: (a) outlet works with surcharge detention for water quality, (b) negatively sloped pipe outlet with riser, and (c) multiple-orifice outlet (Schueler, 1987; UDFCD, 2010).

should be small enough to trap objects that may clog outlet openings. Overflow trash racks should be sized so their hydraulic capacity is greater than that of the spillway. Vehicle access to trash racks should be provided in case debris needs to be removed if it causes excessive flow blockage during a severe storm event.

The channel that receives discharge from the basin's outlet should be protected from erosive discharge velocities greater than 1.2 m/s (4 fps). Options include rip-rap lining of the channel or the provision of stilling basins, check dams, rock deflectors, or other devices to reduce outfall discharge velocities to non-erosive levels.

8.4   Aesthetic and Safety Considerations

Well-designed wet basins are often considered a community amenity, increasing property values and creating open space. They typically are more attractive than dry basins because sediment and debris accumulated within the sediment forebay and permanent pool are out of sight. Wet basins with healthy, diverse aquatic environments seldom become a mosquito or midge breeding area. However, some concern about safety may exist where there is public access to the basin. Urban Drainage and Flood Control District (2010) provides guiding principles to design aesthetically pleasing wet basins, whether they are architectural or naturalized. Architectural basins are intended to appear as part of the built environment; naturalized basins are designed to appear as part of the landscape. For a naturalized look, it is important to attempt to hide the presence of drainage structures and replicate forms that appear shaped by water. For example, the sides in the area of the surcharge volume should have varying slopes. Additional details on safety features of wet basins are presented in Chapter 5.

An emergency spillway must be provided and designed using accepted engineering practices to protect the basin's embankment. The designer should be certain that the basin embankment and spillway are designed in accordance with federal, state, and local dam safety criteria. As discussed previously, side slopes along the shoreline of the wet basin should be 4:1 or less to facilitate maintenance (such as mowing) and reduce risks to the public of slipping and falling in the water. In addition, a littoral zone should be established around the perimeter of the permanent pool to promote the growth of emergent vegetation along the shoreline and deter individuals from wading. A safety bench may be designed providing a shallow area that allows people or animals that inadvertently enter the open water to exit the basin. If public access is not desired, a fence around the basin should also be considered, although this measure is typically considered unsightly.

8.5   Access and Maintenance Features

Pretreatment with a forebay will reduce sediment in the main basin and thus reduce the need to manually remove it from a larger area. A maintenance ramp should be included in the design to facilitate access to the forebay for maintenance activities and for vector surveillance and control. In general, basins should have a sluice gate or drain with a manual valve that can be opened to draw down the basin for vegetation harvesting or the more infrequent dredging of the main cell of the basin. Because wet basins are often selected for their aesthetic considerations and pollutant removal, they are often sited in areas of high visibility. Consequently, floating litter and debris need to be removed more frequently than would be required simply to support proper functioning of the basin and outlet. Where permitted, wet basin wetlands should be regularly stocked with mosquito fish (*Gambusia* spp.) to enhance natural mosquito and midge control. If endangered species take residence in the wet basin, preserving their habitat during regular maintenance can become an issue.

A common maintenance concern with both wet and dry basins is clogging of the outlet. Principal outlets of wet and dry basins should be designed to be nonclogging, with a minimum pipe diameter of 300 mm (12 in.); if smaller openings are needed to control peak rates of outflow from the basin, a T-weir, V-notch weir, or other non-clogging devices should be used, as discussed earlier. In locations where clogging may be an issue, an emergency access area and valve should also be provided at the outlet to perform maintenance and allow water to pass.

9.0   WETLANDS

Wetlands include shallow pools that store stormwater between events and promote the growth of rooted vegetation such as reeds, rushes, willows, and cattails (see Figure 6.13). The resistance of the vegetation moderates the incoming flowrate and a temporary rise in the water level occurs. As the flowrate slows, pollutants are removed through sedimentation and other physical, chemical, and biological processes. The outlet may or may not be restricted to increase HRT and/or provide additional peak-flow attenuation to meet channel and flood control protection goals of the downstream waterbody. Typically, the bottom bathymetry is contoured with sinuous pathways to increase retention time and contact area and to encourage a diversity of rooted species. Invasive species are controlled or otherwise discouraged. Gravel wetlands, or subsurface-flow wetlands, are discussed in Chapter 8, Filters, because these types of wetlands are designed to act like filters.

9.1   Typical Applications

9.1.1   Physical Site Suitability

Wetland basins are appropriate where there is a need to achieve pollutant removal in small-to-medium-sized tributary areas with available open space, where base flow-rates are relatively consistent year round, and in locations where wildlife habitat benefits can be enhanced. Specific site conditions are important to the proper design of a wetland basin. Key site characteristics include soils, hydroperiod, and plant species and density. The siting and configuration of the created wetland depend on adjacent land uses, the magnitude of contributing surface runoff, and the type of collection system (e.g., shallow ditches or underground piping). Variations in topography and plant types will create more suitable habitat for wildlife. If the proposed site is large enough, some upland areas (peninsulas or islands) are preferable. Upland buffers increase the habitat value of a created wetland.

Constructed wetlands can be constructed online or offline and should be sited along drainage ways with consistent baseflow. An offline design is preferred.

9.1.2   Water Quantity Control

Wetland basins provide peak-flow attenuation and may reduce runoff volumes through evapotranspiration. The vegetation within the wetland slows the flow and controls hydraulics; however, a flow restrictor may be needed to achieve the desired level of peak-flow attenuation.

9.1.3   Water Quality Control

Wetland basins are designed for the removal of dissolved pollutants and can be viewed as a variant of wet basins, with many of the same unit processes. As stormwater runoff flows through the wetland, pollutant removal is achieved through settling and biological uptake within the wetland. Flow through the root systems allows vegetation to remove nutrients and dissolved pollutants from stormwater. Biological processes include organic matter degradation, nitrification, denitrification, organic compound degradation, pathogen die-off, and evapotranspiration. With wetlands, precipitation and sorption of key pollutants occurs in bottom soils and, perhaps, in the water column as well. Important removal reactions are dissolved phosphorus with iron, aluminum, manganese oxides, and dissolved metals with sulfides and organic matter. Several of these removal mechanisms are affected by the dissolved oxygen concentration. The thin aerobic soil layer may become anaerobic if thermal or saline stratification occurs. Conversely, the lower soil area that is anaerobic may become aerobic if the basin dries. A wetland may dry between events from evaporation and infiltration. Much of the knowledge about nutrient removal by wetlands has been derived from the wastewater industry. The behavior of stormwater wetlands with respect to phosphorus is more consistent with wastewater influents than with nitrogen (Minton, 2011). Studies are inconsistent regarding the effect on nitrogen removal (Kadlec, 2007; Thullen et al., 2002).

9.2 Limitations

Constructed wetlands offer aesthetic and wildlife habitat advantages over wet basins. Wetlands, however, require more space than basins for the same volume. Pollutants released from decaying vegetation in constructed wetlands may be of concern with respect to phosphorus and nitrogen, in which total loading to the receiving water can be more important than concentration.

Design and construction of wetland basins are constrained in a fashion similar to wet basins. Physical constraints and environmental effects are identical, except that wetlands may be less prone to vectors and have the ability to provide habitat for predators that reduce the mosquito population. Because constructed wetland are typically shallow and more difficult to enter, safety issues are reduced compared to those of a wet basin. Wetland aesthetics may or may not be a constraint, depending on design, maintenance, and the opinions of adjacent residents.

Because of regulatory protection of wetlands in the United States regardless of their origin, federal or state regulatory agencies can assume control of these artificially "constructed" wetlands and require owners to obtain permits before they can perform needed maintenance. Failure to obtain such permits can become a problem for the owner, individual, or organization performing mechanical cleaning, excavation, or dredging operations within these controlled treatment facilities.

The following are potential constraints in the siting and design of wetland basins:

- Aesthetic concerns about a facility that looks swampy;
- Concern about safety when constructed where there is public access;
- Potential for mosquito and midge breeding because of dense vegetation;
- Inability to place wetlands on steep, unstable slopes;
- Need for baseflow or supplemental water if the water level is to be maintained;
- Relatively large footprint;
- Greater head loss than wet basins;

- Potential increased temperatures in the effluent; and

- Potential export of pollutants.

9.3 Design Procedure and Criteria

9.3.1 Typical Configurations

Figure 6.13 shows a typical configuration of a wetland basin. Wetland basins are often organic in shape and include various features such as pools, embayments, islands, and peninsulas to provide diverse habitat and improve the functionality of the wetland.

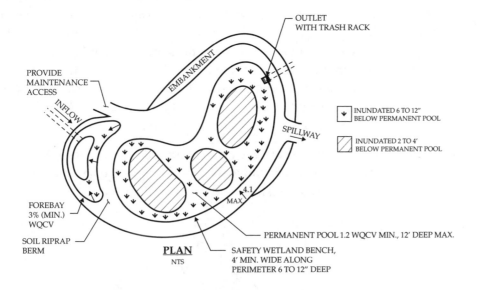

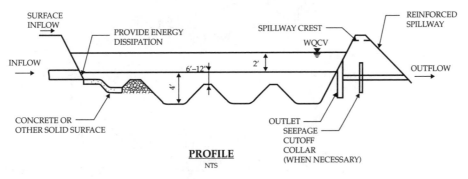

FIGURE 6.13   Schematic of a wetland basin (1 ft × 0.3048 = m; 1 in. × 25.4 = mm).

This unit operation has two primary variants. They are referred to as *variants* rather than *separate unit operations* because field data have not established significant differences in performance. Variants illustrated in Figure 6.14 include

- The surface flow wetland is similar to a shallow marsh with essentially complete coverage by rooted vegetation. Water depths typically vary from 0 to 0.6 m (2 ft). There may be a deep open water forebay and/or an afterbay.

- The hummock wetland is an alternating sequence of deep and shallow pools and has a relatively large area devoid of rooted vegetation because of water depths typically in excess of 1 m. The open water area is typically in the center of the facility. The dividing line between a wet basin and this type of wetland basin is obscure, although 50% coverage is a reasonable demarcation point. A benefit of this configuration compared to the surface wetland is that it covers a smaller area for the same operating volume. To avoid stormwater short-circuiting through the open water, berms are purposefully placed laterally across the basin. Field studies have shown that this configuration improves nitrification and reduces mosquito populations (Thullen et al., 2002).

Gravel wetlands, another type of vegetated control that routes flow through a subsurface gravel layer used in lieu of native soil, are considered to be a filter in this MOP; design guidance for gravel wetlands is provided in Chapter 8.

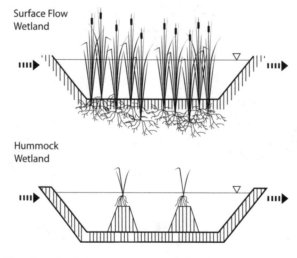

FIGURE 6.14 Wetland variants.

Depth to the confining layer or groundwater is important to design such that the wetland does not dry up during extended periods of no rainfall, unless wetland species are selected that can withstand extended dry periods. In addition, a constant source of surface water is recommended; stagnant water in wetlands causes the underlying soil to become anaerobic, releasing ammonia, phosphorus, and heavy metals to the overlying water for wash-out during the next runoff event. Stagnant water also results in mosquito problems. The depth and duration of maximum submergence are important because an excess of either will kill vegetation. The outlet structure is designed so that the wetland can be periodically drawn down completely to dry the sediments, which also allows for additional aerobic degradation of built-up organics. Wetland design and operation should minimize disruption to flora and fauna during drying and sediment removal or the wetland may need to be revegetated.

9.3.2   Pretreatment Unit

The forebay shown in Figure 6.13 helps settle out the largest sediment particles before flow passes over the areas covered with emergent vegetation. It also helps spread inflow uniformly over the entire wetland. The forebay should also have a baffle near the inlet, as illustrated in Figure 6.13, to break up the inflow jet and facilitate spreading of inflow over the entire surface area of the wetland. Design criteria for forebays and other pretreatment units are presented earlier in this chapter.

Wetlands are typically primary treatment controls; however, in some situations, they may be installed downstream of a larger control. In this instance, biological unit processes of the wetland would typically be the most important aspect of its design.

9.3.3   Main Treatment Unit

9.3.3.1 Sizing the Permanent Pool

Sizing methodologies for wetlands are the same as for wet basins for suspended solid removal or dissolved phosphorus removal. An additional sizing method seeks to minimize the risk of drying during drought and specifies that the permanent pool should be at least 2 times the volume of evapotranspiration during the length of specified drought for the region at summer evaporation rates. In instances where subsurface infiltration to and exfiltration out of the wetland are negligible, the summer evapotranspiration rates may be estimated as 0.75 times the local pan evaporation rate.

Typical practice is to compare the volumes resulting from the aforementioned methods and select the largest.

Wetland basins with a permanent pool volume to mean storm runoff volume ratio close to 1 may be adequate in areas where rain events are longer and less intense or in wetlands where the density of vegetation and a restricted outlet retard flow through the wetland. This flow resistance will cause the water surface elevation in the wetland to rise during the rainfall event and fall slowly following the event (over 12 to 24 hours), minimizing turbulence and allowing time for pollutants in the runoff to settle. A permanent pool volume to mean storm volume ratio greater than 3 may be needed if the basin configuration or large open water features allow runoff to flow quickly through the wetland.

Any rise in the water surface elevation during a water quality event (determined according to the methodology presented in Chapter 3) should not exceed 0.6 m (2 ft); this threshold will reduce stress on herbaceous wetland plants. The 0.6-m depth limitation will determine the surface area required for the wetland.

Dry weather flow depths should vary between 0.1 and 1.2 m (0.5 to 4 ft) through the wetland depending on the types of vegetation planted. The outlet structure should be designed so that the wetland can be periodically drawn down completely to dry the sediments and allow additional aerobic degradation of built-up organics.

The total surface area of the basin should be such that the forebay, outlet, and open water surface areas are 30 to 50% of the total surface area, with a depth of 0.6 to 1.2 m (2 to 4 ft). Wetland zones with emergent vegetation should occupy 50 to 70% of the total areas, with depths of 0.15 to 30 cm (6 to 12 in.); one-third to one-half of this zone should be 15-cm (6-in.) deep.

The inlet and outlet should be separated as much as possible. The primary goals are to increase the contact time of the inflow with wetland surfaces and design so that the inflow does not short-circuit the facility.

9.3.3.2 Sizing the Live Pool

A live pool volume may also be included in wetland design to achieve peak attenuation goals for channel protection and flood control. This live pool should be in addition to any rise in water surface elevation in the wetland during a water quality event, defined according to one of the methods described in Chapter 3. The designer should use principles described in Section 7.0, Dry Basins in this chapter to design the live pool.

9.3.3.3 Vegetation

Suitable plants for wetlands vary between different ecoregions. However, wetland plants chosen for wetland basins should incorporate the following attributes:

- Tolerance to wide ranges of water elevations, salinity, temperature, and pH;

- A mixture of perennials and annuals;

- Moderate amounts of leaf production; and

- Proven removal efficiencies (e.g., of *Scriptus* species).

In some areas, wetland plants are available from local nurseries that can provide additional information on tolerances and growth rates. Plants such as cattail, phragmites, and other noxious plants are undesirable and should be removed.

Retention of water in the basin or the presence of a baseflow is more important to wetland basins than the wet basin because of the need to maintain the health of the plants. It is common to specify a liner if the bottom soils are well-drained in addition to a minimum drainage area that produces flow into the wetland during most of the year. These specifications may not be sufficient in semiarid regions. However, wetland plants can experience desiccated soils for short periods of time.

Rooted vegetation may increase or decrease hydraulic efficiency depending on location and coverage. Placed near the inlet, along a dike located at the inboard edge of the forebay, vegetation spreads the stormwater into the central area of the basin. The benefit of the hummock wetland in improving hydraulic efficiency through the entire basin has been noted. However, vegetation along the longitudinal edges of the basin decreases hydraulic efficiency if the coverage is about 25% of the basin width (Persson, 2005).

Severe water level fluctuations and unnatural concentrations of metals likely reduce the species diversity of constructed wetlands, with dominance by a few tolerant species. These conditions are conducive to invasive species. Research is needed regarding the transition of species as constructed wetlands age.

9.3.3.4 Side Slopes

Side slopes should be stable and sufficiently mild to minimize erosion and facilitate maintenance. A safety wetland bench should exist along the perimeter of the basin that is approximately 1.2-m (4-ft) wide and is situated where the water depth is no more than 15 to 30 cm (6 to 12 in.). Side slopes above the safety bench should be no steeper than 4:1, preferably less.

9.3.3.5 Construction

Construction management of a wetland basin is critical. The elevations and contouring of wetlands are the most important aspects, especially with respect to groundwater. The confining layers of clay will vary from place to place within a specific area. If the clay layer is breached, clay should be replaced and the elevations of that location should be changed in the design.

Proper staging and sequencing will provide areas for dewatering during construction to reduce effects on adjacent waters. Rim ditches are particularly beneficial to avoid excessive pumping. When the wetland basin is adjacent to an existing wetland, a temporary berm is needed until final grade has been achieved.

Use of organic soils is necessary to provide moisture-retaining abilities during drier periods and nutrients. If possible, soils (muck) from displaced wetlands should be stockpiled and used in the created wetland. Care should be taken to use wetland soils with no nuisance or invasive species. The displaced muck will provide root propagules, seed sources, microfauna and mieofauna, and other invertebrates. Topsoil or peat can be substituted in place of wetland muck. The muck and organic layer should be 0.1- to 0.3-m (6- to 12-in.) deep. Greater depths tend to create difficulties in spreading the muck and planting.

If possible, hydration of the newly constructed wetland should be controlled. The installation of plant material is most efficiently accomplished in saturated conditions; however, standing water can cause poorly installed plants to float. Flash-board risers and adjustable gates can aid in controlling water levels during construction. However, if water control is not possible, wetland plants should be acclimated to inundation in the nursery before being shipped to the site.

Keeping the soils saturated for 1 week after the muck and mulch have been spread will encourage seeds and propagules to sprout. If the wetland creation area is flooded with 0.2 m (6 in.) of water, by the second week this flooding will selectively remove upland species. The remaining water can be allowed to fill to design level after 3 weeks (Tesket and Hinckley, 1977).

9.3.4   Outlet Structure

The outlet structure should be designed to control the water surface and protect it from plugging by floatables common to wetlands. An overflow outlet, similar to a riser used in a wet basin, can be placed within a deepened portion near the outlet end of the basin. This deepened basin helps keep the outflow zone free of emergent vegetation and makes the outlet less likely to clog. Wetlands serving small tributary watersheds require small outlets to control the drain time of WQV to be 12 to 24 hours. However, designing small outlets that do not clog is difficult. In this instance, a set of V-notch weirs, a T-shaped weir, or a sawtooth weir may be more appropriate for the outflow control device. A trash rack or screen at the outlet helps maintain that the outlet is unclogged. The rack should allow sufficient hydraulic capacity while the rack is partially clogged. Openings should be small enough to trap objects that may clog outlet openings. Overflow trash racks should be sized so their hydraulic capacity is greater than that of the spillway.

9.4   Aesthetic and Safety Considerations

If properly designed and maintained, a constructed wetland may be of great aesthetic value to the area in which it is installed. However, some may perceive it as "swampy," especially if left unattended and allowed to overgrow. Wetland basins can produce large amounts of algae. Guidelines for creating naturalized wet basins are applicable to wetland basins. Accumulated trash and debris in the basin should be removed at during the middle and end of the wet season. The frequency of this activity may be altered to meet specific site conditions and aesthetic considerations. The safety bench provides a shallow area that allows people or animals that inadvertently enter the open water to exit the basin. Chapter 5 presents additional safety considerations.

9.5   Access and Maintenance Features

A stable driving surface for maintenance vehicles should be provided for access to the forebay and outlet areas. Visual monitoring of the wetlands is needed to check for proper coverage of the planted zones by desirable species. Monitoring should be done quarterly for the first year, semiannually for the second and third years, and, when necessary, annually for the fourth and fifth years. Monitoring the wetland for the following information should help prevent future problems:

- Percent survivorship of planted species (subsamples can be used to provide quantitative results in larger wetlands);
- Percent cover of planted species and recruited desirable plants;
- Percent cover of nuisance species;
- Wildlife use; and
- Qualitative assessments of water quality.

Maintenance includes the following three primary areas: replanting, nuisance and invasive species removal, and excavation of sediment sumps. Replanting as necessary to achieve an 85% survival rate at the end of each year is beneficial. Adjustments in plant type may be needed to accommodate differences in elevations. Typically, this is easier than regrading an established area. If water levels are lower than desired, adjustment of the control structure can increase survival.

It is critical to assess the created wetland for nuisance and invasive species; if coverage is greater than 10%, removal may be necessary to increase the function and value of the wetland basin. Harvesting wetland plants can be considered for nutrient removal, but can resuspend trapped sediments. This resuspension, with habitat disturbance, is likely less beneficial than actual nutrient removal.

10.0   REFERENCES

American Petroleum Institute (1990) *Design and Operation of Oil-Water Separators;* Publication 421; American Petroleum Institute: Washington, D.C.

American Society of Civil Engineers (1985) *Final Report of the Task Committee on Stormwater Detention Outlet Control Structures;* American Society of Civil Engineers: New York.

American Society of Civil Engineers; Water Environment Federation (1992) *Design and Construction of Urban Stormwater Management Systems;* ASCE Manuals and Reports of Engineering Practice No. 77; WEF Manual of Practice No. FD-20; American Society of Civil Engineers: New York.

American Society of Civil Engineers (1996) *Hydrology Handbook;* ASCE, 978-0-7844-0138-5 or 0-7844-0138-1; American Society of Civil Engineers: New York.

Atlanta Regional Commission; Georgia Department of Natural Resources (2001) *Georgia Stormwater Management Manual.* http://www.georgiastormwater.com (accessed Sept 2011).

California Stormwater Quality Association (2003) *New Development and Redevelopment Handbook;* California Best Management Practice Handbooks, TC-20 Wet Ponds; California Stormwater Quality Association: Menlo Park, California.

Camp Dresser & McKee Inc. (2007) *Harvard University Allston Campus Development Utilities Design;* Camp Dresser & McKee Inc.: Cambridge, Massachusetts.

DeGroot, W. G. (1982) *Stormwater Detention Facilities;* American Society of Civil Engineers: New York.

Driscoll, E. D. (1983) Performance of Detention Basins for Control of Urban Runoff Quality. *Proceedings of the International Symposium on Urban Hydrology, Hydraulics and Sediment Control;* Lexington, Kentucky; University of Kentucky: Lexington, Kentucky.

Guo, J. C.; Urbonas, B. (1996) Maximized Detention Volume Determined by Runoff Capture Ratio. *J. Water Resour. Plann. Manage.*, **122** (1), 33.

Hartigan, J. P. (1989) Basis for Design of Wet Detention Basin BMPs. In *Design of Urban Runoff Quality Controls*; Roesner, L. A.; Urbonas, B.; Sonnen, M. B., Eds.; American Society of Civil Engineers: New York.

International Stormwater BMP Database Home Page. http://www.bmpdatabase.org/ (accessed Sept 2011).

Jones, M. P.; Hunt, W. F. (2010) Effect of Storm-Water Wetlands and Wet Ponds on Runoff Temperature in Trout Sensitive Waters. *J. Irrigation Drainage Eng.*, **136,** 656.

Kadlec, R. H. (2007) The Effects of Deep Zones on Wetland Nitrogen Processing. *Water Sci. Technol.*, **56** (3), 101.

Lettenmaier, D.; Richey, J. (1985) *Operational Assessment of a Coalescing Plate Oil/Water Separator*; Municipality of Metropolitan Seattle: Seattle, Washington.

Massachusetts Department of Environmental Protection (2008) *Massachusetts Stormwater Handbook.* http://www.mass.gov/dep/water/laws/policies.htm (accessed Sept 2011).

Mills, W. B.; Dean, J. D.; Porcella, D. B. (1982) *Water Quality Assessment: A Screening Procedure for Toxic and Conventional Pollutants*; EPA-600/6-82-004; U.S. Environmental Protection Agency, Environmental Research Laboratory: Athens, Georgia.

Minton, G. (2011) *Stormwater Treatment: Biological, Chemical, and Engineering Principles*, 3rd ed.; RPA Press: Seattle, Washington.

New Jersey Department of Environmental Protection (2011) *Stormwater Manufactured Treatment Devices.* http://www.nj.gov/dep/stormwater/treatment.html (accessed Sept 2011).

Persson, J. (2005) The Use of Design Elements in Wetlands. *Nordic Hydrol.*, **36,** 113.

Roesner, L. A.; Urbonas, B.; Sonnen, M., Eds. (1989) Design of Urban Runoff Quality Controls; *Proceedings of an Engineering Foundation Conference on Current Practice and Design Criteria for Urban Quality Control*; American Society of Civil Engineers: New York.

Schueler, T. R. (1987) *Controlling Urban Runoff: A Practical Manual for Planning and Designing Urban BMPs*; Metropolitan Washington Council of Governments: Washington, D.C.

Schueler, T. R.; Kumble, P. R.; Heraty, M. A. (1992) *A Current Assessment of Urban Best Management Practices: Techniques for Reducing Non-Point Source Pollution in the Coastal Zone;* Metropolitan Washington Council of Governments: Washington, D.C.

Strecker, E. W.; Quigley, M. M.; Urbonas, B.; Jones, J. (2004) Analyses of the Expanded EPA/ASCE International BMP Database and Potential Implications for BMP Design. *Proceedings of the World Water and Environmental Resources Congress—Critical Transitions in Water and Environmental Resources Management;* Salt Lake City, Utah; June 27–July 1.

Sullivan, R.; Ure, J.; Parkinson, F.; Zielinski, P. (1982) *Design Manual: Swirl and Helical Bend Pollution Control Devices;* EPA-600/8-82/013; U.S. Environmental Protection Agency: Washington, D.C.

Tesket, R. O.; Hinckley, T. M. (1977) Impact of Water Level Changes on Woody Riparian and Wetland Communities; PB-276 036; U.S. Fish and Wildlife Service: Washington, D.C.

Thullen, J. S.; Sartoris, J. J.; Walton, W. E. (2002) Effects of Vegetation Management in Constructed Wetland Treatment Cells on Water Quality and Mosquito Production. *Ecol. Eng.,* **18,** 441.

University of New Hampshire Stormwater Center (2007) *University of New Hampshire Stormwater Center 2007 Annual Report;* University of New Hampshire Stormwater Center: Durham, New Hampshire.

Urban Drainage and Flood Control District (2010) *Urban Storm Drainage Criteria Manual: Volume 3—Best Management Practices;* Urban Drainage and Flood Control District: Denver, Colorado.

Urbonas, B. R.; Roesner, L. A., Eds. (1986) Urban Runoff Quality—Impact and Quality Enhancement Technology. *Proceedings of an Engineering Foundation Conference on Current Practice and Design Criteria for Urban Quality Control;* American Society of Civil Engineers: New York.

Urbonas, B. R.; Stahre, P. (1993) *Stormwater: Best Management Practices and Detention for Water Quality, Drainage, and CSO Management;* Prentice Hall: Englewood Cliffs, New Jersey

U.S. Department of Agriculture (1986) *Urban Hydrology for Small Watersheds;* Technical Release 55; U.S. Department of Agriculture, Natural Resources Conservation Service, Conservation Engineering Division: Washington, D.C.

U.S. Environmental Protection Agency (1986) *Methodology for Analysis of Detention Basins for Control of Urban Runoff Quality*; EPA-440/5-87-001; U.S. Environmental Protection Agency: Washington, D.C.

Walker, W. W. (1985) *Empirical Methods for Predicting Eutrophication in Impoundments— Report 3: Model Refinements*; Technical Report E-81-9; U.S. Army Engineer Waterways Experiment Station: Vicksburg, Mississippi.

Walker, W. W. (1987) *Phosphorus Removal by Urban Runoff Detention Basins. Lake and Reservoir Management: Volume III*; North American Lake Management Society: Washington, D.C.

Washington State Department of Ecology (2005) *Stormwater Management Manual for Eastern Washington*; Washington State Department of Ecology, Water Quality Program: Olympia, Washington.

Washington State Department of Ecology (2011) *Evaluation of Emerging Stormwater Treatment Technologies*. http://www.ecy.wa.gov/programs/wq/stormwater/ newtech/ (accessed Sept 2011).

Wilks, D. S.; Cember, R. P. (1993) *Atlas of Precipitation Extremes for the Northeastern United States and Southeastern Canada*; Publication No. RR 93-5; Northeast Regional Climate Center, Cornell University: Ithaca, New York.

11.0 SUGGESTED READINGS

California Department of Transportation (2002) *Proposed Final Report: BMP Retrofit Pilot Program*; CTSW-RT-01–050; California Department of Transportation: Sacramento, California.

Florida Department of Environmental Protection (1988) *The Florida Development Manual: A Guide to Sound Land and Water Management*; Florida Department of Environmental Protection, Nonpoint Source Management Section: Tallahassee, Florida.

Kadlec, R. H.; Knight, R. L. (1996) *Treatment Wetlands*; Lewis Publishers: Boca Raton, Florida; pp 184–185.

Livingston, E. H. (1989) The Use of Wetlands for Urban Stormwater Management. In *Design of Urban Runoff Quality Controls*; American Society of Civil Engineers: New York.

National Oceanographic and Atmospheric Administration (1982) *Mean Monthly, Seasonal, and Annual Pan Evaporation for the United States;* NOAA Technical Report NWS 34; National Oceanographic and Atmospheric Administration: Washington, D.C.

Persson, J.; Somes, N. L.; Wong, T. H. (1999) Hydraulic Efficiency of Constructed Wetlands and Ponds. *Water Sci. Technol.,* **40,** 3, 291.

Randall, C. W.; Ellis, K.; Grizzard, T. L.; Knocke, W. R. (1982) Urban Runoff Pollutant Removal by Sedimentation; *Proceedings of the Conference on Stormwater Detention Facilities: Planning, Design, Operation and Maintenance;* Henniker, New Hampshire; Aug 1–6; American Society of Civil Engineers: New York.

Strecker, E. W.; Kersnar, J. M.; Driscoll, E. D.; Horner, R. R. (1992) *The Use of Wetlands for Controlling Stormwater Pollution;* Terrene Institute: Washington, D.C.

U.S. Environmental Protection Agency (1983) *Results of the Nationwide Urban Runoff Program, Volume I—Final Report;* U.S. Environmental Protection Agency, Water Planning Division: Washington, D.C.

U.S. Environmental Protection Agency, National Pollutant Discharge Elimination System Home Page. http://cfpub.epa.gov/npdes/home.cfm?program_id=6 (accessed Sept 2011).

Whipple, W.; Hunter, J. V. (1981) Settleability of Urban Runoff Pollution. *J.—Water Pollut.* Control Fed., 53, 1726.

Chapter 7

Swales and Strips

(continued)

1.0 DESCRIPTION

Swales are shallow channels with mild longitudinal slopes (preferably 1 to 2.5%) and flow depths below the height of the vegetation that grows within them or rocks that line them. Strips are vegetated surfaces over which water flows in a thin sheet. Strips convey overland flow whereas shallow, concentrated flow takes place in swales. Both swales and strips are designed to slow down and strain suspended pollutants from stormwater by achieving shallow flow depths and thus they are wider than channels designed solely to convey runoff. Planted vegetation can be turf grasses, wetland plants, or a mixture of shrubs, grasses, and other landscaped plants, using species most appropriate for the climatic region. The best effect is achieved with dense vegetation.

Swales and strips are one of the five categories of stormwater controls addressed by this manual of practice (MOP). Guidelines for determining the water quality volume (WQV), water quality treatment (WQT) rate, channel protection volume (CPV), overbank flood volume (OFV), and extreme flood volume (EFV) may be derived using guidelines found in Chapter 3 or those defined in pertinent state or local design manuals. Selection criteria for determining if swales or strips are appropriate for a particular application are found in Chapter 5.

2.0 BASIC DESIGN PRINCIPLES

2.1 Typical Applications

In this MOP, swales and strips designed to store runoff, commonly called dry or wet swales, are considered to be basins (see Chapter 6), those designed with amended soils and underdrains are considered to be filters (see Chapter 8), and those designed to infiltrate most runoff into native soils are considered to be infiltrators (see Chapter 9). This chapter addresses solely those swales and strips designed to slow down velocities to cause sedimentation of pollutants. The main pollutant removal mechanism is the sedimentation that occurs as the vegetation or rock lining slows down flow velocities, allowing suspended particles to settle. Some stormwater may infiltrate through the bottom of the swale or strip, depending primarily on the antecedent moisture condition of the soil, but it is typically not a significant amount unless the control has been specifically designed to provide this additional unit process. To maintain the conveyance functionality distinction, this chapter applies the following characteristics to swales:

- Large length-to-width ratio;
- Sized to effectively treat to the WQT rate;
- There is no significant storage and the majority of the stormwater that enters the upper end is discharged at the lower end; and
- The surface is vegetated or rock-lined.

As noted, vegetation or rock slows down stormwater, providing the opportunity for particles to settle. Turf grass works most effectively while erect, offering the greatest resistance to flow. Once flattened, turf grass offers little resistance and performance is significantly reduced. Below the top of the grass, stormwater spreads laterally across the swale width and its longitudinal velocity decreases accordingly. The effect is to provide a relatively low hydraulic loading rate (HLR).

In some communities, swales and strips are used as the sole treatment device, whereas other communities only allow them if they are one of two or more unit operations (Chapter 4). Swales or strips can also be intentionally placed and maintained in dry basins to provide or improve treatment using the design procedures presented in this section.

2.2 Limitations

Limitations to the use of swales and strips are related to factors that affect the flow-retarding effect. For example, vegetation type and density may not be able to be sustained because of the lack of water in semiarid environments and, therefore, rock-lined systems may be more effective. In cold climates, dormant vegetation may provide poor resistance to flow during the spring melt, and the type and density of vegetation may be affected by salt and sand use unless salt-tolerant plants are used.

It is difficult to sustain vegetation in gravelly and coarse sandy soils. Heavy clay soils, materials toxic to vegetation, stones, and debris should also be avoided. When suitable, on-site materials should be used and compacted soils should be scarified and tilled before planting. The incorporation of amendments such as mature compost can alleviate these natural disadvantages.

2.3 Design Criteria

Effective swales and strips use mild longitudinal slopes (e.g., 1. to 2.5%) and shallow flow depths to maximize water contact with the vegetated or rock lining and the soil surface (see Figure 7.1). Most runoff passes through a swale or strip because there is no significant infiltration or evapotranspiration during the flow event.

Swales and strips should be rock-lined or uniformly vegetated with fine, turf-forming, water-tolerant grasses. Salt-tolerant species should be used for swales and strips where salt is used as a deicing agent. In semiarid areas, drought-tolerant grasses should be used and supplemental irrigation may be needed to maintain healthy vegetation. Alternatively, a rock lining may be used. In wet climates, poorly draining soils that retain water over extended periods of time should be avoided because they may result in the death of turf grass not suited to such conditions. Alternatively, where swales and strips intercept groundwater or where there is little slope for proper drainage, emergent herbaceous wetland vegetation is an acceptable planting alternative. Some shrubs and trees are acceptable as long as they do not significantly alter the shallow flow regime needed for successful pollutant removal. It is important to select grass and wetland species that work best for the region, climate, and native soils. These can be obtained from the U.S. Department of Agriculture Extension Service at a local land-grant university, referred to in this chapter as the "agricultural extension." Native shrubs and forbs may be preferred over turf grass species given

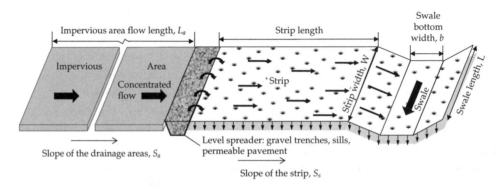

FIGURE 7.1 Typical swale and strip (not to scale).

the tendency to water and fertilize the latter; however, the cover must be capable of slowing doing the flow of stormwater. In addition, if wildlife habitat is being provided, vegetation should be selected accordingly.

The designer should use grass seed and mulch application rates specified by the supplier. If possible, animal manure should not be used as an amendment and fertilizers should be avoided. Instead, compost should be incorporated to the native soil as excavation commonly removes native organic matter. Compost replaces this organic matter, improving water retention capabilities of the soil and biota that will naturally incorporate nitrogen to the soil (Lenhart, 2007). These attributes reduce the need for fertilizers and irrigation. If fertilizer must be used, only the amount needed by the selected plants in existing soil conditions should be applied; in addition, a slow-release fertilizer should be used. The designer should establish grasses when natural moisture is adequate, but irrigate if necessary. If wetland plants are used, they may need to be protected from predation with netting during establishment. If possible, runoff, other than necessary irrigation, should be diverted during the period of vegetation establishment. Pesticides are not typically needed when using native species and should be avoided.

Side slopes should be vegetated or rock-lined to prevent erosion. There are a number of turf-reinforcement products that are resistant to erosive and tractive forces. They can be placed on the slopes and bottom. In addition, they provide mechanical support to maintenance equipment. The designer should use barrier shrubs to reduce intrusion by the public and domestic animals without preventing access for maintenance. The designer should avoid trees that shade grasses and deposit heavy leaf loads into swales and strips. If trees cannot be avoided, space them at least 7 m (20 ft) apart. Landscape beds near swales and strips should be at a slightly lower elevation than the adjacent ground surface.

A high-flow bypass is not needed if the swale is preceded by or incorporates a runoff quantity control device designed to release flow at rates that will not cause erosion or scour within the swale. When a bypass is used, inflow should be regulated and a pipe or a stabilized channel should be used to convey the excess flow without erosion.

3.0 SWALES

Swales are shallow channels on mild longitudinal slopes with flow depths below the height of the vegetation or rock lining up to the peak of the treatment design event.

Planted vegetation can be turf or native grasses, shrubs, trees, wetland plants, or a mixture of these. Numerous studies have documented the stormwater management effects of swales (Bäckström, 2002, 2003; Barrett et al., 1998, 2004; Deletic, 1999, 2005; Deletic and Fletcher, 2006; Fassman et al., 2010; Yu et al., 2001).

3.1 Typical Applications

3.1.1 *Physical Site Suitability*

Swales are commonly placed along roadways or property lines or within medians in parking lots, most effectively in a manner that integrates the swale with a site's infrastructure and landscape. For example, roadside ditches and medians can be designed as stormwater swales and as landscaped amenities. Swales may also be retrofitted to existing roadside ditches in currently developed areas.

3.1.2 *Water Quantity Control*

Attenuation of peak flows is minimal for the WQT rate; however, for large events, a long swale may provide some attenuation because of channel routing. Water that enters the root zone is removed from runoff and later released into the atmosphere as infiltration and evapotranspiration. If the swale is designed to maintain standing water for a period of time, the evapotranspiration volume will increase.

3.1.3 *Water Quality Control*

The primary water quality unit process in swales is sedimentation of coarse particles. As important as settling, which happens typically in the upstream end of the swale, finer suspended sediments are removed as laminar flow develops through grass blades. Through its resistance to flow, vegetation or rock slow the water, increasing its depth and causing particle settling (Barrett et al., 1998; Pitt et al., 2007). Swales improve water quality for sediment with particle sizes greater than 6 to 15 μm and pollutants attached to sediment. They are not particularly effective for dissolved pollutants, such as nitrogen; they may be removed through chemical or biological mechanisms mediated by vegetation and the soil, but the results of field studies have been inconsistent (Barrett, 2004; SWPCD, 1992). The mechanism is unknown, but could be sorption to thatch or sediment. Release of dissolved phosphorus from turf grass has been observed in the fall in temperate climates, presumably because the grass is entering dormancy, and also from swales that have been excessively fertilized or where grass clippings are not collected after mowing. Some studies have attempted to develop treatment model equations for swales based on experimental data (Fletcher et al., 2002).

3.2 Limitations

Swales require relatively mild slopes and soil and climatic conditions that support dense vegetated cover, unless they are rock-lined. Maximum drainage areas are typically 0.4 ha (1 ac) or less, particularly in areas of high rainfall intensity, to support a shallow flow regime during the peak of the treatment design flow.

Swales require a portion of the site to be set aside, compared to storm sewers that do not take up surface area. If the hydraulic grade is too deep, the footprint of the swale can become large. Erosion problems may occur if the swale is not designed and constructed properly.

3.3 Design Procedure and Criteria

3.3.1 Typical Configuration

The designer should use a trapezoidal cross section for ease of construction, with side slopes no steeper than 4H:1V or less for ease of maintenance. Terracing needs to be used when side slopes become steeper than this threshold. It is preferable to provide for a 1 to 2.5% slope in the direction of flow, with 5% being the maximum and 0.5% being the minimum. When the longitudinal slope is less than 1 to 2% and moisture is adequate, wetland species should be established. Otherwise, an underdrain should be installed, which changes unit processes in the swale to filtration. If the slope is greater than 5%, depending on soils and rainfall intensities, the designer should use check dams or drop structures with level spreaders at the entrance and intermediate points to reduce the effective slope to 2 to 2.5% and to maintain uniform cross-section flow. Check dams introduce storage and associated unit processes. Energy-dissipating riprap should be installed at the toe and for a short distance downstream of the toe of these check dams to control erosion. In steeper slopes, swales can be installed to traverse the grade at a lesser slope. Swales should be constructed carefully to attain a flat cross-sectional bottom and uniform longitudinal and lateral slopes and to eliminate high and low spots.

3.3.2 Pretreatment Unit

A pretreatment device such as a simple drop inlet with a sump should be installed at the inlet of a swale receiving stormwater with moderate-to-high total suspended solids (TSS) concentrations. A sump is not needed for stormwater with low TSS concentrations, such as those found in most residential developments. Operations using large amounts of oil should be contained at their source or removed with an oil and water separator or equivalent pretreatment device. Hydrocarbons can affect vegetation health.

Flow should be uniformly distributed into the top of the swale or along its longitudinal slope. In the latter instance, the side slopes behave like a strip. Ideally, upslope areas should be graded to maintain sheet flow at the edge of the strip or along the slope of a swale. The designer should place the pavement slightly above the adjacent swale elevation. A flow-spreading device with sediment cleanouts (such as weirs, stilling basins, and perforated pipes) should be installed to uniformly distribute flow at an inlet to the swale. Inlet areas should be protected from erosion by using stilling basins and rip-rap pads with rock sized large enough not to be moved by inflow. If a curb is placed along the strip or swale, it should be placed perpendicular to the flow. Curb cuts at least 0.3-m (12-in.) wide should be placed perpendicular to the flow and graded to maintain minimum velocities, prevent sediment deposition, and reduce clogging. If a gutter is used to route flow along the curb to an inlet, appropriate calculations should be used for highway drainage to properly size the gutter and inlet to completely capture the design flow WQT rate. Inlet areas should be protected from erosion using 150-mm (6-in.) cobble underlain by a reinforcing grid or a similar approach; a level spreader or similar mechanism should be used to uniformly distribute the flow (Lenhart, 2010).

3.3.3   Main Treatment Unit

At a minimum, it is important to design for the peak runoff rate during the water quality design storm (i.e., WQT rate) using one of the methodologies presented in Chapter 3 or a locally accepted method. The swale should be designed to safely convey the 2-year peak flow. Unless larger events will bypass the swale, its capacity should be enlarged for passage of the 10- to 100-year peak flow. The following criteria are typically used:

- Longitudinal slope between 0.5 to 5%;
- Maximum bottom width of 2.5 m (8 ft);
- Minimum bottom width of 0.5 m (2 ft);
- Maximum depth of flow no greater than 75% of the vegetation height, at the peak of the treatment design event.

It is possible to have some combinations of slope and flow that do not allow a swale because the flat slope and maximum bottom width are unable to convey water at a depth below the grass height. In this case, a wetlands basin (Chapter 6) may need to be considered.

To size the cross section of the swale, the designer should first determine the minimum bottom width of the swale to accommodate the WQT rate at the maximum allowable depth for effective treatment and the ground slope of the site. Next, the designer should check that the swale is large enough to convey the WQT rate without eroding, given the bottom width and side slopes that are selected. It is important to note that the width that is determined from this procedure is only the minimum. The engineer can widen the swale within the limits of the maximum width specification.

The maximum flow velocity should be below the maximum permissible velocity for the soils and vegetation in the swale (Table 7.1). The maximum flow depth should not exceed 0.6 m (2 ft) at the peak flowrate for the design event that needs to be contained in the swale. It is important to check the conditions for other extreme flows to verify that flooding will not occur. The hydraulic calculations make use of well-known relationships between Manning's n roughness coefficient and the

TABLE 7.1   Permissible velocities for channels lined with grass (Chow, 1959).

| | | Permissible velocity, m/s (ft/s) | |
| | | Erosion-resistant soils | Easily eroded soils |
Cover	Slope range, %		
Bermuda grass	0–5	2.4 (8)	1.8 (6)
	5–10	2.1 (7)	1.5 (5)
	>10	1.8 (6)	1.2 (4)
Buffalo grass, Kentucky bluegrass, smooth brome, blue grama	0–5	2.1 (7)	1.5 (5)
	5–10	1.8 (6)	1.2 (4)
	>10	1.5 (5)	0.9 (3)
Grass mixture	0–5	1.5 (5)	1.2 (4)
	5–10	1.2 (4)	0.9 (3)
	>10	Do not use	Do not use
Lespedeza sericea, weeping love grass, ischaemum (yellow blue-stem), kudzu, alfalfa, crabgrass	0–5	1.1 (3.5)	0.8 (2.5)
	>5	Do not use	Do not use
Annuals— used on mild slopes or as temporary protection until permanent covers are established, common lespedeza, Sudan grass	0–5	0.1 (3.5)	0.8 (2.5)
	>5	Not recommended	Not recommended

Note: The values apply to average, uniform stands of each type of cover. Use velocities exceeding 1.5 m/sec (5 ft/sec) only with good cover and where proper maintenance takes place.

VR product, where *V* is the velocity (m/s) and *R* is the hydraulic radius (m) of the flow in the channel (Stillwater Outdoor Hydraulic Laboratory, 1947). Kirby et al. (2005) extended this analysis by 1 order of magnitude to cover smaller values of *VR*. The two sets of curves are depicted in Figure 7.2.

As with all other stormwater controls based on the sedimentation unit process, the design of a swale is dictated by the HLR. However, for conditions typically achieved during flow, the hydraulic residence time (HRT) is an acceptable criterion (Minton, 2011). Hydraulic residence times of 5 to 9 minutes have been recommended, and equations such as the following have been derived from field measurements (Minton, 2011):

$$\text{HRT} = 0.014 \left(L/V \right)^{1.003}$$

(7.1)

where

HRT = in minutes;

L = length of the swale in feet (1 ft = 0.3048 m); and

V = velocity at the design flow in feet per second (1 ft/s = 0.3048 m/s).

Knowing the HRT, this equation can be used to estimate L.

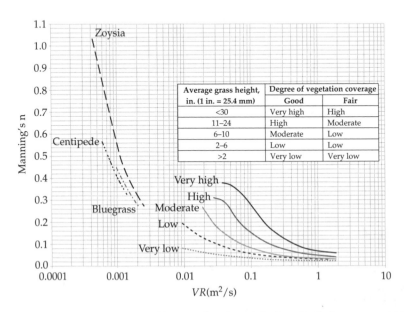

FIGURE 7.2 Manning's *n* vs *VR* (Stillwater Outdoor Hydraulic Laboratory, 1947; Kirby et al., 2005).

Vegetation should be dense and comprise drought-tolerant grasses, preferably turf grasses that will form a mat. Bunch grasses may leave bare ground susceptible to erosion. When selecting grasses, the designer should consider establishment and long-term maintenance requirements, given that some varieties have higher maintenance requirements than others. A suitable growing layer (e.g., a sandy loam) needs to be provided for the vegetation after the swale is graded. This layer may also be achieved by tilling compost to a depth of 15 cm (6 in.). Local guidelines from agricultural extensions should be followed with regard to seed-mix selection, soils, and planting.

The bottom of the swale should be placed at least 300 mm (12 in.) higher than the seasonal high water table to avoid extended periods of standing water within the swale, unless a wetlands condition is desired.

3.4   Aesthetic and Safety Considerations

Properly designed swales present few safety hazards given the shallow water depths at the treatment design capacity. Greater depths can occur if there is no bypass for the extreme events, but the swales will have lesser depths and velocities than found in traditional road ditch design. Rock treatments may be used at inlets where sediments may accumulate or where erosion may occur. The design should include some means of reducing the energy of the flow as it enters the upper end of the swale and spreading the flow across the swale width.

Swales should be naturalized to fit into site features. This is an essential consideration in residential areas because it will encourage swale upkeep by homeowners. Swales have the potential to be accumulation areas for litter or animal waste that may contribute pathogens. Homeowner actions are often the only options to address such issues. Aesthetically pleasing swales also discourage property owners from filling or otherwise modifying what could be considered an unsightly ditch.

Depending on climate, provisions for irrigation may be needed to maintain aesthetics and performance. An underdrain will reduce excessively wet areas, which can damage vegetation or affect mowing operations.

3.5   Access and Maintenance Features

Maintenance access easements to the swale and inclusive of swale width should be provided to facilitate inspection, monitoring, and maintenance. Maintenance requirements should define vegetation heights for mowing, watering, and fertilizing requirements for vegetation, and sediment removal and erosion repair frequencies (Lampe et al., 2005). If the swale is on private property, a maintenance agreement between the local jurisdiction and the property owner should spell out these requirements and establish a legally binding requirement that routine maintenance be performed.

3.6 Design Example

3.6.1 Preliminary Steps

As an example, design a vegetated swale for a 0.4-ha (1-ac) drainage area with 50% imperviousness in Columbus, Ohio. From the hydrologic analysis, the peak flow through the swale (WQT) is 0.026 m³/s (0.93 cfs). The swale must also be able to convey the 10-year event of 0.17 m³/s (6.15 ft³/s). Based on site conditions, the longitudinal slope is determined to be 2%.

Assume Kentucky bluegrass is specified. The swale will be mowed regularly and the height of vegetation expected to occur during the storm runoff season is about 100 mm (4 in.). Figure 7.2 indicates a low level of retardance; a Manning's n of 0.2 is assumed.

3.6.2 Design for Swale Capacity

This analysis emphasizes maximizing resistance to flow rather than efficient hydraulic conveyance, thereby promoting sedimentation. Typically, the design yields a maximum velocity lower than that required for soil stability, and the swale dimensions typically do not have to be modified after a stability check.

Set the maximum water depth y in the swale during the WQT below the vegetation height at 80 mm (3 in.), to maximize resistance to flow. The swale will be designed with a trapezoidal section with a side slope of 4H:1V.

Use Manning's formula to calculate the bottom width b:

$$\text{WQT} = \frac{1}{n} A R^{2/3} S^{1/2} \qquad (7.2)$$

where
$\quad$ WQT = water quality treatment rate in m³/s (cfs);
$\qquad n$ = Manning's roughness coefficient;
$\qquad A = (b+zy)y$ cross-sectional area of flow in m² (sq ft);
$\qquad y$ = flow depth in m (ft);
$\qquad z$ = side slope, ratio of horizontal distance to vertical distance; and
$\qquad R$ = hydraulic radius in m (ft), given by

$$R = \frac{(b+zy)y}{b+2y\sqrt{1+z^2}} \qquad (7.3)$$

where

    b = bottom width of the swale in m (ft); and

    S = slope of the swale in m/m (ft/ft).

In English units, the numerator over n is 1.486.

Equation 7.2 is solved by trial and error to determine the value of b = 2.4 m (7.7 ft), which falls within an acceptable range of 0.5 to 2.5 m (2 to 8 ft). With this depth, the cross-sectional area is A = [2.4 m + 4(0.08 m)](0.08 m) = 0.22 m^2 (2.34 ft^2). The flow velocity for the design flow rate is

$$V = WQT/A = (0.026 \text{ m}^3/\text{s})/0.22 \text{ m}^2 = 0.12 \text{ m/s } (0.4 \text{ ft/s}) \qquad (7.4)$$

A check needs to be made using the retardance curves in Figure 7.2. Equation 7.3 yields a hydraulic radius of R = 0.07 m (2.8 in.); therefore, VR = (0.12 m/s)(0.07 m) = 0.01 m^2/s. For the low retardance curve in Figure 7.2, the corresponding n value is nearly 0.2, which coincides with the initial assumption. If there had been a significant difference, the n value read from the chart would be used to recompute the design until there is a convergence. It should be noted that there is considerable scatter in data that led to the curves shown in Figure 7.2; therefore, a match for n within 0.05 is more than sufficient.

The flow velocity during the design event meets the requirement of being less than 0.3 m/s (0.9 ft/sec), and is much less than the maximum permissible velocities in Table 7.1 for Kentucky bluegrass, that is, 2.1 m^3/s (7 ft/s).

Using an HRT of 9 minutes in eq 7.1, the length of the swale is 77 m (251 ft).

3.6.3 Check for Stability to Reduce Erosion

The stability check is performed for the combination of highest expected flow and least vegetation coverage and height. For this example, the 10-year peak flow of 0.17 m^3/s (6.15 cfs) is the maximum that the swale will contain.

Deeper flow and a higher velocity are expected for the 10-year peak flow; therefore, the VR product will be higher and the Manning's n lower, according to Figure 7.2. An initial estimate is n = 0.04.

Equation 7.2 is used to determine the flow depth. By trial and error, the flow depth is y = 0.09 m (0.31 ft). The flow area is A = 0.26 m^2 (2.81 sq ft), the hydraulic radius is R = 0.08 m (0.27 ft), and the velocity is V = 0.67 m/s (2.2 ft/s). Therefore, VR = (0.67 m/s)(0.08 m) = 0.05 m^2/s (0.37 sq ft/s). From Figure 7.2, the corresponding n value is 0.043. One additional iteration with this new value yields y = 0.1 m (0.33 ft). The corresponding flow area is A = 0.28 m^2 (3.01 sq ft), the hydraulic radius is $R = 0.09$ m (0.28 ft), and the velocity is $V = 0.64$ m/s (2.1 ft/s). This velocity also meets the maximum permissible value in Table 7.1.

The last step is the addition of freeboard to arrive at the final channel size. Typically, 0.3 m (1 ft) is added. One final check is to estimate the maximum capacity of the channel with the freeboard.

4.0 STRIPS

Vegetated strips are densely vegetated surfaces over which water flows in a thin sheet. Planted vegetation is most often turf grasses, but it could also be other species. Like swales, strips strain pollutants by slowing down the flow of water.

4.1 Typical Applications

4.1.1 Physical Site Suitability

Strips are laid on mild slopes and runoff passes through the vegetation at depths below the height of the vegetation. A strip is often used upstream of filters or infiltrators to pretreat flows before they enter the facility. It may also be appropriate to use a strip for "backyard" drainage directly into a stream. Backyard strips may be integrated with a vegetated stream corridor protection zone if sheet flow is maintained.

Strips can be incorporated to parking lots, roadways, and other impervious areas, provided that the flow is distributed uniformly over the width of the strip.

4.1.2 Water Quantity Control

Attenuation of peak flow is minimal. Water infiltrating to the root zone will either percolate to interflow groundwater or be released to the atmosphere by evapotranspiration. Strips operate under sheet flow conditions, unlike the shallow concentrated flow in swales.

4.1.3 Water Quality Control

As with swales, the primary unit process in vegetated strips is sedimentation. Vegetation slows the stormwater, providing the opportunity for particles to settle. Some stormwater volume reduction also occurs through infiltration and evapotranspiration in the root zone. Barrett et al. (2004) found that buffer strips used along highways consistently reduced the concentration of suspended solids and total metals in runoff, but were less effective at removing dissolved metals. However, no change in concentration was observed for nitrogen and phosphorus.

4.2 Limitations

Strips require slopes that maintain sheet flow and soil and climatic conditions that support dense vegetated cover.

4.3 Design Procedure and Criteria

4.3.1 Typical Configuration

Vegetated strips are gently sloping areas with a dense vegetative cover to maintain sheet flow. Slopes are typically between 1 and 15%, but can be steeper as long as concentrated flow does not occur along the strips because it causes erosion that effectively eliminates water quality benefits. Strips typically discharge to a swale at the upstream end of the swale (see Figure 7.1) or the side slopes of the swale act as strips. A flow distribution device is deployed at the upstream end of the strip, either as a level spreader, slotted curb, or any other means of distributing the flow uniformly at the top of the strip.

4.3.2 Pretreatment Unit

Runoff must enter vegetated strips as sheet flow. Concentrated flow may be avoided by limiting the length of impervious surface flowing toward the strip, sloping the impervious surface uniformly toward the strip, limiting the width of the impervious surface to the strip width, or placing a level spreader at the interface between the impervious surface and the strip. The length at which flow concentrates typically ranges from 15 to 45 m (50 to 150 ft), depending on slope and rainfall intensity. If a level spreading device (vegetated berm, sawtooth concrete border, rock trench, etc.) is used, it should be inspected frequently for signs of concentrated flow or standing water.

4.3.3 Main Treatment Unit

Strips should be designed to carry the WQT rate determined according to one of the methods presented in Chapter 3 or based on local design guidance. The following specifications may be used:

- Average velocity not greater than 0.3 m/s (1 ft/s);
- Manning's n = 0.20 to 1.0;
- Maximum slope of 5 to 10%; steeper slopes up to 15% are acceptable in regions with milder rainfall intensities;
- Strip width limited to achieve uniform flow distribution;
- Average depth of flow no more than approximately 50 mm (2 in.);

- Maximum length should not exceed length that maintains sheet flow. In general, sheet flow occurs at the downstream end of an overland flow path. The criterion for sheet flow is $L_a S_a \leq 0.3$, where L_a is the length of the drainage area (m) and S_a is the slope of the flow surface as it drains toward the strip (see Figure 7.1). Sheet flow length rarely exceeds 90 m (300 ft) in mildly sloped, undeveloped areas. In developed areas, sheet flow lengths are typically less than 30 to 45 m (100 to 150 ft) along pervious surfaces; and

The top of the strip should be 25 to 75 mm (1 to 3 in.) below the pavement draining to it so that vegetation and sediment accumulated at the edge of the strip do not block runoff. To provide adequate treatment, the minimum length of the strip in the direction of flow of at least 4.5 m (14 ft) is recommended (Barrett et al., 2004).

The strip must be protected from vehicular traffic on parking lots and roadways. Slotted curbs can be used to allow water to flow into the strip while providing a barrier to traffic. Alternatively, reinforced grass pavement could be used. The vegetated strip should be placed at least 300 mm (12 in.) higher than the seasonal high water table to avoid extended periods of standing water within the strip.

Healthy vegetation is a critical factor to adequate performance of strips. Performance deteriorates significantly if the vegetation coverage is less than 80% (Barrett et al., 2004). Vegetation should be dense and comprise drought-tolerant grasses, preferably turf grasses, that will form a mat. Bunch grasses may leave bare ground susceptible to erosion. When selecting grasses, the designer should consider establishment and long-term maintenance requirements because some varieties have higher maintenance requirements than others. A suitable growing layer (e.g., a sandy loam) needs to be provided for vegetation after the strip is graded. This layer may also be achieved by tilling compost to a depth of 15 cm (6 in.). Local guidelines from agricultural extension should be followed regarding seed-mix selection, soils, and planting. In arid and semiarid areas, vegetated strips may need irrigation to maintain a dependable grass cover.

Also essential is to achieve the desired final grade. Because some of the design dimensions are of the order of centimeters (inches), tolerances are low. Vertically, the placement of soil and vegetation may raise the grade above the pavement that is intended to drain to the strip. Horizontally, grading must be carefully executed to minimize flow concentration. Careful inspection during construction is needed to verify the final grade.

4.4   Aesthetic and Safety Considerations

Properly designed vegetated strips present few safety hazards as they should support shallow water depths at design capacity. As with swales, strips should be designed to blend into the landscape in a natural manner.

4.5   Access and Maintenance Features

Local jurisdictions need to provide for access easements on private land for their inspection, monitoring, and maintenance, and they need to enforce long-term maintenance commitments by private parties to the control facilities owned by private parties. Where vehicle access is needed, reinforcing geotextiles and grids may be used to stabilize the surface and reduce traffic depressions.

Depending on the geographic region, strips may need irrigation, either temporarily during vegetation establishment or permanently as with arid or semiarid climates. If irrigation is not cost-effective, a rock-lined strip may be considered. Also, these strips are frequently integrated to the landscape turf and are often fertilized; applied with preemergence herbicides; and, in some cases, insecticides for control of crane fly, ants, and other turf grass pests.

4.6   Design Example

As an example, design a grass strip serving a 15 m by 60 m (49 ft by 196 ft) strip of parking lot in Columbus, Ohio. The slope of the parking lot toward the strip is 0.5%. The design rainfall is 110 mm/h (4.3 in./h). The runoff coefficient Rv is 0.9. The strip will be planted with zoysia grass that will be mowed to a height of 100 mm (4 in.) and will have a slope of 2%.

The criteria for sheet flow are based on $LS_a = (15 \text{ m})(0.005) = 0.075$, which is less than 0.3; therefore, sheet flow will arrive at the top of the strip.

The design flow is calculated as WQT $= RvIA = 0.9(110 \text{ mm/h})(15 \text{ m})(60 \text{ m}) = 0.03 \text{ m}^3/\text{s}$ (0.87 cfs).

Assuming that the maximum water depth is 25 mm (1 in.) within the strip, the flow velocity is $V = (0.03 \text{ m}^3/\text{s})/[(0.025 \text{ m})(60 \text{ m})] = 0.02 \text{ m/s}$ (0.07 cfs). The strip behaves like a wide rectangular channel such that the hydraulic radius R can be assumed equal to the flow depth y; therefore, $VR = (0.02 \text{ m/s})(0.025 \text{ m}) = 0.0005 \text{ m}^2/\text{s}$. Figure 7.2 is used to determine Manning's n for given VR. Note that this value is below the minimum available in the Stillwater charts; rounded to one decimal place, the Kirby et al. (2005) curves indicate an n value of 0.49.

Manning's formula for a wide channel can be approximated as

$$\text{WQT} = \frac{1}{n} \, Wy^{5/3} S_s^{1/2} \tag{7.5}$$

where

W = width of the strip perpendicular to the flow (m or ft); in this example, 60 m (196 ft); and

S_s = slope of the strip; 2% for the example.

In English units, the numerator above n is equal to 1.486.

Solving eq 7.5 for y yields

$$y = \left[\frac{n\,WQT}{WS_s^{1/2}} \right]^{3/5}$$

and results in y = 32 mm (1.3 in.), which is less than the maximum allowed of 50 mm. The recalculated velocity is V = (0.03 m³/s)/[(0.032 m)(60 m)] = 0.02 m/s (0.04 ft/s), which is less than the maximum recommended velocity of 0.3 m/s (1 ft/s). The corresponding VR is (0.02 m/s)(0.032 m) = 0.0006 m²/s, which is close to the initial assumption. Select a length of the strip in the direction of flow of 5 m (15 ft). For this length, eq 7.1 indicates that the HRT is 5 minutes.

The top of the grass strip is installed 25 to 75 mm (1 to 3 in) below the adjacent pavement so that vegetation and sediment accumulation at the edge of the strip do not obstruct runoff from entering. Depending on the situation, a level spreader may be needed at the top.

5.0 REFERENCES

Bäckström, M. (2002) Sediment Transport in Grassed Swales During Simulated Runoff Events.\ *Water Sci. Technol.*, **45** (7), 41–49.

Bäckström, M. (2003) Grassed Swales for Stormwater Pollution Control During Rain and Snowmelt. *Water Sci. Technol.*, **48** (9), 123–134.

Barrett, M. E. (2004) Performance and Design of Vegetated BMPs in the Highway Environment. *Proceedings of the 2004 World Water and Environmental Resources Congress*; Salt Lake City, Utah; June 27–July 1.

Barrett, M. E.; Walsh, P. M; Malina, J. F.; Charbeneau, R. J. (1998) Performance of Vegetative Controls for Treating Highway Runoff. *J. Environ. Eng.*, **124** (11), 1121.

Barrett, M. E.; Lantin, A.; Austrheim-Smith, S. (2004) Stormwater Pollutant Removal in Roadside Vegetated Buffer Strips. *Transportation Research Record* No. 1890; pp 129–140.

Chow, V. T. (1959) *Open Channel Hydraulics*; McGraw-Hill: New York.

Deletic, A. (1999) Sediment Behaviour in Grass Filter Strips. *Water Sci. Technol,* **39** (9), 129–136.

Deletic, A. (2005) Sediment Transport in Urban Runoff Over Grassed Areas. *J. Hydrol.,* **301,** 108–122.

Deletic, A.; Fletcher, T. D. (2006) "Performance of Grass Filters Used for Stormwater Treatment–A Field and Modelling Study. *J. Hydrol.,* **317,** 261–275.

Fassman, E. A.; Liao, M.; Shadkam Torbati, S.; Greatrex, R. (2010) *Stormwater Mitigation through a Treatment Train.* Prepared by Auckland UniServices, Ltd., for Auckland Regional Council (Auckland, New Zealand); Auckland Regional Council Technical Report TR19/2010.

Fletcher, T. D.; Peljo, L.; Wong, T. H. F.; Weber, T. (2002) The Performance of Vegetated Swales for Urban Stormwater Pollution Control. *Proceedings of the Ninth International Conference on Urban Drainage;* Portland, Oregon; Sept 8–13.

Kirby, J. T.; Durrans, S. R.; Pitt, R.; Johnson, P. D. (2005) Hydraulic Resistance in Grass Swales Designed for Small Flow Conveyance. *J. Hydraul. Eng.,* 131 (1), 65.

Lampe, L. K.; Barrett, M.; Woods-Ballard, B.; Kellagher, R.; Martin, P.; Jefferies, C.; Hollon, M. (2005) *Performance and Whole Life Costs of Best Management Practices and Sustainable Urban Drainage Systems.* Water Environment Research Foundation Report No. 01-CTS-21T; Water Environment Research Foundation: Alexandria, Virginia, 697 pp.

Lenhart, J. (2007) Compost as a Soil Amendment for Water Quality Treatment Facilities. *Proceedings of the 2nd National Low Impact Development Conference;* Wilmington, North Carolina; March 12–14; American Society of Civil Engineers: Reston, Virginia.

Lenhart, J. (2010) The Urban Green Biofilter, An Innovative Tree Box Application. *Proceedings of the 2010 International Low Impact Development Conference;* San Francisco, California; April 11–14; American Society of Civil Engineers: Reston, Virginia.

Minton, G. (2011) *Stormwater Treatment: Biological, Chemical, and Engineering Principles,* 3rd ed.; RPA Press: Seattle, Washington.

Pitt, R.; Nara, Y.; Durrans, S. R. (2007) Particulate Transport in Grass Swales. *Proceedings of the 2nd National Low Impact Development Conference;* Wilmington, North Carolina; March 12–14; American Society of Civil Engineers: Reston, Virginia.

Seattle Water Pollution Control Department (1992) *Biofiltration Swale Performance: Recommendations and Design Considerations;* Seattle Water Pollution Control Department: Seattle, Washington.

Stillwater Outdoor Hydraulic Laboratory (1947) *Handbook of Channel Design for Soil and Water Conservation;* SCS-TP-61; U.S. Department of Agriculture, Soil Conservation Service: Washington, D.C.

Yu, S. L.; Kuo, J.-T.; Fassman, E. A.; Pan, H. (2001) Field Test of Grassed-Swale Performance in Removing Runoff Pollution. *J. Water Resour. Plann. Manage.,* **127** (3), 168–171.

6.0 SUGGESTED READINGS

California Stormwater Quality Association (2003) *New Development and Redevelopment Handbook;* California Best Management Practice Handbooks, TC-20 Wet Ponds; California Stormwater Quality Association: Menlo Park, California.

City of Columbus, Ohio (2006) *Stormwater Drainage Manual.*

Colwell, S. (2001) *Characterization of Performance Predictors and Evaluation of Mowing Practices in Biofiltration Swales.* M.S. Thesis, University of Washington, Seattle, Washington.

Florida Department of Environmental Protection (1988) *The Florida Development Manual: A Guide to Sound Land and Water Management;* Florida Department of Environmental Protection, Nonpoint Source Management Section: Tallahassee, Florida.

King County Department of Natural Resources (1998) *Surface Water Design Manual;* King County Department of Natural Resources: Seattle, Washington.

Roesner, L. A.; Urbonas, B.; Sonnen, M., Eds. (1989) Design of Urban Runoff Quality Controls; *Proceedings of an Engineering Foundation Conference on Current Practice and Design Criteria for Urban Quality Control;* American Society of Civil Engineers: New York.

Schueler, T. R. (1987) *Controlling Urban Runoff: A Practical Manual for Planning and Designing Urban BMPs;* Metropolitan Washington Council of Governments: Washington, D.C.

Urbonas, B. R.; Roesner, L. A., Eds. (1986) Urban Runoff Quality—Impact and Quality Enhancement Technology. *Proceedings of an Engineering Foundation Conference on Current Practice and Design Criteria for Urban Quality Control;* American Society of Civil Engineers: New York.

Urbonas, B. R.; Stahre, P. (1993) *Stormwater—Best Management Practices Including Detention;* Prentice Hall: Englewood Cliffs, New Jersey.

Chapter 8

Filters

(continued)

(continued)

1.0 DESCRIPTION

A filter is a unit operation with the following design characteristics: a bed of specified filter porous media, storage to temporarily hold runoff until it is processed through the filter media, an underdrain system, and a bypass or secondary spillway. Filters may discharge to receiving water bodies, shallow aquifers, other treatment systems, or storm sewers. Due to the very high surface area in the individual grains of the porous media, as well as the size of the pore spaces, these systems enable filtration, adsorption, and ion exchange unit processes. In addition, the infiltrating surface as well as the porous media host populations of attached microorganisms that remove, consume, or reduce organic pollutants and nutrients. Because all of these unit processes are time dependent, the longer the contact time between stormwater and the porous media, the better the treatment. By design, filters also provide settling either in pretreatment locations or in storage just upstream to the filter media. Because the media is in or below the ground, there can be significant moderation of runoff temperatures by filter systems. Filters temporarily store stormwater and therefore can control peak flows depending on the amount of storage provided. In this regard, filters provide the same water quantity control unit processes as basins.

Filters are one of the five categories of storm water controls addressed by this manual. Guidelines for determining the design capture volume typically consisting of the water quality volume (WQV), water quality treatment rate (WQT), channel protection volume (CPV), overbank flood volume (OFV), and extreme flood volume (EFV), may be derived using guidelines found in Chapter 3 or defined in pertinent state or local design manuals. Selection criteria for determining whether filters are appropriate for a particular application are found in Chapter 5.

Filters are divided into two groups: slow- and rapid-rate. The application rate of slow-rate filters is 2 to 6 L/m²·min (0.05 to 0.15 gal/sq ft/min). The sand filter used in stormwater treatment is essentially the same as that one used to produce potable water. In contrast, loading rates on rapid-rate filters are 80 to 400 L/m²·min (2 to 10 gal/sq ft/min). For the same flow, the surface area of a rapid-rate filter is about 100 times smaller than for a slow-rate filter. Most manufactured filters are within the rapid-rate range. These high rates are achieved with coarse media at a shallow depth (media thickness), implying that rapid-rate filters generally achieve lower pollutant removal than a slow-rate filter such as a flatbed sand filter.

The porous media may be any material ranging from clean, uniform sand to a manufactured biologically active soil mixture composed of gravel, native soil, and organic matter. Other manufactured granular material such as zeolite and other commercial products may also be used as the media and can be selected on a contaminant-specific basis. Filters may be classified based on the number of filter media; for instance, mono-media, dual-media, tri-media, and quad-media filters contain one to four layers, respectively. A mono-medium filter like sand removes solids from the incoming water on its entry face and within the first few centimeters of the media: this process is called cake-filtration. The objective of a dual-, tri-, and quad-medium filter is to remove particles through the depth of the media rather than just at the surface: this process is called depth filtration. The intent is to make more effective use of the entire filter bed by placing relatively coarse media in the surface layer with smaller media in each successive layer in the direction of the flow. Another concept is to place an inert media like sand in the upper layer, protecting a lower layer of sorptive media for dissolved pollutants. Different media may be mixed together, whether in a slow or rapid rate application, as with bioretention filters. Layers may be placed horizontally or vertically, differing by media type, size, and density. Water may flow downward, upward or laterally through the media. All these concepts are currently used in stormwater treatment.

Hydraulic equalization and peak flow attenuation is accomplished by a basin or storage volume upstream of the media. In general, the larger the particle size of the porous media, the higher its permeability and therefore the faster water is capable of moving through it. The porous media itself may act as a restrictive primary spillway to influent stormwater, and therefore hydraulically just upstream of the filter media, storage must be included in the design. Often, the media's flow capacity is high and the entire hydraulic control for the filter is not the media itself but rather the outlet by means of a hydraulically restrictive orifice, pipe, or valve. In this way, the removal effectiveness of a coarser media is improved by the restrictive outlet, which slows down the flow through the media, thereby increasing contact time. Some filter designs incorporate an upstream basin (forebay) to provide pretreatment and peak flow attenuation, thereby regulating flow to the filter bed and also extending the time between required cleaning of the filter media. The operating head or water depth is the height of the water above the bed of a gravity filter that drives the water through the bed. When the rate of flow through the bed is momentarily less than the rate of flow entering the filter unit, the water level rises above the bed. A balance occurs at the water elevation where incoming and outgoing flow rates are equal. The rate of flow through the filter media decreases as the stormwater hydrograph recedes at the end of a storm and when the flow through the filter exceeds the rate of stormwater inflow. As particles accumulate in and on the filter, the pore space in the media clogs causing the rate of flow to decrease for a given head or water depth. The filter media must be cleaned or replaced once the flow rate reaches unacceptably low levels. This condition is typically monitored by assessing the time it takes the filter to drain after runoff ceases. An outlet restriction often maintains a constant flowrate through the media as the sediment accumulates. This feature creates a "flat" characteristic on a curve of flow vs accumulated sediment load that continues until clogging causes the media to control the flowrate, at which time the filter requires maintenance.

Filters may be located at the land surface or subsurface. When underground, it is possible to locate other infrastructure, for example parking, above the filter, a common advantage for some of the manufactured systems. Filtration systems may include vegetation on the surface of the porous media. Although infiltration may also occur with the filtration systems, it will not be discussed in this chapter other than when it affects design. Infiltrators are discussed in Chapter 9. Filtration alone may be the preferred system performance when constraints such as high groundwater table or groundwater contamination exist.

2.0   DESIGN PRINCIPLES

2.1   Sizing the Filter

The filtration class of technologies can be conveniently conceptualized as basins that employ restrictive primary spillways. In this case, the restrictive primary spillway, or hydraulic control, is the porous media or its outlet structure. Hydraulic design uses one or more of WQV, CPV, OFV, and EFV as performance parameters. It is also possible to design filters to meet a flow design criterion (Lenhart, 2004). Filters can be located inline or offline, and often flows higher than the EFV volume are bypassed.

Prior to flowing through the porous media, filtration systems are designed to hold 100% of the WQV. Ordinarily the filtration systems will have two stages: a forebay and the filter cell, and the WQV can be split between them. The common range for complete drainage of the WQV through the filter is 12 – 48 hours, with 48 hours being the maximum in order to minimize the potential for the filter to be partially full if another storm arrives. In arid climates, drain times can be as long as 72 hours.

2.2   Permeability and Hydraulic Conductivity

The key aspect of the porous media design is its permeability k. To be clear and to be consistent with hydrogeologic terminology, permeability is not the same as hydraulic conductivity K, although many stormwater guidance documents consider the two the same. Hydraulic conductivity has the units of velocity (L/T) whereas permeability (or coefficient of permeability) has the units of length squared (L^2). Permeability is a true porous media property in that it describes the ability of the porous media to pass a fluid (any fluid). Hydraulic conductivity is a combined fluid and porous media property (McWhorter and Sunada, 1977). The relation between the two variables is

$$K = \frac{k\rho g}{\mu}$$
(8.1)

where

  ρ = fluid density (kg/m^3);
  g = gravitational acceleration (m/s^2); and
  μ = fluid dynamic viscosity (N s/m^2).

Conveniently, permeability may be estimated from particle size (Shepherd, 1989; Fair and Hatch, 1933; and Hazen, 1892). Often, texts on the subject of groundwater will identify the hydraulic conductivity associated with descriptions of porous media (Driscoll, 1986; Fetter, 1988; Freeze and Cherry, 1979; or McWhorter and Sunada, 1977). It is important to understand that for stormwater filtration the lower the permeability and therefore the hydraulic conductivity of the porous media, the larger the size of the system. Therefore, permeability affects system dimensions, cost, hydraulic performance, and treatment effectiveness. Viscosity is a function of temperature; therefore, the performance of filters is affected by cold temperatures (Braga et al., 2007).

Associated with the concepts of permeability and hydraulic conductivity are two other terms: filtration rate and infiltration rate. Both of these terms correspond to the product of hydraulic conductivity and a driving hydraulic gradient. This product essentially represents the essence of Darcy's law, to be discussed soon. It is important to understand that neither filtration rate nor infiltration rate are equal to the hydraulic conductivity or the permeability. The filtration rate is the flow rate that actually passes through the filter. As the filter removes solid particles, this rate usually decreases with time until the filter media is renovated.

2.3 Pretreatment

As mentioned earlier, a common design feature for filters is the use of a forebay, or pretreatment cell, to remove large particles from the influent stream and also to potentially remove gross solids and floating debris. Criteria for sizing pre-treatment units are included elsewhere in this MOP. Forebays and other basins used for pre-treatment units are included in Chapter 6, swales and strips are discussed in Chapter 7, and gross pollutant traps are included in Chapter 10. Both primary and secondary spillways may lead from the pre-treatment unit to the filter, and care must be taken that the energy of flows does not erode or disturb the porous media surface or the embankments and sidewalls that surround the media. One design consideration is whether it is desired to have the filter "inline" or "offline." An inline filter accepts all inflow from the forebay. In this case, for events more severe than the design storm, the filter component will require a high flow bypass. In the offline configuration, flows up to the design flow are directed to the filter component, and higher flows are bypassed just before or right after the forebay.

2.4 Underdrains

In media systems that utilize downward vertical flow (gravity-driven systems), the effluent may either flow into a collection system (stone and perforated/slotted pipe) at the base of the filter media (or the downstream end in horizontal media systems), or infiltrate into the native soil underneath. Underdrains are not needed when the native soil has a sufficiently high hydraulic conductivity to allow the water to percolate into the native soil. If a collection system is used, it may then discharge to receiving waters or be plumbed into other stormwater conveyance infrastructure or to subsequent stormwater control (e.g., wetlands). In vertical flow filters the stone layer in the collection layer is at least 15 cm (6 in.) thick or twice the diameter of the collection perforated or slotted pipe, whichever is larger. In smaller filters, the stone completely underlies the media and in large filters stone trenches are used. If infiltration is desired, the collection pipe may be vertically centered in the stone layer (i.e., above the bottom of the stone) to provide for water storage and infiltration in between runoff events. Storage may also be enabled by the addition of an elbow in the underdrain piping at a 90-deg angle vertically perpendicular to the horizontal underdrain. The effluent infiltrates at the base of the collection system and before it can enter the collection pipe, it must refill this storage of the drained stone below the bottom of the perforated pipe. In addition, this zone of saturation below the system may aid in nutrient removal if it is anaerobic (Hunt et al., 2006, 2011). Stone size is typically in the range of 2 to 5 cm (¾ to 2 in.) and washed clean to remove fines, debris, and organic matter. The collection system pipe should be connected to risers that act as clean-outs, one at each end of each collection pipe and at each bend in excess of 22.5 degrees. These clean-outs extend above the filter media surface and are capped. Caps should be locked, screwed, or attached to the riser pipe. If perforated collection pipe is used, 10 to 13 mm (⅜ to ½ in.) perforations are recommended, spaced no closer than 150 mm (6 in.), with three or four rows of perforations. If slotted pipe is used, 20- to 50-slot pipe is recommended. The drain pipe is sloped at 0.5 to 2%. For large surface-area filters, the collection pipe should be spaced every 3 m (10 ft) and connected to a header. The collection pipe diameter is sized to have greater hydraulic capacity than the filter media filtration rate; normally 150 mm (6 in.) or larger diameter pipe is used. However, as discussed later, it is usually necessary to install restrictions in this pipe to control the outflow from the filter. The pipe diameter sizing is accomplished by comparing the flow through the filter media at the design level of ponding against the pipe capacity at the same condition using the pipe slope and roughness in Manning's formula.

2.5 Design of the Filter Bed

The flow through the filter media is computed from Darcy's law as

$$Q = \frac{K\left(h_{SF} + d\right)}{d} A_{SF} \tag{8.2}$$

where

Q = flow through the filter media (m³/s);
K = filter media hydraulic conductivity (m/s);
h_{SF} = depth of ponding over the filter media surface (m);
d = thickness of the filter media (m); and
A_{SF} = surface area of the filter media (perpendicular to Q) (m²).

Geotextiles are not recommended in the vertical layering (filter media to stone) of the filter or to wrap the collection system pipe due to the potential for clogging of the geotextile. Geotextiles can be used on the walls of the excavation to reduce migration of the native soil into the filter media. If particle stability analysis indicates the need for a transition between the filter media and the stone, a graded filter should be designed (U.S. Army Corps of Engineers, 2000). A geotextile filter may be used at the base of the collection stone to separate the stone from underlying soil. The geotextile should not be used here if infiltration is desired. If the collection pipes are constructed in stone trenches, a geotextile strip may be used between the stone and filter media, but not completely wrapping the stone. This geotextile strip can be 250 to 600 mm wide (1 to 2 ft), and centered over the collection pipe at the top of the stone.

If infiltration through the native soil is acceptable, the collection system may be completely unnecessary in high permeability soils.

2.6 Outlet Structures

An orifice plate (restrictor plate) or some other control such as a valve should be located downstream of the collection system to reduce velocities through the filter, increase residence time in the filter media, and control the discharge. The orifice plate or valve is often necessary because of the high permeability of the filter media: without the restriction, the filter drains faster than the minimum drain time (12–48 hours). The orifice opening is sized at the design depth of ponding on the filter with an orifice equation. Once the restrictor is sized, the WQV, CPV, OFV, and EFV hydrographs should be routed through the forebay, filter media, and orifice or valve to ensure that the WQV is contained, the CPV is met, and, if applicable, flood control requirements are met. In cold climates, care must be taken to locate the orifice plate or valve where it will not be subject to freezing.

2.7 Maintenance Considerations

Inspection and maintenance will vary based upon the specific type of filter; however the commonality is that the filter media surface clogs with time resulting in increased drain times. Limited field data and laboratory studies indicate that significant clogging occurs with the accumulation of 1.2 to 5 kg/m^2 of sediment per filter media surface area (0.25 to 1 lb/sq ft) (Minton, 2011; Woelkers et al., 2006). Because surface clogging is directly related to sediment load and debris, filters are not recommended for sites with high sediment loads (e.g., construction, agriculture, and silviculture), unless deployed with a suitable pretreatment control. Performance degradation depends on the characteristics of the contributing area. Filters that receive roof runoff may never experience clogging; similarly, a filter receiving drainage from a well-established development may experience a low suspended solids load so that the filter may perform well for decades. Pretreatment delays the onset of clogging and processes ongoing in certain filters can also increase longevity. For example, the biological processes in bioretention filters contribute to maintain the pore structure in the root zone (Emerson and Traver, 2008; Hatt et al., 2009). Periodic checks should include visual inspection of the media surface when water is not ponded as well as observation of the time required for ponded water to drain after storms (i.e., drain time). When it is determined that the filter system is not meeting the desired drain time criteria, the filter media is cleaned of the clogging sediments and debris, which is usually accomplished by removing and replacing the top few centimeters. The material should be tested and used or disposed of in accordance with applicable regulations. After maintenance, some filter media may need to be replenished.

Inspection of drain time should also occur for the storms immediately after maintenance. If systems still do not drain after routine maintenance, the entire filter media
bed and the underdrain collection system need to be inspected and then maintained
or replaced. The clean-out risers for underdrain piping should be flushed once every
one to two years.

3.0 SURFACE SAND FILTER

The surface sand filter uses clean sand or gravel for the filter media. Influent stormwater flows from the forebay to a surface filter cell where it flows vertically through
the sand media (Figure 8.1). At that point, water can infiltrate into the ground or be
collected and sent to receiving waters or a storm sewer. These filters can provide
modest water quantity control (Figure 8.2) and significant water quality improvement
(Figure 8.3), both being related to the grain size distribution and media thickness.

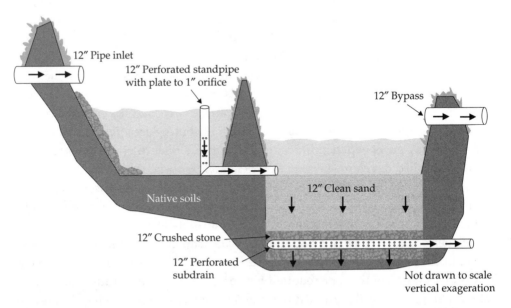

FIGURE 8.1 Typical surface sand filter, with dimensions provided for illustration only; actual facility dimensions should be developed based on site specific
conditions (1 in. = 25.4 mm) (UNHSC, 2007) (Courtesy of the University of New
Hampshire Stormwater Center).

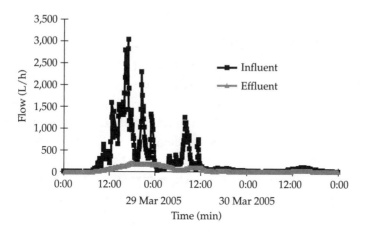

FIGURE 8.2   Example surface sand filter inflow and outflow hydrographs for a system that receives runoff from 2.5 ha (1 ac) of impervious area during two-day storm of 55 mm (2.2 in.) (1 gpm = 227 L/h) (UNHSC, 2007).

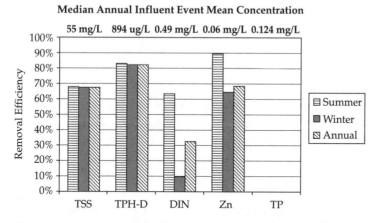

FIGURE 8.3   Representative water quality performance of a sand filter that receives runoff from 2.5 ha (1 ac) of impervious area (TSS = total suspended solids, TPH-D = total petroleum hydrocarbons in the diesel range, DIN = dissolved inorganic nitrogen, Zn = Zinc, TP = total phosphorus) (UNHSC, 2007).

If the stormwater inflow to the surface sand filter cell is less than the filtration rate of the sand media, no water ponds; and when the stormwater inflow rate exceeds the filtration rate of the sand media, water ponds above it.

3.1 Typical Applications

3.1.1 Physical Site Suitability

Individual surface sand filters have been designed to accommodate runoff from up to 100 ha (250 ac) of watershed area; however, watershed areas less than 2 ha (5 ac) are more common in most applications in the United States. As the surface sand filter area increases, it becomes more difficult to uniformly load the surface with stormwater, which may then lead to successive clogging of portions of the surface during the more frequent small storms thereby rendering the filter incapable of performing acceptably during the design events. The surface sand filter is not recommended in areas with high sediment loads (e.g., construction sites) because the surface will quickly clog.

Surface sand filters may have vegetation on the media surface. The vegetation requires a thin layer of organic material or topsoil. Rye or other shallow-rooted grasses are used for this purpose, and care must be taken that the soil layer is not more restrictive (i.e., has a lower hydraulic conductivity) than the sand below. Ultimately, when the surface clogs and needs to be maintained, this layer is lost and must be replaced. Because of the frequency of replacement (2 to 6 times per year), vegetation is not commonly used.

3.1.2 Water Quantity Control

Sand filters provide modest peak flow attenuation in the filter bed; most of the peak flow control is provided by the pre-treatment basin. Stormwater volume control is dependent on whether underlying soils are suited for infiltration, in which case the infiltrated volume is removed from the direct runoff. Some volume is kept in the pore space of the media and removed by evaporation between storm events.

3.1.3 Water Quality Control

In sand filters filtration is the primary water quality unit process, combined with sedimentation from storing runoff on the surface of the control (see Figure 8.1).

3.2 Limitations

There are very few constraints to installation of sand filters. The site must be relatively flat to promote uniform surface ponding. Frozen filter media may inhibit performance in cold climates. Experience with the freeze-thaw cycle of pervious pavement, which has a granular structure like sand in a sand filter, indicates that the surface remains open to water flow in as much as the water freezes to the surface of the grains. The hydraulic conductivity is reduced but no more than what likely occurs due to sediment accumulating on the top of the sand filter. While this is a valid concern, cold region data (Roseen et al., 2009, 2007, and 2005) demonstrate that even though the sand media freezes, it quickly thaws during runoff. The worst case scenario is that the system remains frozen, fills, and flows out the secondary spillway, thereby performing much like a basin. There are no significant environmental, performance, or social impacts associated with filters.

3.3 Design Procedure and Criteria

3.3.1 Typical Configurations

The media may be contained in an excavation or a vault. If located in an excavation, geotextile may be used to line the walls of the excavation to preserve the separation for soil from sand media. The filter is located at least 0.6 m (2 ft) and preferably 1.2 m (4 ft) or more, above the estimated seasonal high groundwater table. Installation on steep slopes is not recommended because of potential problems with embankment height, excavation depth, groundwater breakout, or slope stability. A geotechnical investigation should be conducted when soils may present stability issues. The footprint of the media area is dictated by the depth of water at the design flow and the outlet's discharge curve characteristics (Claytor and Schueler, 1996).

There are various variants of the basic surface sand filter system. One is to design a linear system around the perimeter of impervious areas. These linear filters are typically long and narrow and are constructed in vaults. The forebay side of the perimeter system runs parallel to the impervious surface, and water enters through near-continuous grates on the top of the forebay vaults. These grates can trap gross solids. Parallel to the forebay is the sand media filter, and the two are separated by a knee wall that acts as a weir. The collection system is located below the sand media and the collection pipe either runs below the media, or connects to a header pipe away from the media.

3.3.2 Pretreatment Unit

Runoff is often pretreated before entering a surface sand filter to remove coarse sediments, gross solids and debris, which extends the period between cleanings. Pretreatment units may also regulate the flow into the filter. Usually, a forebay or other type of basin is used for pretreatment. The pretreatment volume commonly does not exceed of 25% of the WQV. Chapter 6 provides several methods for sizing a basin for pretreatment. As the flow leaves the forebay and enters the filter, it needs to be adequately dispersed to avoid erosion in the filter and to overload one area of the filter.

3.3.3   Main Treatment Unit

The recommended volume storage for the main sand filter unit varies as a function of the storage available in the forebay. Overall, the total storage volume of the forebay and sand filter is from 75% to 100% of the WQV. The lower value (75%) is justified by the fact that there is storage volume in the sand media itself as well as the fact that the sand filter is draining during the time that it is filling. As the sand filter clogs, the filtration rate reduces; therefore, careful consideration should be used to weighing the storage volume size against the maintenance frequency. The sand media thickness (d_{SF}) is generally between 450 and 600 mm (18 and 24 in.) with a common value of 450 mm (18 in.). Some states will accept as little as 300 mm (12 in.) on a case by case basis, when thicker depths are infeasible. The surface area (A_{SF}) of the sand media is calculated in a few ways. In some instances, an initial estimate is based on the filter "duty": the amount of filter area per unit of watershed or impervious area. Another estimate for filter area is to take the WQV and divide it by the maximum operating depth (water depth above the sand) for a site, to yield an estimate of filter area. Some design methods also look at designing the filter area based upon desired TSS removal (Urbonas, 2003), which requires estimates of sediment loading rates at the site. Many state and local drainage manuals use the WQV, infiltration rate, and drain time to size the filter area, for example as done by the City of Austin, Texas (1996):

$$A_{SF} = \text{WQV}\, \frac{d_{SF}}{K(h_{SF} + d_{SF})t_{SF}} \tag{8.3}$$

where
  d_{SF} = sand filter bed depth (m);
  K = hydraulic conductivity for sand bed (m/s);
  h_{SF} = average height of water above the sand bed (m); and
  t_{SF} = time required for WQV to filter through the sand bed (s).

While eq 8.3 will give the filter media surface area to process the WQV in the required drain time, it assumes that the filtration rate is constant. Because the filtration rate decreases with time, a factor of safety is included that reduces the hydraulic conductivity by a factor of 2 to 3.

3.3.4   Filter Media

The range of hydraulic conductivity for sand is 0.6 – 6 m/d (2 to 20 ft/d) with a recommended range of 0.6 – 1.2 m/d (2 to 4 ft/d). It is best to obtain samples of the sand prior to construction and measure the hydraulic conductivity, for example using method ASTM, D5084–03, 2007. After construction, the hydraulic conductivity of the sand can be measured in-situ using methods (ASTM, 2007a, b, c). The in-situ techniques can also be employed during routine inspection. A common sand size is fine aggregate or "washed concrete" sand as specified in ASTM C-33 (ASTM, 2007d); it is however recommended that all material smaller than mesh size 100 (less than 0.15 mm) be removed from the ASTM C33 specification to minimize the potential for clogging within the filter bed by fines present in the original sand.

Using the units of feet and days in eq 8.3, the equation reduces to $A_{SF} = (WQV)/B$, where B ranges from 1.5 to 12 m (5 to 40 ft) for most common designs.

Surface sand filters often use a similar gradation of sand or other media as that specified for water and wastewater treatment filters. The specification consists of four criteria: 10-percentile diameter (D_{10}), 60-percentile diameter (D_{60}), effective size, and uniformity coefficient. The effective size is specified as the D_{10}, the diameter at which only 10% of the granular media is smaller by weight. With sand filters the intent is to minimize the fraction of fines in the media, reducing clogging potential and the influx of the fine material to the treated effluent. A common effective size for sand is 0.3 mm, ranging from 0.15 to 0.45 mm. For high rate treatment filters using coarse media, the effective size is in the range of 1 to 2 mm.

The uniformity coefficient is the ratio D_{60}/D_{10}. The D_{60} is the particle diameter for which 60% of the media by weight is smaller. This ratio has relevance to performance, avoiding media that is too coarse relative to the specified effective size. For sand, the uniformity coefficient should be in the range of 1.5 to 3.5, with 2 being the norm. It has been found with potable water treatment that a uniformity coefficient within this range results in better filtration. The effective size and uniformity coefficient are not specified explicitly for stormwater filters. However, the effective size and uniformity coefficient values for the sand in sand filters are within the above ranges. Nonetheless it is advisable to remove the silts and clays given that stormwater filters receive less maintenance attention than filters used for potable water treatment (Clark and Pitt, 1999).

The above specifications are what can be called fine gradation, applicable to sand and recycled glass. Pea gravel, commonly used in manufactured filters, is larger, as is perlite. Most manufactured filters use a coarser gradation, which is acceptable as long as the performance goal is reached.

A coarser gradation of sand or recycled glass can be used in a horizontal bed (vertical flow) filter. The filter operation would then last longer before clogging because particles in stormwater could penetrate deeper into the bed as it does with the coarse media used in manufactured filters. However, this deeper penetration complicates cleaning. Other parameters that might be used in media specification include cleanliness, hardness, sphericity, density, and bed void ratio.

As discussed previously, the storage volume in the surface sand filter cell is the remaining volume of the portion of the WQV not contained by the forebay. For example, if the forebay is sized at 25% of WQV, the volume for the surface sand filter cell is 75% of WQV, if 100% of the WQV is the design storage. Larger forebay volumes afford better pretreatment prior to the sand filter, and generally increase the time between maintenance visits. The surface of the sand filter is the bottom dimension of the sand filter cell; additional volume can be stored in the slopes above the filter bed. Side slopes for the surface sand filter cell should be no steeper than 2.5:1 and typically 3:1 or flatter for ease of mowing, inspection, and maintenance.

The surface sand filter secondary spillway starts at the maximum elevation of the design storage ponding for the WQV and CPV. The upper elevation of the secondary spillway is set to pass the design extreme event. The maximum elevation for the cell is commonly 30 cm (1 ft) or higher above the design extreme event elevation. The secondary spillway rating curve commonly is designed to pass the peak flows for the CPV and EFV conditions.

The surface sand filter and forebay may be constructed within vaults or in excavations. If constructed in excavations, care should be taken that there is no leakage or soil piping in the embankment between the forebay and the surface sand filter cell. In general, ponding depths h_{SF} less than 1.2 m (4 ft) are recommended to limit embankment heights and to prevent piping of the sand into the collection system or through embankments; however, ponding depths as much as 3 m (10 ft) are reported in some state drainage guidelines. Geotextile placed on the excavation walls can reduce the possibility of developing piping problems.

In a vault system, the native soil subbase is compacted after excavation and a foundation of 150 to 300 mm (6 to 12 in.) of gravel or stone is placed, leveled, and compacted. The vaults are then placed on the foundation. The collection system is then constructed in lifts (stone-pipe-stone) and compacted. The sand is then placed in 200 to 300 mm (8 to 12 in.) lifts, each lift lightly compacted with a plate compactor. The vaults are then backfilled and the backfill compacted. The construction area is then stabilized. The vault typically bypasses flows higher than the design flow.

3.3.5 Outlet Structure

The primary spillway for the sand filter is the drainage network after the influent storm-water has passed through the sand media. In high permeability soils with infiltration rates generally higher than 25 mm/h (1 in./h), no collection system may be necessary, and water may be allowed to infiltrate into the ground. In these cases, the collection system can be a simple layer of stone sized to store a particular depth of water (for example, the WQV). In general, and particularly for low infiltration soils or sites where infiltration is undesirable, a collection system is installed comprised of stone and perforated or slotted pipe. The stone is sized to afford rapid collection of water at the base of the sand media and to deliver it to collection drain pipes. Common stone sizes range from 13 to 40 mm (½ to 1½ in.). Stability, uniformity, and permeability criteria are employed (eq. 8.4) between the sand and the stone as well as between the stone and the underlying soil (Lagasse, 2006). If these criteria are not met, then a graded filter layer should be designed. Often, a pea gravel will meet these specifications.

$$\frac{D_{15_{coarse\ layer}}}{D_{85_{fine\ layer}}} < 5 < \frac{D_{15_{coarse\ layer}}}{D_{15_{fine\ layer}}} < 40 \qquad \text{and}$$

$$\frac{D_{50_{coarse\ layer}}}{D_{50_{fine\ layer}}} < 25 \qquad (8.4)$$

Collection drain pipes run in the stone collection layer and remove the water away from the bottom of the system. This pipe can be perforated with perforation sizes smaller than the stone size, or slotted (20- to 50-slot). If isolation from the soil below the base of the stone is desired, a low permeability soil or high-density polyethylene (HDPE) liner may be installed at the base of the excavation to minimize infiltration. When infiltration is desired, the soil at the base of the collection system is lightly compacted (no more than 85% of the maximum dry weight density according to the modified Proctor test) and scarified. If infiltration is not desired, the base soil may be compacted at greater than 95% of the maximum dry density. Then the stone may sit on the underlying soil or a graded filter. Infiltration quantity is increased if the collection drains are set at the top of the stone. This configuration leaves void space available for the next storm, and between storms the water below the drain invert may then infiltrate. In addition the zone of saturation below the drains and above the soil can enhance the removal of nutrients, especially if the zone is anaerobic (Hunt et al. 2006). The walls of the excavation can be lined with geotextile.

The collection system is then constructed (stone-pipe-stone) and the stone lightly compacted. The collection drains are tied into a header pipe, which may be solid, perforated, or slotted. When the header pipe leaves the stone, it is solid pipe. This pipe may then direct the water to a storm sewer, a receiving water body, or another stormwater control. The collection drains and header pipe should be fitted with cleanouts for future maintenance purposes. Additional criteria for sizing underdrain systems are found in the design principles presented at the beginning of this chapter. Depending on the type of secondary spillway, this component may also be installed or initiated at this time. If a graded filter (e.g., pea gravel) is needed, it is then placed above the stone and lightly compacted with a plate compactor. The sand is then placed in 200- to 300-mm (8- to 12-in.) lifts, each lift lightly compacted with a plate compactor. An energy dissipater is then constructed where the forebay (primary and secondary spillways) flows into the sand media.

Construction phasing is important. Adjacent areas must be stabilized to avoid premature clogging of the sand filter surface. Protective erosion control measures during construction (silt fencing, hay bales, water diversion, straw mulching, or filter berms) help minimize clogging.

The outflow primary control from the surface sand filter can be the hydraulic conductivity of the sand media itself; however preferably, it is the drain pipe in the downstream collection system. As mentioned earlier, flow restrictors are installed in the header pipe downstream of the sand media to force the drain pipe to be the hydraulic control. The drain time of the system (t_{SF}) is designed to meet the WQV and CPV criteria; for example, the CPV may be required to drain in 24 hours or longer. Typically, t_{SF} is in the range of 12 to 48 hours. Longer drain times will increase removal of some stormwater pollutants, but at the same time will require larger storage above the sand media surface or in the stone in the collection system. The rating curve for the outlet pipe hydraulic control is developed from pressure flow calculations. Because the WQV and smaller events use just the primary spillway, storage indication routing (e.g., Wanielista, et al., 1997) can route the inflow hydrograph through the system, using the outlet rating curve.

The secondary (emergency) spillway for the structure is designed in consideration of whether the structure is inline (all site stormwater piped to the sand filter) or offline (all flows higher than the WQV and CPV are bypassed). Inline sand filters can present significant problems because the rare but very high flows move through the forebay and into the sand filter bay. These high flows have the potential to erode slopes as well as resuspend sediments that collected on the sand filter surface. The higher flows will then flow out an emergency spillway in the sand filter bay, and thus possibly contain very high loads of sediment and other contaminants. For this reason, sand filters are most effective when used offline. The first flush is generally captured, and even when high flows are bypassed, stormwater volumes greater than the WQV can still be treated.

Bypassing of flows greater than the design flow is necessary to provide adequate treatment and protect the integrity of the filter. The system can be designed to trigger a bypass when the filter is full and the hydraulic grade line forces the excess water around the filter. The flow restrictor at the inlet can also be used to trigger a bypass that limits the flow that can enter the filter. This approach prevents scouring of the filter bed but may allow high flows to bypass before the WQV is accumulated. Combinations of weirs and orifices offer the best control for bypassing high flows.

3.4 Aesthetic and Safety Considerations

Materials collected by surface sand filters will build up on the surface, creating unsightly conditions if not routinely maintained. Filter areas should have mild side slopes to minimize the risk of falls, or be fenced to prevent entry. Other stormwater facility safety recommendations are provided in Chapter 5.

3.5 Access and Maintenance Features

The filter media surface clogs with time, which manifests itself by increased drain times. Because surface clogging is directly related to sediment load and debris, sand filters are not recommended for sites with high sediment loads. Periodic checks should include visual inspection of the media surface when water is not ponded as well as observation of the time required for ponded water to drain after storms (i.e., drain time). When it is determined that the filter is not meeting the desired drain time criteria, the filter media needs to be cleaned. As mentioned earlier, the removed material needs to be tested and used or disposed of according to pertinent regulations. After maintenance, some filter media may need to be replenished. Inspection of drain time should also occur for the storms immediately after maintenance.

3.6 Sand Filter Design Example

3.6.1 Given Information

Assume the following sizing information for the sand filter design example:

- WQV = 800 m^3
- Required drain time, t_{SF} = 24 hours = 1 day
- Forebay to hold 25% of WQV

- Saturated hydraulic conductivity measured at 3 m/day
- Maximum head at the site is 1 m

3.6.2   Sand Filter Sizing

Assume the following sizing information for the sand filter design example:

- Sand filter thickness selected at 0.46 m (18 inches)
- Because the maximum head at site is 1 m, reserve 0.4 m for freeboard and secondary spillway, leaving 0.6 m for maximum head on the filter h_{SF}

Using eq. 8.3, the sand filter surface area is

$$A_{SF} = WQV \frac{d_{SF}}{K(h_{SF} + d_{SF})t_{SF}}$$

$$= [(800 \text{ m}^3)(0.46 \text{ m})]/$$
$$\{(3 \text{ m/d})/3)[0.6 \text{ m} + 0.46 \text{ m})1 \text{ day}\}$$
$$= 347 \text{ m}^2 \text{ for example, } 10 \text{ m} \times 35 \text{ m}$$

The volume of the sand filter bay is

$$\text{Volume} = WQV - \text{Forebay volume} = WQV - 0.25 \, WQV$$
$$= 0.75 \, WQV = 0.75 \, (800 \text{ m}^3)$$
$$= 600 \text{ m}^3$$

For maintenance, allow 1 m all around the sand filter surface, which can be turf; therefore, the base of the sand filter bay is 12 m ×37 m. For h_{SF} = 0.6 m and 3H:1V side slopes, this bay would only hold 323 m³. To increase the volume, the side slopes can be flattened, the base dimension increased, or both. For example, side slopes of 14.1:1 with the base dimension of 12 m ×37 m yields a volume of 600 m³ at a depth of 0.6 m. At the maximum depth of 1 m, this configuration yields surface dimensions of 40 m ×65 m. It might be difficult to fit this large facility on a site; therefore, another possibility is to increase the base dimension to 19 m ×47 m and use 3:1 side slopes, which yields 611 m³ at a depth of 0.6 m, and dimensions of 25 m ×53 m when filled to a depth of 1 m. Other possibilities are to vary freeboard, maximum depth of ponding, and drain time. In this example, the factors that control the footprint are the WQV and drain time, and not the hydraulic conductivity of the sand.

The maximum media flowrate at the design WQV depth of 0.6 m can be computed from eq. 8.2 as follows:

$$Q = (3 \text{ m/d})(0.6 \text{ m} + 0.46 \text{ m})(390 \text{ m}^2)/0.46 \text{ m} = 2696 \text{ m}^3/\text{d} = 31.2 \text{ L/s}.$$

If the underdrain piping is fitted with an orifice plate, for example, at the design water depth of 0.6 m above the sand filter surface, and the hydraulic conductivity safety factor is 3, then the orifice plate is sized to pass one third of the maximum flowrate through the filter, or (0.0312 m³/s) / 3 = 0.01 m³/s. Therefore the hydraulic control for the system will be at the orifice plate as long as the hydraulic conductivity remains greater than 3 m/d.

The emergency or secondary spillway for the sand filter has the invert elevation at 0.6 m above the sand surface. The maximum depth at the site is 1 m. Of the remaining 0.4 m, 0.2 m can be reserved for freeboard, and the other 0.2 m can be used to size the spillway. In this case, the hydraulic rating curve for this spillway should be such that at a water depth of 0.8 m, the system can pass the design extreme event, for example the 10-year flood.

4.0 SUBSURFACE SAND FILTER

The subsurface sand filter locates both the forebay and sand filter cell below ground in vault structures (Figure 8.4). The stormwater moves through the sand media in a manner similar to the surface sand filter; however, typically a more conservative design should be employed. For example, the factor of safety applied to the sand hydraulic conductivity should be set to 2–5 times lower than the measured value, or the maximum depth of ponding should be reduced. Therefore the footprint of the subsurface system can be larger than the similar surface system. There are many variations, such as the Austin sand filter, Alexandria Underground Sand Filter, and the Delaware sand filter (FHWA, 1996, Claytor and Schueler, 1996). An example inflow and outflow hydrograph for a subsurface sand filter is shown in Figure 8.5.

4.1 Typical Applications

4.1.1 Physical Site Suitability
The underground placement may be a space saving advantage in that above ground land use is then possible (recreation, buffer, garden, parking, etc.). A foundation design for the vaults and pipe bedding is necessary to accommodate the load of the sand system plus that of the land use above, which can include the cover fill, infrastructure, and traffic. Care must be employed to fully understand groundwater conditions and how groundwater may affect filter performance and physical stability.

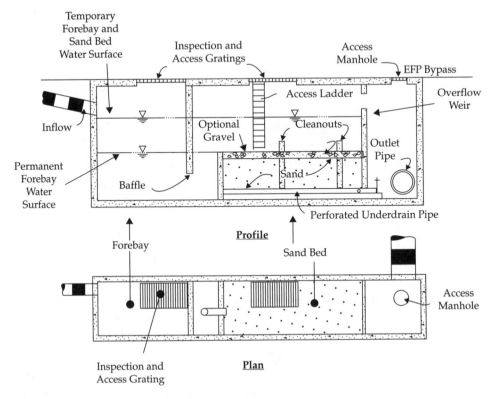

FIGURE 8.4 Schematic of a subsurface sand filter.

4.1.2 Water Quantity Control

Subsurface sand filters provide peak flow attenuation mostly by virtue of having a pre-treatment basin, although the storage in the filter media and surcharge may be significant for large facilities. Stormwater volume control is dependent on whether underlying soils are suited to infiltration, in which case runoff volume will be reduced by the infiltrated amount.

4.1.3 Water Quality Control

Subsurface sand filters are water quality controls that use filtration as the primary unit process, combined with sedimentation from storing runoff on or below the surface of the control. Specialized media can remove pollutants by adsorption. Some filters may be designed to maintain a permanent storage at the bottom where anaerobic biological processes may remove nitrogen and other biodegradable pollutants.

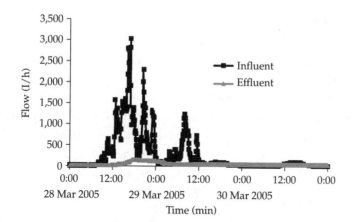

FIGURE 8.5 Example inflow and outflow hydrographs for a manufactured subsurface sand filter that receives runoff from 2.5 ha (1 ac) of impervious area during a two-day storm of 55 mm (2.2 in.). The filter is an ADS Water Quality Unit followed by an ADS Infiltration System (1 gpm = 227 L/h) (UNHSC, 2007).

4.2 Limitations

There are very few constraints to installation of subsurface sand filters. Shallow depth to groundwater can be a limitation and may require anchoring considerations. The site must be relatively flat to promote even surface ponding. There are no significant environmental, performance, or social impacts. Maintenance schedules must be carefully followed because poor performance issues may not be readily visible due to the underground location of the filter.

4.3 Design Procedure and Criteria

4.3.1 Typical Configurations

Subsurface sand filters are typically housed in a vault. Pertinent considerations in Section 3.3.1 for surface sand filters apply to subsurface sand filters.

4.3.2 Pretreatment Unit

The forebay is sized using the same equations and specifications as for the surface sand filter. Because the subsurface systems are enclosed, there is the opportunity to use the forebay roof in the design. A weir or similar restrictive primary outlet provides ponding to trap heavy sediments in the forebay. An inverted or hanging weir can be included to remove floating contaminants and debris.

4.3.3   Main Treatment Unit

The sand thickness, sand specification, sand surface area, storage volume, and sand cell secondary spillway are defined using the same equations and specifications as for the surface sand filter. After excavation, soil is compacted and a foundation of 150 to 300 mm (6 to 12 in.) of gravel or stone is placed, leveled, and compacted. The vaults are then placed on the foundation. The collection system is then constructed in lifts (stone-pipe-stone) and compacted. The sand is then placed in 200- to 300-mm (8- to 12-in.) lifts, each lift lightly compacted with a plate compactor. The vaults are then backfilled and the backfill compacted. The construction area is then stabilized.

4.3.4   Outlet Structure

The filter bed serves as the primary outlet of the subsurface sand filters. Underdrains are commonly provided to collect the filtered runoff. An orifice may be inserted into the outlet of the underdrain system if the infiltration rate through the sand media is faster than the required drawdown time to meet water quality or channel protection objectives. Underdrains are not needed if the hydraulic conductivity of the native soil allows adequate percolation.

4.4   Aesthetic and Safety Considerations

Subsurface sand filters are generally not visible and thus present few aesthetic and safety concerns if routinely maintained. Poor maintenance may cause the filter to clog, restricting release rates and potentially causing flooding or bypassing without adequate treatment. Often, entrance into the subsurface sand filters for maintenance or inspection is considered a confined space entry, and therefore proper personnel training and equipment are necessary.

4.5   Access and Maintenance Features

All vault structures (forebay, media cell) should have at least one point of entry, and preferably more. These entry points are typically constructed with riser structures topped by a manhole cover. The riser structure should have permanent scaffolding, ladder, or steps, and these should extend down to the floor of the forebay or the surface of the sand media. The entry locations must be sized to easily accommodate personnel and equipment for maintenance and inspection. For example, multiple manholes are needed to accommodate ventilation and lighting (if needed) and removal and replacement of material. Doors work better and can significantly reduce maintenance costs. Therefore, this means that maintenance and inspection equipment characteristics, including the equipment and method of replacing filter media, should be known or specified at the time of design. Care should be taken during construction to seal all entry points for control of mosquitoes and other vectors. Periodic inspection and maintenance is similar to the surface sand filter; however, in addition, inspections should include monitoring for vectors. In the sand media cell, wells can be used to monitor the water level to assess infiltration capacity and determine any need for maintenance. The wells avoid the need to enter the vaults for water level inspection. This type of inspection should occur after every major storm or quarterly, whichever is more frequent.

5.0   BIORETENTION FILTER

Bioretention filters are an extension of the surface sand filter concept. The bioretention filter aims to support plants and help more closely mimic the original site hydrology through evapotranspiration. The primary differences between the two kinds of filters are a mulch or cover layer, the media mix, and vegetation (Figure 8.6). These differences also affect the maximum ponding depth. The media mix for bioretention systems, sometimes referred to an engineered soil or a biological soil mix, is a mixture of sands, gravels, compost, wood chips and shreds, and native soil. The organic matter in the bioretention media mix and plants at the surface enhances the ability

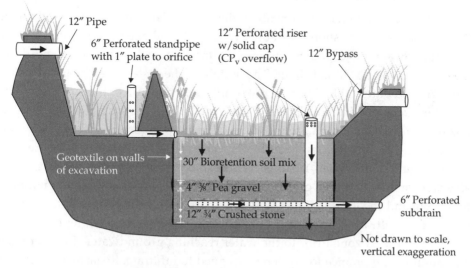

FIGURE 8.6   Schematic of a bioretention filter, with dimensions provided for illustration only; actual facility dimensions should be developed based on site specific conditions. (1 in. = 25.4 mm).

to support plants, promote nutrient uptake, hold moisture, and increase evapotranspiration. This media and vegetation harbor microbial populations with the overall effect of enhancing biological processes for nutrient removal and treatment of infiltrating stormwater.

Bioretention designs have been around since the early 1990s. Much of the original design guidance was founded in conceptually sound logic, however there was little scientific basis to support the guidance at the time. Since then, many successful designs were constructed and are still functioning. Design guidance changed slowly in response to system failures, but design changes have taken place and appear in many of the state stormwater manuals. There is an increasing volume of field studies and scientific literature on bioretention filters, which is expected to further enhance the function and acceptability of these systems. It should be noted that many of the design variables today have recommended values or ranges, and modifying these values does not necessarily imply poor design or ultimate system failure, rather that there are few examples at this time on which to base these modifications. Several state-of-the-knowledge articles have been published summarizing performance (Dietz, 2007; Davis et al., 2009; Roy-Poirier et al., 2010).

5.1   Typical Applications

5.1.1   Physical Site Suitability

The siting consideration for bioretention filters is similar to those for the sand filters. The base of the system should be at least 0.6 m (2 ft) above the estimated seasonal high groundwater table, and if infiltration is undesirable the system may need to be lined with clay or a synthetic liner. The bottom of the systems can be located closer to the groundwater table, but this proximity then may affect the system hydraulic performance. When considering placing the base of the system closer than 0.60 m (2 ft) to the seasonal high groundwater table, more rigorous analysis of hydraulic mounding and hydrograph routing is warranted. If infiltration is desirable, as a general guide, more than 1.2 m (4 ft) of distance above the seasonal high water table is recommended. The greater the separation distance between the bottom of the system and the groundwater table, the more pore volume available to accommodate the infiltrating water and the higher the degree of polishing of the water in the unsaturated zone prior to the water reaching groundwater. Chapter 9 contains additional guidance for systems designed to infiltrate. Regardless of exfiltration through the bottom, bioretention filters take advantage of evapotranspiration for volume control.

Installation on steep slopes is not recommended; a geotechnical investigation should be conducted when soils may present stability issues. The maximum size of the catchment area feeding runoff to a bioretention filter is still under debate. The original concept of bioretention was deployment as a decentralized control, with drainage areas smaller than 0.4 ha (1 ac). However, bioretention filters should be able to serve drainage areas up to 2 ha (5 ac). It is possible to design much larger systems that serve large drainage areas, but in these cases greater care would be necessary to ensure proper energy dissipation of water entering the control and effective distribution of runoff over the entire surface of the filter for the small precipitation events. In general, the higher the percent of impervious area in a watershed, the smaller the recommended watershed area served by the bioretention filter to achieve better decentralization. On the other hand, if the size of the bioretention filter becomes very small, it is subjected to greater environmental stress (heat, freezing, wetness, dryness, etc.), which will then affect the planting scheme and specifications.

A key difference between sand filters and bioretention filters is the maximum depth of ponding. Whereas sand filters can accommodate ponding depths up to a few meters, the common recommendation for bioretention filters is to limit the ponding depth at the design event (the WQV) to no more than 300 or 600 mm (12 or 24 in.) provided that the drain time criterion is met. Depending on site specific conditions and the selected vegetation for the system, higher ponding depths are possible. The concern with a large depth of ponding is both vegetation survival as well as particle stability within the filter layers.

Bioretention filters are designed to drain within 12 and 24 hours after a storm. Longer drain times can be used, especially in arid regions; however, 48 hours is typically a sufficiently long drain time.

5.1.2 Water Quantity Control

Bioretention filters possess the runoff quantity control unit processes of volume reduction by infiltration, if soils are appropriate, and evapotranspiration. Bioretention filters also reduce the peak flow of inflow hydrographs (Figure 8.7) by the storage provided in the systems and the slow rate of water movement through the filter.

The available storage volume in a bioretention filter is calculated as the sum of the storage in the surface ponding area and that within the pore space in the media. The larger the storage volume with respect to the contributing watershed, the better the performance of the filter in terms of infiltration, evapotranspiration, and lower

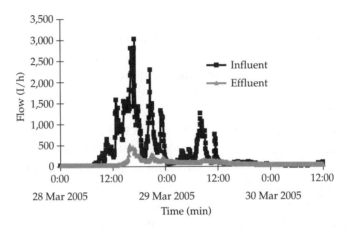

Figure 8.7   Hydraulic performance of a bioretention filter that receives runoff from 2.5 ha (1 ac) of impervious area during a two-day storm of 55 mm (2.2 in.) (1 gpm = 227 L/h) (UNHSC, 2007).

flow release. This storage is the design variable to meet a given capture requirement (Davis et al., 2011).

5.1.3   Water Quality Control

Bioretention filters are filtration systems that have been designed specifically to incorporate biological processes. Water quality unit processes include sedimentation from surface ponding, and sorption and filtration from the filter media. Surface plantings and the organic material in the media provide biological processes of plant metabolism, organic matter degradation, nitrification and denitrification, and organic compound degradation. Bioretention filters are generally effective at controlling runoff temperature due to their thicker below grade profile (Jones and Hunt, 2009). Bioretention filters exhibit very good removal of common stormwater contaminants (Figure 8.8). Nitrogen and phosphorus removal is not as efficient as for other contaminants. Nitrate and nitrite removal can be enabled by provision of an internal water storage (IWS) zone at the bottom of the filter, where anaerobic conditions facilitated denitrification (Davis, 2007).

Bioretention filters may contain additive sorptive soil media. In this case the sorptive media is a general-purpose remover not specifically selected or designed to target any specific contaminant. For example water treatment plant waste (alum) or zero-valent iron. These media prefer to remove aluminum or iron to zinc or copper, yet the latter are usually of greater environmental interest. Unfortunately, for these media, metals of lesser interest consume some of the sorption capacity. Also, due to

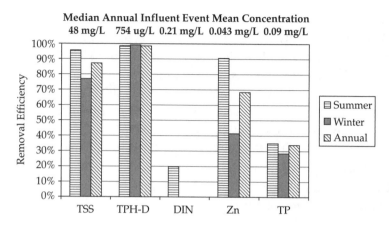

FIGURE 8.8   Water quality performance of a bioretention filter that receives runoff from 2.5 ha (1 ac) of impervious area (TSS = total suspended solids, TPH-D = total petroleum hydrocarbons in the diesel range, DIN = dissolved inorganic nitrogen, Zn = Zinc, TP = total phosphorus) (UNHSC, 2007).

selectivity a particular media may be fairly effective with one metal of interest but not another (Minton, 2011). Recent research has shown that various additives to the media can target specific pollutants. For example, water treatment residuals are effective at phosphorus removal (Lucas and Greenway, 2011). Wanielista and Chang, (2008) found that media containing sawdust and tire crumb, combined with sand, silt, and limestone are effective for nutrient removal. Ericson et al. (2007) showed that addition of steel wool, calcareous sand, or limestone can remove dissolved phosphorus.

Bioretention filters can also remove pathogens. Filtration is the primary removal mechanism as microbes can strongly sorb to the organic component of the media. In general, field studies of bioretention have shown capture of indicator species (Hathaway et al., 2009; Passeport et al., 2009). Higher removal is attained with relatively lower infiltration rates as shown by laboratory studies (Rusciano and Obropta, 2007; Bright et al., 2010; Zhang et al., 2010).

5.2   Limitations

Bioretention is similar to other filtration systems and has few constraints. The filters are easier to design and site on gentle slopes. Steeper slopes may present problems with embankment height, excavation depth, groundwater breakout, or slope stability. The filter should be built above the estimated high water table as high groundwater may adversely affect the hydraulic performance. Consideration should be given to site maintenance, especially during the first growing season. If the site and biological functions cannot be adequately maintained then this stormwater control should not be considered. Frozen filtration media may cause problems in cold climates. While this is a valid concern, cold region data (Roseen et al., 2005, 2007, 2009) demonstrate that even though the soil media freezes, it quickly thaws during runoff. In addition, the data demonstrate that bioretention filters are less prone to freezing than sand filters (Figure 8.9). The worst case scenario is that the system remains frozen, fills, and flows out the secondary spillway, thereby performing much like a basin. In addition, these areas are typically used to store snow removed by snow plows. As the snow melts, it infiltrates and does not become runoff.

5.3   Design Procedure and Criteria

5.3.1   Typical Configurations

Bioretention filters may be constructed in open excavations or within vaults. There are variations of bioretention designs, from long and narrow to nearly rectangular, to free form plan views. When using this control for very small watershed areas consisting of primarily impervious surface, a large diameter pipe (e.g., 180 cm [6 ft] or larger) can be placed vertically, and the filter built within the vertical pipe. In this case a single shrub or tree is planted, and a grate is placed over the top and

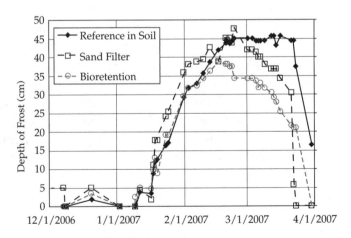

FIGURE 8.9   Frost depth penetration in a sand filter and bioretention filter compared to the nearby soil (UNHSC, 2007).

surrounding the plant. Flows higher than the design flow are either bypassed, or a secondary spillway (for example an overflow pipe) is connected into the collection system pipe.

5.3.2 Pretreatment Unit

Forebays or strips may be included as pretreatment in bioretention designs. Generally the smaller the catchment draining to the bioretention system, the less need for pretreatment. Pretreatment can remove floating and gross solids, and extend the life of the bioretention filter surface. The forebay and strip are designed using criteria in Chapters 6 and 7 respectively. However, it should be noted that the upper layers of soil mantle can act essentially as pretreatment by assimilating light suspended solid loads that may be typical of established developments.

5.3.3 Main Treatment Unit

5.3.3.1 Mulch

Very commonly a mulch layer resides at the surface of bioretention filters but is not requisite. The mulch layer prevents soil erosion and helps hold the soil moisture below. If mulch is used, the layer should be no thicker than 70 mm (3 in.). Chipped mulch should be avoided as it tends to float and may either redeposit in isolated pockets in a thicker layer (thereby choking vegetation), clog the secondary spillway, or leave the filter altogether. Shredded bark mulch is preferred. Mulch is generally replaced annually and the old layer can be tilled into the upper part of the soil as part of the maintenance procedures. If a thick groundcover is grown on the bioretention surface, the mulch may be unnecessary.

5.3.3.2 Filter Media

The bioretention soil mix is a high permeability manufactured soil, although there are some locations where a native soil has all the desirable characteristics for the bioretention mix. This soil possesses a texture of a sandy loam, loamy sand, or loam, and should be homogeneous and free of stones, stumps, and roots. Media specification varies depending on the geographic location and the pollutants to be removed but, in general, it should have a very high sand fraction, with small fractions of fines and organic matter. The significant component is a high permeability sand and fine gravel mixture (50 to 70%); large organic particles such as wood chips or shredded mulch (5 to 20%); native soil, preferably a loam (10 to 25%); and fine organic material such as compost (10 to 20%). In lieu of the compost and wood chips, humus from debarking logs has been used. Mixes that demonstrate good water quality improvement and permeability are 50–20-10–10 to 60–10-10–10 (sand-compost-wood chips/shredded mulch-loam) (Roseen, et al., 2009). This soil mix may be designed to sequester or target a specific contaminant for removal. The slower the infiltration rate, the higher the removal rate of fines (Patel et al., 2004). The most important aspect of this mix is that it possesses no more than 2% fines (silt and clay) because these fines in the mix will work their way to either a thin, hard pan layer or flow into the effluent. Some soil mixes still specify higher clay content, upwards of 10% (Roseen et al., 2005). These mixes provide for much slower percolation and while they have been found to greatly improve water quality, the soil mix itself becomes the hydraulic control. It is because of the fines content in the media that geotextiles are not recommended in the vertical profile of the bioretention systems.

Media selection is critical. For example high-phosphorus soils can cause leaching of that pollutant. The ideal phosphorus index (P-index) should be in the range of 10 to 30 (Hunt et al., 2006). The P-index is an indicator of the relative risk of phosphorus migration to receiving water, in this case from the engineered soil (NRCS, 1994). The organic matter content should be limited as well; organic matter will break down and lead to leaching of phosphorus (Clark and Pitt, 2009).

Bioretention mixes should be prepared by commercial providers of soils and mulch because media created at the construction site are often not sufficiently mixed. The uniformity coefficient of the soil media mixture is commonly greater than 6. The recommended range for soil mix hydraulic conductivity is 0.3 to 6 m/d (1 to 20 ft/d), and should be tested before and after construction. Because vegetation is expected to grow in this soil mix, the pH should be in the range of 5.5 to 6.5, and there should be less than 500 mg/L of soluble salts. Chemical testing of the individual components to the soil mix and the final soil mix is recommended prior to construction, to include pH, phosphate, nitrate, and cation exchange capacity. Soil recommendations can also be checked at local soil conservation offices.

The bioretention soil mix depth is generally between 0.6 – 0.9 m (2 to 3 ft). However if deep-rooted plants are to be included in the planting plan, then depths as much as 1.5 m (5 ft) are acceptable. In general, the thicker the soil media layer, the better the removal of nutrients (Davis, et al., 2001; Prince George's County, 2001). Deep-rooted plants increase the storage available and allow greater evapotranspired volume than shallow root vegetation (Davis et al., 2011). However, root depth should not extend below the soil mix and into the collection system to prevent clogging of the collection system pipes. A soil mix depth thinner than 0.60 m (2 ft) can be used if the filter receives runoff from small watersheds (less than 0.2 ha [0.5 ac]) with less than 25%

imperviousness, but the real limit on the thickness of the soil media is rooting depth of the mature plants. The minimum soil mix thickness of 400 mm (15 in.) is sufficient for grass covers.

After excavation, the soil can be compacted if no infiltration is desired and a liner or geotextile can be placed on top of it. If infiltration is desired, then the excavation should be only lightly compacted. Scarification of the soil surface at the bottom of the filter before media placement enhances exfiltration (Brown and Hunt, 2010). The infiltration rate should be measured in several areas of the bottom to adjust the design if necessary according to actual field conditions. The walls of the excavation can be lined with a geotextile to prevent mixing of the native soils with the engineered soil media.

When the soil media is placed in the excavation, it should be done in 300 mm (12 in.) lifts, and lightly compacted. Excessive compaction reduces the infiltration capacity of the soil. On the other hand, inadequate compaction leads to settling when the facility is exposed to runoff. This settling may cause the plant root balls to protrude out of the water-compacted soil surface. The soil should not be compacted when saturated or at high moisture contents. The City of Seattle, Washington, specifies 85% of the maximum dry weight density according to the modified Proctor test. Water compaction may be induced by flooding the bioretention filter after installation to a water depth of at least 25 mm (1 in.) (Seattle Public Utilities, 2009). Nevertheless, it should be noted that compaction requirements have not been formally developed for bioretention filters.

Where flow enters the bioretention filter, the water should have low, non-erosive velocities or proper design for energy dissipation should be employed.

5.3.3.3 Vegetation

The bioretention plants have extremely important roles of evapotranspiration, shading, nutrient removal, and phytoremediation as well as in maintaining the infiltration properties of the media. Variable plant communities should be selected. Monocultures should generally be avoided, although Passeport et al. (2009) indicate good performance of grass bioretention filters. Vegetation variability includes plant height, density, water requirements, inundation tolerance, and salt tolerance. The planting mix for the bioretention filter should be native species that match the setting in which the control is located. Plants should include wetland species, grasses, forbs, and deep-rooted species. Plantings are not restricted to facultative wetland species. The plants that seem to survive the best are the more common of native field and forest species suited to the climatic and geographic location of the site.

5.3.4 Outlet Structure

The primary spillway for the bioretention filter is the drainage after the influent stormwater has passed through the soil media. This outlet could be infiltration into the underlying native soil; in this case the control is often known as a rain garden. The outlet can also be an underdrain collection system, which is the same as for sand filters, and the reader is referred back to Section 3.0 for design details.

As stated earlier, nitrogen removal is greatly enhanced by designing an IWS zone at the base of the system, where denitrification can take place in an anaerobic environment. To create this condition, the drain pipe can be raised off the bottom of the underlying stone layer, or the outlet to the drain pipe is upturned vertically to discharge above the drain pipe. Percolation through the bottom may need to be restricted to provide adequate time for denitrification. In either case, an IWS zone of 0.3 to 0.60 m (1 to 2 ft) is recommended (Hunt et al., in press).

5.4 Aesthetic and Safety Considerations

Materials collected by bioretention filters will clog the infiltrating surface and create unsightly conditions if not routinely removed. Vegetation needs to be maintained regularly for the same reason. Small bioretention filters do not involve substantial ponding depths; therefore, the associated risk is reduced but public safety needs to be considered if the ponded depth is significant. Safety considerations for open water are presented in Chapter 5. Abrupt drops along sidewalks and pedestrian walkways may pose fall risks. In addition, in facilities along roads overgrown vegetation may become a sighting distance hazard for traffic. In most cases, maintenance is no more than what landscapers typically provide for any vegetation in median strips. It is important to remove grass cuttings to both remove nutrients and prevent clogging of the infiltration surfaces.

5.5 Access and Maintenance Features

Maintenance tasks unique to bioretention systems include the occasional removal of surface silt, removal and replacement of the mulch layer, and vegetation care. During the first three to six months, plants may need to be watered. If the system does not meet drain time performance (e.g., because of improper construction or large sediment loads), the surface may need to be removed, new soil mix added, and the surface re-planted. Maintenance can include replacing dead vegetation, pruning live vegetation, removing trash and debris, removing accumulated sediment and debris, replacing mulch, and irrigation if needed during extreme droughts. Effective maintenance of these controls is best accomplished as part of regular landscaping tasks, which often include monthly maintenance visits during the growing season.

5.6 Bioretention Filter Design Example

5.6.1 Given Information

Assume the following formation for the bioretention filter design example:

- Drainage area A = 2.7 ha = 27 000 m^2
- WQV = 25 mm, equivalent to (27 000 m^2)(0.025 m) = 675 m^3
- Design hydraulic conductivity K = 0.20 m/d, by state regulation that already includes a safety factor
- Maximum drain time t_{SF} = 24 h= 1 d
- No forebay
- 75% of WQV is required to be stored over the filter before treatment
- Maximum design depth of ponding h_{SF} = 300 mm

5.6.2 Bioretention Filter Sizing

The ponded volume is

$$Vd = 0.75 \text{ WQV}$$
$$= 0.75(675 \text{ m}^3) = 493 \text{ m}^3$$

Select a soil media thickness d_{SF} of 0.75 m.

Equation 8.3 yields the bioretention filter surface area:

$$= [(493 \text{ m}^3)(0.75 \text{ m})]/\{(0.2 \text{ m/d})[(0.3 \text{ m} + 0.75 \text{ m})(1 \text{ d})]\}$$
$$= 1761 \text{ m}^2 \text{ for example, 30 m} \times 60 \text{ m}$$

This design methodology is conservative in that it assumes that the volume is stored above the filter before it begins to infiltrate. In reality, water begins to flow into the pore space and out through the underdrain or into the soil, simultaneously as it enters the filter. The assumption that only 75% of the WQV needs to be ponded accounts for the pore storage. Assuming a maximum water content of 0.3, the pore space available for storage is (0.3)(1761 m^2)(0.75 m) = 396 m^3, which is significant given that the WQV is 675 m^3; even if only one-half of the pore space is available, the stored volume is 198 m^3, which is 29% of the WQV and consistent with the assumption. It should be noted that additional storage exists in the underdrain and gravel pack, and in the IWS zone if present. Other design methodologies exist that consider storage and outflow effects in the sizing (Engineers Australia, 2006).

6.0 LANDSCAPED ROOFS

Landscaped roofs receive various terms depending on the location; some of the more common are green roofs, vegetated roofs, and ecoroofs. A landscaped roof is meant to collect, store, and evapotranspire precipitation on building rooftops thereby reducing the amount of runoff compared to impervious roofs. In addition, the fact that an inert media or active soil media and root zone exists, makes the landscaped roof capable of removing certain airborne contaminants that become dry or wet deposition on typical impervious surfaces. A landscaped roof moderates the temperature or runoff and also helps insulate the building against weather and sound. They also protect the roof membrane. The ability to grow plants for pollinators and other wildlife is also a potential benefit from landscaped roofs.

Roofs can be vegetated or non-vegetated; in arid regions or Mediterranean climates the latter may be preferable. An important consideration is the micro-climate that the roof must endure depending on the nature of the building. For example, the top of a high-rise building may behave like an alpine desert with high winds.

The components of a landscaped roof include plants, soil media (or inert porous media), root barrier, drainage layer, and an impermeable membrane (Figure 8.10). Many configurations are available from installers, including modular units.

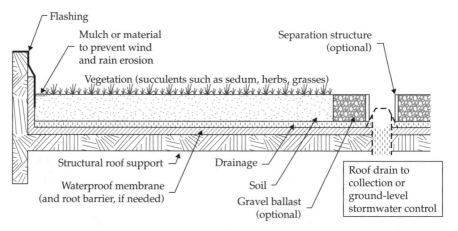

Figure 8.10 Schematic of typical extensive landscaped roof.

6.1   Typical Applications

6.1.1   Physical Site Suitability

A sound, properly functioning, waterproof membrane must underlay the landscaped roof. The building roof itself will need to be structurally designed to accommodate the additional load of the landscaped roof, including media, plants, and the moisture stored during storms.

6.1.2   Water Quantity Control

The soil or media absorbs precipitation on the landscaped roof, allowing evaporation and vegetation transpiration of the absorbed precipitation. Volume control achieved by landscaped roof systems varies depending on the season, the amount of precipitation, and the depth of the soil media. A drainage system is commonly provided to drain excess precipitation that is not absorbed by the soil or evapotranspired by the vegetation. With flow restriction controls, some peak flow attenuation may be provided.

6.1.3   Water Quality Control

Landscaped roofs are a method to bring some of the unit processes of pervious vegetated areas to the built environment. The unit processes include sedimentation, filtration, adsorption, and biological processes from the vegetation and microbes in the media.

6.2   Limitations

There are no significant constraints to landscaped roofs. Load restrictions are usually the main limitation for landscaped roofs in retrofit applications. Proper drainage and waterproofing are also essential for proper functioning. In addition, care must be exercised in specifying the growth media. Improperly formulated media can leach pollutants into the effluent.

6.3   Design Procedure and Criteria

6.3.1   Typical Configurations

Landscaped roofs typically include layers of drainage material and planting media or other porous media on an impermeable membrane to minimize leakage. There are two types of landscaped roofs:

- Extensive landscaped roofs (thinner profile), illustrated in Figure 8.10, typically use drought-tolerant roof covers of succulents, grasses, and mosses that require little to no maintenance. Extensive landscaped roofs have been observed to remove 50 to 80% of the average annual precipitation volume (Berghage et al., 2007). These roofs are not intended for recreation and are typically not designed for public access. The fully saturated weight is typically in the range of 50 to 170 kg/m^2 (10 to 35 lb/sq ft). Because of the thin soil medium, plant diversity is low and in many instances may be absent altogether. Sedums are a common plant in extensive landscaped roofs.

- Intensive Landscaped Roofs (thicker profile) are typically more elaborately designed roof landscapes, such as roof gardens, that are intended for human interaction and need to be engineered to conform to the additional load requirements for such activities. They are generally more costly than extensive landscaped roofs. The fully saturated weight is typically in the range of 240 to 1500 kg/m^2 (50 to 300 lb/sq ft). Because of the thick soil medium, plant diversity can be very high.

6.3.2   Pretreatment Unit

Landscaped roofs do not use a pretreatment unit. Precipitation generally falls uniformly across the surface of the roof. If portions of a roof without vegetation are directed to the landscaped portion, flow must be distributed uniformly across that part of the roof to avoid erosion, overloading, or short-circuiting.

6.3.3   Main Treatment Unit

At the base of the landscaped roof is a concrete or metal decking (the roof). Care should be taken to ensure that this is a corrosion resistant base. The roof slope is commonly between 0.02 and 0.05. Located on top of the deck is an impermeable membrane intended to be a waterproofing layer against leaking of the captured runoff. This membrane is either manufactured as one sheet, or constructed in the field by welding together pieces of membrane. In both cases, any seams require strict quality control to ensure that they are watertight. The membrane is either loosely laid on the roof or attached to the roof by adhesives. Desirable characteristics of the membrane include less than 1% water absorption, water vapor transmission less than 0.2 perms, ability to field splice, and high tensile strength. See *Vapor Barriers or Vapor Diffusion Retarders* (USDOE, 2007) for additional information on perms, the unit to measuring the ability of a material to retard the diffusion of water vapor. Commonly used landscaped roof membranes are hot-applied rubberized asphalt membranes, thermoplastic membranes, modified bituminous membranes, or cold-applied liquid membranes.

These materials include vulcanized elastomers, nonvulcanized elastomers, thermo-plastics, hot-applied rubberized asphalt, modified bituminous, cold-applied liquid, and built-up bituminous membranes (AIA, 2007). The impermeable membrane must be an inert material.

Above the impermeable membrane is the drainage layer. The drainage layer is sized to collect the infiltration through the media above and then move it laterally to roof drains, gutters, or the roof edge. The drainage layer can be a layer of 10 to 13 mm ($^3/_8$ to ½ in.) clean stone or a manufactured layer of geosynthetics composites. If stone is used, a protective layer of synthetic or natural, inert, or fine material should be first placed on the membrane to prevent the stone from damaging the membrane.

Above the drainage layer is a root barrier that is sufficiently strong to prevent root penetration into the drainage layer (which would clog the drainage layer) yet with high permeability to easily accommodate infiltration from above. Geotextiles are commonly used for this layer, with an apparent opening size smaller than the number 140 sieve. The root barrier must be an inert material. If plants are not to be used, then the root barrier may be unnecessary.

The media is a manufactured mix that must be free draining, have less than 2% fines, and be capable of supporting plant growth. The thickness varies from 80 mm (3 in.) for extensive landscaped roofs to 1 m (3 ft) for intensive landscaped roofs. If no plants are used, then pea gravel up to small stones may be used for this layer. Media thickness is designed based upon both the intended plants as well as the desired hydrologic control. The media can hold 20 to 35% of the field water capacity, although not all of this capacity is available every storm, depending on antecedent precipitation patterns. The thicker the layer, the more water it can hold prior to grav-ity drainage, and therefore the greater the ability to evapotranspire water in between precipitation events. The thinner the layer, the less the evapotranspiration and there-fore the more water will flow through the bottom drainage layer. When considering that the landscaped roof is replacing a nearly impervious surface, peak flows from extreme storm events can be dramatically reduced (Jarrett and Berghage, 2008).

The plants for landscaped roofs should be species that prefer well drained soils and full to partial sun. Species that can tolerate strong winds will also be more suc-cessful, although windbreaks can be included in the design. Perennial plants such as sedums are preferred; however mosses, shrubs, and trees can be successful. Diverse plantings tend to work better than monocultures. The selected plant species should be a function of the soil thickness and the geographic location. Variables of lesser impor-tance include slope, aspect, and building height. Plants should be locally grown and hardened for the local climatic conditions. It is best to consult local landscape architects, nurseries, or plant biologists on plant selection among the growing industry of suppliers for landscaped roof plants. In general, mosses, grasses and bulbs can be supported by 80 to 200 mm (3 to 8 in.) of soil; 600 mm (24 in.) for shrubs, 800 mm (30 in.) for small trees; and deeper for larger trees. Additional specifications for landscaped roofs are provided in detail by Forschungsgesellschaft Landschaftsentwicklung Landschaftsbau (2008). Because numerous components of landscaped roofs are fabricated, design should be closely coordinated with the manufacturers.

System construction occurs from the roof upwards. The soil can be moderately compacted. After planting, irrigation may be required to establish strong, healthy plants. During this time erosion and sediment control aspects need to be implemented and maintained. These factors should be considered during the design phase. Plants can be supplied in trays, plugs, or by sprigging. Each option has its advantages in terms of cost, plant size, and success rate of establishment.

Any penetration through the roof system, for example vents, must be appropriately sealed to the impermeable barrier membrane to prevent leaks into the building at these locations.

6.3.4   Outlet Structure

As described in the previous section, a drainage layer must be installed between a watertight membrane and a root barrier to direct precipitation not absorbed by the landscaped roof to a drainage system that then directs runoff safely off the roof. The drainage layer is plumbed into the roof gutter or roof drain system, or simply directed to the roof edge.

6.4   Aesthetic and Safety Considerations

Extensive landscaped roof systems are not typically designed for public access and thus present few aesthetic concerns. Intensive roof designs require more maintenance, largely to support their aesthetic and recreational uses. The attraction of birds and insects may be seen as a limitation or a benefit and needs to be considered. If the vegetation is allowed to become dry, it may become a fire hazard.

Roofing materials and drainage principles appropriate for any roofing system also apply to landscaped roofs to prevent leakage. It is also important to consider the weight of mature plants for structural stability. Trees and shrubs can become heavy, especially when turgid and while they hold rain in their foliage. As with any roofing system, designers also need to consider factors such as wind loads and uplift, roof slopes, and deflections caused by loads caused by plants, snow, or water accumulated on the roof.

Roofs with access by casual tenants or the public need to have fall protection in place and, as with any roof, access to roof appurtenances such as air conditioners, vents, and window washing gear should be restricted.

6.5 Access and Maintenance Features

Large landscaped roofs may include walkways to accommodate inspection and maintenance. Inspection should look for dead plants, dry regions of the surface, eroded soil, ponded water, and any evidence of leakage (staining) inside the building. Maintenance includes replanting, replacing soil, irrigation during prolonged dry spells, and patching the impermeable membrane. In case of a leak, detection can be challenging and repair may require significant disturbance of the landscaped roof. Vegetation-free zones must be allowed around the entire perimeter of the landscaped roof to allow access for inspections and maintenance and as a fire barrier. Penetrations through the membrane should also have this provision, for example, vents, drains, and utility conduits. The integrity of the membrane is essential for the landscaped roof's performance; therefore, these areas should be inspected three times a year (Tolderlund, 2010). Additional information on maintenance can be found in Chapter 11.

7.0 DRAIN INLET INSERTS

Drain inlet inserts are simply filter devices located at stormwater drains or inlets (catch basins). Drain inlet filters are most commonly manufactured proprietary devices. The devices consist of an inert filter material, often polypropylene, and a support structure or housing. The support structure not only holds the filter material but it allows installation into a wide variety of inlet geometries.

7.1 Typical Applications

7.1.1 Physical Site Suitability

Inserts are installed near the curb opening in a storm drain inlet, within catch basins, or in their own vault system.

7.1.2 Water Quantity Control

Inserts are not intended to provide stormwater volume control or peak flow attenuation. Inserts may cause water to pond if installed without a bypass or inadequately maintained, thereby sealing and causing flooding or bypass. Some inserts do have a bypass as part of the system. This minimal amount of ponding will result in some peak flow attenuation, but in general should not be included in peak flow attenuation calculations.

7.1.3 Water Quality Control

Inserts are considered pre-treatment units for filtering debris, trash, or larger solids from the runoff from smaller storms. Designs, sizes, and applications vary greatly between products and manufacturers. Many use a fabric consisting of polypropylene, primarily to remove petroleum hydrocarbons. Others use various types of filter media, singly or in combinations.

7.2 Limitations

Drain inlets provide modest performance (Pitt, 1998) and therefore should not be used in new development design or disturbed sites (high soil erosion potential). They are best used in retrofits to mitigate existing problems or to serve as pretreatment prior to other stormwater management strategies. Various drain inlet inserts can be seen in Figure 8.11.

7.3 Design Procedure and Criteria

7.3.1 Typical Configurations

There are basically three different types of drain inlet inserts: unsupported fabric, framed fabric, and fabric/media on horizontal grids. The unsupported fabric inserts consist of filter material that may or may not be attached to a frame. In some models the grate of the inlet itself holds the fabric material. The fabric material can be a funnel, cup, bag, or otherwise shaped to hold water and allow it to strain out. The unsupported fabric inlet inserts (Figure 8.11a) are intended for vertical (drop) inlets. The framed fabric systems use a frame constructed of plastic or wire mesh, and inside of this mesh frame a filter material is placed. The filter material then takes the shape of the frame. The horizontal grid (Figure 8.11c) systems are composed of one or more horizontal mesh grates. The grates may hold different types of media or filter fabric, each grate targeting a different contaminant or particle size.

7.3.2 Pretreatment Unit

Drain inlet inserts can function as pre-treatment for primary controls installed at the outfall of the storm drain system.

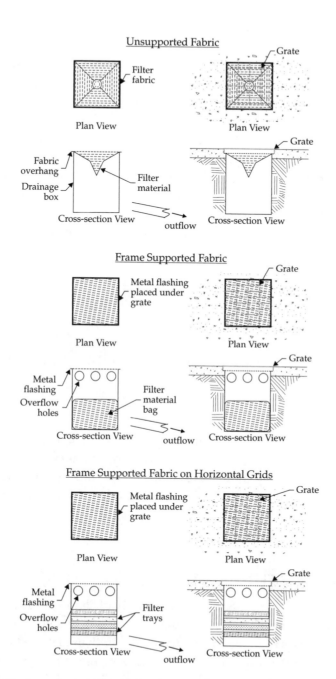

FIGURE 8.11   Various drain inlet inserts.

7.3.3   Main Treatment Unit

There is no common hydrologic or hydraulic design guideline for the drain inlet inserts. Rather, guidelines are specific to each manufacturer. These guidelines normally consider the existing infrastructure, the drainage area, and site specific inlet geometry.

Construction normally consists of fastening the insert into an existing inlet. Inspection focuses on whether the insert is deemed to be at or near capacity (for example, full of sediment), as well as if it is securely fastened and in place. Inspection should also look for excessive bypassing, which would indicate that the filter needs to be cleaned or that the inlet structure is poorly situated. If there are any holes or punctures in the filter material, the insert should be replaced or the material repaired.

7.3.4   Outlet Structure

The fabric or filter media serves as the primary outlet of an insert. Some form of bypass or overflow is advised to prevent flooding during major storm events.

7.4   Aesthetic and Safety Considerations

Clogged filter inserts provide little pollution removal and may result in flooding unless a bypass or overflow is provided.

7.5   Access and Maintenance Features

Maintenance includes removing sediment and debris; and replacing the fabric material or the entire insert. Since most drain inlet inserts are intended to remove sediment and gross debris, any preventive removal of sediment from the catchment, for example street sweeping, can increase the duration between insert maintenance efforts. Whenever possible, inserts should be installed with easy access in mind to avoid maintenance tasks in confined spaces.

8.0   MANUFACTURED FILTERS

Manufactured filter systems take on a wide variety of shapes, functions, and sizes owing to the various manufacturers and their products in this market. Most but not all manufactured filters use filter media that is coarser than that used in sand filters. The purpose is to employ high filtration rates thereby reducing the footprint of the filter. As a result, manufactured filters generally require much less space than sand filters or basins, which is one advantage of manufactured filters. However, coarse media generally provides a lower pollutant removal than fine media, particularly with respect to sediment and attached pollutants. Nevertheless, manufactured filters can help meet pollutant removal performance goals when properly designed, installed, and maintained.

8.1 Typical Applications

8.1.1 Physical Site Suitability

The filters may be located at or near to the ground surface or buried deeper underground to allow for additional aboveground land use. An example of a manufactured filtration system is shown in Figure 8.12 in which the system has sedimentation and floatables pretreatment before the stormwater flows to the filter media. This system can also provide infiltration if desired.

8.1.2 Water Quantity Control

Manufactured filters generally are not intended to provide volume control or peak flow attenuation. They may be coupled with basins, infiltrators, or other controls if these functions are desired. Depending on the type and size of filter, some peak flow attenuation may occur.

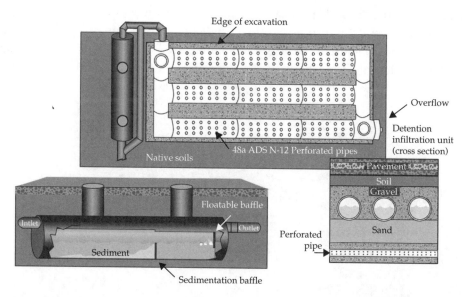

FIGURE 8.12   Manufactured subsurface filter (Courtesy of the University of New Hampshire Stormwater Center).

8.1.3 Water Quality Control

Some filters target specific contaminants, for example phosphorus or metals; others function much like a sand filter that primarily targets sediment and also removes other pollutants. Due to the proprietary nature of this class of systems, designers must go directly to the manufacturer for the proper sizing, construction, and installation specifications.

8.2 Limitations

Manufactured filters may cause water to pond if installed without a bypass or inadequately maintained, causing flooding. These systems are more effective when employed offline so that flows greater than the design flow are bypassed upstream of the filter.

8.3 Design Procedure and Criteria

8.3.1 Typical Configurations

Manufactured filters are typically intended to be inserted into the drainage system. Configurations are varied, depending on the manufacturer.

8.3.2 Pretreatment and Main Treatment Units

Configurations may include pretreatment and main treatment units (Figure 8.13), or may combine several unit processes into a single unit, depending on the proprietary design of the manufacturer. The size of a manufactured filter is based on the design peak flow, as described in Chapter 3. The design peak flow is divided by the unit

FIGURE 8.13 Example manufactured separator followed by a manufactured filter.

design discharge rate for the particular product, either as volumetric flow rate or as flow per unit of filter or filter area. Manufactured filters are often sized based on the expected mass load. This situation takes place when the flow-based design results in a small filter that will likely clog rapidly with sediments. Accordingly, the designer needs to understand the mass load the filters can handle, the event mean concentration of the influent TSS, and the annual runoff volume to reduce the maintenance costs.

8.3.3 Outlet Structure

Outlet structures of these facilities vary depending on the proprietary design of the manufacturer.

8.4 Aesthetic and Safety Considerations

Manufactured filters are generally installed underground in chambers and present few aesthetic and safety concerns if designed to completely drain and are routinely maintained thus avoiding breeding mosquitoes and other vectors. Because these are typically underground vault systems, confined-space entry considerations exist. Caution is always urged to understand access and maintenance equipment, training, personnel, and associated challenges.

8.5 Access and Maintenance Features

Construction, inspection, and maintenance of these systems is very similar to surface or subsurface sand filters. The longevity of all filters involving a pretreatment element depends on proper sizing and configuration given the expected sediment characteristics. In addition, inspection and timely maintenance improve longevity and performance. Most manufactured filters perform best in an offline configuration, which allows better control of the hydraulic loading rate. These factors minimize the amount of sediment that may enter the filter area. Some accumulation is expected as the finer sediments not captured in the pretreatment unit settle on the filter media.

9.0 SUBSURFACE GRAVEL WETLAND

The subsurface gravel wetland differs from most other filtration devices in that flow is directed horizontally through a porous media composed of stone or gravel. As the name implies, the primary media is below ground. Immediately above the gravel is a graded filter and above that a wetland or manufactured soil mix suitable for supporting wetland plant species (Figure 8.14). As in other vegetated systems, the objective

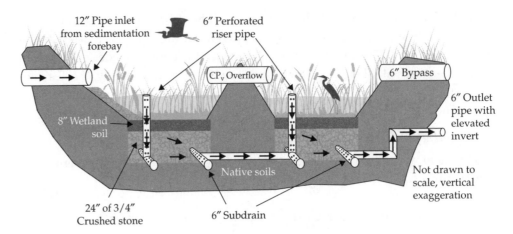

FIGURE 8.14 Subsurface gravel wetland, with dimensions provided for illustration only; actual facility dimensions should be developed based on site specific conditions (1 in. = 25.4 mm) (Courtesy of the University of New Hampshire Stormwater Center).

of the wetland plants is nutrient uptake as well as evapotranspiration and potentially phytoremediation.

Influent stormwater first enters a forebay and then travels to the first of two subsurface gravel wetland cells. Water enters the first cell at the soil surface. On the upstream end of this cell, a vertical perforated or slotted pipe directs the water down into a horizontal perforated or slotted distributor pipe, located at the upstream end of the stone. The water then leaves this distributor pipe and flows through the stone. At the downstream end of the stone, water is collected in a horizontal perforated or slotted header pipe and then directed to the second cell where it is again distributed laterally across the stone. At the downstream end of the stone in the second cell, water is collected in another horizontal perforated or slotted header pipe and discharged to receiving waters (Figure 8.14).

9.1 Typical Applications

9.1.1 Physical Site Suitability

Siting considerations for subsurface gravel systems are similar to those for sand filters however not as limiting because subsurface wetlands can be located close to or just above the estimated seasonal high water table. To inhibit infiltration the system may need to be lined with clay or an impermeable liner (HDPE). Generally the system should serve drainage areas less than 2 ha (5 ac), although some filters have been designed to serve larger catchments. Installation on steep slopes is not recommended; a geotechnical investigation should be conducted when soils may present stability issues. The maximum depth of ponding should not be more than 150 mm (6 in.) at the design condition although depths up to 300 mm (1 ft) may be acceptable, the primary concern being plant survival.

9.1.2 Water Quantity Control

Subsurface gravel wetland systems are designed to drain within 12 to 48 hours after a storm. Longer drain times can be used, especially in arid regions; however this will affect system size as well as limit the types of plants that can be used. The fundamental hydraulic control for the system is at the downstream end, where a valve or orifice plate is the hydraulically restrictive element. Because the primary spillway is horizontal flow through porous media followed by a pipe restriction, the system provides excellent reduction of peak flows (Figure 8.15).

9.1.3 Water Quality Control

Sedimentation occurs in the forebay as well as above and within the two gravel wetland cells. Filtration and sorption also occur as the water flows through the gravel. The wetland plants provide nutrient reduction and evapotranspiration as well as potential phytoremediation. Although the systems occupy a relatively large area, their treatment performance is some of the best for stormwater management (Figure 8.16).

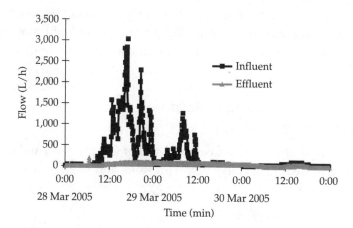

FIGURE 8.15 Example inflow and outflow hydrographs for a subsurface gravel wetland that receives runoff from 2.5 ha (1 ac) of impervious area during a two-day storm of 55 mm (1 gpm = 227 L/h)(UNHSC, 2007).

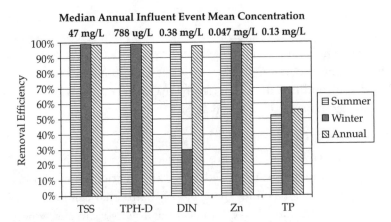

FIGURE 8.16 Representative performance for a subsurface gravel wetland that receives runoff from 2.5 ha (1 ac) of impervious area (TSS = total suspended solids, TPH-D = total petroleum hydrocarbons in the diesel range, DIN = dissolved inorganic nitrogen, Zn = Zinc, TP = total phosphorus) (UNHSC, 2007).

9.2 Limitations

The water level in the subsurface gravel wetland is carefully controlled by the outlet piping, with the water level in between storms normally a few centimeters below the soil surface. The intent is to preserve wetland conditions with this artificial "water table"; however during extended dry periods in the growing season, the high water table can drop. This is also why the subsurface gravel wetland is not intended to be an infiltration system: water lost to infiltration may limit the ability to sustain the wetland plants.

9.3 Design Procedure and Criteria

9.3.1 Typical Configurations

The typical configuration is that discussed earlier (Figure 8.14) and consisting of a forebay with two treatment cells filled with stone and overlain with wetland substrate and vegetation.

9.3.2 Pretreatment Unit

The forebay should be sized according to criteria in Chapter 6 providing flow attenuation and capture of coarse sediments and debris.

9.3.3   Main Treatment Unit

The system retains and filters the entire WQV; 10% of the WQV is used to size the forebay, and 45% of the WQV is distributed above each of the respective treatment cells. The maximum design water depth of the WQV should be no more than 150 mm (6 in.) above the wetland surface and preferably less. The CPV is retained for 12 to 48 hours through appropriate design of the outlet structure, typically an orifice plate or valve. A length-to-width ratio of 0.5 or greater is needed for each treatment cell with a minimum flow path within the gravel substrate of 4.5 m (15 ft). Berms and weirs on the surface that separate the forebay and treatment cells should be constructed with clay, or non-conductive soils, a fine geotextile, or a combination thereof to avoid water seepage and soil piping through and under the berms. Standard design approach for basins (Chapter 6) should be followed regarding side slopes, erosion control, and stabilization of outlet locations.

At its base the subsurface gravel wetland has a 600 mm (24 in.) minimum thickness of 20 mm (¾ in.) crushed-stone as the active zone where treatment occurs. Below this stone is either native soil or a geotextile. Infiltration must be minimized; therefore, in pervious soils, a low permeability liner or soil with hydraulic conductivity less than 10^{-5} cm/s (0.03 ft/d) should be used to limit infiltration, maintain horizontal flow in the stone, and preserve a "water table" for the wetland plants.

The plumbing system is standard 150-mm (6-in.) diameter solid or perforated/slotted plastic pipe. Other pipe materials can be used if conditions warrant. Because water is to flow primarily through the stone layer, it must be first directed down to the stone, distributed across the stone, and then collected at the downstream end of the stone. There should be a minimum flow distance of 4.5 m (15 ft) in the stone, which dictates the spacing of distribution lines, at the leading edge of the treatment cell and collection subdrains at the tail end of the treatment cells. Water is directed downward to the upstream end of the stone in vertical perforated or slotted risers set at a maximum spacing of 4.5 m (15 ft). Oversizing of the perforated vertical risers is useful to allow a margin of safety against clogging. The top elevation of the risers is situated at the design elevation for the WQV above the wetland soil surface. The vertical risers shall not be capped, but rather left open and covered with a grate or screen to allow overflow to enter when the water level exceeds the WQV. Within the stone layer the risers are connected to a horizontal perforated/slotted pipe distributor running the width of the gravel wetland stone. At each end of the distributor pipe are solid, vertical clean-out pipes, which are capped. The horizontal distributor pipe is vertically centered in the stone. At the downstream end of the stone is another horizontal perforated or slotted pipe, also vertically centered in the stone. This subdrain collects the water that flowed through the stone and directs it to the next subsurface gravel wetland cell. At either end of the subdrain are solid, vertical clean-out pipes capped at the top. At one or more locations along the subdrain but no closer than 4.5 m (15 ft) on centers, T-connections conduct the water in the solid pipe to the horizontal, perforated or slotted header pipe distributor pipe in the second cell stone. This distributor also has vertical risers to allow surface overflow water from the second cell to enter the stone. This distributor also has vertical clean-out pipes at either end capped at the top. At the downstream end of the second cell stone, another horizontal subdrain collects the water with vertical clean-outs at either end, capped at the top. A single T-connection at the center of this subdrain directs the water to the restrictive outlet and then to a receiving water body. From this connection and downstream until it comes above ground, the pipe is solid. The water level in the subsurface gravel wetland is maintained at 100 mm (4 in.) below the soil surface by locating the invert of the outlet pipe at the same distance below the wetland surface. Care should be taken not to enable a siphon that would drain the wetland. Therefore the elevated invert of the discharge pipe should be adequately vented. The invert should include an orifice (restrictor) plate or valve appropriately sized or set to drain the WQV in 12 to 48 hours. In cold regions the flow restrictor should be located where it is not subject to freezing. If an orifice is used, the orifice diameter should be at least 2 times the diameter of the perforations in the riser pipes to minimize the possibility of clogging. The easiest installation of the orifice plate is between a pipe and fitting using a 10-mm ($^3/_8$-in.) or thicker HDPE plate. This hydraulic control (valve or restrictor plate) should be easily accessible.

If possible, the riser discharge pipe should also have a connection to a solid pipe at the same elevation as the lowest distributor pipes in the system. This pipe is used only when the gravel wetland needs to be completely drained.

If perforated pipe is used, 10- to 13-mm ($^3/_8$- to ½-in.) perforations are recommended, spaced no closer than 150 mm (6 in.), with three or four rows of perforations. This pipe may need to be enclosed in pea gravel or a filter course that meets stability criteria between the perforation size and the soil particle size distribution (U.S. Army Corps of Engineers, 2000). If slotted pipe is used, 20- to 50-slot pipe is recommended.

Above the stone at the base of the subsurface gravel wetland is an 80- to 150-mm (3- to 6-in.) graded filter course (for example pea gravel) that meets the stability and permeability criteria for graded filter courses (U.S. Army Corps of Engineers, 2000). Geotextiles are not recommended between the vertical layers in the subsurface gravel wetland system due to potential clogging.

Above the filter course is the top soil layer of the subsurface gravel wetland system that supports the wetland plants. This is a 200- to 400-mm (8- to 15-in.) thick top-layer wetland soil. A high organic content soil similar to the bioretention engineered soil can be used, but should be at the fine end of the typical bioretention soil mixes. The gravel wetland surface infiltration rates should be similar to a low hydraulic conductivity wetland soil (4×10^{-5} cm/s to 4×10^{-6} cm/s [0.1 to 0.01 ft/d]). This soil can be manufactured using compost, sand, and fine soils to blend into a high organic matter content soil (>15% organic matter). Avoid using clay contents in excess of 15% because of potential migration of fines into the subsurface gravel layer. Do not use geotextiles within this system as they will clog due to fines and may restrict root growth. The final wetland soil mixture should not possess more than 10% fines.

The system should be planted to achieve a vigorous root mat with grasses, forbs, and shrubs with obligate and facultative wetland species. Successful plant species are typically the hardier common species for the region.

9.3.4 Outlet Structure

The forebay spillways have been previously discussed. The primary spillway for each subsurface gravel wetland cell is through the stone below. The secondary spillway for the first subsurface gravel wetland cell has its invert set at or below the WQV design elevation. The secondary spillway can be a pipe, weir, or open channel that directs the high flows, aboveground, into the second cell. If the primary spillway of the second cell (the stone) is exceeded, the secondary spillway for the second cell directs the high flows to either receiving waters or a stormwater collection system. The invert for the secondary spillway for the second subsurface gravel wetland cell is set at or just above the design WQV elevation.

9.4 Aesthetic and Safety Considerations

Subsurface gravel wetlands are similar in context to bioretention filter and thus present few aesthetic and safety concerns if routinely maintained. Poor maintenance may cause the stone to clog, restricting release rates and potentially causing flooding or bypassing without adequate treatment. The subsurface gravel wetland is not limited by cold weather and freezing of the stone.

9.5 Access and Maintenance Features

Construction is very similar to that of the bioretention filter. Inspection should include monitoring the rate at which water drains after storms. In addition, wetland plant health should be periodically monitored. Slope instability and erosion should be repaired. Any litter or gross solids should be periodically removed. Finally, the flow restrictor should be inspected for blockages. Maintenance includes removing gross pollutants, preserving a free-flowing invert, replanting as necessary, flushing distribution pipes and subdrains as necessary, and possibly mowing of the side slopes. In cold regions, the perforated/slotted risers may need to be inspected and cleared of ice.

9.6 Subsurface Gravel Wetland Design Example

9.6.1 Given information

For the subsurface gravel wetland design example, assume that WQV equals 50 m³.

9.6.2 Subsurface Gravel Wetland Sizing

For sizing, assume the following:

- Forebay: 10% of WQV = (0.1)(50 m³) = 5 m³
- Cell 1 and cell 2 above ground volumes = 0.45 WQV = 0.45 (50 m³) = 22.5 m³

The ground footprint of each cell requires a minimum length of 4.5 m (distance between horizontal headers in the stone) and a length to width ratio greater than 0.5. For a length to width of 1.0, the footprint at the wetland soil surface could be 4.6 m by 4.6 m. If 4H:1V side slopes are used, at the maximum permissible depth of 0.15 m, the volume of water above one of the cells is only 4.1 m³, yet 22.5 m³ is required. At this point, a smaller length to width ratio can be used as well as increasing other dimensions, for example considering a higher ponding depth. These dimensions should be appropriate to get the system to fit into the site constraints. A system with a wetland soil (and therefore stone) footprint of 8 m (length) by 15.5 m (width) yields the necessary volume. At the design depth of 0.15 m, the footprint is 9.3 m by 16.8 m; however additional constructed depth should be included for freeboard, especially if the system is constructed inline.

10.0 REFERENCES

American Institute of Architects (2007) Green Roof Design; Adapted from an AIA Convention Seminar by C. Garrett, K. Klein, and A. Phelps; American Institute of Architects: Washington, D.C.

American Society for Testing and Materials (2007a) Standard Guide for Comparison of Field Methods for Determining Hydraulic Conductivity in the

Vadose Zone; ASTM-D5126–90; American Society for Testing and Materials: Conshohocken, Pennsylvania.

American Society for Testing and Materials (2007b) Standard Specifications for Concrete Aggregates; ASTM-C-33–07; American Society for Testing and Materials: Conshohocken, Pennsylvania.

American Society for Testing and Materials (2007c) Standard Test Method for Field Measurement of Infiltration Rate Using a Double-Ring Infiltrometer with a Sealed-Inner Ring; ASTM-D5093–02; American Society for Testing and Materials: Conshohocken, Pennsylvania.

American Society for Testing and Materials (2007d) Standard Test Methods for Measurement of Hydraulic Conductivity of Saturated Porous Materials Using a Flexible Wall Permeameter; ASTM-D5084–03; American Society for Testing and Materials: Conshohocken, Pennsylvania.

American Society of Civil Engineers; Water Environment Federation (1992) *Design and Construction of Urban Stormwater Management Systems;* ASCE Manuals and Reports of Engineering Practice No. 77; WEF Manual of Practice No. FD-20; American Society of Civil Engineers: New York.

Berghage, R.; Jarrett, A.; Beattie, D.; Kelley, K.; Husain, S.; Rezai, F.; Long, B.; Negassi, A.; Cameron, R.; Hunt, W. (2007) Quantifying Evaporation and Transpirational Losses from Green Roofs and Green Roof Media Capacity for Neutralizing Acid Rain; National Decentralized Water Resources Capacity Development Project, The Pennsylvania State University, University Park, Pennsylvania. http://www.epa.gov/region8/greenroof/pdf/Green%20 Roofs%20and%20acid%20rain.pdf (accessed Oct 20, 2010).

Braga, A.; Horst, M.; Traver, R. G. (2007) Temperature Effects on the Infiltration Rate through an Infiltration Basin BMP. *J. Irrig. Drainage Eng.,* **133** (6), 593–601.

Bright, T. M.; Hathaway, J. M.; Hunt, W. F.; de los Reyes, F. L.; Burchell, M.R. (2010) Impact of Stormwater Runoff on Clogging and Fecal Bacteria Reduction in Sand Columns. *J. Environ. Eng.,* **136** (12), 135–141.

Brown, R. A.; Hunt, W. F. (2010) Impacts of Construction Activity on Bioretention Performance. *J. Hydrol. Eng.,* **15** (6), 386–394.

City of Austin, Texas (1996) *Design of Water Quality Controls;* City of Austin, Texas.

Clark, S.; Pitt, R. (1999) *Stormwater Runoff Treatment: Evaluation of Filtration Media;* EPA-600/R-00–010; U.S. Environmental Protection Agency, Water Supply and Water Resources Division, National Risk Management Research Laboratory: Cincinnati, Ohio.

Clark, S. E.; Pitt, R. (2009) Storm-Water Filter Media Pollutant Retention under Aerobic versus Anaerobic Conditions. *J. Environ. Eng.,* **135** (5), 367–371.

Claytor, R. A.; Schueler, T. R. (1996) *Design of Stormwater Filtering Systems;* Center for Watershed Protection: Ellicott City, Maryland.

Davis, A. P.; Hunt, W. F.; Traver, R. G.; Clar, M. E. (2009) Bioretention Technology: An Overview of Current Practice and Future Needs. *J. Environ. Eng.,* **135** (3), 109–117.

Davis, A. P.; Shokouhian, M.; Sharma, H.; Minami, C. (2001) Laboratory Study of Biological Retention for Urban Stormwater Management. *Water Environ. Res.,* **73** (1), 5.

Davis, A. P.; Traver, R. G.; Hunt, W. F.; Brown, R. A.; Lee, R.; Olszewski, J. M. (2011) Hydrologic Performance of Bioretention Stormwater Control Measures. *J. Hydrol. Eng.,* **16** (10).

Dietz, M. E. (2007) Low Impact Development Practices: A Review of Current Research and Recommendations for Future Directions. *Water Air Soil Pollut.,* **186** (1–4), 351–363.

Driscoll, F. G. (1986) *Groundwater and Wells,* 2nd ed.; Johnson Division: St. Paul, Minnesota.

Emerson, C. H.; Traver, R. G. (2008) Multiyear and Seasonal Variation of Infiltration from Storm-Water Best Management Practices. *J. Irrig. Drainage Eng.,* **134** (5), 598–605.

Erickson, A. J.; Gulliver, J. S.; Weiss, P. T. (2007) Enhanced Sand Filtration for Storm Water Phosphorus Removal. *J. Environ. Eng.,* **133** (5), 485.

Fair, G. M.; Hatch, L. P. (1933) Fundamental Factors Governing the Streamline Flow of Water Through Sand. *J—Am. Water Works Assoc.,* **25,** 1551.

Fetter, C. W. (1988) *Applied Hydrogeology,* 4th ed.; Prentice Hall: Upper Saddle River, New Jersey.

Federal Highway Administration (1996) *Evaluation and Management of Highway Runoff Water Quality;* FHWA-PD-96–032; Federal Highway Administration: Washington, D.C.

Forschungsgesellschaft Landschaftsentwicklung Landschaftsbau e.V. (2008) *Guidelines for the Planning, Construction and Maintenance of Green Roofing.* http://www.fll.de/shop/product_info.php?info=p152_Green-Roofing-Guideline--2008--download-edition-.html (accessed Oct 2011).

Freeze, R. A.; Cherry, J. A. (1979) *Groundwater;* Prentice Hall: Englewood Cliffs, New Jersey.

Hathaway, J. M.; Hunt, W. F.; Jadlocki, S. J. (2009) Indicator Bacteria Removal in Stormwater Best Management Practices in Charlotte, North Carolina. *J. Environ. Eng.,* **135** (12), 1275–1285.

Hatt, B. E.; Fletcher, T. D.; Deletic, A. (2009) Hydrologic and Pollutant Removal Performance of Stormwater Biofiltration Systems at the Field Scale. *J. Hydrol.,* **365** (3–4), 310–321.

Hazen, A. (1892) *Some Physical Properties of Sands and Gravels;* Massachusetts State Board of Health, Annual Report; pp 539–556.

Hunt, W. F.; Davis, A. P.; Traver, R. G. (in press) Meeting Hydrologic and Water Quality Goals through Targeted Bioretention Design. *J. Environ. Eng.*

Hunt, W. F.; Jarrett, A. R.; Smith, J. T.; Sharkey, L. J. (2006) Evaluating Bioretention Hydrology and Nutrient Removal at Three Field Sites in North Carolina. *J. Irrigation Drainage Eng.,* **132** (6), 600.

Lagasse, P. F. (2006) *Riprap Design Criteria, Recommended Specifications,and Quality Control;* NCHRP Report 568; National Cooperative Highway Research Program: Washington, D.C.

Lenhart, J. H. (2004) Methods of Sizing Water Quality Facilities. *Stormwater Magazine.* Jul–Aug.

Lucas, W.; Greenway. M. (2011) Phosphorus Retention by Bioretention Mesocosms Using Media Formulated for Phosphorus Sorption: Response to Accelerated Loads. *J. Irrig. Drainage Eng.,* **137** (144).

Maryland Department of the Environment (1998) *Maryland Stormwater Design Manual, Volumes I & II;* Maryland Department of the Environment, Water Management Administration: Baltimore, Maryland.

McWhorter, D. B.; Sunada, D. K. (1977) *Ground-Water Hydraulics and Hydrology;* Water Resources Publications: Fort Collins, Colorado.

Minton, G. R. (2011) *Stormwater Treatment: Biological, Chemical, and Engineering Principles,* 3rd ed.; RPA Press: Seattle, Washington.

Natural Resources Conservation Service (1994) *The Phosphorus Index A Phosphorus Assessment Tool.* http://www.nrcs.usda.gov/technical/ecs/nutrient/pindex.html (accessed Oct 2010).

New Hampshire Department of Environmental Services (2008) *New Hampshire Stormwater Manual.* http://des.nh.gov/organization/divisions/water/stormwater/manual.htm (accessed Oct 2011).

Patel, D.; Hauser, J.; Johnston, J.; Curtis, J. (2004) Pilot Filtration Studies for Turbidity and Nutrient Removal at Lake Tahoe. *Proceedings of the 3rd Annual North American Surface Water Quality Conference;* Palm Springs, California; May 17–19.

Pitt, R. (1998) An Evaluation of Storm Drainage Inlet Devices for Stormwater Quality Treatment. *Proceedings of the Annual Water Environment Federation Technical Exposition and Conference;* Orlando, Florida; Oct 3–7. http://rpitt.eng.ua.edu/Publications/StormwaterTreatability/Storm%20drain%20inlets%20weftec98%20paper.PDF (accessed Oct 2010).

Prince George's County, Maryland (2001) *The Bioretention Manual;* Prince George's County, Maryland, Department of Environmental Resources, Environmental Services Division.

Roseen, R. M.; Ballestero, T. P.; Houle, J. P. (2009) University of New Hampshire Stormwater Center 2009 Bi-Annual Report; University of New Hampshire: Durham, New Hampshire.

Roseen, R. M.; Ballestero, T. P.; Houle, J. P. (2007) University of New Hampshire Stormwater Center 2007 Annual Report; University of New Hampshire: Durham, New Hampshire.

Roseen, R. M.; Ballestero, T. P.; Houle, J. P. (2005) The UNH Stormwater Center's 2005 Data Report; University of New Hampshire: Durham, New Hampshire.

Roy-Poirier, A.; Champagne, P.; Filion, Y. (2010) Review of Bioretention System Research and Design: Past, Present, and Future. *J. Environ. Eng.,* **136** (9), 878–889.

Rusciano, G. M.; Obropta, C. C. (2007) Bioretention Column Study: Fecal Coliform and Total Suspended Solids Reductions. *Trans. ASABE,* **50** (4), 1261–1269.

Seattle Public Utilities (2009) *Updated SPU Bioretention Soil—Modeling Inputs and Water Quality Treatment.* http://www.seattle.gov/util/groups/public/@spu/@usm/documents/webcontent/spu02_019972.pdf (accessed Oct 2011).

Shepherd, R. G. (1989) Correlations of Permeability and Grain Size. *Groundwater*, **27** (5), 633.

Tolderlund, L. (2010) *Design Guidelines and Maintenance Manual for Green Roofs in the Semi-Arid and Arid West*; University of Colorado: Denver Colorado, 59 pp.

Urbonas, B. R. (2003) *Stormwater Sand Filter Sizing and Design: A Unit Operations Approach*; Urban Drainage and Flood Control District: Denver, Colorado.

U.S. Army Corps of Engineers (2000) *Design and Construction of Levees*; EM 1110-2-1913; U.S. Army Corps of Engineers: Washington, D.C.

U.S. Department of Agriculture (1986) *Urban Hydrology for Small Watersheds*; Technical Release 55; U.S. Department of Agriculture, Natural Resources Conservation Service, Conservation Engineering Division: Washington, D.C.

U.S. Department of Energy (2007) Vapor Barriers or Vapor Diffusion Retarders. http://www.eere.energy.gov/consumer/your_home/insulation_airsealing/index.cfm/mytopic=11810 (accessed Oct 2011).

Wanielista, M.; Chang, N.-B. (2008) *Alternative Stormwater Sorption Media for the Control of Nutrients*; Final Report for Project B236; Stormwater Management Academy, University of Central Florida: Orlando, Florida.

Wanielista, M.; Kersten, R.; Eaglin, R. (1997) *Hydrology: Water Quantity and Quality Control, Second Edition*; Wiley & Sons: New York.

Woelkers, D.; Clark, S.; Pitt, B. (2006) Stormwater Treatment Filtration as a Stormwater Control. *Proceedings of the North American Surface Water Quality Conference and Exhibition*; Denver, Colorado; July 24–27; Forester Communications: Santa Barbara, California.

Zhang, L.; Seagren, E. A.; Davis, A. P.; Karns, J. S. (2010) The Capture and Destruction of Escherichia coli from Simulated Urban Runoff Using Conventional Bioretention Media and Iron Oxide-Coated Sand. *Water Environ. Res.*, **82,** 701–714.

Chapter 9

Infiltrators

(continued)

1.0 DESCRIPTION

Infiltrators are unit operations in which the entire design capture volume infiltrates to the soil and percolates to shallow aquifers from which it flows to streams as inter-flow. Water is also removed by plants via evapotranspiration. Figure 9.1 illustrates the following two types of infiltrators:

- Surface infiltrators (see Figure 9.1a), where water ponds on the ground until it can infiltrate to the soil. Infiltration rates and storage volumes of these types of infiltrators depend on the infiltration properties of the soil; buildup of sediment deposited on the surface of the infiltrator; the root structure, evapotranspira-tion, and water tolerance of the vegetation growing on the infiltrator; the effect of freeze–thaw cycles on seasonal infiltration; and other climatic conditions. Surface infiltrators are most commonly configured as basins or trenches.

- Underground infiltrators (see Figure 9.1b), where water enters an under-ground reservoir that is either empty or filled with rock or other material providing support, and infiltrates through the bottom and sides of this reser-voir. Underground infiltrators are less prone to freeze–thaw issues and other climatic conditions, but lack evapotranspiration and infiltration-enhancing

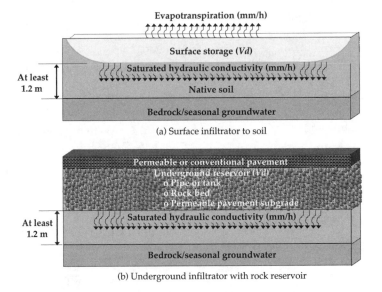

(a) Surface infiltrator to soil

(b) Underground infiltrator with rock reservoir

FIGURE 9.1   General types of infiltrators.

properties of plants. Pretreatment is often required to prevent sediment from entering the underground infiltrator, where plugging could result in expensive maintenance or reconstruction. Underground infiltrators are commonly configured as infiltration vaults (including perforated pipes and half pipes), dry wells, or rock-filled basins that overlay permeable soils.

The design capture volume (Vd) of an infiltrator is determined based on site conditions and may include the groundwater recharge volume, water quality volume (WQV), and channel protection volume (CPV), as specified in local regulations or determined using methods described in Chapter 3. Volumes exceeding the design capture volume, including the overbank flood volume (OFV) and the extreme flood volume (EFV), are typically either diverted around the infiltrator to a suitable control facility or safely routed through the infiltrator.

2.0 DESIGN PRINCIPLES

2.1 Physical Site Suitability

Infiltrators require pervious soils, favorable site geology, and proper groundwater conditions to manage the intended design capture volume. Properly sited, installed, and maintained infiltrators may

- Recharge groundwater and help maintain baseflow;
- Reduce ground settlement in areas of groundwater depletion;
- Help preserve and enhance vegetation;
- Reduce pollutant loads transported to receiving waters; and
- Reduce runoff volumes, peak flows, and temperatures.

In the evaluation of infiltration feasibility, the proximity of buildings or other features that may be damaged by infiltration should be considered. Also, there may be applicable groundwater discharge regulations that need to be considered.

2.2 Hydraulic Control

By definition, infiltrators do not directly discharge the design capture volume to a receiving surface waterbody. It is important to properly measure site infiltration rates and depth to the seasonal groundwater level and to consider gradual clogging in the sizing of the surface area of the infiltrator. Infiltrators are less prone to clogging where runoff contains low total suspended solids (TSS) concentrations, for example from roofs.

The infiltration rate, evapotranspiration rate, and moisture-retaining properties of the soil within infiltrators control the water balance within the soil column, as illustrated in Figure 9.2. Surface ponding will occur whenever the precipitation intensity exceeds the infiltration rate or whenever the volume of water within the soil column exceeds the maximum saturation of the soil. Porosity is the ratio of pore volume to bulk soil volume and the maximum saturation is the fraction of the porosity that can be occupied by water. Therefore, the maximum volume of water that can be contained within the soil column is the maximum saturation times the porosity times the depth of the soil layer from the surface to rock, groundwater, or some other barrier that limits infiltration to groundwater. The maximum saturation is commonly approximated as 1; therefore, the porosity is assumed to be the maximum water content in the soil. Some materials such as pumice, zeolites, and perlites have closed pores that are part of the total porosity but do not contribute to water-holding capacity because they are closed. In such cases, the porosity and maximum saturation volume are different. The moisture-holding capacity of the soil layer may be a limiting factor if the water table or an impervious layer such as fragipan is relatively close to the surface. Otherwise, the hydraulic conductivity of the soil is typically the limiting condition.

Gravity drainage will occur whenever the volume of water within the soil exceeds its field capacity, defined as the water content at which capillary forces holding the

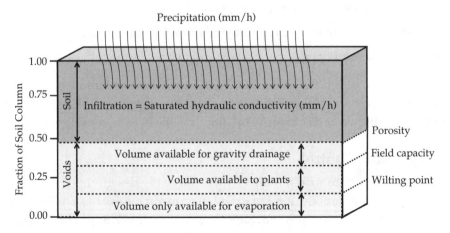

FIGURE 9.2   Definition of soil infiltration and water retention properties.

water within the soil exceed gravitational force. For design storm calculations, it is assumed that the antecedent moisture condition equals the field capacity of the soil. Alternatively, typical year estimates may be performed to track the soil moisture between rainfall events.

Evapotranspiration is the combination of direct evaporation to the atmosphere and uptake of water by plants. In general, water available to plants is defined as the difference between the field capacity and the wilting point, which is the moisture content at which plants can no longer extract water against the capillary forces within the soil to transpire normally. If watered after this threshold has been reached, plants will recover; however, there is a permanent wilting point at which the plant will be unable to recover. The soil column depth available for evapotranspiration is limited to the root zone of the plants. All other factors being equal, plants with deeper roots achieve larger volumes of evapotranspiration. In general, plants should be selected based on their ability to withstand both saturated conditions within the soil column (i.e., periods when soil moisture exceeds the field capacity) and drought conditions (i.e., periods when soil moisture falls below the wilting point).

The general infiltrator types in Figure 9.1 include a storage volume on the ground surface or in an underground reservoir to hold the design capture volume until it can infiltrate to the soil. The duration of infiltration should occur within a maximum allowed ponding time (e.g., 48 to 72 hours) to satisfy public health, safety, and aesthetic considerations (e.g., to avoid mosquito breeding). The drain time for the ponded water is a critical design parameter. Infiltration within reasonable time periods is typically achievable when underlain by soils with relatively high infiltration rates. Although infiltrators may be used in clayey soils, their surface area will be significantly larger to allow the entire design capture volume to infiltrate in the same amount of time.

Performance of infiltrators is dependent on the characteristics of the soil. While the hydrologic soil groups (HSGs) (USDA, 2009) are commonly used to assess infiltration capacity, the USDA soil texture classifications are preferred to assess hydraulic conductivity, field capacity, wilting point, and other properties of soils (Saxton and Rawls, 2006). Calculators have been created to estimate hydraulic properties based on the sand, silt, clay, and organic matter content of soils (e.g., Saxton, 2009). These estimates are adequate for preliminary sizing of infiltrators but field tests are indispensable for final design. The hydraulic conductivity of soils can vary widely, often by orders of magnitude; therefore, tests spatially representative of the infiltration surface of the infiltrator must be conducted to provide a reliable design.

In loamy soils, it may be appropriate to replace the upper layer of organically rich soil that is commonly removed by excavation. The native soil may be modified to enhance surface infiltration and treatment as long as subsurface conditions such as impermeable layers, high groundwater tables, and bedrock do not inhibit adequate infiltration. Where native soil infiltration rates are unable to completely dispose the design capture volume within the maximum allowed ponding time, an infiltrator–basin or infiltrator–filter system may be designed, where a portion of the design capture volume is disposed through infiltration and the remainder discharged through an underdrain at a flowrate able to achieve water quantity and quality objectives (see Figure 9.3). It should be noted that an underdrain could reduce the volume captured in the root zone.

To minimize the risk of clogging, runoff containing sediment should either be diverted from infiltrators to another type of control or receive pretreatment (e.g., using a forebay, strip, or vault) to remove coarse sediment, defined as particles 0.075 mm or larger that are retained by a no. 200 sieve size according to the Unified Soil Classification System. Silt and clay particles less than 0.05 mm may fill the pore space in coarser soils, significantly reducing infiltration capacity. Infiltration capacity may recover, however, as roots create macropores in the soil, particularly plants with thicker roots (Le Coustumer et al., 2008). Runoff from roof drains from large

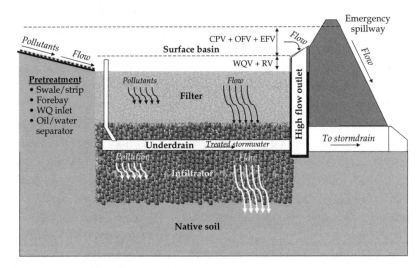

FIGURE 9.3 Schematic representation of combination infiltrator–filter with pretreatment (RV = recharge volume).

buildings and mature developments with light traffic has low suspended solid concentration and may not require pretreatment.

2.3   Unit Processes

Water quantity unit processes present in infiltrators reduce the amount of runoff by infiltration and evapotranspiration. Water quality unit processes remove pollutants by filtering, sorption, and various biological mechanisms. Loamy soil (e.g., HSG-B) provides relatively high infiltration rates coupled with effective treatment through the presence of organic matter and clay. Coarse soil (e.g., HSG-A) provides higher infiltration rates, but minimal treatment before the groundwater is reached. In these cases, it may be appropriate to use a filter (see Chapter 8) to fully treat stormwater before entering the infiltrator.

Current specifications regarding the distance to the groundwater table are mostly based on engineering judgment. Only a few field studies on separation exist, such as the Los Angeles Basin Water Augmentation Study (Los Angeles and San Gabriel Rivers Watershed Council, 2005). Separation serves the following functions: ensuring sufficient treatment before reaching groundwater, avoidance of mounding, and protecting drinking water supplies. The coarser the media, the greater the separation should be unless pretreatment is included. Special consideration is needed if the aquifer is used for potable water. Mounding is more likely with tighter soils; hence, greater separation is needed than that with coarse soils. Mounding may occur during large rainfalls or extended periods of infiltration and is a function of basin size and geometry. The likelihood of mounding is greater for larger infiltrators and for those in which the ratio of horizontal dimensions is close to unity, such as with square or round basins (Carlton, 2010). However, the extent of mounding is localized under the infiltrator (Machusick et al., 2011) and related to the storm size.

Although surface infiltration has received much attention in recent years, it has long been practiced in situations with inadequate surface drainage (Ferguson, 1994). The practice has gained renewed emphasis under the green infrastructure approach to stormwater management, which focuses on capturing runoff from impervious surfaces and immediately conveying it to infiltrating surfaces (Fassman and Blackbourn, 2011; Smith and Hunt, 2010).

Infiltrators can be infiltration basins, infiltration trenches, dry wells, and permeable pavements. These facilities need to be designed to provide good surface and subsurface site drainage. Infiltration is most successful when it is distributed on the drainage area and a single infiltrator is used to control runoff from an individual building site or small urban catchment (i.e., up to 4 ha [10 ac] of single-family residential and up to 2 ha [5 ac] of commercial or industrial land use, which have larger impervious areas thus producing more runoff volumes).

Infiltrators are susceptible to failure when improperly designed, poorly constructed, infrequently maintained, or subjected to large sediment loads from construction-site runoff (Haselbach, 2010). Failure of an infiltrator occurs when stormwater no longer drains into the ground at design rates. Early signs of failure include excessively long periods of standing water on infiltrating surfaces or within infiltration trenches, or flow through underdrains under conditions other than those for which they were designed. When an infiltrator fails, runoff bypasses the infiltrator untreated and may cause nuisance flooding locally.

2.4   Limitations

The following issues are associated with infiltrators:

- Infiltration practices typically require wide-scale implementation to significantly affect downstream peak flows and runoff volumes, particularly to control runoff from streets and large paved areas. When peak flow control is required, infiltrators may need to be combined in a system with other unit operations that provide peak attenuation;

- Infiltrating surfaces clog if they receive large concentrations of sediment not removed through pretreatment. Under such circumstances, the infiltration surface will fail as the solids accumulate. Low concentrations such as those from established developments and roofs do not present this problem;

- Individual infiltrators may not receive proper maintenance because they are below ground;

- Algae growth within the infiltrator may form hydrated units that prevent water from infiltrating;

- If improperly situated, local groundwater mounding under these facilities can cause them to fail or affect nearby infrastructure and foundations;

- They may provide a pathway to groundwater in case of accidental spills involving pollutants from certain types of industrial and commercial materials (Section 2.3.6).

- Unless other appropriate unit processes are provided, soluble pollutants such as nitrate will not be removed by infiltrators and may enter shallow aquifers.

2.5   Design Capture Volume

The amount of urban surface runoff arriving at infiltrators is affected by the watershed's size and imperviousness, local rainfall, and snowmelt characteristics, in addition to dry weather activities such as lawn watering, car washing, and hydrant flushing. Of these, stormwater and snowmelt runoff typically are the most significant considerations for design, and the choice of a design is often dictated by local conditions or criteria. It is recommended that an infiltrator be designed to infiltrate the entire design capture volume within the maximum allowed drain time of 48 to 72 hours to avoid frequent occurrences of standing water that may create health, safety, or aesthetic issues. Local regulations may allow longer drain times. The design infiltration rate of the basin should be 0.3 to 0.5 times the measured saturated infiltration rate of the soils at the site to account for increased water viscosity at lower temperatures, which reduces the hydraulic conductivity (Braga et al., 2007), and diminishing infiltration rates over the life of the infiltrator (Engineers Australia, 2006). Larger infiltration areas and shorter design drain times are required if the depth of the underlying soil to seasonal groundwater or bedrock limits infiltration.

An infiltrator designed solely for water quality control should be able to infiltrate WQV, which is either specified by local regulations or calculated using the procedures in Chapter 3. The design capture volume may also include recharge volume and CPV. Estimation of the design capture volume for infiltration trenches is somewhat more complex and is described later in this chapter.

2.6   Soil Infiltration and Storage Properties

For design, it is recommended that several surface infiltration tests be performed at each site, with an average of several of the lowest measured infiltration rates used for design. It is important to recognize that, as sediment accumulates on the infiltrator's bottom, the effective infiltration rate will be governed by the sediment layer, which, in turn, will be affected by the presence or absence of a healthy vegetated surface. Therefore, when local soils exhibit high surface infiltration rates, the infiltrator's design should be based on infiltration rates that do not exceed 50 mm/h (2 in./hr). When native soils have infiltration rates less than 50 mm/h (2 in./hr), the designer should consider using a reduced rate to account for the fact that soil infiltration rates will decline as sediment builds up on the bottom of the basin.

To determine the infiltration rates of in-situ soils and verify that subsurface conditions are appropriate for infiltration, the designer should conduct a geotechnical investigation of the infiltrator's site. According to a recognized method for establishing hydraulic conductivity, the following investigation techniques are suggested for the design of infiltration basins (CASQA, 2003):

- Perform at least three inhole conductivity tests using the *Procedure for Performing Field Permeability Testing by the Well Permeameter Method* (DOI, 1990). If groundwater is present in the borehole, the Bouwer–Rice procedures (1976) should be used. At least two of these tests should be performed at different locations within the proposed infiltrator and the third performed down-gradient no more than approximately 10 m (30 ft). The tests should measure hydraulic conductivity in the side slopes and the bed within a depth of 3 m (10 ft) of the invert. Alternatively, a cone penetrometer test could be conducted to support creation of microzonation maps (Zhang and Tumay, 2003);

- The minimum acceptable hydraulic conductivity as measured in any of the three required test holes is 13 mm/h (0.4 in./hr). If any test hole shows less than the minimum value, the site should be disqualified from further consideration;

- The designer should exclude from consideration sites where the invert of the infiltrator is constructed in fill or partially in fill, or where fill is excavated to uncompacted levels unless no silts or clays are present in the soil boring. Fill tends to be compacted, with clays in a dispersed rather than flocculated state, thereby greatly reducing permeability; and

- The geotechnical investigation should provide a good understanding of how stormwater will move in the soil (horizontally or vertically) and whether there are any geological conditions that could inhibit the movement of water.

It should be noted that there are several additional standard methods to estimate in situ hydraulic conductivity, for example the single-ring infiltrometer test (Bouwer, 1986; Wu and Pan, 1997) and, *Standard Test Method for Infiltration Rate of Soils in Field Using Double-Ring Infiltrometer* (ASTM D 3385). Detailed treatment of these field measurements is beyond the scope of this manual. A comprehensive geotechnical evaluation of the site is needed to ensure that the designer has reliable hydraulic conductivity data.

2.7 Arid or Semiarid Climates

Infiltrators can effectively recharge groundwater in arid or semiarid climates, although there is the potential for increased clogging because of high sediment loads typical of these regions. Vegetation over the infiltrating surface needs to be a drought-tolerant species; otherwise, the surface should be covered with sand or gravel because it may be too costly to water vegetation in these climates (Clark et al., 2009).

2.8 Cold Climates

Infiltrators can be used in cold climates, but are not recommended in areas with permafrost. Deicers may increase the sodium adsorption ratio in the soil and could destabilize the clay in soils, which could clog the infiltrator. Vegetation associated with infiltrators should be salt tolerant in these climates. A minimum setback from roads is needed and minimizes the chance that the infiltrator may cause frost heaving. Pervious pavements need to have the base of the gravel storage reservoir below the frost line or an underdrain system should be designed to remove stormwater before it freezes (Clark et al., 2009).

In some locations, snowmelt can govern the size of infiltrators, especially where frozen ground or saturated soils may seasonally increase pervious area runoff to the infiltrator. Under extreme conditions, snowmelt rates can equal 4 mm (0.6 in.) of water per hour. Although it is not possible to generalize snowmelt runoff rates across the United States, the following snowmelt rates may be used to determine if snowmelt governs the size of these facilities: snowmelt from impervious surfaces, 1.0 mm/h (0.04 in./hr), and snowmelt from pervious surfaces, 0.5 mm/h (0.02 in./hr). The designer should use locally derived rates whenever they are available.

2.9 Groundwater Contamination Potential

There is regulatory concern about the effect of untreated infiltrated runoff on groundwater quality, especially when the separation between groundwater and the surface is small. However, Clark et al. (2009) indicate that infiltrators can treat runoff for at least several decades without substantial migration to the groundwater. The exceptions are pollutants like chloride and nitrate, which are mainly conservative substances and are poorly treated in the soil under most conditions.

As mentioned in Section 2.3.1, infiltrators may provide a pathway to groundwater in case of accidental spills involving pollutants from certain types of industrial and commercial materials. The severity of such an event depends on the properties of the substance. Heavy hydrocarbons may be unable to flow through the porous media and effectively remain contained in the infiltrator, while lighter substances may easily migrate downwards. Some of these materials persist in groundwater for long periods and remediation is expensive, for example chlorinated hydrocarbons heavier that water. It should be noted that the effect of these types of accidents is not limited to infiltrators. Any stormwater control affected by such an event will be severely affected and will likely have to be rebuilt.

2.10   Karst Terrain

Many jurisdictions prohibit infiltration in karst terrain because of the concern of concentrated water inflows that may erode the karst and cause sinkholes. However, complete elimination of infiltration in karst does not allow groundwater replenishment, which may also cause structural stability problems in the surface because of air pockets. Limited infiltration in these areas using dispersed infiltrators is recommended as a compromise (Clark et al., 2009).

2.11   Urban Soils

Urban areas are typically underlain by highly disturbed soils. In general, compacted fill is not appropriate for infiltration. Although compacted soil may allow infiltration, local testing should be performed to determine actual infiltration rates. Amendments with organic matter have been used to recover infiltration capacity on these soils, but have shown mixed results (Clark et al., 2009). Typically, only a small amount of organic matter (less than 5% tilled into the upper layers) is needed to improve infiltration capacity.

2.12   Estimating the Life Span of Infiltrators

Most infiltrators fail because of surface clogging. Research on stormwater filters shows significantly reduced infiltration after approximately 5 to 25 kg/m^2 (1 to 5 lb/sq ft) of particulate solids have been loaded (Clark, 1996; 2000; Clark and Pitt, 2009). Healthy vegetation and a well-developed soil structure extend the useful life because more of the surficial soil depth is used to filter solids, while the roots of plants maintain flow channels. Clark et al. (2009) present methodologies for clogging calculations, which can be used to determine the life span of an infiltrator. In the simplest case, TSS loading can be estimated based on local event mean concentrations and the annual runoff volume. The load varies depending on the land use; TSS concentrations from roofs and established developments are lower than other areas. This load can be compared to the thresholds provided previously to estimate the time it would take for the infiltrator to experience noticeable decreases in infiltration. Engineers Australia (2006) applies this concept to set aside an area of the infiltrator that is expected to become clogged. Lenhart and Calvert (2006) present a method to estimate the life span of infiltrating surfaces using a volumetric approach.

3.0   INFILTRATION BASINS

An infiltration basin is essentially a dry basin (Chapter 6) with the soil–air interface as the outlet rather than orifices or weirs. The design capture volume typically includes WQV and, where site conditions allow, recharge volume and CPV. The general design requirements in Section 2 for drain time and infiltration area apply to infiltration basins.

A design consideration is which of the surface areas to recognize as the points of infiltration (i.e., the bottom, sidewalls, or both). All three approaches are in use. Inclusion of sidewalls becomes less relevant as the footprint of the infiltration basin increases; therefore, their exclusion provides for a conservative design. While the bottom can gradually clog from sediments, bacterial growth can reduce the infiltration rate of sidewalls. In addition, filter fabrics between gravel and/or soil media and underlying soils may clog.

3.1   Typical Applications

3.1.1   Physical Site Suitability

A qualified geotechnical engineer, geologist, or soil scientist should identify sites for infiltration basins with appropriate soil and hydrogeologic properties, which are critical for long-term performance (CASQA, 2003). A study of 23 infiltration basins in the Pacific Northwest showed better long-term performance in an area with highly permeable soils (Hilding, 1996). In this study, few of the infiltration basins had failed after 10 years. Consequently, the following guidelines for identifying appropriate soil and subsurface conditions should be followed:

- The entire design capture volume should infiltrate within 24 to 36 hours when the infiltration basin is new, and in no more than the maximum allowed ponding time of 48 to 72 hours within older basins and during cold weather when infiltration rates are reduced;

- Infiltration rates should be established by a qualified professional through a geotechnical investigation of subsurface soils and conditions, including long-term infiltration tests in multiple dimensions (e.g., single-ring or double-ring infiltrometer) and establishment of depth to rock, seasonal water tables, and other conditions limiting infiltration;

- For feasibility assessments, infiltration rates may be estimated using information for the site from the Natural Resources Conservation Service (NRCS) Soil

Survey (see the NRCS Web Soil Survey at http://websoilsurvey.nrcs.usda. gov/app/HomePage.htm), such as soil texture, HSG, the fraction of silt and clay, presence of a restrictive layer or seasonal high water table, and estimated hydraulic conductivity;

- Large, shallow basins over soils with lower surface infiltration rates (e.g., clayey soils) may be used in low-density development where sufficient space can be allocated for infiltration;

- The basin invert should be at least 1.2 m (4 ft) above the seasonal high groundwater elevation. Infiltrators should not be used in coarse, gravelly soils that do not remove pollutants or where pollutants able to migrate through the soil may be present. Instead, the designer should consider a filter with a media able to remove the anticipated pollutants (see Chapter 8), followed or underlain by an infiltrator to control the discharge of water (Pitt et al., 2010);

- Bedrock or an impervious soil layer should not exist within 1.2 m (4 ft) of the infiltrating surface;

- Infiltration basins should be located away from buildings, slopes, highway pavement, wells, and bridge structures. The separation distance depends on the volume of water infiltrated, the infiltration rate of the soil, the drain time of captured runoff, the depth of the basin, the presence of underlying impermeable layers, and other factors that may create subsurface flow gradients toward such areas. Sites constructed on fill, or where infiltration may destabilize a slope, should not be considered; and

- Adequate head should be available for off-line basins to operate flow splitter structures without ponding in the splitter structure or creating backwater upstream of the splitter.

Infiltration basins should completely drain between almost all storms. Otherwise, a groundwater mound may form under the basin. In soils with low hydraulic conductivity or underlying impermeable layers, groundwater mounding may slowly drain off laterally and then surface, causing a failure. These failures can be reduced if infiltrators are distributed uniformly throughout a development site to more closely reproduce the predevelopment hydrologic condition. Thus, instead of concentrating all site runoff at one infiltration basin, it is better to install many small infiltration basins throughout the development site. The designer should try to fit them into the landscape, even into individual residential or commercial lots.

If the aforementioned conditions do not rule out the site as a candidate for infiltration, its suitability can be assessed using a point-evaluation system suggested by Swedish Water and Sewage Works Association (1983) and Urbonas and Stahre (1993) that assesses various site conditions by assigning points for each category listed in Table 9.1.

A site with fewer than 20 points is considered unsuitable, whereas a site with more than 30 points is considered a good candidate. A site with 20 to 30 points is considered to be a fair candidate, with occasional standing water on the infiltration surfaces likely. This preliminary screening technique, however, is not a substitute for detailed site-specific engineering investigations. When the initial screening process finds the site acceptable, the infiltration surface area and the stormwater storage volume above this surface must then be determined. Table 9.1 suggests that the infiltration surface area include all pervious areas within the site in addition to the surface area of all stormwater controls able to infiltrate runoff (including strips and swales) and that the surface area be no less than one-half of the tributary impervious surface areas.

This screening procedure can best be illustrated by an example. An infiltration site is to manage runoff from a roof having a 1.0-ha (2.5-ac) area. The site is a new lawn with a surface area of 1.6 ha (4.0 ac) and a 0.20% slope. The topsoil is normal humus (e.g., loam), and the underlying soils are composed mainly of coarse silt. Determine if the site is suitable for infiltration.

Using the evaluation point system presented in Table 9.1, the results are as follows:

- The infiltrating area is 1.6 times larger than the impervious surface (i.e., $A_{INF} = 1.6\ A_{IMP}$) = 10 points;
- The top soil layer is of normal humus type = 5 points;
- The underlying soil layers are coarse silt = 5 points;
- The slope of the infiltration surface is 0.002 = 5 points;
- The infiltration surface is a new established lawn = 0 points; and
- The lawn is expected to have normal foot traffic = 3 points.

The total is 28 points for this site. This site is judged to be an above-average candidate, runoff is not likely to puddle frequently, and occasional periods of standing water are likely. It should be emphasized that this method is only an example of a feasibility evaluation process.

TABLE 9.1   Point system for the evaluation of potential infiltration sites (Urbonas and Stahre, 1993) (adapted by permission of Prentice-Hall, Inc., Upper Saddle River, New Jersey).

Site condition	Evaluation points to award
Ratio of tributary impervious area (A_{IMP}) to the infiltrating surface area (A_{INF})	
$A_{INF} > 2 \cdot A_{IMP}$	20 points
$A_{IMP} < A_{INF} < 2 \cdot A_{IMP}$	10 points
$0.5 \cdot A_{IMP} < A_{INF} < A_{IMP}$	5 points
Urban catchments with infiltrating surface areas less than one-half of the impervious surfaces are poor candidates.	
Surface soil layer type	
Coarse soils with low organic material content	7 points
Normal humus soil	5 points
Fine-grained soils with high ratio of organic matter	0 points
Underlying soils	
If the underlying soils are more coarse than surface soil, assign the same number of points for underlying soils as were given for the surface soil layer soils above.	
If the underlying soils are finer grained than the surface soils, use the following points:	
Gravel, sand of glacial till with gravel or sand	7 points
Silty sand or loam	5 points
Fine silt or clay	0 points
Slope (S) of the infiltrator's site	
S < 0.007 ft/ft (m/m)	5 points
0.007 < S < 0.020 ft/ft (m/m)	3 points
S > 0.020 ft/ft (m/m)	0 points
Vegetation cover	
Healthy natural vegetation cover	5 points
Lawn well established	3 points
Lawn new	0 points
No vegetation, bare ground	−5 points
Degree of traffic on infiltration surface	
Limited foot traffic	5 points
Average foot traffic (park, lawn)	3 points
Much foot traffic (playing fields)	0 points

3.1.2   Water Quantity Control

Infiltration basins reduce runoff volumes through groundwater recharge and evapo-transpiration. They may also provide peak-flow attenuation during flood events if an outlet is elevated above the ponding stage of the design capture volume, additional OFV or EFV is provided, and the outlet is designed to meet downstream flood control objectives.

3.1.3   Water Quality Control

Infiltration basins filter pollutants as runoff passes into the ground, where filtering, sorption, and biological processes remove pollutants. As with all infiltration systems, basins are capable of reducing runoff temperature.

3.2   Limitations

The aforementioned limitations cited for infiltrators in Section 2 apply to basins. Infiltration basins, like dry ponds, require a fairly large area for installation and may not be suitable for karst terrain. High water tables and impermeable soils limit their effectiveness. Pretreatment to remove coarse sediment is required for areas with potentially high TSS loading and recommended for all other sites. Regular maintenance is required to minimize clogging.

3.3   Design Procedure and Criteria

3.3.1   Typical Configurations

A typical infiltration basin looks like a dry basin except that it empties through the basin's bottom and has a pretreatment forebay and an emergency spillway. The basin must drain within the maximum allowed ponding time, typically no more than 48 to 72 hours. Otherwise, boggy and undesirable site conditions will occur and the vegetation lining these basins will die unless water-tolerant species are used. Vegetation should have long root systems to maximize evapotranspiration and be tolerant of both wet and dry conditions. Salt-tolerant vegetation should be used when salt is applied for winter pavement deicing. In addition, the available soil pore volume will amplify each 0.3 m (1 ft) of ponding depth into 1 to 1.2 m (3 to 4 ft) of groundwater depth mounding under the basins; these mounds need to drain off laterally to provide sufficient volume for subsequent events.

3.3.2   Pretreatment Unit

Forebays, vaults, strips, swales, or similar unit operations that promote sedimentation may be used as pretreatment units for infiltration basins to prevent high sediment loads from clogging the soil and reduce its infiltration capacity. If infiltration rates exceed 50 mm/h (2 in./hr), such as those commonly experienced in glacial outwash, fractured geology, or karst, then the runoff should be treated before infiltration.

3.3.3   Main Treatment Unit

During intense rainfall events, an infiltration basin cannot transfer stormwater to the soil void space within the root zone as rapidly as stormwater arrives at the basin. As a result, the infiltration basin should include a surface depression or underground reservoir to temporarily store this excess runoff. This volume should equal the design capture volume determined as described earlier in this chapter and in Chapter 3, plus any additional runoff volume required to meet groundwater recharge and flood control criteria. The area of the basin's bottom is estimated as

$$A = Vd/D_b \qquad (9.1)$$

where
   A = average surface area of the basin (m^2);
   Vd = design capture volume (m^3); and
   D_b = maximum depth of the basin (m).

The maximum depth of the basin is determined from the minimum values of eq. 9.2 and 9.3. The first equation determines the maximum depth that can infiltrate to the soil within the maximum allowed surface ponding time, t, as follows:

$$D_b = \text{FS}\, u\, k\, t \qquad (9.2)$$

where
   k = saturated hydraulic conductivity (m/h);
   t = maximum allowed ponding time (h);
   u = soil moderation factor; and
   FS = factor of safety.

The factor of safety accounts for uncertainties in the saturated infiltration rate and reductions caused by future clogging of the basin (0.3 to 0.5 is recommended). Saturated hydraulic conductivity, porosity, and field capacities for various soil types, shown in Table 9.2, may be used at the concept design stage. However, field hydraulic conductivity tests are essential to confirm the assumptions of saturated hydraulic conductivity. Soils are inherently heterogeneous and field tests can often misrepresent the areal hydraulic conductivity of a soil. Field tests of point soil hydraulic conductivity often lead to underestimating the areal hydraulic conductivity of clayey soils and overestimating sandy soils. Engineers Australia (2006) recommends that a soil moderation factor be applied to field hydraulic conductivity values (see Table 9.3).

TABLE 9.2   Typical infiltration rates of various soil groups.

NRCS hydrologic soil group	Typical soil texture	Saturated infiltration rate*		Porosity	Field capacity
		mm/h	In./hr		
A	Sand	200	8.0	0.437	0.062
A	Loamy sand	50	2.0	0.437	0.105
B	Sandy loam	25	1.0	0.453	0.190
B	Loam	12.7*	0.5	0.463	0.232
C	Silt loam	6.3*	0.25	0.501	0.284
C	Sandy clay loam	3.8	0.15	0.398	0.244
D	Clay loam and silty clay loam	<2.3	<0.09	0.465	0.325
D	Clay	<1.3	<0.05	0.475	0.378

*Values recommended for screening and selection only, as actual infiltration rates may vary significantly within each soil group. Minimum acceptable infiltration rate is 8 mm/h (0.3 in./hr). Soils with lesser rates can be used, but the infiltrators will require a large area.

TABLE 9.3   Soil moderation factors (Engineers Australia, 2006).

Soil type	Soil moderation factor (u) (To convert point k to areal k)
Sand	0.5
Sandy clay	1.0
Medium and heavy clay	2.0

The second equation for determining the basin depth is based on the available pore space under the basin to hold infiltrated volume. A conservative estimate would assume that the infiltrated water would mound directly under the footprint of the basin (i.e., no lateral movement during the event). Therefore, the entire design capture volume would need to fit into the pores in the soil below the basin under typical climatic conditions, limiting the maximum depth in the basin to

$$D_b = (p - f)D_g \tag{9.3}$$

where

D_g = depth below the basin to seasonal high groundwater or bedrock (m);
p = porosity of the soil (dimensionless); and
f = field capacity of the soil (dimensionless).

The smaller value of D_b determined in eq 9.2 and 9.3 is used to calculate the average surface area of the basin according to eq 9.1. The designer should grade the site so that the entire volume is stored at the calculated depth. Continuous simulation methods that integrate surface runoff, infiltration, groundwater recharge, and evapotranspiration are available to optimize basin sizing (see Chapter 14 for an overview of such methods). The area of the basin will have to be increased if it needs to handle snowmelt.

All infiltrating surfaces should be vegetated with grasses that can withstand and survive prolonged periods of inundation, followed by extended dry periods. Healthy vegetation is essential; without it, the surface soil pores quickly clog. Deep grass roots reopen soil pores and maximize evapotranspiration, even when considerable deposition of silt has occurred. Biological processes contribute to maintain the pore structure in the root zone (Emerson and Traver, 2008; Hatt et al., 2009). Eventually, the deposited sediment layer and old grass may need to be removed, the soils rehabilitated, and the basin revegetated.

3.3.4   Outlet Structure

In infiltration basins, the outlet for the design capture volume is the bottom of the facility. Outlets may be provided if the infiltration basin also provides peak-flow attenuation for larger design storms to prevent downstream flooding. See the recommendations for dry basins in Chapter 6.

3.4   Aesthetic and Safety Considerations

Infiltration basins should be vegetated to help maintain their infiltration capacity and to avoid unsightly conditions. Basins with insufficient infiltration capacity will form wet areas where wetland vegetation will grow. For safety reasons, basin side slopes should be no steeper than 4H:1V or the basin should be fenced. However, fences are often considered unappealing visually. In general, safety and aesthetic considerations for dry basins are applicable to infiltration basins. See Chapter 5 for a more detailed discussion of these issues.

3.5   Access and Maintenance Features

Infiltration basins must be accessed periodically to remove accumulated sediments to rejuvenate their infiltration capacity. Stable surfaces must be provided for maintenance vehicle access, but care should be taken not to compact the infiltrating surface.

3.6 Design Example

A 2.22-ha (5.5-ac) catchment located in Minneapolis, Minnesota, is located on sandy loam soils with saturated hydraulic conductivity k of 25 mm/h (1 in/h), a 3-m (10-ft) depth to the seasonal high water table D, and a maximum allowed ponding time t, of 48 hours. The catchment is 44% impervious (runoff coefficient $Rv = 0.3$). Using Table 9.2, the porosity of sandy loam soil p is 0.453, the field capacity f is 0.190, the soil moderation factor is 1.0, and a factor of safety of 0.5 is chosen.

First, determine the maximum infiltration depth and draw-down time for the basin using eq 9.2 and 9.3, as follows:

$$D_b = \text{FS } u\, k\, t$$

$$= (0.5)(1.0)(25 \text{ mm/h})(48 \text{ h})$$
$$= 0.6 \text{ m (2 ft)}$$
$$D_b = (p - f)D_g$$
$$= (0.453 - 0.190)\,(3 \text{ m})$$
$$= 0.8 \text{ m (2.6 ft)}$$

Based on these calculations, the lowest D_b, 0.6 m (2 ft), is used for sizing the basin, with a maximum ponding time of 48 hours. According to the methodology in Chapter 3, the mean precipitation P_{avg} of 12.7 mm (0.5 in.) for Minneapolis and the event capture ratio a of 1.545 for a 48-hour drain time are used to calculate the "maximized" volume for the infiltration basin, as follows:

$$P = P_{avg}\, a \tag{9.4}$$
$$= (12.7 \text{ mm})(1.545)$$
$$= 19.6 \text{ mm, or } 0.77 \text{ in.}$$

The design capture volume then is

$$Vd = R_v P\, A \tag{9.5}$$
$$= (0.3)(19.6 \text{ mm})(2.22 \text{ ha})$$
$$= 129 \text{ m}^3\text{, or } 4650 \text{ ft}$$

Using eq 9.1 and the maximum ponding depth D_b of 0.6 m (2 ft) establishes the basin's surface area at 215 m² (2350 sq ft). The total exfiltration rate then is

$$Q_{out} = A\, D_b/t \tag{9.6}$$
$$= (215 \text{ m}^2)(0.6 \text{ m})/48 \text{ h}$$
$$= 2.7 \text{ m}^3/\text{h, or } 96 \text{ cu ft/hr}$$

This exfiltration rate will empty the design volume in 48 hours. Tripling the basin's surface area to 645 m² (6940 sq ft) will empty the design volume in 16 hours at a rate of 8.1 m³/h (288 cu ft/hr). The designer should note that the resultant basin area occupies almost 3% of the total catchment area.

Next, check to see if the basin will handle prolonged snowmelt periods without overtopping. Using the snowmelt rates cited previously, the snowmelt rate for the site is 0.71 mm/h (0.028 in./hr), equal to a 15.6-m³/h (559-cu ft/hr) flowrate, which is nearly double the design rate of 8.1 m³/h (288 cu ft/hr). Further adjustment to the basin's size may be justified depending on the design snow pack.

4.0 INFILTRATION TRENCHES AND VAULTS

Infiltration trenches are small-scale infiltration systems designed to collect runoff and infiltrate it to the soil. Its name implies, the length of an infiltration trench is much greater compared to its width and depth. Trenches are filled with rock to support the earthen walls. Plastic lattice structures may be used in lieu of rock to increase the pore space and thus reduce the volume of the trench. Strips or other unit operations that remove suspended solids are deployed upstream of infiltration trenches to provide pretreatment. Infiltration vaults are similar to infiltration trenches, but have a permanent engineered cover and may be placed under parking areas.

4.1 Typical Applications

4.1.1 Physical Site Suitability

The same factors that affect an infiltration basin should be considered to assess site suitability for an infiltration trench. Therefore, if the following conditions are discovered or are likely to be at the site, stormwater infiltration is not recommended:

- Seasonal high groundwater is less than 1.2 m (4 ft) below the bottom of the infiltration trench or more depending on the anticipated pollutant loading, soil type, and relative emphasis on groundwater quality protection;

- Bedrock or impervious soils are within 1.2 m (4 ft) of the bottom of the infiltration trench;

- The infiltration trench is located within or on top of fill or recompacted soils; or

- Soils adjacent to the trench have estimated or field-measured saturated hydraulic conductivity of the soils is less than 2.0×10^{-5} m/s (6.5×10^{-5} ft/s).

If the aforementioned conditions do not rule out the site, the Swedish Water and Sewage Works Association (1983) provides additional feasibility guidance as described in Section 3.1.1.

4.1.2   Water Quantity Control

The main unit processes for water quantity afforded by infiltration trenches and vaults is volume reduction. Individually, infiltration trenches and vaults provide minimal peak attenuation because of their relatively small size. With distributed deployment of a significant number of devices, the watershed can experience considerable volume reduction and peak attenuation.

4.1.3   Water Quality Control

Unit processes for quality control include sorption and filtration. There could also be some biological activity taking place in the stone filling the trenches; however, this is nonexistent if synthetic devices are used. As noted earlier, sediment removed by the trench contributes to clogging. Thermal control occurs through cooling of runoff from heated surfaces upon contact with the soil.

4.2   Limitations

Constraints of infiltration trenches and vaults are similar to those of infiltration basins, with the exception that they are small-scale systems that do not require a large land area and they likely will not result in tree clearing or forest effects. Geology, soils, water table, and climate can all influence the effectiveness of these controls. Pretreatment to remove coarse sediment (larger than 0.075 mm) is required, as is regular maintenance to avoid clogging.

4.3   Design Procedure and Criteria

4.3.1   Typical Configurations

Infiltration trench design uses the pore volume of trench fill media as the storage volume. Table 9.4 lists the porosity of the more typical trench fill materials. The stone aggregate should be washed to remove dirt and fines before being placed in the trench. The bottoms of these trenches tend to clog first, often shortly after installation. As a result, the bottom of the trench is considered impervious and all water is assumed to infiltrate out only through its walls. Typically, long and deep trenches with flat or terraced bottoms are most efficient and require the least amount of porous media. The maximum trench depth is limited by trench wall stability, seasonal high groundwater levels, and the depth to any impervious soil layer. Trenches that are 1-m (3-ft) wide and 1- to 2-m (3- to 6-ft) deep seem to be most efficient.

TABLE 9.4   Porosity of commonly used granular materials.

Material	Effective porosity, %
Plastic crates	95
Crushed and blasted rock	30
Uniform-sized gravel	40
Graded gravel, 2 cm (0.75 in.)	30
Sand	25
Pit run gravel	15–25

4.3.2   Pretreatment Unit

The most important factor of infiltration trench longevity is to provide pretreatment to remove coarse sediment (0.075 mm and larger), typically using a swale or strip (see Chapter 7), followed by a sand layer overlaying the trench. If stormwater is permitted to enter the trench without first being filtered, pores in the media and adjacent soils will fill over time and the facility will fail.

Figure 9.4 illustrates an infiltration trench with a surface sand filter layer on top. This sand filter layer has to have sufficient surface area to permit stormwater to enter the trench with minimal ponding above it. However, some ponding volume will be needed above the sand filter to accept higher flow rates. Such a sand surface filter layer may also be provided within a modular pervious pavement. Other filter configurations are possible (Urbonas and Stahre, 1993). Infiltration trenches may also be arranged in systems. For example, an infiltration trench may also receive the effluent from a landscaped roof. Geotextiles are discouraged because they tend to clog quickly. All filter devices will need adequate routine maintenance to maintain design infiltration capacity.

4.3.3   Main Treatment Unit

Darcy's law provides a basis for estimating the rate at which water can infiltrate to the ground and through the sides of an infiltration trench.

$$q = FS\, u\, k \tag{9.7}$$

where
   q = specific discharge per bulk area of soil (m/s);
   FS = factor of safety;
   u = soil moderation factor; and
   k = hydraulic conductivity (m/s).

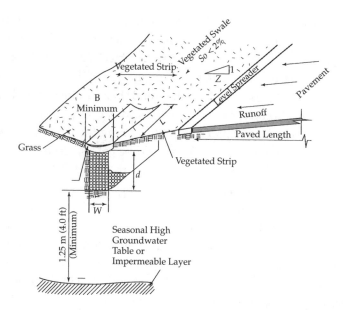

FIGURE 9.4 An infiltration trench with a sand filter layer for surface inflow (Urbonas and Stahre, 1993) (adapted by permission of Prentice Hall, Inc., Upper Saddle River, New Jersey).

Because the bottom of the facility is above high seasonal groundwater, the hydraulic gradient is assumed equal to 1 in Darcy's law, which results in eq 9.7, corresponding to flow in unsaturated media.

It is best to perform several site-specific hydraulic conductivity tests because hydraulic conductivities can vary by orders of magnitude for a single soil group. Section 2 of this chapter describes acceptable geotechnical investigations. For initial site screening and planning, hydraulic conductivity values typical of local soil types may be used, such as those listed in Table 9.2. The soil moderation factor, u, found in Table 9.3 should be applied to field hydraulic conductivity values to properly represent the areal hydraulic conductivity of the soil (Engineers Australia, 2006).

A factor of safety of 0.3 to 0.5 times the lowest field measured in situ hydraulic conductivities should be used for design purposes to account for eventual loss of infiltration capacity as sediments accumulate. An infiltration trench is expensive to construct and more expensive to rebuild. Therefore, being conservative in its design is appropriate. As stated in Section 2, the hydraulic conductivity is a function of temperature; therefore, performance during cold weather needs to be considered.

Depending on the stormwater management objective for the facility, the design capture volume of the trench must be established to effectively infiltrate recharge volume, WQV, and CPV discussed in Chapter 3. Larger storm events are typically routed around infiltration trenches to other controls designed to provide OFV and EFV. If the methodology in Chapter 3 for determining the maximized water quality volume is used to size the trench, WQV should be calculated using eq 3.1, 3.2, and 3.4 for a 12-hour drain time, using an event capture ratio a of 1.109. One alternative, particularly if the design rainfall intensity is significantly greater than the rate of infiltration, is to set the volume of the void space within the trench equal to the design capture volume, which can be a combination of recharge volume, WQV, or CPV. This approach yields a conservatively large design able to compensate for loss of storage and infiltration capacity over time. In areas with less intense design storms or higher infiltration rates, the routing calculation described in the infiltration trench design example typically yields a smaller trench volume.

The next step is to select a cross section for the trench and the type of fill material to define the void ratio (see Table 9.4). The trench is designed to infiltrate runoff through the sides; the bottom area is not included. The length is calculated through the trial-and-error process illustrated in the design example in Section 4.6.

Because the water depth in the trench varies during the storm, the sides of an infiltration trench are not fully inundated during most runoff events. To simplify the sizing process, the designer can assume that the average outflow rate is the result of one-half of the trench depth being inundated. With this assumption, the average effective area of infiltration for a rectangular trench footprint is $H(L + W)$, where H is the height of the trench, L the length, and W the width. The hydraulic gradient is assumed equal to 1. Thus, the infiltrated volume at time t is

$$V_{out} = A_{inf}\, q\, t \qquad (9.8)$$

where

V_{out} = volume infiltrated into the soil during the storm duration t (m³);

$A_{inf} = H(L + W)$ half of the total area of the sides of the infiltration trench (m²);

q = specific discharge per bulk area of soil, m/s (from eq 9.7); and

t = storm duration (s).

Similarly, for a storm duration t, the inflow into the trench is

$$Vd\,(t) = Rv\, I\, A\, t \qquad (9.9)$$

where

Rv = the runoff coefficient;

I = average storm intensity (m/s); and

A = drainage area (m^2).

The volume of water stored in the trench for a storm duration t, is

$$Vd(t) - V_{out}(t). \tag{9.10}$$

The maximum of this difference for various storm durations is the design volume for the trench, as follows

$$V = \max_t \left[Vd(t) - V_{out}(t) \right] \tag{9.11}$$

Once the volume of the trench has been determined, the length can be computed with knowledge of the height and width. Standard storage routing computations (e.g., Maidment, 1993) can be used to adjust the dimensions by simulating inflow to and outflow from the trench. An inflow hydrograph for the design event needs to be derived using appropriate hydrologic methods.

4.3.4   Outlet Structure

If an infiltration trench cannot be made sufficiently large to empty its fully available storage volume within the desired drain time, it is recommended that a collector pipe be installed at an appropriate elevation above the bottom to release the stored water slowly through a flow controller. The outlet of this pipe should be located so that it can be tied to a nearby stormdrain. The pipe is designed to supplement the infiltration outflow so that both combine to empty out the trench-full volume during the duration of rain time if the soil is not sufficiently permeable (Engineers Australia, 2006). This type of installation behaves like the underdrain in a filter (see Chapter 8). In addition, it is necessary to install an overflow spillway to safely convey storm events greater than the design capacity of the trench.

4.4   Aesthetic and Safety Considerations

Properly functioning infiltration trenches present few aesthetic and safety concerns. Clogged infiltration trenches with standing water are unsightly and can become a nuisance because of mosquito breeding. Standing water also can encroach into travel areas and be hazardous to traffic or threaten buildings with localized flooding. If the trench takes more than 72 hours to drain, then it must be rehabilitated. All dimensions of the trench should be increased by 50 mm (2 in.) or more, if necessary, to provide fresh surfaces for infiltration.

4.5 Access and Maintenance Features

Unlike infiltration basins, failure of an infiltration trench or vault can go unnoticed for long periods of time because the trench is out of sight. Therefore, a routine inspection program is needed to discover failed infiltration trenches. One or more observation wells with locked well caps should be provided to facilitate inspections. A record of water in the trench not draining within 2 days after a storm ends can indicate incipient failure and should be investigated. Care must be taken to avoid vehicular or excessive foot traffic over infiltrating surfaces. Grass clippings should not be allowed to accumulate over the trench.

4.6 Design Example

Table 9.5 presents an example of an infiltration trench design accomplished using a spreadsheet. After the known parameters are entered, the iterative process begins by entering an assumed trench length needed for storms of various intensities that represent rainfall events with the same return period (i.e., the intensity-duration-frequency curves discussed in Chapter 3) and calculating the "needed trench length." New "assumed length" values are entered until a balance is achieved between the "assumed length" and the maximum of the "needed" lengths for all storms. Table 9.5 presents the final solution. The resulting dimensions would be refined using a routing method to evaluate performance under various storm scenarios and their corresponding inflow hydrographs.

5.0 DRY WELLS

Dry wells are underground structures typically designed to infiltrate small volumes of stormwater. They may be configured as excavated pits filled with aggregate to prevent collapse (Connecticut DEP, 2004), deep manholes typically 0.6 to 1.2 m (2 to 4 ft) in diameter, small vaults with open or perforated bottoms that are typically surrounded by a gravel pack, or excavations filled with plastic crates. The last two configurations provide more storage and facilitate removal of accumulated sediment.

5.1 Typical Applications

5.1.1 Physical Site Suitability

Dry wells are appropriate for use in small drainage areas of 0.4 ha (1 ac) or less that generate low sediment loads. They should be placed in soils with sufficient hydraulic

TABLE 9.5   Example of infiltration trench sizing.

Tributary catchment area [A]:	2.2 ha (5.50 ac)
Impervious fraction [i]:	44%
Runoff coefficient [$Rv = 0.858\ i^3 - 0.78\ i^2 + 0.774\ i + 0.04$]:	0.3
Maximized rainfall depth ($I_{1\text{-hour}}$); $C = 1.0$ and 12-hour drain time:	1.3 cm (0.50 in.)
Soil's hydraulic conductivity:	0.3 mm/sec (0.001 ft/s)
Trench width (W):	0.9 m (3 ft)
Trench height (H):	1.8 m (6 ft)
Assumed length (L):	46 m (151 ft)
Hydraulic gradient:	1
Average infiltration outflow rate $Q_{out} = kH(L + W)$:	0.04 m³/s (1.39 cfs)
Rock media porosity (p):	0.35
Rainfall intensity I at duration t: $I = aI_{1\text{-hour}}/(T + b)^c$	$a = 28.5$ $b = 10.0$ $c = 0.786$

Storm duration (min)	Rainfall intensity (cm/h)	Inflow Vd (m²)	Outflow V_{out} (m³)	Volume stored (m³)	Needed trench volume (m³)	Needed trench length (m)
t	I	$Rv\ I\ A\ t$	$Q_{out}\ t$	(3) - (4)	(5)/p	(6)/WH
(1)	(2)	(3)	(4)	(5)	(6)	(7)
10	3.52	38.7	15.2	23.5	67	41
20	2.56	56.3	30.4	25.9	74	46*
30	2.04	67.3	45.6	21.7	62	38
40	1.71	75.3	60.8	14.5	42	26
50	1.48	81.6	76.0	5.6	16	10
60	1.31	86.7	91.2	−4.5	−13	−8

* Maximum value in column (6) matches the assumed value.
  Note: All values in bold are input data.

conductivity to allow reasonable rates of infiltration. In some communities, dry wells are used in lieu of a centralized stormdrain system. Dry wells have been used for decades as a stormwater discharge in areas with coarse soil such as glacial out-wash, fractured geology, or karst. The bottom of the dry well should be located at least 1.2 m (4 ft) above the seasonally high water table or bedrock as documented by on-site soil investigations.

5.1.2   Water Quantity Control

Dry wells function as infiltration systems to reduce the quantity of runoff from a site and recharge groundwater.

5.1.3   Water Quality Control

Unit processes for quality control include sorption and filtration. There could also be some biological activity taking place in the stone filling the wells. Thermal control occurs through reduction of runoff from heated surfaces and cooling upon contact with the fill material and soil.

5.2   Limitations

Dry wells are subject to underground injection control permits and regulations administered by the U.S. Environmental Protection Agency. Consequently, they should only be used to infiltrate relatively clean water such as rooftop runoff. Dry wells should not be used to infiltrate runoff containing significant suspended solid concentrations or soluble pollutants that could contaminate groundwater. Some communities now include pretreatment or a specified layer of media placed on top of the native soil. Dry wells should not be placed over fill materials, should be located a minimum of 3 m (10 ft) down slope from building foundations (or further, depending on geotechnical considerations), and, unless otherwise required, should be located at least 25 m (75 ft) away from

- Drinking water supply wells;
- Septic systems (any components); and
- Surface waterbodies.

5.3   Design Procedure and Criteria

5.3.1   Typical Configurations

Dry wells are small-scale infiltration devices similar to the infiltrators described in previous sections of this chapter. Siting, design, construction, and maintenance considerations for dry wells are similar to those of infiltration trenches.

5.3.2   Pretreatment Unit

Pretreatment should be provided to remove sediment, floatables, and oil and grease. Appropriate pretreatment technologies include strips, oil and water separators, leaf gutter guards, screen cleanouts at the base of roof leaders, roof washers for cisterns and rain barrels, catch basin inserts, or other pretreatment practices.

5.3.3   Main Treatment Unit

Dry wells should be designed to completely drain the design capture volume consisting of recharge volume, WQV, or CPV within 24 hours after the storm event. Dry wells should completely dewater between storms. A minimum draining time of 6 to 12 hours is recommended to provide adequate pollutant removal. Dry wells should be equipped with overflows to handle larger runoff volumes or flows.

Dry wells should only be used with soils having suitable capacity to infiltrate the design capture volume within the maximum allowed drain time of 48 to 72 hours or less, as confirmed through field testing. This limitation generally restricts application to well drained soils. One infiltration test and test pit or soil boring is recommended at the proposed location of the dry well.

The dry well should be filled with or surrounded by 40- to 80-mm (1.5- to 3-in.) diameter clean washed stone. Stone placed within excavated pit dry wells should be wrapped with filter fabric, if necessary, to prevent surrounding soil from intruding to the rock. Sediment-laden runoff entering dry wells should be pretreated to minimize clogging of filter fabrics. Excavated pit dry wells should be covered by a minimum of 300 mm (12 in.) of soil.

5.3.4   Outlet Structure

The outlet of a dry well is the soil. In some instances, it may be necessary to divert flows larger than the infiltration capacity of the dry well to a safe discharge point downstream in the storm drainage system.

5.4   Aesthetic and Safety Considerations

Without adequate treatment, dry wells should not be used to infiltrate runoff containing significant suspended solid concentrations or soluble pollutants that could contaminate groundwater.

5.5   Access and Maintenance Features

An observation well consisting of a well-anchored, vertical perforated polyvinyl chloride pipe with a lockable aboveground cap should be installed to monitor dry well performance.

6.0   PERMEABLE PAVEMENT

Permeable pavements are stormwater controls consisting of a load-bearing, durable but permeable paving surface course that rapidly passes the rainwater falling on it and any runoff flowing to it into an underlying layered structure where it is temporarily stored until it infiltrates to the underlying soil or is released slowly through an underdrain (see Figure 9.5). Permeable pavement can be installed as pervious asphalt, pervious concrete, permeable interlocking concrete pavers, concrete grids, or reinforced grass.

Permeable pavements reduce runoff volume while providing treatment, are unobtrusive, and may reduce development costs by reducing the need for other stormwater infrastructure such as inlets, pipes, and basins. Properly designed, installed, and maintained permeable pavement can infiltrate, or otherwise treat, the runoff from up to 100% of all storm events, depending on the size of the contributing drainage area, the infiltration properties of native soils, and the sediment concentrations in runoff onto the pavement. Permeable pavement able to infiltrate most stormwater in effect reduces the amount of directly connected impervious surface within a catchment. Pollutant removal may occur at the surface of the pavement, within the

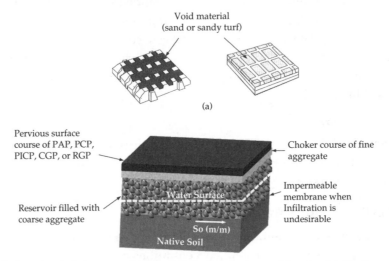

FIGURE 9.5   Permeable pavement: (a) two examples of individual concrete grid pavement and (b) typical cross section.

open-graded granular base course supporting the pavement, within an underground reservoir filled with coarse aggregate, and where water enters the underlying soil. Some designs incorporate a filter media within voids in the pavement or under the pavement to increase pollutant removal.

6.1   Typical Applications

6.1.1   Physical Site Suitability

The suitability of a pervious pavement system at a particular site depends on the loading criteria required of the pavement. Permeable paving is most commonly used where traffic volumes are light and where vehicle turning is minimal (e.g., parking areas, residential streets, cul-de-sacs, driveways, walkways, and patios). The surface may be a continuous permeable slab such that water infiltrates across the entire surface of the material or it can be built of impermeable blocks separated by open spaces and joints through which water can drain. Permeable pavement designed to infiltrate only the precipitation falling upon it has the lowest potential for surface clogging and water ponding. Designs that direct runoff from other paved and unpaved areas to the pervious pavement for infiltration experience larger sediment loads and water depths, increasing the potential for surface clogging and ponding.

Permeable paving may be used where grades, subsoils, drainage characteristics, and groundwater conditions are suitable. Slopes should be flat or gentle, or the underlying stone reservoir may be terraced. Neither the underlying soil nor the pavement subgrade should be compacted when installing permeable paving intended to infiltrate the captured runoff. However, compaction may be necessary to protect earth fill, buried utilities, or nearby basements from infiltrated water. If compaction is required, the aggregate underlying the permeable pavement will serve as a basin and should be provided with an underdrain regulated to discharge the captured runoff at the design drain time, as described in Chapter 3.

Experience has shown that pervious paving systems can be installed in a wide range of ground conditions. The vulnerability of local groundwater sources to pollution from the site should be low and the seasonal high water table should be at least 1.2 m (4 ft) below the surface.

The aforementioned concepts allow for categorizing areas where permeable pavement can be used in the following three types of sections (UDFCD, 2010):

- Full infiltration sections, where the water is allowed to infiltrate to the native soil and this soil has sufficient infiltration capacity to meet a given drain time;

- Partial infiltration sections, where the water is allowed to infiltrate to the soil below the facility, but the soil does not have sufficient infiltration resulting in longer drain times. An underdrain is needed to empty the reservoir; and

- No infiltration section, where the water may not be infiltrated to the soil below the facility because of groundwater issues or infrastructure at risk. An underdrain is needed to empty the reservoir and an impermeable liner must be installed above the native soil.

When an underdrain is needed, a flow control device must be installed to meet discharge requirements. A filter layer is needed to remove pollutants prior to discharge to the underdrain. An aggregate filter may be necessary at the interface of the gravel reservoir and the native soil to prevent migration of fine material into the reservoir.

Use of permeable pavement in highways is slowly being introduced. Pervious pavements that discharge horizontally to the side of the roadway have been used as a friction course on highways to minimize hydroplaning and reduce noise. Moreover, friction courses have demonstrated water quality benefits (Barrett, 2008). Some state transportation departments, such as the Ohio Department of Transportation (2010), have developed design criteria for use of permeable pavement along the curb of highways to infiltrate runoff from the entire highway cross section. However, concentrating runoff and its pollutants into a small area may clog the pavement, demanding more frequent maintenance and requiring higher hydraulic conductivities to infiltrate this concentrated volume to the soil.

Permeable pavements can be used in cold climates and are less likely to form ice on the surface than conventional pavements (UDFCD, 2010). Guidelines for design and installation of permeable pavement in cold climates have been developed by the University of New Hampshire Stormwater Center (2009).

6.1.2   Water Quantity Control

The main unit process for water quantity afforded by permeable pavement is stormwater volume reduction. Peak attenuation also takes place (Collins et al., 2008), even when the systems are lined and discharge through underdrains (CASQA, 2003). With distributed deployment on substantial portions of the watershed, significant volume reduction and peak attenuation can be realized. Horst et al. (2011) found that the infiltration rate of permeable pavement controls is cyclical, with higher infiltration rates during warmer periods and lower rates during colder periods.

6.1.3   Water Quality Control

Permeable pavements trap sediments at the pavement surface and further remove pollutants within the base course and underlying soil. Unit processes for quality control include sorption and filtration. There could also be some biological activity taking place in the stone filling the gravel reservoir. Thermal control occurs through reduction of runoff from heated surfaces and cooling upon contact with the fill material. Recent studies have demonstrated the pollutant reduction capability of permeable pavement (Barrett, 2008; Bean et al., 2007), although nitrate and nitrite removal seem to require the presence of a sand layer to act as a filter (Collins et al., 2010).

6.2   Limitations

There are some specific disadvantages associated with permeable pavement:

- Permeable pavement can become clogged if improperly installed or maintained or if excessive sediment reaches the pavement surface. However, this issue is countered by the ease with which small areas of paving can be cleaned or replaced when blocked or damaged.

- Historically, permeable pavements have not provided adequate load-bearing strength or durability for higher volume roadway use. Consequently, their use has been limited to highways with low traffic volumes, low axle loads, speed limits less than 50 km/h (30 mph), car parking areas, and other lightly trafficked or nontrafficked areas. Research into appropriate applications for pervious pavements on high-volume roadways is ongoing. As noted previously, permeable friction courses are being used to reduce hydroplaning and noise in highways (Barrett, 2008).

- Pervious pavement systems designed for infiltration should not be used in areas where heavy pollutant loads may be able to migrate into the soil, such as in industrial areas.

- Use of permeable pavement is restricted to gentle slopes, unless the underlying rock reservoir in the pavement is terraced or otherwise divided into cells that prevent reservoir water from flowing down slope (UDFCD, 2010).

- Permeable pavement is generally more expensive to install than traditional pavement. The cost gap, however, is closing as more installers enter the market.

- Inexperienced paving contractors cause failures in permeable pavement installations.

6.3 Design Procedure and Criteria

6.3.1 Typical Configurations

As mentioned previously, there are five types of permeable pavement. These are as follows:

- Pervious asphalt pavement, often called *porous asphalt*, consists of regular bituminous asphalt in which the fines have been screened and reduced, creating void spaces and making it permeable. The void space of porous asphalt is approximately 15%, compared to 2 to 3% for standard asphalt. The National Asphalt Pavement Association (2008) provides installation and maintenance guidance for pervious asphalt pavement.

- Pervious concrete pavement (PCP) is monolithically poured concrete produced by binding aggregate particles with a mortar created with water and cementitious materials. Minimal sand content creates a large porosity, typically between 15 and 25%. This high porosity and the weaker mortar bond result in less strength compared to conventional concrete. National industry standards and guidelines for PCP have been established by the American Concrete Institute (2008).

- Permeable interlocking concrete pavement (PICP) is achieved with high-strength concrete units separated by stone-filled joints that allow stormwater to infiltrate. The concrete units have beveled corners, spacers, ridges, or irregular slopes at the edges and are laid on an open-graded, single-sized granular base. The open surface is between 5 and 15% of the pavement surface. The stone filler and ridges in the joints help the pavers interlock and distribute vehicle loads. National industry installation guidelines for PICP have also been established by the Interlocking Concrete Pavement Institute.

- Concrete grid pavement (CGP) is made of flat lattices of modular units arranged in a continuous pattern (see Figure 9.5a). The open space in the lattice can be 20% of the surface and is filled with aggregate, sand, or planted with grass.

- Reinforced grass pavement (RGP), also known as *turf pavement systems*, refers to a number of systems such as plastic grids to increase the bearing capacity of turf while allowing a large fraction of open surface available for infiltration. Many of these systems are proprietary and require specific grass varieties that can survive intermittent load application. This type of permeable pavement is not designed to capture a particular volume, but to maintain a pervious surface.

- Porous gravel pavement uses the open-graded, single-sized granular base as both the driving surface and the rock reservoir subgrade.

Except for reinforced grass, all of the aforementioned systems share similar features. The subsequent discussion focuses on the generic configuration in Figure 9.5b, which illustrates a typical cross section applicable to the first four types of permeable pavements. While design mixes and specifications continue to evolve, typical permeable concrete and asphalt pavements consist of the following four permeable layers (from top to bottom):

- A pervious paving surface course;
- A "choker" course composed of intermediate-sized, open-graded aggregate such as American Association of State Highway and Transportation Officials (AASHTO) No. 57 washed aggregate, designed to provide a stable foundation for construction of the paving surface course and prevent its smaller, open-graded aggregate from migrating downward (AASHTO, 2010);
- A clean, uniformly graded coarse aggregate (e.g., AASHTO No. 3) serves as a gravel-filled reservoir to store runoff prior to infiltration or discharge; and
- A subgrade of native soil.

Design criteria in this section address permeable pavement systems that act as infiltrators, that is, pavements that pass runoff rapidly through the surface layer and into the open-graded (single-sized) granular base that serves as a rock-filled reservoir and provides storage until the stormwater can infiltrate to the underlying soil for treatment and groundwater recharge. Concrete grids pavement, PICP, and other similar systems where the voids in the surface are filled with sand or another filter media function like a filter and should be designed according to the criteria in Chapter 8, where the surface area of the filter is the area of the voids between the modular blocks. This observation also applies to underdrained permeable pavement where a filter is installed to treat stormwater prior to discharge to the underdrain.

6.3.2 Pretreatment Unit

Permeable pavements are prone to clogging where there is a sediment source. Adjacent earth slopes should be assumed to be potentially erodible sediment sources; as such, drainage from them should be directed away from the pavement to another stormwater control, where possible. Pretreatment is partially effective at controlling sediment loads in runoff that cannot be diverted away from the permeable pavement.

One method of pretreatment involves allowing the runoff to flow through a fully stabilized strip surrounding the pavement, designed according to the criteria in Chapter 7. In some installations, off-site runoff from fully stabilized areas is intercepted by a border of clean washed stone surrounding the pavement that extends up from the underlying stone reservoir and connects with perforated pipes to distribute stormwater through the rock reservoir (Adams, 2003). Such systems may also allow pavement runoff to overflow onto the rock reservoir in case the pavement clogs.

6.3.3   Main Treatment Unit

The permeable pavement should be designed to infiltrate the design capture volume, consisting of recharge volume, WQV, or CPV, into the underlying soil according to criteria presented in Chapter 3. Larger storm events should be safely conveyed from the permeable pavement facility. Water should rapidly pass through the surface of the permeable pavement to minimize surface ponding; this condition is readily achieved where the pavement is designed to infiltrate only the precipitation on its surface and is well maintained. Runoff from paved or unpaved areas directed toward the pervious pavement increases water depths on the surface and may convey sediments that reduce the infiltration capacity. If a filter layer is incorporated within the pavement, it should be designed, according to the criteria in Chapter 8, to pass the design capture volume rapidly enough to minimize surface ponding.

To protect the integrity of the pavement, the entire design capture volume should be contained in the gravel reservoir. As indicated previously, in situations of limited or no infiltration into the native soil, an underdrain is installed to dewater this reservoir. This underdrain can be perforated round pipe, flat geocomposite panel pipe, or other suitable conveyances. The drainage system should be placed at an elevation within the reservoir that allows the volume of runoff captured below the drainage system to infiltrate to the underlying soil within the specified drain time (e.g., 48 to 72 hours).

The reservoir volume placed above the drainage system behaves as a basin that temporarily stores the fraction of design capture volume unable to infiltrate to the soil. The drainage system should regulate the discharge, as necessary, to provide appropriate peak-flow attenuation for pollutant removal, channel protection, and flood control. Flow regulation may be provided by the size, shape, and perforation pattern of the drainage system itself, or a restrictive orifice sized to achieve peak-flow attenuation goals may be provided at the discharge point of the drainage system. Additional guidelines for designing this underground reservoir may be found in Chapter 6.

The design of each layer of pavement must be determined by the likely traffic loadings and their required operational life. To provide satisfactory performance, the following criteria should be considered:

- Any permeable pavement must be constructed of proper materials including aggregate gradation and durability and controlled concrete water content;

- The subgrade should be able to sustain traffic loading without excessive deformation;

- The granular capping and sub-base layers should give sufficient load-bearing to provide an adequate construction platform and base for the overlying pavement layers; and

- The pavement materials should not crack or suffer rutting under the influence of traffic. This property is controlled by the horizontal tensile stress at the base of the layers.

For performance and durability, permeable pavements must be installed by a qualified, experienced contractor. Among the criteria for such a contractor is a special pervious installer certification by the National Ready Mixed Concrete Association (2010). Paving blocks used for permeable pavements should meet or exceed American Society for Testing and Materials (2010) Standard Specifications for Solid Concrete Interlocking Pavement Units to minimize risk of abrasion and damage.

The structural design of permeable pavement follows the same criteria and procedures as impermeable pavements. Software typically used for conventional pavement design can be used to properly design permeable pavements by entering the known characteristics of pervious concrete material and expected subgrade moisture conditions. The following factors should be considered in the design and specification of materials:

- Pervious pavements use materials with high permeability and void space. Therefore, the stiffness of the materials must be considered.

- Water present during construction can soften and weaken materials and must be accounted for in pavement structural design.

- Existing design methods assume full friction between layers. Any geosynthetics necessary in the design must be carefully specified to minimize loss of friction between layers.

- Pervious asphalt pavement loses adhesion and becomes brittle as air passes through the voids. Its durability may be lower than conventional materials.

- Most designs line the bottom and sides of the rock reservoir with geotextiles to prevent migration of finer-grain materials from underlying and surrounding uncompacted soils from entering the voids.

- Pervious pavements require a single size grading or a controlled, limited mixture of different sizes to produce open voids. The choice of materials is, therefore, a compromise between stiffness, permeability, and storage capacity.

- Because the sub-base and capping will be in contact with water for a large part of the time, the strength and durability of the aggregate particles when saturated and subjected to wetting and drying should be assessed.

- A uniformly graded single-size material cannot be compacted and is liable to move when construction traffic passes over it. This effect can be reduced by the use of angular crushed rock material with a high surface friction. In pollution control terms, these layers represent the site of long-term chemical and biological pollutant sorption and degradation processes. In addition to their structural strength properties, construction materials should be selected for their ability to sustain such processes. In general, this means that materials should create neutral or slightly alkaline conditions and should provide favorable sites for colonization by microbial populations.

- Whenever the permeable pavement is expected to infiltrate water to the underlying soil, the pavement subgrade should be placed at least 1 m (3 ft) above the seasonal high groundwater and at least 1.2 m (4 ft) above bedrock.

6.3.4   Outlet Structure

Permeable pavement applications able to infiltrate all runoff do not require an outlet. When the underlying soils, groundwater depth, or bedrock do not qualify the site for stormwater infiltration, permeable pavement accompanied by a regulated drainage system can be designed to be an underground detention facility using criteria from Chapter 6. As mentioned earlier, the facilities need to be underdrained (e.g., with perforated pipes installed at 3- to 8-m [10- to 25-ft] intervals). The release rate is controlled by a flow regulator, such as an orifice, which is designed to empty the pore storage volume within the specified drain time.

6.4   Aesthetic and Safety Considerations

Pervious concrete and asphalt pavements have rougher surfaces than conventional pavements, which affects site aesthetics. The additional roughness can cause more severe skin abrasions if a person falls. By eliminating ponded water, permeable pavements are less prone to icing over, thereby enhancing safety. Voids within modular paving materials may create safety problems for pedestrians (e.g., high-heeled shoes), which can be alleviated by providing walkways that do not contain voids.

6.5 Access and Maintenance Features

Permeable pavement is prone to clogging depending on the amount of sediment deposition on the pavement and the frequency of maintenance. Sediment deposition tends to accumulate on or directly below the pavement surface and can be removed by high-power vacuuming, which restores the pavement's porosity and permeability. Dougherty et al. (2011) describe a rapid procedure to evaluate the infiltration capacity of pervious concrete. Faster clogging rates occur in areas with extensive winter sanding, increasing required maintenance frequency. Semifluid binders in some asphalt pavements may migrate into voids within the pavement, causing clogging. Pavement sealers should never be used on permeable pavements. After being sealed, this type of pavement has to be replaced.

Permeable interlocking concrete pavement seems to clog at a slower rate than asphalt and concrete pervious pavement and has a good record of service under a wide range of climatic conditions. The open spaces of CGP can be cleaned out by vacuuming or, if severely clogged, by removing the vegetated soil or the sand layer and replacing it with fresh material. Joint fill should be routinely replaced after vacuuming. Individual blocks can settle and become misaligned if the pavement is not properly installed.

7.0 REFERENCES

Adams, M. (2003) Porous Asphalt Pavement with Recharge Beds: 20 Years and Still Working. *Stormwater*, **4** (3).

American Association of State Highway and Transportation Officials (2010) *Standard Specifications for Transportation Materials and Methods of Sampling and Testing,* 30th ed.; ISBN No. 1–5605 1–479–4; American Association of State Highway and Transportation Officials: Washington, D.C.

American Concrete Institute (2008) *ACI 522.1–08 Specification for Pervious Concrete Pavement;* American Concrete Institute: Farmington Hills, Michigan.

American Society for Testing and Materials (2010) Standard Specifications for Solid Concrete Interlocking Pavement Units; ASTM-C936/C936M-09; American Society for Testing and Materials: West Cochohocken, Pennsylvania.

Barrett, M. E. (2008) Effects of a Permeable Friction Course on Highway Runoff. *J. Irrigation Drainage Eng.*, **134** (5), 646.

Bean, E. Z.; Hunt, W. F.; Bidelspach, D. A. (2007) Evaluation of Four Permeable Pavement Sites in Eastern North Carolina for Runoff Reduction and Water Quality Impacts. *J. Irrigation Drainage Eng.*, **133** (6), 583.

Bouwer, H. (1986) Intake Rate: Cylinder Infiltrometer. In *Methods of Soil Analysis. Part 1*, 2nd ed.; Klute, A. (Ed.); Agronomy Monograph 9; ASA and SSSA: Madison, Wisconsin.

Bouwer, H.; Rice, R. C. (1976) A Slug Test for Determining Hydraulic Conductivity of Unconfined Aquifers with Completely and Partially Penetrating Wells. *Water Resour. Res.*, **12,** 423.

Braga, A.; Horst, M.; Traver R. G. (2007) Temperature Effects on the Infiltration Rate through an Infiltration Basin BMP. *J. Irrig. Drainage Eng.*, **133** (6), 593–601.

California Stormwater Quality Association (2003) *New Development and Redevelopment Handbook;* California Best Management Practice Handbooks, TC-10, TC-11, and SC-20; California Stormwater Quality Association: Menlo Park, California.

Carlton, G. B (2010) *Simulation of Groundwater Mounding Beneath Hypothetical Stormwater Infiltrated Basins;* U.S. Geological Survey Scientific Investigations Report, 2010–5102; U.S. Geological Survey: Reston, Virginia.

Clark, S. E. (1996) *Evaluation of Filtration Media for Stormwater Runoff Treatment.* M.S. Thesis, University of Alabama at Birmingham, Alabama.

Clark, S. E. (2000) Urban Stormwater Filtration: Optimization of Design Parameters and a Pilot-Scale Evaluation. Ph.D. Dissertation, University of Alabama at Birmingham, Alabama.

Clark, S. E.; Pitt, R. (2009) Solids Removal in Stormwater Filters Modeled Using a Power Equation. *J. Environ. Eng.*, **135** (9), 896.

Clark, S. E.; Baker, K. H.; Treese, D. P.; Mikula, J. B.; Siu, C. Y. S.; Burkhardt, C. S. (2009) *Sustainable Stormwater Management: Infiltration vs. Surface Treatment Strategies;* Project 04-SW-3; Water Environment Research Foundation: Alexandria, Virginia.

Collins, K. A.; Hunt, W. F.; Hathaway, J. M. (2008) Hydrologic Comparison of Four Types of Permeable Pavement and Standard Asphalt in Eastern North Carolina. *J. Hydrologic Eng.*, **13** (12), 1146.

Collins, K. A.; Hunt, W. F.; Hathaway, J. M. (2010) Side-by-Side Comparison of Nitrogen Species Removal for Four Types of Permeable Pavement and Standard Asphalt in Eastern North Carolina. *J. Hydrologic Eng.*, **15** (6), 512.

Connecticut Department of Environmental Protection (2004) *2004 Connecticut Stormwater Quality Manual;* Connecticut Department of Environmental Protection: Hartford, Connecticut.

Dougherty, M.; Hein, M.; Martina, B. A.; Ferguson, B. K. (2011) Quick Surface Infiltration Test to Assess Maintenance Needs on Small Pervious Concrete Sites. *J. Irrig. Drainage Eng.*, **137** (8), 553.

Emerson, C. H.; Traver R. G. (2008) Multiyear and Seasonal Variation of Infiltration from Storm-Water Best Management Practices. *J. Irrig. Drainage Eng.*, **134** (5), 598–605.

Engineers Australia (2006) *Australian Runoff Quality—A Guide to Water Sensitive Urban Design;* Wong, T. H. F., Ed.; Engineers Media: Crows Nest, New South Wales, Australia.

Fassman, E.; Blackbourn, S. D. (2011) Road Runoff Water Quality Mitigation by Permeable Modular Concrete Pavers. *J. Irrigation Drainage Eng.*, **138** (1), 177.

Ferguson, B. K. (1994) *Stormwater Infiltration;* Lewis Publishers: Boca Raton, Florida.

Haselbach, L. M. (2010) Potential for Clay Clogging of Pervious Concrete under Extreme Conditions. J. Hydrologic Eng., **15,** 67.

Hatt, B. E.; Fletcher, T. D.; Deletic, A. (2009) Hydrologic and Pollutant Removal Performance of Stormwater Biofiltration Systems at the Field Scale. *J. Hydrol.*, **365** (3–4), 310–321.

Hilding, K. (1996). Longevity of Infiltration Basins Assessed in Puget Sound. *Watershed Protection Tech.*, **1** (3), 124.

Horst, M.; Welker, A. L.; Traver, R. G. (2011) Multiyear Performance of a Pervious Concrete Infiltration Basin BMP. *J. Irrig. Drainage Eng.*, **137** (6), 352.

Le Coustumer, S.; Fletcher, T. D.; Deletic, A.; Potter, M. (2008) *Hydraulic Performance of Biofilter Systems for Stormwater Management: Lessons from a Field Study;* Facility for Advancing Water Biofiltration and Melbourne Water Corporation (Healthy Bays and Waterways): Melbourne, Victoria, Australia.

Lenhart, J.; Paula, C. (2007) "Mass Loading and Mass Load Design of Stormwater Filtration Systems. *Proceedings of the ASCE/EWRI, World Environmental and Water Resources Congress,* Tampa, Florida.

Los Angeles and San Gabriel Rivers Watershed Council (2005) *Los Angeles Basin Water Augmentation Study Phase II Final Report.* http://www.swrcb.ca.gov/ water_issues/programs/climate/docs/resources/labwas_phase2report2005. pdf (accessed Nov 15, 2010).

Machusick, M.; Welker, A.; Traver, R. (2011) Groundwater Mounding at a Storm-Water Infiltration BMP. *J. Irrigation Drainage Eng.,* **137,** 154.

Maidment, D. (Ed.) (1993) *Handbook of Hydrology;* McGraw-Hill: New York.

National Asphalt Pavement Association (2008) *Porous Asphalt Pavements for Stormwater Management: Design, Construction, and Maintenance Guide;* Information Series 131; National Asphalt Pavement Association: Lanham, Maryland.

National Ready Mixed Concrete Association (2010) *Pervious Concrete Certification Program.* http://www.nrmca.org/Education/Certifications/Pervious_ Contractor.htm (accessed May 16, 2011).

Ohio Department of Transportation (2010) Location and Design Manual, Volume 2, Drainage Design, Section 1117.1 Exfiltration Trench; Ohio Department of Transportation: Columbus, Ohio.

Pitt, R.; Clark, S.; Steets, B. (2010) Engineered Bioretention Media for Industrial Stormwater Treatment. *Proceedings of the 2010 Watershed Management Conference: Innovations in Watershed Management under Land Use and Climate Change;* Madison, Wisconsin; Aug 23–27.

Saxton, K. E. (2009) Soil Water Characteristics: Hydraulic Properties Calculator. http://hydrolab.arsusda.gov/soilwater/Index.htm (accessed Oct 2011).

Saxton, K. E.; Rawls, W. J. (2006) Soil Water Characteristic Estimates by Texture and Organic Matter for Hydrologic Solutions. *Soil Sci. Soci. Am. J.,* **70,** 1569–1578.

Smith, D. R.; Hunt, W. F. (2010) Structural/Hydrologic Design and Maintenance of Permeable Interlocking Concrete Pavement. *Proceedings of the Green Streets and Highways 2010: An Interactive Conference on the State of the Art and How to Achieve Sustainable Outcomes;* Denver, Colorado; Nov 14–17.

Swedish Water and Sewage Works Association (1983) *Local Disposal of Storm Water;* Publication VAV P46; Swedish Water and Sewage Works Association: Stockholm, Sweden.

University of New Hampshire Stormwater Center (2009) *UNHSC Design Specifications for Porous Asphalt Pavement and Infiltration Beds;* University of New Hampshire Stormwater Center: Durham, New Hampshire.

U.S. Department of Agriculture (2009) *National Engineering Handbook, Title 210-VI, Part 630, Chapter 7 Hydrologic Soil Groups;* U.S. Department of Agriculture, Natural Resources Conservation Service: Washington, D.C.

Urban Drainage and Flood Control District (2010) Urban Storm Drainage Criteria Manual, Volume 3. http://www.udfcd.org/downloads/down_critmanual_volIII.htm (accessed July 9, 2011).

Urbonas, B. R.; Stahre, P. (1993) *Stormwater: Best Management Practices and Detention for Water Quality, Drainage, and CSO Management;* Prentice Hall: Englewood Cliffs, New Jersey.

U.S. Department of the Interior (1990) Procedure for Performing Field Permeability Testing by the Well Permeameter Method (USBR 7300–89). In *Earth Manual, Part 2, A Water Resources Technical Publication,* 3rd ed.; U.S. Department of the Interior, Bureau of Reclamation: Denver, Colorado.

Wu, L.; Pan, L. (1997) A Generalized Solution to Infiltration from Single-Ring Infiltrometers by Scaling. *Soil Sci. Soc. Am. J.,* **61,** 1318–1322.

Zhang, Z.; Tumay, M. T. (2003) *The Nontraditional Approaches in Soil Classification Derived from the Cone Penetration Test;* ASCE Special Publication No. 121, Probabilistic Site Characterization at the National Geotechnical Experimentation Sites. American Society of Civil Engineers: Reston, Virginia.

8.0 SUGGESTED READINGS

California Department of Transportation (2003) *Infiltration Basin Site Selection Study;* Report No. CTSW-RT-03–025; California Department of Transportation: Sacramento, California.

Ferguson, B. K. (2005) *Porous Pavements;* CRC Press: Boca Raton, Florida.

Florida Department of Environmental Protection (1988) *The Florida Development Manual: A Guide to Sound Land and Water Management*; Florida Department of Environmental Protection, Nonpoint Source Management Section: Tallahassee, Florida.

Jerome W. Morrissette & Associates Inc. (1998) *Stormwater Facilities Performance Study: Infiltration Pond Testing and Data Evaluation*; Jerome W. Morrissette & Associates Inc.: Olympia, Washington.

Massman, J. W. (2003) *A Design Manual for Sizing Infiltration Ponds*; Final Research Report 578.2; Washington State Department of Transportation: Olympia, Washington.

Minnesota Pollution Control Agency (2005) *State of Minnesota Stormwater Manual*; Minnesota Pollution Control Agency: St. Paul, Minnesota.

Roesner, L. A.; Urbonas, B.; Sonnen, M., Eds. (1989) Design of Urban Runoff Quality Controls; *Proceedings of an Engineering Foundation Conference on Current Practice and Design Criteria for Urban Quality Control*; American Society of Civil Engineers: New York.

Schueler, T. R. (1987) *Controlling Urban Runoff: A Practical Manual for Planning and Designing Urban BMPs*; Metropolitan Washington Council of Governments: Washington, D.C.

Smith, D. R. (2007) *Permeable Interlocking Concrete Pavements*, 3rd ed.; Interlocking Concrete Pavement Institute: Herndon, Virginia.

Urbonas, B. R.; Roesner, L. A., Eds. (1986) Urban Runoff Quality—Impact and Quality Enhancement Technology. *Proceedings of an Engineering Foundation Conference on Current Practice and Design Criteria for Urban Quality Control*; American Society of Civil Engineers: New York.

U.S. Environmental Protection Agency (1994) *Potential Groundwater Contamination from Intentional and Nonintentional Stormwater Infiltration*; EPA-600/R-94–051; U.S. Environmental Protection Agency: Washington, D.C.

Chapter 10

Gross Pollutant Traps and Mechanical Operations

(continued)

(continued)

1.0 BASIC DESIGN PRINCIPLES

1.1 Description

A gross pollutant trap (GPT) is a unit operation designed to remove trash, litter, debris, coarse sediment, vegetation, and other large pollutants from stormwater. This group of stormwater controls primarily uses the water quality unit processes of screening and skimming. Gross pollutant traps that remove pollutants primarily by screening include screens, nets, baskets, and racks, while hoods primarily use skimming to remove pollutants.

Gross pollutants are large-size pollutants that can impair aquatic habitat, injure aquatic biota, degrade aesthetic conditions, threaten human health, and cause clogging of drainage infrastructure. By virtue of remaining within the flow, gross pollutants may undergo a variety of physicochemical reactions that create a second source of water pollution.

The size designation of what constitutes a gross pollutant is still under debate. The Los Angeles Regional Water Quality Control Board, Los Angeles, California, has created a trash total maximum daily load (TMDL) regulation that places the distinction at 5 mm, 0.2 in. (LARWQCB, 2001). Sansalone and Kim (2008) recommended a formal delineation at 75 μm (0.0030 in.), which is the limit between fine sands and silt per American Society for Testing and Materials D422, "Standard Test Method for Particle-Size Analysis of Soils." The U.S. Geological Survey (2005) has used 63 μm (0.0025 in.) to distinguish silt and sand from sand-suspended sediments. The American Society of Civil Engineers (ASCE) Committee on Gross Solids has proposed to formalize a classification following more thorough studies (see Figure 10.1) (Roesner et al., 2007). The ASCE proposed classification scheme (England and Rushton, 2007) includes the following classes:

- Litter—anthropogenic trash or rubbish, such as paper, plastic, polystyrene products, metal, and glass greater than 4.75 mm (0.19 in.) or no. 4 U.S. Standard Sieve Size;

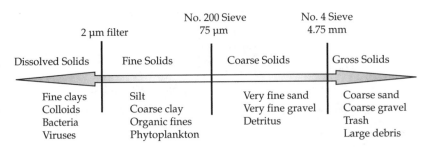

FIGURE 10.1   Solids size classification scheme (after Roesner et al., 2007).

- Organic debris—for example, leaves, branches, seeds, twigs, and grass clippings greater than 4.75 mm (0.19 in.); and

- Coarse sediments—organics or inorganics that can be derived from soils, pavement, building materials, litter, or other materials greater than 75 μm (0.003 in.) or no. 200 U.S. Standard Sieve Size.

Currently, only a handful of gross solids studies have sought to classify the various types of litter and debris that make up gross pollutants. Sartor and Boyd (1972) originated much of the research in an early U.S. Environmental Protection Agency study that defined the knowledge of street-surface pollution. This study found a high variability in loading rates based on land use type samples from eight cities in the United States. A South African study found that litter wash-off rates varied from 0.53 to 96 kg/ha-y for residential areas (Armitage et al., 1998). A series of Australian studies found similar variability (Allison, 1998a; 1998b). The California Department of Transportation (2000) performed a litter management pilot study and found that freeway surfaces generated 97.6 L/ha (892.6 ft³/mi²). There is no consistent relationship between litter volume and mass because litter is generated in such a variety of sizes and shapes and can change with time and degradation (URS Corporation, 2004). A summary of these studies is presented in Table 10.1. Another study performed by the City of New York (HydroQual, 1995) found that 2.3 floatable litter items per day per 30 m (100 ft) of curb were discharged through storm drain inlets; the total litter load was two times this floatables quantity. The City of New York study also characterized the types of litter collected (see Table 10.2).

1.2 Typical Applications

Traditionally, gross pollutants have been screened by either adding bars or grates in the front of inlet openings or by adding sumps built into storm drain inlets, which are

TABLE 10.1 Litter loading data.

Source	Land use	Loading rate
Ballona Creek and Wetland Trash TMDL (LARWQCB, 2001)	Default	9.3 L/ha (640 gal/sq mile), or 0.009 m³/ha (85.6 cu ft/sq mile) Based on uncompressed litter
Ballona Creek and Wetland Trash TMDL (LARWQCB, 2001)	Freeways	13.1 kg/ha (7479.4 lb/sq mile), or 0.1 m³/ha (892.6 cu ft/sq mile)
South Africa (Armitage et al., 1998)	Residential	0.53 kg/ha·yr (0.47 lb/ac/yr), Minimum residential value
South Africa (Armitage et al., 1998)	Residential	96 kg/ha·yr (86 lb/ac/yr), Maximum residential value
Australia (Allison et al., 1998b)	Urban	30 dry kg/ha·yr (27 lb/ac/yr)
Australia (Allison et al.,1998a)	Commercial / residential / light industrial mix	81 and 236 g/ha-storm (46 and 135 lb/sq mile-storm) Noted for individual storm
Sartor and Boyd (1972) Residential	Low/old/single Med/new/single Low/old/multi Med/old/multi	310 kg/km (1100 +/− lb/curb mile) 140 kg/km (500 +/− lb/curb mile) 280 kg/km (1000 +/− lb/curb mile) 340 kg/km (1200 +/− lb/curb mile)
Sartor and Boyd (1972) Industrial	Light Medium Heavy	650 kg/km (2300 +/− lb/curb mile) 540 kg/km (1900 +/− lb/curb mile) 1130 kg/km (4000 +/− lb/curb mile)
Sartor and Boyd (1972) Commercial	Shopping center Central business district	113 kg/km (400 +/− lb/curb mile) 85 kg/km (300 +/− lb/curb mile)

known as *catch basins* in the United States and *gully pots* in the United Kingdom and the British Commonwealth. Lager et al. (1977) proposed sizing of such catch basin sumps to have the following dimensions: if the outlet pipe is of diameter D, then the outlet pipe invert should be 2.5 D below street level and the catch basin sump bottom should be 4 D below street level.

Pitt (1985) reported that for these traditionally sized sumped basins, pollutant removals of conventional pollutants such as total and suspended solids may be reduced by up to 45% for low gutter flows, and that sediments will accumulate until they reach 60% capacity of the sump, at which point equilibrium will occur between scour and new depositions. This study, which sampled more than

TABLE 10.2   Types of floatable litter found on the streets of New York City.

Category	No. of items (%)	Wt. of items (%)	Density, g/L (lb/cu ft)
Plastics	57.2	44.3	44.9 (2.8)
Metals	18.9	12.0	60.9 (3.8)
Paper	5.9	4.0	32.0 (2.0)
Wood	5.9	5.3	123 (7.7)
Polystyrene	5.4	1.3	11.2 (0.7)
Cloth/fabric	2.5	12.5	133 (8.3)
Sensitive items	1.7	0.4	N/A
Miscellaneous	1.0	3.6	157 (9.8)
Glass	0.4	15.6	221 (13.8)

200 locations in Bellevue, Washington, including mixed residential and commercial drainage areas, found that sediment recovered from catch basins corresponded to the largest particles washed from the streets. These particles had a smaller median particle size than dirt found on the street that could be mechanically removed by street cleaning.

Pitt and Field (1998) further researched catch basin configurations, including the addition of screens and hoods, and found that the only arrangement to produce statistically significant removals of conventional pollutants was the traditional sumped catch basin arrangement. The addition of a screen or a hood did not produce a significant difference between influent and effluent waters for total suspended solids, suspended solids, turbidity, or color.

In the southwestern United States, catch basins typically do not contain the sumps that are designed in other regions' catch basin standard drawings or plans. More recently, local health departments have enforced this practice so that there are no locations of freestanding water for more than 3 days; this measure helps regulate vector pathways for mosquito development.

1.2.1 Physical Site Suitability

Gross pollutant traps can be designed as additions to various elements of drainage infrastructure, as illustrated in Figure 10.2. Gross pollutant traps can be deployed at the entrance to the storm drain system, within the storm drain system, or at the outlet from a storm drain system into another conveyance or receiving water. Inline and

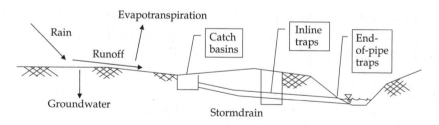

FIGURE **10.2** Typical applications of gross pollutant traps.

end-of-pipe devices can be configured with screens, racks, or nets. Some configurations, such as baskets and inclined wedge-wire screens, require a certain amount of elevation drop to properly function. Traps may also be added as inline installations, such as in a vault with a given trap mechanism.

1.2.2 Water Quantity Control

Gross pollutant traps are typically designed to convey flow through the system with no storage or peak-flow attenuation. Partial clogging of the trap should be assumed when sizing the trap to pass the design flow; bypasses are incorporated to some devices for large, infrequent events or in instances when the trap has become completely clogged with debris.

1.2.3 Water Quality Control

All traps work by capturing gross solids in a location that is easily accessible for poststorm retrieval. Traps are not designed to actually perform any treatment on the trapped items. Some traps have been modified to include media for other unit processes, including oil and grease sorption.

Depending on the arrangement, traps may provide sedimentation and may be designed to hold water and wet gross solids (e.g., in sumps), or without such so that collected items may dry. One advantage to dry collections is the reduced weight and the decreased potential for physicochemical reactions with the water that may add to the fraction of dissolved pollutants. The rate of accumulation is based on the size of the opening relative to the size, shape, and direction of the gross solids either screened or skimmed by the trap.

1.3 Limitations

Maintenance is the most significant constraint for these stormwater controls. All GPTs must be cleaned out regularly to maintain their function. Without a complete operations and maintenance plan that is legally enforceable, proper cleaning is challenging. Without enforcement, traps often only get cleaned after they are clogged because subsequent flooding makes their inoperability obvious.

1.4 Access

Access is essential to maintaining GPTs. Siting the traps for ease of collection and proper cleaning is also essential. Therefore, the designer should eliminate as many hazards and obstructions as possible in locating these controls.

1.5 Aesthetic and Safety Considerations

Most GPTs are incorporated to subsurface drainage systems and thus are not visible to create any aesthetic displeasure. The only visible items are nets that can be seen when they are applied to end-of-pipe outlet structures, inline nets systems within open channels, or open channel bar racks. When maintenance of GPTs at storm drain inlet and catch basins is inadequate, the quantity of gross pollutants in some instances can be unsightly. Many catchbasin inserts and trash excluders do not have a bypass; if not cleaned regularly, they can clog and cause localized flooding in streets.

2.0 SCREENS

2.1 Description

A screen is a sieve or other meshlike device used to separate gross pollutants from stormwater. Screens may be mounted on a flat or curved frame (see Figure 10.3) or on a drum that rotates (see Figure 10.4). Finer mesh screens are able to remove finer

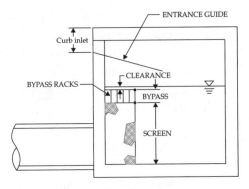
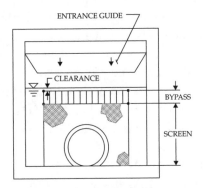

FIGURE 10.3 Typical configuration of a vertical screen with a weir bypass.

FIGURE 10.4   Externally fed rotary drum screen with paddle drive in Okanogan County, Washington.

sediments and debris, thereby increasing effectiveness; however, they tend to clog faster, which increases maintenance requirements. Screen features such as percent open area, smoothness, materials, aperture geometry, and others can affect clogging rates, costs, and design configuration.

2.2 Typical Applications

2.2.1 Physical Site Suitability

Screens are typically used as inline systems and can either be retrofitted to existing catch basins or created in separate manhole structures; they may also include other parts, as with rotary drum and step screen arrangements.

It is recommended that screens be used for coarse litter and debris of 4.75 mm (0.19 in.) and larger. Screens should be considered in design as being partially effective because of clogging.

2.2.2 Water Quantity Control

Screens do not provide water quantity unit processes for peak attenuation or volume reduction. In fact, they should be designed to convey flow efficiently. The designer should assume that the screen will be partially clogged when sizing to pass the design flow; in addition, the designer should incorporate a bypass for large, infrequent events and for the situation in which the screen has become completely clogged with debris.

2.2.3 Water Quality Control

Screens remove gross solids from stormwater at a location that is easily accessible for poststorm retrieval. Screens do not provide unit processes to treat the trapped items.

2.3 Limitations

Screens tend to clog frequently; they are more prone to clogging as the mesh size decreases. Mechanical screens include self-cleaning mechanisms to reduce clogging. Static screens must be cleaned by hand or be replaced when clogged.

2.4 Design Procedure and Criteria

2.4.1 Typical Configurations

Screens can be designed for the water quality treatment (WQT) rate as defined in Chapter 3 but all range of flows need to be analyzed for proper sizing. They may be additions to existing drainage infrastructure or may be designed into new elements. Screens may also be added as inline installations upstream of a vault or downstream at pipe outlets.

Microscreens typically used in publicly owned treatment works (POTWs) have been applied to stormwater. They consist of filter fabric with opening sizes ranging from 10 to 35 μm (0.000 39 to 0.0014 in.). However, to be cleaned, these devices have to be high-pressure backwashed, which makes them less attractive for stormwater systems. Microscreens have reported efficiencies of total suspended solids removal of 10 to 80%, with an average of 55% (Metcalf and Eddy, 2003).

Common screen configurations include a screen weir, a static inclined wedge-wire screen, and rotating cylindrical screen. The latter devices have undergone extensive field and laboratory testing by the California Department of Transportation (2003). Screens used in catch basins (see Figure 10.5) provide a cost-effective retrofit option. Although proven to be effective, applications of wedge wire screen applications for stormwater treatment are few mostly because of large head losses and cost. Cylindrical screens that use continuous deflection are widely used in the U.S. and Australia. Sizing of screens needs to consider an appropriate bypass overflow capacity.

The static inclined wedge-wire screens exhibit self-cleaning ability (see Figure 10.6). This configuration includes placing a concave wedge-wire screen off of the downstream face of a weir. Flow will accelerate down the face of the screen, which allows the water to pass through the screen and solids to slide down the face of the screen to a collection device. Wahl (1995) performed a series of capacity tests on such screens

FIGURE 10.5   Typical screen retrofit inside existing catch basin in Los Angeles County.

FIGURE 10.6   Static inclined wedge-wire screen.

for the U.S. Bureau of Reclamation and found that "the high capacity of the static screens is due primarily to a tilted-wire construction in which each wire is tilted so that its upstream edge is offset into the flow. A thin layer of the flow is sheared off the bottom of the water column and directed through the screen. This shearing action may depend somewhat on a phenomenon known as the Coanda effect.... The Coanda effect is the tendency of a fluid jet to remain attached to a solid boundary, flow entrainment into the jet is inhibited on the surface side."

Rotary drum screens have two different configurations that feed the influent either internally or externally across the screen. Internally fed screens are suited for removal of fibrous solids or solids with shear resistant properties, and that are not amorphous or do not smear (e.g., oils and grease). These screens typically provide more retention time on the screen and, therefore, typically drier mass solids. However, the screens require sophisticated cleaning systems, including high-pressure water, and removal of amorphous solids such as oils and grease can be difficult.

Externally fed screens are suited for removal of a wide range of gross pollutants including amorphous solids. The externally fed screen includes a back of screen knife that helps remove adhered solids. Also, the system cleans itself as the filtrate backwashes through the drum. Externally fed screens are not suited for high flows. The solids content tends to be wetter and the potential exists for free oils to be discharged with the solids. Figure 10.4 shows an example of how stream flow can produce the power required to rotate the drum and continue the self cleaning. The device can also be actuated by solar power.

Reciprocating step type mechanically actuated screens typically used in wastewater treatment are also available for stormwater applications (see Figure 10.7). In this configuration, gross pollutants are moved up the screen by means of movable and fixed vertical screen plates (Metcalf & Eddy, 2003). These devices require more power to operate and, therefore, may not be as advantageous as the previous examples.

2.4.2 Pretreatment Unit

Screens are most often used as a pretreatment unit for other stormwater controls and seldom include a pretreatment unit themselves.

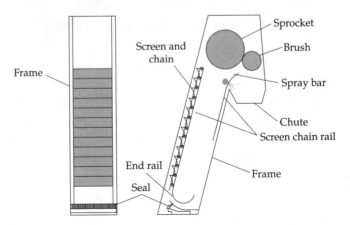

FIGURE 10.7   Typical step screen design (Parkson Corporation).

2.4.3 Main Treatment Unit

Fine screens have been routinely used in treatment plants to add redundancy in primary and preliminary unit processes. In some instances, screens have even replaced primary treatment clarifiers for flowrates up to 11 ML/d (3 mgd) (Metcalf and Eddy, 2003). Head loss through treatment plant screens ranges from 0.75 m (2.5 ft) to 1.5 m (4.5 ft). Typical configurations consist of static wedge-wire systems, rotating drum systems, and mechanically operated step screen systems. These performance characteristics have been applied to screens for stormwater. However, stormwater applications typically are not electrically powered and use hydraulics for self cleaning.

For the purposes of design and performance evaluation, screens are often treated as devices that introduce minor head losses. The hydraulic effects of screens depend on numerous factors, including position with respect to flow, geometry of the openings, degree of submergence, and the degree of clogging as litter and debris accumulate and obstruct the openings. One approach is to use a relationship analogous to an orifice discharge equation:

$$Q_{screen} = c_{screen} A_{screen} \sqrt{2gh}$$

(10.1)

where

Q_{screen} = the design flow capacity of the screen (m³/s);

c_{screen} = the screen discharge coefficient;

A_{screen} = total gross area of the screen (not the net opening area) (m²);

g = acceleration caused by gravity (9.81 m²/s); and

h = difference in depth of flow across the screen (m).

The discharge coefficient depends on the factors enumerated above and must be determined through laboratory experiments for a suitable range of flow conditions. The designer must consult the manufacturer to obtain appropriate design parameters.

Equation 10.1 is included in the overall energy equation of the system to calculate the flow rate through the screen. The bypass flow is obtained by removing this flow from the incoming flow, and is used to design bypass conveyances. Depending on the situation, design formulas for the bypass may correspond to open channel, orifice, or weir flow.

The design should include a check on the forces exerted on the screen through the application of the momentum equation for the worst possible conditions. These forces are needed to verify the integrity of the screen, the fasteners, and the supporting structural elements.

2.5 Aesthetic and Safety Considerations

Most screens are incorporated to subsurface drainage systems and thus are not visible to create any aesthetic displeasure. With inadequate maintenance, the accumulation of gross pollutants in some instances can be unsightly.

2.6 Access and Maintenance Features

Screens must have structural supports to withstand applied forces and vertical pieces must be removable to enable access to downstream pipes for cleaning.

In addition, a breaking capacity is often provided to allow the system to self-clean to prevent damage to the screen and the downstream infrastructure. Such situations may also release the captured gross pollutants and negate any positive effects of the device.

3.0 NETS

3.1 Description

Nets are composed of meshlike material, somewhat less rigid than screens, and trap gross pollutants as stormwater flows through them. They may be placed within the drainage system, at an outfall, or within the receiving water.

3.2 Typical Applications

3.2.1 Physical Site Suitability

Nets are provided in various proprietary configurations along with other traps such as screens, typically in end-of-pipe locations (see Figure 10.8). Nets have been installed in open channels as inline configurations (see Figure 10.9). Problems encountered in such applications include localized flooding because of the accumulation of gross pollutants and subsequent creation of a hydraulic jump. Unless a bypass is installed, some jurisdictions choose to remove these devices when rain is predicted to be greater than the design flow rate. The cost of constructing a bypass structure must be weighed against the consequences of violating a water quality requirement. Buoyed boom systems are available. However, these devices have a tendency to be

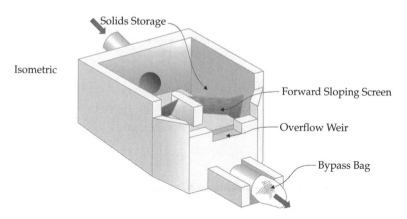

Isometric

Solids Storage

Forward Sloping Screen

Overflow Weir

Bypass Bag

FIGURE 10.8   Dual screen and net system (Caltrans, 2005).

FIGURE 10.9   Net system during storm event (Caltrans, 2005).

influenced by the velocities experienced in the channels and can eliminate floatables captured as the device is driven below the water surface at higher velocities. If nets are designed for open channels, a thorough review of the resident biota should be performed to allow for the safe passage of aquatic life.

3.2.2 Water Quantity Control

Nets should be designed to convey flow through the system with little storage or peak-flow attenuation. The designer should assume that the net will be partially clogged when sizing to pass the design flow; in addition, a bypass should be incorporated for large, infrequent events and for the condition in which the net has become completely clogged with debris.

3.2.3 Water Quality Control

Nets remove gross solids from stormwater, trapping them in a mesh bag that can be easily removed after storm events. Nets are not designed to treat the trapped items.

3.3 Limitations

Nets tend to fill with debris following moderate storm events. Occasionally, a net may be torn away during extreme storm events. Nets typically require construction of a chamber large enough to accommodate increased head loss across the net and a bypass, and to provide access for net removal and replacement.

3.4 Design Procedure and Criteria

3.4.1 Typical Configurations

End-of-pipe and inline systems are available. The California Department of Transportation (2005) has performed several pilot studies that use end-of-pipe netting to catch gross solids that pass through various other trap techniques such as wedge-wire and radial screens.

3.4.2 Pretreatment Unit

Nets are most often used as a pretreatment unit for other stormwater controls and seldom include a pretreatment unit themselves.

3.4.3 Main Treatment Unit

Head losses should be determined through the net using eq 10.1. The design should include a check on the forces exerted on the net through the application of the momentum equation for the worst possible conditions. These forces are needed to verify the integrity of the net, the fasteners, and the supporting structural elements.

3.5 Aesthetic and Safety Considerations

Most nets are incorporated to subsurface drainage systems and, therefore, are not visible to create any aesthetic displeasure. With inadequate maintenance, the accumulation of gross pollutants in some instances can become unsightly.

3.6   Access and Maintenance Features

Nets must be provided with structural supports to withstand applied forces and vertical pieces must be removable to enable crews to access downstream pipes for cleaning. In addition, nets may be designed to "break away" during extreme storm events to prevent damage to the frame.

4.0   BASKETS

4.1   Description

Baskets, or insert screens, are manufactured filters or fabric placed in a storm drain inlet to remove sediment and debris. Inserts come in a variety of shapes and configurations and typically fall into one of the following groups: socks, boxes, and trays. Essentially, all baskets skirt the entrance to the curb inlets. For on-grade inlets, bypass of the basket should be provided for flows exceeding the design flow rate to reduce potential flooding (CASQA, 2003).

Socks are meant for vertical (drop) inlets. A sock consists of a fabric, typically constructed of polypropylene, attached to a frame or the grate of the inlet. Boxes are constructed of plastic or wire mesh (CASQA, 2003). Typically, a polypropylene "bag" is placed in the wire mesh box. The bag takes the form of the box. In most products the settling and filtration through media occur in the same box.

Some manufacturers state that the bag has the ability to increase in volume up to 3 times before uptake capacity is exhausted. To maintain integrity of the inlet, the engineer must ensure such volumes will not clog the inlet.

Some products consist of one or more trays or mesh grates. The trays may hold different types of media. Filtration media vary by manufacturer and include polypropylene, porous polymer, treated cellulose, activated carbon, peat, and zeolite.

4.2   Typical Applications

4.2.1   Physical Site Suitability

Typically, the most important advantage of baskets or other devices that insert to inlets is that they do not require additional space as inserts to drain inlets are already a component of the standard drainage systems. These inserts effectively decrease the hydraulic capacity of the inlets.

4.2.2 Water Quantity Control

These devices do not reduce peak flows or runoff volumes. Inlet basket design should follow typical inlet design, with careful selection of the clogging factor. Generally, inlets work as weirs or orifices. This means that the flow rate into an inlet can be determined using the corresponding equations, for example, eq 10.1.

Typically, a clogging factor of 50% is applied to account for clogging at the inlet entry. To account for clogging to a basket within the inlet opening, an additional amount of blockage should be considered because of the likelihood that clogging increases with more screening devices (e.g., the basket plus the inlet bars). It is suggested that engineers use clogging factors somewhat larger than the standard without baskets. Engineering experience and judgment should guide selection of this clogging factor.

4.2.3 Water Quality Control

Baskets screen gross solids from stormwater to a location that is easily accessible for poststorm retrieval. Baskets are not designed to treat the trapped items.

4.3   Limitations

Baskets tend to clog frequently, with clogging more pronounced as the mesh size decreases. Baskets must be cleaned by hand or replaced when clogged. In a study by Pitt and Field (2004), screen insert devices were found to foul after only 1 to 2 mm accumulation of sediment.

4.4   Design Procedure and Criteria

4.4.1 Typical Configurations

Typical configurations consist of inlets that are placed either on-grade or with the slope of the conveyance or in sag, or sump, conditions.

4.4.2 Pretreatment Unit

Baskets are most often used as a pretreatment unit for other stormwater controls and seldom include a pretreatment unit themselves.

4.4.3 Main Treatment Unit

Design of the basket or other insert to a drain inlet must be consistent with the hydraulic design of the inlet itself, accounting for increased resistance as the unit clogs along with a mechanism for bypassing flows larger than the design flow rate. There are many inlet configurations in use and municipalities rely on design manuals to size the inlets (e.g., County of San Diego, 2005). Inlet design procedures are based on discharge equations through weirs and orifices (e.g., eq 10.1). The basic design procedure for a basket consists of estimating the capacity of the inlet and verifying that the basket will not substantially reduce this capacity for an assumed level of clogging.

4.5 Aesthetic and Safety Considerations

Most baskets are placed directly into the storm drain inlet and, therefore, are not visible to create any aesthetic displeasure. With inadequate maintenance, the accumulation of gross pollutants in some instances can be unsightly. Unless a bypass is provided, reduced inlet capacity may cause surface flooding, which may create safety hazards.

4.6 Access and Maintenance Features

Baskets are accessed directly from the storm drain inlet. Frequent maintenance should be anticipated to address clogging.

5.0 RACKS

5.1 Description

Racks are a series of circular or rectangular bars on a frame, spaced to trap gross solids. They have traditionally been designed to protect inlets from drainage waters and for use as headworks to treatment plants.

5.2 Typical Applications

5.2.1 Physical Site Suitability

Racks are placed to maintain the hydraulic integrity of the downstream drainage system. They are often placed over outlet works for basins.

5.2.2 Water Quantity Control

Racks should be designed to convey an appropriate design flow with little storage or peak flow attenuation. An appropriate design flow may be the WQT rate for pollution control, or a larger flow if the intent is to protect the drainage system from large debris. The designer should assume that the rack will be partially clogged when sizing to pass the design flow; in addition, a bypass should be incorporated for large, infrequent events and for the situation when the rack has become completely clogged with debris.

5.2.3 *Water Quality Control*

Racks remove gross solids from stormwater through physical separation. Some designs divert the trapped solids to a storage area as flows increase, reducing clogging of the rack. Racks are not designed to treat the trapped items.

5.3   Limitations

Racks may clog with debris following moderate storm events, with clogging more pronounced as bar spacing decreases. Mechanical racks include self-cleaning mechanisms to minimize clogging. Static racks and associated debris traps must be cleaned by hand when clogged.

5.4   Design Procedure and Criteria

5.4.1 *Typical Configurations*

Racks are typically designed to slope from 3H:1V to 5H:1V to allow trash to slide up the rack with increasing flows. Engineering judgment should be used to estimate the opening space required to pass items that may clog when in areas of large debris yield (i.e., silviculture, preserves, open space, etc.).

Collapsible racks are also available to allow for debris release and to maintain operability of the conveyance during peak flow conditions. These racks may also be used as a safety precaution should people become trapped against the device.

Racks can be configured similar to screens. They can be retrofitted to catch basins or they can be constructed inline. A technique proposed by the University of Guelph

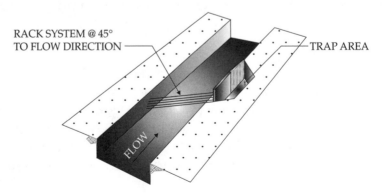

FIGURE 10.10   In-channel rack installation.

in Ontario, Canada places the racks at a 45-deg angle to the flow direction (see Figure 10.10), which guides gross pollutants into a separate trapping compartment off of the main open channel. The device must be designed to avoid overtopping as debris collects in the trap.

5.4.2 Pretreatment Unit

Racks are most often used as a pretreatment unit for other stormwater controls and seldom include a pretreatment unit themselves.

5.4.3 Main Treatment Unit

Two design equations are currently in use. Metcalf & Eddy (1972) presents the following equation based on tests done in Germany:

$$H_g = K_{g1}\left(\frac{w}{x}\right)^{\frac{4}{3}}\left(\frac{V_u^2}{2g}\right)\sin\theta_g \qquad (10.2)$$

where

H_g = head loss through rack (m);

K_{g1} = bar shape factor: 2.42—sharp-edged rectangular, 1.83—rectangular bars with semicircular upstream and downstream faces, 1.79—circular bars, and 1.67—rectangular bars with semicircular upstream and downstream faces;

w = maximum cross-sectional bar width facing the flow (mm);

x = minimum clear spacing between bars (mm);

V_u = approach velocity (m/s); and

θ_g = angle of the rack with respect to the horizontal (degrees).

The second methodology was developed by the U.S. Army Corps of Engineers (1988) based on laboratory testing for trash racks. These equations were developed for vertical racks; however, adjustments could be made to account for the angle of the bars as in the previous method. The set of equations is as follows:

$$H_g = \frac{K_{g2}V_u^2}{2g} \qquad (10.3)$$

where K_{g2} is defined from a series of equations that depend on the shape of the bars:

Sharp-edged rectangular (length/thickness = 10)

$$K_{g2} = 0.00158 - (0.03217A_r) + (7.1786A_r^2) \qquad (10.4)$$

Sharp-edged rectangular (length/thickness = 5)

$$K_{g2} = -0.00731 + (0.69453 A_r) + (7.0856 A_r^2) \qquad (10.5)$$

Round-edged rectangular (length/thickness = 10.9)

$$K_{g2} = -0.00101 + (0.02520 A_r) + (6.0000 A_r^2) \qquad (10.6)$$

Circular cross section

$$K_{g2} = 0.00866 + (0.13589 A_r) + (6.0357 A_r^2) \qquad (10.7)$$

$$\text{and } A_r = \frac{A_b}{A_g} \quad (10.8)$$

where
A_b = the area of the bars (m²); and
A_g = the area of the grate section (m²).

The design should include a check on the forces exerted on the rack through the application of the momentum equation for the worst possible conditions. These forces are needed to verify the integrity of the rack, the fasteners, and the supporting structural elements.

5.5   Aesthetic and Safety Considerations

A proper break-away mechanism should be provided for large inlet structures. Flow near outlet works from wet basins may drag people, pets, or wildlife into the drop structure and barrel. Unprotected pipe inlets present similar hazards. Racks may reduce this danger but the trapped debris may injure victims. The size of the openings needs to be small enough to keep people from getting swept into the downstream conduit. The bars of racks should be rounded to minimize injury should a person come in contact with them. The racks should be positioned at a distance upstream from the opening so that flow velocity will not pin victims against the rack. Additional information on the deployment of racks in culverts can be found in Urban Drainage and Flood Control District (2001).

5.6   Access and Maintenance Features

Access must be provided to allow maintenance crews and equipment to reach the rack. Frequent maintenance should be anticipated to address clogging of the rack.

5.7 Design Example

An 8-ha (20-ac) basin through an urban area discharges into a trunk storm drain collector pipe. The pipe is 1.5 m (60 in.) in diameter and is designed to flow with $Q_{peak} = 3.5$ m³/s (125 cfs) and WQT = 0.7 m³/s (25 cfs). The slope of the pipe is 0.004. Design a bar rack inline to trap solids 60 m (200 ft) upstream of the discharge of this pipe to a river that has a gross solids water quality standard. The rack is inclined 67 deg with respect to the flow direction in the pipe.

For a 1.5-m (60-in.) diameter reinforced concrete pipe (RCP) pipe with slope of 0.004, use Manning's formula to find the depth of flow and velocity at the given design flows, as follows:

At $Q_{peak} = 3.5$ m³/s (125 cfs), $h = 1$ m (39.1 in.), $V = 2.8$ m/s (9.2 ft/sec) and
At WQT = 0.7 m³/s (25 cfs), $h = 0.4$ m (15.8 in.), $V = 1.85$ m/s (6.1 ft/sec).
Assume that the bars are 50-mm (2-in.) wide with 75-mm (3-in.) spaces.
For the Q_{peak} condition,

$$H_g = K_{g1}\left(\frac{w}{x}\right)^{\frac{4}{3}}\left(\frac{V_u^2}{2g}\right)\sin\theta_g = (1.83)\left(\frac{50}{75}\right)^{\frac{4}{3}}\left(\frac{(2.8\ m^2/s)}{2(9.8\ m^2/s)}\right)\sin 67° = 0.39\ m\ \ (1.29\ ft)$$

(10.9)

Therefore, the head with the addition of the grates, makes the water depth in the pipe 1 m (39.1 in.) + 0.39 m (1.29 ft) = 1.39 m (54.6 in.), which is less than the pipe diameter of 1.5 m (60 in.).

For WQT,

$$H_g = K_{g1}\left(\frac{w}{x}\right)^{\frac{4}{3}}\left(\frac{V_u^2}{2g}\right)\sin\theta_g = 1.83\left(\frac{50}{70}\right)^{\frac{4}{3}}\left(\frac{(1.8m^2/s)}{2(9.8m^2/s)}\right)\sin 67° = 0.17m\ (0.57\ ft)$$

(10.10)

The water depth in the pipe under these conditions is 0.4 m (15.8 in.) + 0.17 m (0.57 ft = 0.47 m (22.6 in.), which is less than the pipe diameter of 1.5 m (60 in.).

6.0 HOODS

6.1 Description

Hoods are covers at the entrance to a pipe which leaves a basin, for example, a wet basin or a vault. The cover is placed such that the bottom extends below the invert of the discharge pipe. As a result, a sump or permanent pool must exist. The hood keeps floatables out of the discharge by eliminating their path into the outlet. Hoods may have to be outfitted with antisiphon devices. Hoods must also allow access to the discharge point to allow for proper cleaning. The City of New York study (HydroQual, 1995), discussed in Section 1.1, found that catch basins with hoods outperformed those without hoods by an average of 55%.

6.2   Typical Applications

6.2.1 Physical Site Suitability

Hoods may be used at the outlet of a basin with a sump or permanent pool.

6.2.2 Water Quantity Control

Hoods do not attenuate peak flows or reduce stormwater volume. The depth of water in the basin regulates discharge through the hood.

6.2.3 Water Quality Control

Hoods primarily use skimming to remove floating gross pollutants and oils.

6.3   Limitations

Floatables trapped by hoods need to be removed frequently to prevent unsightly buildup or the creation of a floatable layer so deep that it could enter the hood and clog the outlet pipe.

6.4   Design Procedure and Criteria

6.4.1 Typical Configurations

Hoods need to be oriented such that they extend from above the outlet pipe entrance to below the invert of the pipe. The basin must be designed with a sump or permanent pool. With the exception of the Southwestern United States, sumps are standard for catch basins in most of the United States. Hydraulic loss factors have been provided by vendors for use in design (see Figure 10.11 for a typical hood structure installation).

6.4.2 Pretreatment Unit

Hoods are most often used as a pretreatment unit for other stormwater controls and seldom include a pretreatment unit themselves.

6.4.3 Main Treatment Unit

The hood consists of a solid cover around the pipe outlet that extends for a distance below the invert of the pipe. The depth below the invert should extend below the drought-level water elevation of a permanent pool within the basin. If the basin has a

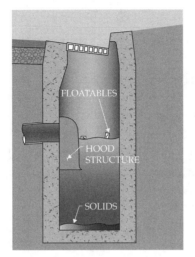

FIGURE 10.11   Typical hood installation.

dry sump, then it may be necessary to use a screen under the hood to keep floatables in the sump from rising into the hood as the water level increases. The hood must extend sufficiently deep below the pipe invert to reduce the potential for this situation to develop. Sloping the screen toward the interior of the sump will allow floatables that may have fallen below the entrance to the hood to rise in the sump rather than becoming trapped against the screen as water rises. Approach velocities toward the entrance to the hood must be checked to verify that they will not resuspend settled material at the bottom of the sump.

The area inside the hood should be larger than the outlet pipe size so that the hood does not become the hydraulic control. Standard hydraulic calculations are used to size the hood. However, because of the variations in shape, head loss coefficients are supplied by manufacturers.

6.5   Aesthetic and Safety Considerations

Floatables captured by the hood should be removed routinely to prevent their buildup on the surface of permanent pools.

6.6   Access and Maintenance Features

Access should be provided to the basin outlet to allow routine maintenance for floatables removal. Settled material at the bottom of the sump needs to be removed to avoid resuspension and entry into the hood.

6.7 Design Example

A land development project is converting an existing apartment complex into condominiums and local regulations require a decrease in the quantity of floatables from the property. Hoods need to be designed for addition to the catch basins.

The Q_{peak} is 0.08 m³/s (3 cfs) and the WQT rate is 0.02 m³/s (0.75 cfs). The manufacturer provides a loss coefficient K of 3.8 for a 600-mm (24-in.) hood that fits over the 450-mm (18-in.) RCP storm drain, which is sloped at 0.75%. The catch basin internal dimensions are 1.2 m × 1.2 m × 1.8 m (4 ft × 4 ft × 6 ft). The distance between the invert of the pipe and the bottom of the sump is 1.14 m (3.75 ft).

Head loss through the hood is given by

$$H = K \frac{V_{peakflow}^{2}}{2g} \qquad (10.11)$$

Given that Q_{peak} = 0.08 m³/s (3.0 cfs), the depth of flow in the pipe can be calculated from Manning's formula applied to a circular pipe. Using the slope of 0.75% and a value of 0.013 for n, the corresponding depth is h = 0.18 m (7.1 in.) and V = 1.4 m/s (4.6 ft/sec).

The head loss through the hood is

$$H = K \frac{V^{2}}{2g} = 3.8 \frac{(1.4 m/s)^{2}}{2(9.8 m^{2}/s)} = 0.38 \text{ m } (1.25 ft) \qquad (10.12)$$

The depth of water over the pipe invert upstream of the hood is then 0.18 m (7.1 in.) + 0.38 m (1.25 ft) = 0.56 m (1.83 ft), which is less than the clearing to the top of the inlet of 1.83 m (6 ft) - 1.14 m (3.75 ft) = 0.69 m (2.25 ft). Therefore, the hood will not cause localized flooding for the design flow.

6.0 REFERENCES

Allison, R. A.; Chiew, F. H. S.; McMahon, T. A. (1998a) *A Decision-Support-System for Determining Effective Trapping Strategies for Gross Pollutants;* Cooperative Research Centre for Catchment Hydrology, Department of Civil Engineering, Monash University: Melbourne, Victoria, Australia.

Allison, R. A.; Walker, T. A.; Chiew, F. H. S.; O'Neil, I. C.; McMahon, T. A. (1998b) *From Roads to Rivers Gross Pollutant Removal From Urban Waterways;* Cooperative

Research Centre for Catchment Hydrology, Department of Civil Engineering, Monash University: Melbourne, Victoria, Australia.

Armitage, N.; Rooseboom, A.; Nel, C.; Townshend, P. (1998) *The Removal of Urban Litter from Stormwater Conduits and Streams*; WRC Report No. TT 95/98; Water Research Commission: Pretoria, South Africa.

California Department of Transportation (2003) *Phase 1 Gross Solids Removal Devices Pilot Study: 2000–2002*; CTSW-RT-03–072; California Department of Transportation: Sacramento, California.

California Department of Transportation (2005) *Phase III: Gross Solids Removal Devices Pilot Study: 2002–2005*; Final Report No. CTSW-RT-05–130–03.1; California Department of Transportation: Sacramento, California.

California Department of Transportation (2000) District 7 Litter Management Pilot Study; Caltrans Document No. CT-SW-RT-00–013; California Department of Transportation: Sacramento, California.

California Stormwater Quality Association (2003) *New Development and Redevelopment Handbook;* California Best Management Practice Handbooks, TC-10, TC-11, and SC-20; California Stormwater Quality Association: Menlo Park, California.

County of San Diego (2005) *San Diego County Drainage Design Manual;* County of San Diego, Department of Public Works: San Diego, California.

England, G.; Rushton, B. (2007) ASCE Guideline for Monitoring Stormwater Gross Solids; American Society of Civil Engineers: Reston, Virginia.

HydroQual, Inc. (1995) *Floatables Pilot Program Final Report: Evaluation of Non-Structural Methods to Control Combined and Storm Sewer Floatable Materials;* Department of Environmental Protection, Division of Water Quality Improvement: New York.

Lager, J. A.; Smith, W. G.; Lynard, W. G.; Finn, R. M.; Finnemore, E. J. (1977) *Urban Stormwater Management and Technology: Update and Users' Guide;* EPA-600/8–77–014; U.S. Environmental Protection Agency: Cincinnati, Ohio.

Los Angeles Regional Water Quality Control Board (2001) *Trash Total Maximum Daily Loads for the Los Angeles River Watershed;* Los Angeles Regional Water Quality Control Board: Los Angeles, California.

Metcalf and Eddy, Inc. (1972) *Wastewater Engineering: Collection, Treatment, Disposal;* McGraw-Hill: New York.

Metcalf and Eddy, Inc. (2003) *Wastewater Engineering: Treatment and Reuse;* McGraw-Hill: New York.

Pitt, R. (1985) *Characterizing and Controlling Urban Runoff through Street and Sewerage Cleaning;* U.S. EPA. Contract No. R-805929012; EPA-2/85–038. PB 85–186500/AS; U.S. Environmental Protection Agency: Cincinnati, Ohio.

Pitt, R.; Field, R. (2004) Catchbasins and Inserts for the Control of Gross Solids and Conventional Stormwater Pollutants. Proceedings of the American Society of Civil Engineers World Water and Environmental Resources Congress BMP Technology Symposium; Salt Lake City, Utah; June 27–July 1.

Pitt, R.; Field, R. (1998) An Evaluation of Storm Drainage Inlet Devices for Stormwater Quality Treatment. *Proceedings of the Annual Water Environment Federation Technical Exposition and Conference;* Orlando, Florida; Oct 3–7.

Roesner, L. A.; Pruden, A.; Kidder, E. M. (2007) *Improved Protocol for Classification and Analysis of Stormwater-Borne Solids;* WERF 04-SW-4; Water Environment Research Foundation: Alexandria, Virginia.

Sansalone, J.; Kim, J. Y. (2008) Transport of Particulate Matter Fractions in Urban Source Area Pavement Surface Runoff. *J. Environ. Qual.,* **37** (5), 1883.

Sartor, J. D.; Boyd, G. B. (1972) *Water Pollution Aspects of Street Surface Contaminants;* EPA-R2–72–081; U.S. Environmental Protection Agency, Office of Research and Monitoring: Washington, D.C.

U.S. Army Corps of Engineers (1988) *Hydraulic Design Criteria;* U.S. Army Engineer Waterways Experiment Station: Vicksburg, Mississippi.

Urban Drainage and Flood Control District (2001) *Urban Storm Drainage Criteria Manual, Volume 2;* Denver, Colorado.

URS Corporation (2004) *Draft Engineering Report: Solid Waste Prevention Investigation—Chollas Creek and Paleta Creek.* San Diego, California.

U.S. Geological Survey (2005) Water Resources Data—Definition of Terms. http://water.usgs.gov/ADR_Defs_2005.pdf (accessed May 18, 2011).

Wahl, T. L. (1995) Hydraulic Testing of Static Self-Cleaning Inclined Screens. *Proceedings of the First International Conference on Water Resources Engineering;* San Antonio, Texas; Aug 14–18; American Society of Civil Engineers: New York.

Chapter 11

Maintenance of Stormwater Controls

(continued)

1.0 INTRODUCTION

1.1 Overview

Maintenance is a necessary activity to preserve the intended water quality bene-fit and stormwater conveyance capacity of stormwater controls. However, there often is little planning regarding future maintenance activities and financial and staff resources that will be needed to perform these activities. The objective of this chapter is to identify maintenance required for various types of stormwater controls and to estimate costs associated with this work, much of which may not be directly related to the functionality of controls. This will allow agencies and municipalities to anticipate future financial requirements and to plan accordingly.

Most of the observations and recommendations presented in this chapter are derived from a study of practices in the United States and United Kingdom funded by the Water Environment Research Foundation (2005) entitled *Performance and Whole Life Costs of Best Management Practices and Sustainable Urban Drainage Systems*. A sur-vey conducted as part of that study of maintenance practices by agencies throughout the United States found that maintenance budgets were sized largely as a function of policy rather than on technical or functional inputs. In addition, agencies interviewed in that study had not allocated the resources necessary to fully maintain stormwater controls in their jurisdiction to the level required by their maintenance guidelines. As expected, those agencies and municipalities with more resources and stronger public support for their programs were generally able to provide more extensive maintenance for their controls. In addition, it was found that vegetation management dominated maintenance activities and that there is a wide variation in the level of maintenance expected by residents.

In many jurisdictions, vegetation management constitutes the majority of maintenance activities rather than tasks one might expect such as sediment, debris and trash removal, or structural repair. The frequency of mowing and other vegetation management activities may have little effect on stormwater control performance, but result from the expected level of service by residents living near these facilities or by regulatory requirements. Consequently, selecting low-maintenance vegetation is important for reducing maintenance costs. The frequency of maintenance has been found to depend on the economic status of the neighborhood (with more maintenance requests generated in affluent neighborhoods) and the visibility of the system. Consequently, the expected maintenance cost for a given type of facility can vary significantly depending on the expectations (mostly aesthetic) of the nearby community.

Stormwater control size and complexity also affect maintenance activities. Large systems, such as wet basins, are easier to track, inspect, and monitor to ensure that they continue to function as intended (because each system treats a larger area, there are fewer of them), but require specialized contractors or agency crews to maintain. Small landscaped systems (e.g., swales and residential rain gardens) are more difficult to track, but are more straightforward to maintain using landscaping contractors or delegating responsibility to homeowners (except some types of rehabilitative work, such as erosion repair). Consequently, the situation has, therefore, arisen in which some municipalities are moving toward small-scale, privately maintained controls (e.g., "low-impact development") while others are insisting on large-scale, publicly maintained controls, with both doing so largely to reduce public maintenance costs (WERF, 2005).

Regardless of the type of control, lack of routine maintenance can lead to disproportionately greater long-term expense. For example, structural damage caused by growth of large trees in outfalls and embankments could be easily prevented with periodic mowing. Costs to repair structural damage and remove tress and other well-established vegetation would more than exceed the cost of mowing. Therefore, there may be little additional cost to maintain best management practices (BMPs) if a frequent landscaping maintenance program is in place.

The following are the principal reasons why maintenance of stormwater controls has been historically difficult to implement (WERF, 2005):

- Inability to physically locate BMPs;
- Inability to track responsible parties;

- Dedicated staff not assigned to inspection;
- Designs not conducive to easy maintenance;
- Lack of enforcement authority and access;
- Owners of BMPs are unaware of their responsibilities;
- Proliferation of BMPs that require intensive maintenance; and
- Insufficient funding sources.

A common theme with each of these issues is funding. Indeed, the long-term maintenance and operation of a control or system of controls require money to

- Hire staff and maintain a database of the physical location of stormwater controls and provide for routine inspections;
- Establish a legal framework (and persistence) to have enforcement authority, ensure access, and track responsible parties; and
- Educate facility owners (which can range into the thousands of individual entities for a single community) about the responsibilities and proper practices needed to maintain stormwater control function.

To address funding needs, some communities have created stormwater utilities, while others insist that private developers or landowners enter into maintenance agreements (i.e., "declaration of maintenance") to ensure that the constructed stormwater control is properly funded and maintained over time.

Agencies do have control over proper facility design and selection, helping them avoid use of those controls that fail frequently and/or require intensive maintenance. However, it requires sufficient staff to review design plans, perform construction inspection, and conduct postconstruction inspection to ensure that the control continues to function as intended. Many agencies do not have the experience or time to investigate which control types might be most appropriate for their needs.

Maintenance of stormwater controls is frequently not the primary focus of municipal governments. In many cases, structural controls were designed and constructed many years before concerted efforts were made to ensure that they were inspected and functioning as intended. Therefore, while structural controls have existed in many areas of the United States for 10 to 20 years, maintenance experience is often much more limited, generally having come about in the last 5 years.

Many agencies require that private entities install and maintain structural controls when they develop or redevelop a property. Public agencies are then expected to perform routine inspections on these controls to make sure that they continue to function. Private developers have a strong financial incentive to complete a project and move on to the next one. Little incentive is provided for the long-term maintenance of the stormwater infrastructure, with still less for the development of a funding mechanism (such as a stormwater utility) to pay for it. In areas with rapid urban growth, municipalities have often had trouble keeping track of the existence and location of new controls, let alone ensuring that all are inspected and operating properly.

1.2 Maintenance Requirements and Level of Effort

1.2.1 Maintenance Drivers

Three main drivers affect the degree and frequency of maintenance. These are

- Protecting human health and safety;
- Maintaining facility functionality; and
- Maintaining facility aesthetics.

Stormwater controls are part of the drainage infrastructure that must be maintained, and there is a minimum level of routine maintenance that must be undertaken for the component or system to operate as designed. As an example, trash and sediment must be removed on a routine basis to maintain the performance of the system and prevent clogging of outlets. In addition, a minimum level of vegetation maintenance is also required to avoid clogging of outlets and stormwater conveyances. The total maintenance requirement of a type of control will vary from location to location. While difficult to define in advance, these requirements need to be determined and considered during the design process. Possible causes of higher maintenance requirements include exceptional sediment load (often the result of ongoing construction activities), invasive vegetation, and/or litter production in the catchment.

Many maintenance activities have less to do with proper function than with appearance. A significant amount of maintenance is undertaken to preserve the desired appearance of the facility rather than to maintain proper function. Aesthetic concerns might lead to grass cutting as frequently as weekly during a wet season, but much less frequently in a dry spell. Publicly visible and privately maintained sites tend to receive more attention than those located in less visible locations, whether or not this additional attention is required for system function.

Vegetation management may also be required to meet different health- or safety- related requirements. Vector (mosquito) control for controls that maintain a permanent pool of water is required in areas such as California and New York to avoid the spread of diseases; however, other states with abundant mosquito populations do little or nothing. In Florida, concerns over alligators have led to the banks of basins being maintained with little to no emergent, near-shore vegetation, thus eliminating alligator habitat. Human safety can also be an issue, especially in the case of catastrophic collapse of embankments. Consequently, a substantial amount of maintenance is directed at preventing the establishment of woody vegetation on embankments and inspecting for structural stability.

1.2.2   Maintenance Categories and Levels

The following two general maintenance categories have been established: routine and intermittent. Routine maintenance consists of basic tasks performed on a frequent and predictable schedule. These include inspections, vegetation management, and litter and minor debris removal. In addition, three levels of routine maintenance can be identified and these relate mainly to frequency of the activity being undertaken. These are defined as

- Low/minimum—a basic level of maintenance required to maintain the function of the stormwater control;

- Medium—The normal level of maintenance to address function and appearance; it allows for additional activities, including preventative actions, at some facilities; and

- High—enhanced maintenance activities required for appearance and amenity only.

Intermittent maintenance typically consists of more heavy-duty, unpredictable, and infrequent tasks to keep systems in working order, such as repair of structural and erosion damage, and, potentially, complete facility reconstruction. The intermittent category can include a wide range of tasks that might be required to address maintenance issues at a BMP (e.g., invasive species removal, animal burrow removal, forebay cleanout, etc.).

2.0   GENERAL MAINTENANCE CONSIDERATIONS

A wide variety of maintenance practices and preferences have been implemented throughout the United States. Differences in geography (climate, topography, soils, etc.), culture (aesthetics, materials, program goals, etc.), and economics (availability and willingness to use financial resources) lead to a variety of alternatives in the selection and maintenance of stormwater controls. There are, however, many similarities in the maintenance activities carried out by state and local regulatory agencies.

Written maintenance schedules are often similar, and maintenance activities actually carried out (or not carried out, as the case may be) have several common traits. Common maintenance activities are discussed in the following sections and include inspections, vegetation management, and sediment removal. Their frequency and thoroughness are often driven by limitations of finance.

It is important for maintenance staff to be properly trained in safety issues associated with stormwater controls such as confined-space entry, fall hazards, operation of heavy equipment, hearing protection around vacuum motors, and contact with contaminants. For example, work in landscaped roofs involves fall hazards, and accumulated trash and debris frequently contain sharps such as hypodermic needles, broken glass, and biological waste. Issues also arise with standing water and associated vectors, as well as other pests; for example, infestations of fire ants in filter beds have been observed.

2.1   Inspection Programs

Many performance problems (and associated repair costs) can be identified and addressed early through a regular inspection program. Inspection during the design and construction phase helps ensure proper design, construction techniques, and sediment and erosion controls. Inspections following the construction phase serve to inspect, track, and help ensure that controls continue to function properly. Regular monitoring not only ensures that maintenance activities are being carried out as specified, but also identifies any areas of potential system failure.

Development of standard procedures is important and aids in evaluating the stability and function of stormwater controls. The inspection protocol should consider features related to site conditions, water quality performance, structural integrity, and overall function. Inspection findings can be used to develop remedial actions or identify the need for additional assessment or engineering analyses.

An important consideration in an inspection program is determining who is responsible for inspecting stormwater controls. There are substantial differences in the way that inspection programs are structured throughout the United States. In many areas, inspections are carried out by municipal or regional regulatory agencies. These agencies often have resource constraints and, consequently, routine inspections do not occur with the frequency typically recommended. In these instances, much of the regulatory response is complaint-based.

Harris County, Texas, has taken a different approach. The County requires that a professional engineer selected by the facility owner certify annually that all required maintenance for a given control has been performed. This reduces the burden on the regulatory agency and transfers the responsibility to a licensed engineer to determine that the facility is functioning properly.

2.2   As-Built Drawings

A factor that has been overlooked in some jurisdictions is the importance of maintaining a database, or inventory, of stormwater control locations that includes the location, type, and other descriptive data for each facility. This is typically accomplished using geographical information system tools. Inspectors need to know where the controls are and what they should look like so that they can be maintained as designed. Another useful resource when conducting inspections of facilities are as-built drawings. It is rare that these drawings are readily available to inspectors. Some programs, such as one in King County, Washington, make these as-built drawings available electronically to their inspectors. The New York City Department of Environmental Protection has developed a maintenance reference card for each control. The letter-sized laminated cards include a complete as-built drawing of each facility with inspection instructions and cleanout procedures. As-built drawings can provide details on components of a control that require inspection and, in some instances, can reference operation and maintenance needs. These drawings also reduce the potential for confusion in the field and allow the inspector to verify that all parts of the facility are functioning as designed.

2.3   Effects of Construction Activities on Stormwater Control Maintenance

Design and operation of BMPs must take into consideration damage that inevitably occurs when construction stage runoff is permitted to enter drainage systems. Repeated examples of almost irreparable damage to downstream controls caused by high sediment loads associated with construction activities, especially those relying on an infiltration component, have been documented. Environmental gains from implementation of stormwater control policies are seriously compromised if construction-derived sediment is not prevented from entering systems and/or inadequate efforts are made to remove sediment prior to the use of controls.

Sediment control is a significant focus and concern for regulatory agencies and the more progressive utilities have addressed this issue in a number of ways. The site of the proposed facility can be used as a dedicated sediment control measure until the watershed is stabilized, and then the dedicated stormwater control components can be added. In areas where a municipality or other authority maintains stormwater controls, it may be advisable to require that the majority of construction (e.g., >80%) in the development be completed before accepting responsibility for the system. When the control is infiltration-based, it may be advisable to have an even greater amount of the site at final stabilization. Other options might involve constructing extra capacity within a facility that is specifically sized to store construction-derived sediment; or, a second facility could be constructed to treat construction stage runoff and not permit any flow into the permanent system until the end of the construction phase. This second option has the added advantage of the permanent controls being allowed to stabilize prior to routine operation. The main conclusions regarding construction sediment accumulation in stormwater controls are

- The majority of sediment problems result from construction activities (both public and private sector), underscoring the need for more effective erosion and sedimentation controls during this phase of system life.

- Long-term performance of a facility can only be guaranteed after completion of the construction phase of the complete site. Some agencies require a waiting period and/or posting of a performance bond to guarantee that sufficient time has passed and/or money is available to perform necessary repairs (including construction sediment removal) prior to the public agency assuming maintenance responsibility for the basin.

- Removal of construction sediment is essential prior to the facility being handed over to the operator; the cost of this activity should be borne by the contractor.

2.4 Vegetation Management

Two important points regarding stormwater control maintenance are the degree to which maintenance is dominated by vegetation management and the variability in the level of maintenance that citizens of different areas expect. As much as 80% of total staff hours spent in the field in many jurisdictions is associated with grass mowing, as opposed to sediment, debris and trash removal, or structural repair. While much of this effort has little effect on control performance, it is driven by the expectations of residents living near these facilities. The frequency of maintenance is often dependent on how visible the system is to those that live and work nearby.

Consider the practices of Baltimore County, Maryland, and Orlando, Florida. In Baltimore, the county maintenance group provides mowing only once per year at wet and dry basins, and does so only on embankments to prevent establishment of woody vegetation on dams and to provide access to the outlet structure and along the fence line. Dense, woody vegetation is actually preferred in the basin itself to prevent warming of stored runoff by sunlight and is acceptable to residents who are comfortable with a more natural look, although leaf accumulation in the basin may exacerbate other maintenance needs such as outlet cleaning. A low-maintenance ground cover is also planted to replace more maintenance-intensive grass cover. This low level of vegetation management does not appear to compromise the performance; for instance, the best performing dry basin in the International Stormwater Best Management Practices Database (www.bmpdatabase.org) at this time is located in Baltimore.

In contrast to Baltimore is Orlando. This program is funded through a stormwater utility fee and is relatively well-financed compared to most other U.S. jurisdictions. Mowing at some city-maintained sites occurs every 6 weeks and, because of the length of the growing season, this means approximately 6 times per year. Basins located in office parks maintained by private commercial operators appear to be mowed at the same frequency as other landscaping activities, or likely as much as 30 times per year.

These examples demonstrate the wide range in vegetation maintenance practices and frequencies among jurisdictions throughout the United States. While climate (e.g., length of the growing season, quantity of rainfall, etc.) will affect mowing frequency in different regions, it is primarily citizen expectations that drive maintenance activities beyond the minimum required for function. Consequently, areas that are just now beginning to implement stormwater controls widely may need to consider the expectations of their local populace when planning for the size and cost of a maintenance program rather than relying on an average cost based on experience in another jurisdiction.

2.5 Sediment Accumulation, Removal, and Disposal

Sediment removal is often viewed incorrectly as a frequent maintenance activity for stormwater controls. Sediment removal frequency is based on the amount of solids removed from the watershed during storms. With the exception of construction-phase sediment loads, stormwater sediment concentrations are generally not excessive.

Consider a stable urban watershed of 10 ha (25 ac) with an average total suspended solids concentration of 100 mg/L and a rainfall of approximately 1000 mm/yr (40 in./yr). This would result in a total solids load to the control of about 10 000 kg/yr (22 000 lb/yr), which would occupy perhaps 8 m³ (280 cu ft). Spread out over a basin with a surface area of, for example, 1000 m² (10 700 sq ft), the annual accumulation of sediment would be less than 1.0 cm/yr (0.4 in.). Consequently, it would take many years to accumulate a substantial amount of sediment. Of course, accumulation does not occur uniformly in the basin, rather, often preferentially in the vicinity of the inlet; as such, minor removal in this area may be required more frequently.

Sediment disposal is often a concern for agencies and others responsible for stormwater control maintenance. There are conflicting perceptions as to the degree of contamination of sediments in stormwater systems, and there is also concern among operators that there will be high costs associated with disposal of contaminated sediments. Sediment quality datasets from around the country generally do not support the concern that these materials are hazardous based on the mass of metals contained in the sediment. Maximum concentrations from controls constructed in the United States by the California Department of Transportation (Caltrans) (2004) on transportation facilities are presented in Table 11.1. The concentrations of the samples are compared with concentrations for U.S. hazardous waste thresholds. The results indicate that sediment pollutant concentrations from stormwater controls are generally well below thresholds for categorization as hazardous waste in the United States, and could be disposed of in a municipal landfill as a "special waste" or used as fill for another project. However, it is important to note that controls treating runoff from "hot spots" or where spills of hazardous materials have occurred in the watershed may have substantially higher sediment concentrations than shown here; in these instances, the sediment may need to be tested to determine the proper disposal method.

It should be noted that total suspended solids is only one component of the mass of solids coming into a stormwater control. Heavier solids, leaves, trash, and debris frequently outweigh the load based on total suspended solids. Chapter 4 summarizes several studies on litter loads.

2.6 Liquid Removal and Disposal

Liquid removal and disposal is of particular concern in the maintenance of many proprietary devices that maintain a permanent pool of water between events. Cleanout of these facilities typically is done with an eductor truck that removes both the accumulated pollutants and the overlying water. Eductor trucks vacuum stormwater,

TABLE 11.1. Maximum concentrations of selected constituents in sediments from various sources (WERF, 2005).

Site name	Structure	Maximum concentration (mg/kg)						
		As	Cd	Cu	Pb	Zn	Ni	Hg
605/91 (U.S.)	Biofiltration strips	2.90	1.2	60	144	337	13	0.05
Alameda (U.S.)	Oil and water separator	5.00	1.7	106	189	702	27	0.07
Termination P&R (U.S.)	Sand filter	0.76	0.3	11	11	70	3.40	0.04
Eastern regional middle states (U.S.)	Sand filter	1.20	0.3	8	25	61	3.10	0.04
Foothill middle states (U.S.)	Sand filter	1.70	0.2	7	16	77	2.40	0.04
Via Verde P&R (U.S.)	Sand filter treatment train	3.1	1.5	41	54	535	22	0.05
Kearny Mesa (U.S.)	Compost filter	1.7	5.0	120	110	670	18	0.5
Escondido (U.S.)	Sand filter	1.1	5.0	10	10	140	10	0.5
U.S. threshold values for hazardous waste		5000	1000	25 000	5000	250 000	20 000	

wastewater, and associated solids into a tank located on a truck for transport and disposal. The trucks are generally known as *Vactor trucks*, which references a popular brand name of truck manufactured by Vactor, a subsidiary of Federal Signal Corporation (Streator, Illinois).

The mixture is hauled to the operator's plant for decanting and liquid and sediment separation. Analysis of the solids portion often indicates elevated levels of metals and other pollutants; however, the material, like that collected in dry systems, does not rise to the level of hazardous waste (Serdar, 1993). The liquid portion could be discharged to the local sanitary sewer system. It should be noted that this likely will require an industrial waste discharge permit. Once dried, the solids can typically be disposed of in a municipal landfill.

2.7 Role of Stormwater Systems and Pretreatment

The use of sediment forebays, secondary upstream controls, and other treatment devices in a series prevents the accumulation of sediment in downstream controls and may significantly lower maintenance costs, although there will be some capital costs associated with pretreatment. A survey in the United Kingdom indicated that in 85% of the stormwater controls where sediment was a problem, no upstream pretreatment was provided (WERF, 2005). Pretreatment is especially desirable for wet basins because removal of wet sediment from the main pool is much more expensive than dry sediment from a pretreatment swale or sump. Several U.S. agencies, such as King County, have moved to sediment pretreatment in catch basins prior to entry into stormwater facilities.

2.8   Vector and Pest Management

Many areas experience unique maintenance requirements related to wildlife, including beavers, muskrats, geese, gophers, and alligators. It was only a few years ago that widespread concern about the West Nile virus in the United States changed the way that agencies and the public viewed systems that maintain a permanent pool, such as wet basins and underground vaults. Efforts are also underway to determine if these controls are significant sources of mosquito problems. Reactions to real or potential threats vary and vigorous debate continues as to the nature and level of threat posed by wet basins and wetland systems as breeding grounds for mosquitoes.

2.9   Privately Owned Low-Impact Development Systems

Privately owned low-impact development systems present a unique set of maintenance challenges. The presence of numerous, small, and potentially inaccessible on-lot systems makes inspections by regulatory agencies far more difficult than if a few large regional stormwater controls had been constructed. In addition, the large number of homeowners that need to be educated about the function and specific maintenance requirements also reduces the likelihood that 100% compliance can be achieved, especially if one looks at a 50-year life of the facility and the large number of people that might own that system during its life span. The thought of potentially bringing enforcement actions against many homeowners who don't comply with recommended maintenance guidelines is also problematic. Consequently, regulatory agencies should give serious thought about maintenance of these systems and how that might affect expected performance and create downstream effects.

3.0 DETAILED GUIDELINES FOR STORMWATER CONTROL MAINTENANCE

The previous sections of this chapter describe a variety of global issues related to maintenance of stormwater controls. This section focuses on stormwater control of specific maintenance issues for swales and strips, basins, filters, infiltrators, and catch basins. The goal is to provide the designer with specific information about the type of maintenance, frequency (based on level of maintenance), manpower, and equipment required. This should help municipalities and others responsible for stormwater control maintenance to make a better estimate of the resources that will be required to maintain these facilities.

3.1 Maintenance of Vegetated Swales and Strips

Maintenance of swales and buffer strips is reasonably straightforward and consists primarily of vegetation management, ensuring that flow is spread evenly across the system, and preventing ponding of water. Trash needs to be removed, inflow and outflow structures checked and kept unblocked, side slopes kept vegetated and stabilized, and sediment removed periodically.

Swales and strips tend to be treated as an integral, rather than separate, part of an easement or landscape. When the public right-of-way is mowed, so, too, is the swale or strip. In addition, most swales and buffer strips are not inspected. When problems arise (e.g., a blocked flow path), they are noted (typically on a citizen complaint basis) and corrected, but not necessarily anticipated.

Swales engineered for water quality (with lengths, widths, and slopes calculated to achieve a certain retention time) tend to be lumped in with other grassed conveyance ditches and swales that are not engineered as such. Open swales and drainage ditches are ubiquitous in the United States. Thousands of road miles are drained with swales as are innumerable commercial and residential developments. Many rural areas have virtually no curb-gutter-and-pipe drainage systems and rely entirely on open swales (also known as "borrow" or "bar" ditches). Swales designed specifically for water quality are actually uncommon in most communities, although a few states such as Florida have used them for many years. Jurisdictions with progressive stormwater regulations specify how to design and build these swales and credit them toward required water quality controls; however, despite this institutional support and their touted simplicity, swales are used in an official capacity for stormwater control much less often than wet basins and dry basins. Therefore, the experience level and data available from which to base maintenance conclusions is somewhat limited.

Maintenance activities for swales and strips include the following:

- Routine maintenance—inspection, reporting, and information management, vegetation management; and trash and minor debris removal; and

- Intermittent facility maintenance—erosion repairs, landscaping, animal control, and sediment removal.

Each of these items is discussed in this section. Estimates of "best practices" levels of maintenance are presented for typical applications. Where appropriate, "minimum" levels and other options are also discussed. Conclusions presented in this section were drawn from quantitative data and interviews with stormwater agency representatives.

3.1.1 Inspections

Some public agencies perform or contract out maintenance of stormwater controls; other agencies do not maintain any controls, leaving this to private owners. In most instances, public entities provide some form of periodic field inspection. Important elements to evaluate during the inspection include

- Determining that the control exists (and has not been eliminated by a change in land use);

- Assessing if erosion or damage to vegetation has occurred;

- Checking for uniformity of grass cover, debris and litter, and areas of sediment accumulation; and

- Replanting and restoring bare spots and areas of erosion identified during semiannual inspections to original specifications.

Table 11.2 summarizes the most typical inspection program for swales. "Default" values for use in the whole life costing (WLC) model described in Chapter 12 are included in boldface type. The designer should note that, where available, local data are preferable to that of nationwide averages or literature values.

At a minimum, annual inspections are recommended for swales; however, more frequent inspections of grass cover during the first few years after establishment will

TABLE 11.2 Inspection, reporting, and information management for swales and strips (WERF, 2005).

Description: visit site; review comprehensive checklist of items; note and refer problems to maintenance staff; document findings in database.

Frequency		
Default	**Once per year**	Self-explanatory.
High	Twice per year	Work crews sometimes asked to do informal inspections; formal inspections typically every 3 years. Many agency representatives recommended more frequent, annual inspections for small controls (swales, bioretention, and infiltration trenches) than the standard 3-year cycle for larger ponds and basins.
Medium	Once per year	Typical frequency, especially for agencies with large numbers of BMPs.
Low	No scheduled inspections; respond to citizen complaints	Not recommended. Need more timely observations.
Time required		
Default	**2 hours**	Includes recording field data into computer database.
Range	1 to 3 hours	Depends on distance and speed of travel between sites, level of detail of reporting required.
Labor		
Default	**1 person**	Calculate cost by multiplying the number of persons times local wage rate(s).
Range	1 to 2 persons	Typically one person; some agencies prefer two.
Skill level		
Default	**Skilled Professional**	Determines wage level.
Range	High school trainee to skilled professional	Dictated by budget; higher turnover typically for lower paid employees; depends on complexity of BMPs.
Equipment and materials		
Default	**Vehicle; field data form; computer database**	Determines equipment cost. Select an hourly expense.
Range	See above; also digital camera and Global Positioning System devices to record and track control locations.	Depends on level of sophistication desired.

help determine if any problems are developing so designers can plan for long-term restorative maintenance needs. Some agencies inspect more frequently and some ask that routine mowing contractors or crews report problems as they see them, which provides additional inspection capability. Unfortunately, because of budgetary constraints, many stormwater agencies do not provide this level of inspection and are visited only on a citizen-complaint basis.

Swales have long been a concern as places that breed mosquitoes. However, properly designed and maintained dry swales should not harbor mosquitoes because of the way they are graded to provide uniform sheet flow with thick vegetation for slope and bottom stability. Poorly maintained swales may form inadvertent temporary pools that can hold standing water long enough for mosquito larvae to mature. Temporary pools can be a particular problem in driveway culverts when sediment and vegetation builds up near the outlet. Inspectors must be able to view these systems following wet conditions to determine if inappropriate ponding is occurring. Levels of perceived and real threat vary enormously from community to community and no "average" condition or needed expenditure is available at present.

3.1.2   Vegetation Management

Vegetation management constitutes the dominant maintenance activity for swales and strips in terms of labor, equipment, and overall cost. In many ways, it is equivalent to standard practices for landscaped areas such as grassed medians and parkland. Most agencies have guidelines to cut the grass to maintain a maximum height, typically recognized as 100 to 150 mm (4 to 6 in.) in height. Periodic mowing is necessary to prevent takeover of woody vegetation and to ensure a proper flow path for water through the swale. Table 11.3 summarizes the vegetation management program common among agencies in the United States.

The level of vegetation management is controlled by the following interrelated factors: aesthetics, vegetation choice, and climate. Mowing often occurs on a schedule dictated by aesthetic concerns rather than for water quality function. In commercial complexes, for example, mowing vegetation under landscaping contracts is not distinguished from that of the surrounding lawn and garden areas. Proximity to well-tended public and private developments increases the chance these vegetated controls also will be frequently maintained. Conversely, some prefer a more natural look and use native or low-growing species that do not have to be maintained as frequently.

TABLE 11.3 Vegetation management with trash and minor debris removal for swales and strips (WERF, 2005).

Description: mow grounds; cut small woody vegetation to prevent unwanted tree growth. Walk or drive site; pick up obvious litter; informal inspection: check outfalls for blockage and notify maintenance staff if significant problems are observed.

Frequency		
Default	**Once per year**	Self-explanatory.
High	Every 4 to 6 weeks	Done for aesthetics, especially for controls with high public visibility; not required in low rainfall areas (except, possibly, trash control component). Commercial areas often maintain on same schedule as rest of grounds.
Medium	Once or twice per year	Typical frequency. Aesthetics still is impetus; depends on community expectations, rainfall level, and plant growth rate.
Low	Every 3 years, plants selected for slow growth	Minimum required to ensure woody plants do not compromise flow path and outfall areas. Use of native grasses and/or wetland plants can potentially decrease maintenance frequency.
Time required		
Default	**4 hours**	Assumes small (2-person) crew. Larger crew could maintain an "average"-sized facility more quickly. Each agency strikes its own balance.
Range	2 to 5 hours per crew per facility	Depends largely on the size of control site and level of maintenance, distance and speed of travel between sites, and size and equipment of crew. Large equipment may slow transport between sites. Supervisor spends fraction of time at each site.
Labor		
Default	**2 persons**	Calculate cost by multiplying number of persons times local wage rate(s). If contracted, use lump sum.
Range	1 to 5 workers plus supervisor	Depends on equipment used and level of maintenance. Large one-person mowers used by some; minimal maintenance site requires much less labor than manicured site.
Equipment and materials		
Default	**Truck, trailer, tractor with mower, miscellaneous landscaping tools.**	Determines equipment cost. Select an hourly expense.
Typical	See above; equipment varies.	Greatly varies on size of BMPs, budget, and level of maintenance desired. Some agencies much more tolerant of plant growth on site.
Options	Public crew vs contracted services	Market-driven factors determine choice. Both inhouse labor and subcontracted labor used by agencies interviewed. Usually maintained by property owners except in public property or rights-of-way.

The United States has extreme climatic variations and mowing frequency follows these differences. In Florida, where rainfall is frequent and substantial, mowing is done as often as every 6 weeks (nine times per year; it is important to note that many of the facilities are also in close proximity to homes and are part of the landscaped grass area). This differs substantially from that required in dry areas. In California and Washington, swales and strips may only need to be cut twice a year, once in the dry season and once in the wet season. On public right-of-ways, most agencies simply mow as often as they can afford to financially and as dictated by public complaints.

Frequent mowing serves a purpose beyond aesthetics. It has been observed that frequently mowed areas are less susceptible to erosion. Grass "self-shades" if it is not mowed frequently, leading to spotty, patchy vegetation and insufficient cover; increased periodic maintenance (mowing) helps avoid increased corrective maintenance (particularly erosion and channelization in swales).

Use of native grasses can help in avoiding the added expense of frequent mowing, minimize the use of irrigated water, and provide more natural habitat. Some maintenance guidelines specify mowing heights of 50 to 100 mm (2 to 4 in.) for irrigated grass and 150 to 200 mm (6 to 8 in.) for nonirrigated native grass; however, a study in Portland, Oregon (Liptan, personal communication), where one swale was maintained with mowed turf grass and the other was not maintained at all and featured largely native, volunteer plants, found that the native, messy swale functioned better than the mowed and maintained swale. This finding helped support Portland's decision to minimize routine landscaping on the grounds of its structural water quality controls by planting native vegetation instead of turf grasses.

Excess ponded water (which may occur in swales, but typically not in filter strips) and a desire to reduce mowing has prompted several agencies in the Pacific Northwest to look at wetland plant alternatives to grass for swales. At one King County monitoring site, the pollutant removal effectiveness of wetland plants was examined (the subject swale had previously had problems with dying grass caused by excessive water ponding). Results showed 70% total suspended solids (TSS) removal, which was respectable but not as efficient as monitored in grass-lined swales (80% removal) (Kulzer, personal communication).

3.1.3   Litter Management

Trash and minor debris removal is typically performed by mowing crews as they cut the grass. Cost data were not readily available for distinguishing between routine mowing and litter pickup, although, in some instances, a different contract or crew would take care of each component. Table 11.3 notes that most typical trash and litter removal programs follow the same schedule (and share the same costs with) vegetation management programs.

3.1.4   Intermittent Maintenance

Most agencies do not track maintenance costs, especially those for long-term maintenance (WERF, 2005). Some track the total cost of the maintenance program but not costs for individual stormwater controls. The unit cost per stormwater control is estimated as the total divided by the number of controls, disregarding the type of control or whether maintenance was actually performed in all of them. The result is a unit cost that is lower than actual. Therefore, it is not known with certainty what these long-term infrequent maintenance costs will look like. Average annualized costs are, therefore, speculative. More data are required to increase the accuracy of this information. Table 11.4 summarizes available information on these maintenance tasks, comprised largely of erosion and geometry repairs, minor sediment removal, landscaping, and animal control. Additional discussion is presented by subcategory in this section.

Because swales convey concentrated runoff, they are much more prone to problems than filter strips, which receive sheet flow from contributing areas. King County is now retrofitting old, failing swales to improve water quality performance. The following design issues requiring correction have been identified and are especially common for older swales built prior to the development of improved design criteria:

- Insufficient slope (leading to ponded water and dying grass);
- Excessive slope (leading to insufficient residence time);
- Improper geometry (many are too V-shaped, causing channelization in the center of the swale);
- Baseflow problems (persistent flows, channelized flows);
- Lack of flow spreaders (channelized flows, erosion); and
- Lack of liners in soils with excessively rapid infiltration (insufficient pollutant removal, threat to groundwater).

TABLE 11.4 Intermittent maintenance for swales and strips (WERF, 2005).

Description: miscellaneous maintenance to repair nonroutine problems: repair eroded side slopes, correct geometry (channelization, lack of flow spreaders, etc.), remove sediment, restore landscaping elements, and repair animal damage.

Frequency		
Default	**Every 4 years**	Local conditions (drainage area stability, soils, etc.) will dictate frequency; need to establish long-term averages based on local experience.
High	Every 1 to 2 years	Recommended level in some maintenance guidelines; small number of agencies use this frequency in practice. Caltrans requires annual sediment removal.
Medium	Every 5 to 8 years	More typical frequency. Montgomery County estimates sediment removal every 5 years.
Low	No maintenance (Assume every 10 years for cost model)	Most systems have received no maintenance to date; not an acceptable long-term strategy—will diminish performance.
Time required		
Default	**1 day**	Varies with project size and complexity from 1 hour to several days or more per activity.
Range	4 hours to 2 days	Depends greatly on size and accessibility of control, quantity of sediment, weather, location of disposal site, etc. Long-term averages should be established based on local data.
Labor		
Default	**4 persons**	Crew size varies by agency and project. Calculate cost by multiplying number of persons times local wage rate(s). If contracted, use lump sum.
Range	3 to 6 workers plus supervisor	Depends on equipment used and level of maintenance.
Equipment and materials		
Default	**Backhoe; dump truck; miscellaneous hand tools**	Equipment and materials vary by agency, project size, and complexity.
Typical	Front-end loader, backhoe, dump truck, trailer for vehicles, miscellaneous hand tools, replacement components.	Dependent on size of control, equipment available, and facility design. Controls with no provision for maintenance will require ad hoc measures for access, raising costs and project lengths.

Erosion of strips is typically not a problem because water depths and flowrates tend to be exceedingly small; however, this is not the case for swales. Erosion of the side and bottom surfaces of swales can cause a variety of problems and needs to be repaired. Side slope erosion and sloughing leads to direct sedimentation, which is the very issue the swale is designed to address. If the bottoms of swales become sufficiently irregular and pitted (often initiated by tire tracks), they will no longer have the desired uniform flow and can retain water and harbor pests, such as mosquitoes. Often, swales are not high-profile landscaped features and do not receive maintenance attention beyond routine mowing and litter pickup (WERF, 2005). Eroded stretches, then, may simply be left to "self repair" rather than receive intervention. In more managed landscaped areas, these problems would receive the same type of attention given to a bare patch of ground on a lawn. Therefore, no additional expense is assumed for maintenance; this work (or lack thereof) would be performed for aesthetics whether or not the swale was designed for water quality or was simply just another element of a landscape.

Because swales and strips are vegetated landscape features, they benefit from periodic landscaping approaches such as scarification, thatch removal, aeration (e.g., spiking or hollow tining), and reseeding or overseeding of new grass. These techniques serve to foster vigorous and healthy grass cover. However, unless the swale was in a highly managed landscape setting (with care provided for regardless of whether or not it was a stormwater control), these sorts of techniques do not typically occur.

Vegetated swales and strips are potentially vulnerable to burrowing animals such as moles and gophers. The expense to repair gopher damage in California is typically minor, at less than 5% of annualized maintenance costs (Caltrans, 2004). However, estimated animal burrow removal in Maryland was 30% of annualized costs (WERF, 2005).

Sediment can build up in swales, especially around changes in grade or flow condition (e.g., at a culvert) and can occur near the contact of a strip with the adjacent pavement. This sediment needs to be removed periodically to maintain proper hydraulic performance and to avoid creation of inadvertent ponded areas. Sediment is typically removed when something more obvious occurs, such as a blockage that prevents flow out of the swale or when a sediment delta builds up in the bottom, affecting flow. The quantities required to be removed are typically not very large and require a lower level of equipment and transport. Few agencies have experience removing sediment from swales and even fewer track the costs of this work explicitly (WERF, 2005).

3.2 Basin Maintenance

3.2.1 Wet Basin and Wetland Maintenance

Maintenance activities for wet basins and wetlands include the following significant activities:

- Routine maintenance—inspection, reporting, and information management; vegetation management; trash and minor debris removal; and vector control; and

- Intermittent facility maintenance—forebay sediment removal and dewatering; main pool sediment removal and dewatering; erosion repairs; landscaping; and animal control.

3.2.1.1 Inspections

When possible, inspections should be carried out with as-built basin plans in hand and conducted under a variety of conditions. Wet weather inspections are important and useful for determining if the basin is functioning properly. Seasonal inspections are also important. During winter, erosion and animal burrows are more visible, whereas, during summer, invasive species can be seen. Dry weather inspections allow outlet structures and weirs to be more easily inspected. Inspections of wet basins and wetlands should comprise a variety of activities including

- Checking the embankment for subsidence, erosion, leakage, cracking, and tree growth;
- Assessing the condition of the emergency spillway;
- Inspecting the inlet and outlet structures and assessing their condition;
- Evaluating upstream and downstream channel stability;
- Checking the stability and vegetation coverage of the side slopes; and
- Evaluating the condition of the basin vegetation to determine if removal, harvesting, or replanting is needed.

Table 11.5 summarizes a typical inspection program for wet basins and wetlands found among U.S. agencies. Some agencies inspect more frequently (e.g., annually).

TABLE 11.5 Summary method to estimate effort for inspection, reporting, and information management for wet ponds (WERF, 2005).

Description: visit site; review comprehensive checklist of items; note and refer problems to maintenance staff; document findings in database.

Frequency		
Default	**Every 3 years**	Self-explanatory.
High	Twice per year & following large rainfall events	Work crews sometimes asked to do informal inspections; formal inspections usually every 3 years.
Medium	Every 1 years	Typical frequency, esp. for agencies with large numbers of BMPs.
Low	Every 3 years	Not recommended. Need more timely observations.
Time required		
Default	**2 hours**	Includes recording field data into computer database.
Range	1 to 3 hours	Depends on distance and speed of travel between sites, level of detail of reporting required.
Labor		
Default	**1 person**	Calculate cost by multiplying number of persons times local wage rate(s).
Range	1 to 2 persons	Typically one person. Some agencies prefer two.
Skill level		
Default	**Skilled Professional**	Determines wage level.
Range	High school trainee to graduate student to skilled professional	Dictated by budget; higher turnover typically for lower paid employees; depends on complexity of BMPs.
Equipment and materials		
Default	**Vehicle; field data form; computer database**	Determines equipment cost. Select an hourly expense.
Range	See above; also digital camera and Global Positioning System devices to record and track control locations.	Depends on level of sophistication desired.

However, once wet basins are maintained in good order, most agencies have not found it necessary to perform detailed inspections more than once every 3 years. Some agencies ask that routine mowing contractors or crews report problems as they see them, which provides additional inspection capability. Default values are included in boldface type for use in the WLC model in Chapter 12. It is important to note that local data, where available, are preferable to those of nationwide averages or literature values.

3.2.1.2 Vegetation Management

Vegetation management consists of two different types of activities with substantially different costs. These activities include management of terrestrial vegetation around the perimeter of the basin and management of aquatic vegetation within the basin. Most agencies mow regularly to control the height of grass and other vegetation on the basin perimeter. This task requires a crew with equipment to go to each basin site on a regular basis. Considerable additional expenses can be incurred if vegetation within the basin (emergent wetland and open-water plants) is also maintained.

Some actions (and costs) reflect a commitment to providing improved aesthetic benefits rather than functional benefits essential to system performance and public health protection. While most agencies do not have resources to maintain the facilities more than once or twice a year, they may work with adjacent property owners to address complaints and concerns. At least two options have been developed to address the shortfall of resources to providing more frequent landscaping services.

First, many agencies have begun to work cooperatively with nearby landowners (e.g., homeowners, associations, and businesses) to have these community groups provide day-to-day mowing and litter pickup. For example, in Maryland, stormwater agencies in Baltimore, Montgomery, and Prince George's Counties have all instituted some variation of "adopt a basin" programs for homeowners, whose residential communities contain stormwater basins. Citizens check for obvious problems (i.e., basins not draining properly, etc.) and do routine maintenance, such as trash pickup and mowing. New York City Department of Environmental Protection has instituted a similar program called "Adopt-A-Bluebelt," where citizens, local community groups, and businesses maintain the perimeters of BMPs and are recognized for their efforts with a prominent, personalized sign erected at the site. These programs allow county crews or publicly funded contractors to focus on more serious issues, such as repair of structural components, or removal of trash and debris affecting the hydraulic performance of outlets.

An alternative (and potentially complementary) strategy taken by some agencies is to specify which specific landscaping elements (species of grasses, shrubs, etc.) do not have to be cut, thereby reducing significantly this line item in their maintenance budgets. For example, Baltimore County, Maryland, specifies the use of a low-growing ground cover which does not have to be mowed. County crews only mow on the facility perimeter (i.e., along the fence) and along a strip to provide access to the outflow structure (for inspection purposes). The City of Portland, Oregon, has allocated more than $1 million (U.S. dollars) to replace all landscaping in its publicly owned structural controls with native species (WERF, 2005). These native plants are not mowed and require only occasional landscaping attention to remove invasive vegetation.

In addition to being a nuisance, uncontrolled growth of woody vegetation, particularly trees, can be a significant cost item. Trees flourish around basins, especially in outflow structures and embankments. Trees can compromise the integrity and function of the basins when they grow on embankments. Removing large trees can cost tens of thousands of dollars. However, initial growth of these plants can be controlled at a fraction of the potential cost by ensuring that they are cut on a regular schedule during routine mowing and landscaping visits.

Management of aquatic vegetation is driven by the following factors: aesthetic and vector control. Residents and businesses located adjacent to high-visibility wet basins have historically expressed a clear preference for wet basins as opposed to wetlands, which often come to resemble swamps. Consequently, substantial effort is often exerted to prevent cattails and other aggressive plants from becoming established over the majority of the basin surface. More highly managed approaches can be expensive. The City of Austin, Texas, is now reevaluating its design criteria for wet basins to minimize aquatic vegetation maintenance, provide deeper water areas (with less aquatic bench), and avoid aggressive species like water lilies (which can cover the entire surface of the basin). In less visible locations, many agencies (likely, at least in part, out of financial necessity) have tended toward a hands-off approach, minimizing interventions and associated labor and disposal costs. The focus appears to be on making sure that vegetation does not interfere with the hydraulic function of the design (e.g., block the outlet).

Table 11.6 summarizes the vegetation management program for wet basins found among agencies interviewed.

3.2.1.3 Litter Management

Trash removal falls into a similar category as mowing, although trash poses a significant risk in that it can clog the hydraulic control structures of the basin and cause system failure (as can vegetative debris in sufficient quantities). Therefore, trash collection around the outfall and trash screen provide more than just an aesthetic function; indeed, many agencies want to show that they are removing pollutants, including the most visible form of pollutants (i.e., trash and litter). Table 11.6 notes that most typical trash and litter removal programs for wet basins follow the same schedule (and share the same costs with) as vegetation management programs.

3.2.1.4 Vector Control

As mentioned previously, the emergence of West Nile Virus has led to increased concern about the potential for mosquito breeding in stormwater systems. In California (but not in many other states), vector control agencies have been particularly concerned with the habitat provided in portions of basins covered with emergent vegetation. The organic matter provides food for the mosquito larvae and the vegetation is often dense enough to prevent mosquito fish (*Gambusia affinis*) from reaching their intended prey. Consequently, agencies have required basin operators to harvest all vegetation in the basin annually. This is an expensive and difficult undertaking; as such, agencies should consider this potential maintenance factor when recommending the use of wet basins.

3.2.1.5 Intermittent Facility Maintenance

Intermittent maintenance for wet basins includes repairs of structural elements, dam embankments, and eroded areas around the perimeter; however, the most resource-intensive activity is sediment removal. Wet basins are specifically designed to capture sediment (among other pollutants) and thus fill in with sediment over time. Many are online systems, which can be especially vulnerable to rapid sedimentation. The level of development activity in the contributing area is a key factor in determining this load. Many basins are built during the first stages of development. Subsequent land clearing can produce large quantities of sediment to the downstream control. Once stabilized, the load is reduced. Another factor is drainage area size; large stream systems can move large quantities of sediment bed-load, which contributes significantly to sedimentation.

TABLE 11.6 Summary of vegetation management and trash and minor debris removal for wet ponds (WERF, 2005).

Description: mow grounds; cut small woody vegetation to prevent unwanted tree growth. May or may not include significant care of aquatic vegetation. Walk or drive site; pick up obvious litter; informal inspection: check outfalls for blockage and notify maintenance staff if significant problems are observed.

Frequency

Default	**Once per year**	Assumes not in high visibility area.
High	Every 4 to 6 weeks	Done for aesthetics, especially for BMPs with high public visibility; not required in low rainfall areas (except possibly trash control component). Commercial areas often maintain on same schedule as rest of grounds.
Medium	Once or twice per year	Typical frequency. Aesthetics still is impetus; depends on community expectations, rainfall level, plant growth rate.
Low	Every 3 years, limited area mowed, plants selected for slow growth	Minimum required to ensure woody plants do not take over embankment and outfall areas. Can mow perimeter, embankment, and access points only if desired. Use of native plants can improve appearance. May have to target "problem ponds" for more frequent maintenance.

Time required

Default	**8 hours**	Assumes small (2-person) crew. Larger crew could maintain an "average"-sized facility more quickly. Each agency strikes its own balance.
Range	4 to 16 hours per crew per facility	Depends greatly on size of control and level of maintenance, distance and speed of travel between sites, and size and equipment of crew. Aquatic vegetation maintained at some sites in boat; others not at all; extensive care of aquatic plants could require substantially more time and cost. Large equipment may slow transport between sites. Supervisor spends fraction of time at each site.

Labor and labor rate

Default	**2 persons**	Calculate cost by multiplying number of persons times local wage rate(s). If contracted, use lump sum.
Range	1 to 5 workers plus supervisor	Depends on equipment used and level of maintenance. Large one-person mowers used by some; minimal maintenance site requires much less labor than manicured site. Labor wage rates vary considerably across the country.

Equipment and materials

Default	**Truck, trailer, tractor with mower, miscellaneous landscaping tools.**	Determines equipment cost. Select an hourly expense.
Typical	See above; equipment varies. Boat or aquatic vehicle required to remove trash and plants from pool area.	Greatly varies on size of BMPs, budget, and level of maintenance desired. Some agencies much more tolerant of plant growth (including trees) in pond and on-site.
Options	Public crew vs contracted services	Market-driven factors determine choice. Both inhouse labor and subcontracted labor used by agencies interviewed.

Because their performance is also linked to capture volume, it is important that this sediment be removed periodically to restore each basin to its original design capacity. Without exception, this maintenance task represents the most financially onerous of the many maintenance tasks for wet basins. None of the other five structural control types had a similar maintenance task type of this scale and complexity. In the one instance with specific, itemized data, the CH2M HILL (2001) study in Montgomery County showed that about 40% of annualized costs to maintain wet basins come with removing sediment. Sediment removal requires draining the basin and removing, dewatering, and hauling the sediment to a disposal site. These tasks are individually and collectively difficult and expensive, requiring specific expertise and equipment. In fact, this may be the key reason that most of the wet basins built (many at least 15 years old) have not had significant sediment removal performed. This leaves some doubt as to the exact cost of this task for these agencies.

The logistics of sediment removal are as follows. First, an assessment of the quantity of sediment is made. Work proceeds if there is sufficient sediment to warrant removal and that quantity is roughly estimated, typically using sonar or a simple rod. The difficulty of making accurate quantity estimates is an important factor as this can lead to much higher costs if the contractor has to excavate more than is expected (the bid's price per unit of sediment will depend on the initial quantity estimated). Basins with concrete bottoms (relatively rare) facilitate the quantification of sediment accumulation and its removal.

The Urban Drainage and Flood Control District (UDFCD) in the Denver, Colorado, metropolitan area has considerable experience with sediment removal from their large, inline, regional wet basins. The UDFCD staff require construction of a large rip-rap pad next to the concrete access ramp; the ramp is typically not big enough for both the loader and the truck). The excavator (or backhoe for smaller jobs) can then be located on the pad and a team of dump trucks can use the concrete ramp. A significant amount of time is taken each day to ensure that the footing (rip-rap pad) is structurally sound (to avoid having the loader tip into the basin) and that the machinery is all taken out after each work day (to avoid problems if wet weather occurs and, during cleanup, to avoid tracking and sedimentation); indeed, only 4 to 6 hours of an 8-hour work day will actually involve loading trucks. Either the water is diverted with diversion structures, pumped, and/or the excavator typically digs a trench along one side of the basin to allow water to flow past and to establish a low point to which the rest of the sediment can drain. (Some basins have release valves that allow the water to drain by gravity. The UDFCD has found that underdrains clog with sediment and cannot be relied on.) The excavator piles up the material and moves it around to dewater it and then loads it onto the trucks. If the disposal site is in a distant location, a larger number of trucks are needed to ensure that trucks are continuously available to be filled with the excavator. The excavator is a high-cost item. Large-scaled excavators can cost $200 per hour (2004 cost in U.S. dollars). Dewatering must be accomplished as it is illegal (for health and environmental reasons) to haul material that drips or spills sediment. Waterlogged sediment is also much heavier and expensive to haul and is not accepted in many landfills.

New York City almost exclusively uses an educator truck (or Vactor truck) to clean sediment from its wetland and extended detention facilities. The truck is especially well-suited for cleaning the forebays and micropools of these systems because of the flexibility of the vacuum apparatus and the mobility of the truck-mounted machine. Each of the forebays and micropools has a bottom constructed of rip-rap embedded in concrete. The extended detention controls have built in draw-down valves, which allow maintenance staff to safely drain the system. Once drained, the hose is easily extended into the control for sediment removal. The sediment is then hauled to a nearby maintenance yard for dewatering and disposal.

All of the experienced agencies interviewed stressed the importance of finding a nearby disposal site to control costs. Disposal arrangements typically occur on an ad hoc basis because of the infrequent nature of the work and the distributed location of the basins. In the best-case scenario, sediment is placed on-site (some facilities have land set aside for this purpose) or hauled to close-by locations for use as fill material. In some instances, the contractor secures a disposal site, excavates and sells the topsoil, creating an area large enough to dispose of the dredged material, and vegetates it. In one instance, the material was sold at a relatively low price to an entity that would mix in compost and manure and create soil for sale. In the worst-case scenario, trucks haul the materials great distances to be dumped in a landfill. The UDFCD staff estimated that disposal costs could approximately double the cost of the job relative to a job with low-cost disposal. In general, UDFCD has found that, even for the exact same basin, costs from one maintenance event to the next can vary dramatically. Factors involved include a contractor's bid price, distance to the disposal site, type of disposal site (free vs landfill), volume of sediment to be removed, the weather, and adequacy of access to the basin.

Montgomery County staff predict that, with more regular maintenance of forebays (as opposed to the entire basin), these costs should decrease. Montgomery

County retrofits sediment forebays into their wet basins when they remove sediment from older structures, which did not initially provide this feature.

3.2.2 Dry Basin Maintenance

Maintenance requirements for dry basins are similar to those of wet basins. The lack of a standing pool of water does tend to make dry basin maintenance less complicated and less expensive than that required for wet basins. The greater degree of simplicity is attributable to the absence of a wet component in the design. There are numerous designs possible for dry basins, ranging from a completely dry basin to those including a permanent pool of various sizes. For the purpose of this analysis, it is assumed that all the runoff is discharged within 24 to 48 hours. If wet features and micropools are used, the reader is referred to Section 3.2.1. The same set of maintenance categories for wet basins is suitable for dry basins. As with the retention basin section, conclusions presented in this section were drawn from quantitative data obtained from stormwater agencies nationally and from qualitative insights from interviews with agency representatives. Maintenance activities include

- Routine maintenance—inspection, reporting, and information management; vegetation management; trash and minor debris removal; and vector control; and

- Intermittent maintenance—woody vegetation removal; access; structural repairs; animal control; and sediment removal.

3.2.2.1 Inspection

Inspection, reporting, and information management for dry basins is identical to that of wet basin (see Section 3.2.1.1).

3.2.2.2 Vegetation Management

Vegetation management for dry basins is also similar to that of wet basins in that the grounds are typically vegetated with grass and must be periodically mowed for aesthetic purposes to prevent takeover of woody vegetation and ensure a proper flow path for water through the system. The absence of wetland plantings can greatly reduce costs compared to wet basin. Where aquatic plants are not removed, the cost to maintain remaining landscaped grounds might actually be slightly higher for dry basins than for wet basins given than the interior of the basin would have to be mowed. Table 11.7 summarizes a typical vegetation management program for dry basins.

3.2.2.3 Litter Management

Trash and minor debris removal for dry basins is similar to that of wet basin. However, debris removal from within the basin is significantly easier because it does not (unless the outflow is clogged) require a boat or other means of accessing permanent pool area and riser structure in open water. Table 11.7 notes that most trash and litter removal programs for dry basins follow the same schedule (and share the same costs) as vegetation management programs.

3.2.2.4 Vector Control

Vector control for dry basins is similar to that of wet basin. The lack of a permanent pool does not actually eliminate the need to monitor for mosquitoes and other undesirable animal species. Temporary pools and standing water that can last long enough for mosquito larvae to mature (at least 3 days) can form in dry basins. Inspectors must be able to view these systems following wet conditions to determine if undesired ponding is occurring. Levels of perceived and real threats vary enormously from community to community and no average condition or needed expenditure is available at present.

3.2.2.5 Intermittent Facility Maintenance

Intermittent facility maintenance for dry basins is similar to that of wet basins in that structural, dam embankment, slope and erosion repairs, and cleaning of outfall structures all must be addressed. A common problem identified for dry basins serving smaller drainage areas is clogging of small-sized (in diameter) orifices in the outlet structure. In addition, it has been noted that maintenance crews sometimes blow grass clippings to storm drain inlets or directly into basins, contributing to clogging and failure of these systems.

Access for sediment removal and other repairs has also been a problem with many systems. Dry basins and other facilities have often been designed without consideration for access, increasing the cost and difficulty of maintenance. Roads are sometimes too narrow and the basin is crowded in among houses with no entry.

Many dry basins develop unintended wet areas, typically near outflow structures. In some instances, contractors overexcavate dry basins to allow them to serve as sedimentation basins during construction, but then fail to modify them at project's end; therefore, they do not function hydraulically and convert to de facto wet basins. Unplanned wet areas also develop in dry basins in part because of excessive irrigation or other inputs (e.g., car wash discharges) in upstream contributing areas. Mowing equipment or maintenance of these areas causes rutting and extensive damage to the basin floor. These dry weather flows also keep the basin wet and create more wetland-type conditions than were intended in the original design. If not mowed, the entire floor of the basin may eventually resemble a wetland, which does not dry even during an extended period without rain. Some agencies prefer to allow these wet areas to remain (they can provide a pollutant removal function for low flows) rather than take the time and expense to remove them.

In some areas, beavers have begun to occupy dry systems. These animals can block outfalls to create their preferred habitat and burrow into embankments, potentially compromising their structural integrity. Gophers also pose a challenge in some areas.

Removal of sediment from dry basins tends to be simpler and less costly than for wet basins. The majority of cost savings comes from not having to dewater the system. Localized sediment removal from these basins, from around the inlet, for instance, is often such that a crew with hand tools could likely do the work in a day or two. Crews can wait until the sediment is relatively dry and remove it without concerns about dewatering and transport of wet materials. Avoiding the cost and difficulty of sediment removal from wet basins alone has prompted many agencies and land developers to favor dry systems over wet systems. Clogged systems will still require some degree of dewatering.

3.2.3   Swirl Concentrators and Vaults

There are a variety of below-grade swirl concentrators and vaults marketed by a number of manufacturers. The size and configuration varies substantially between them and, as such, the frequency and type of maintenance is dependent largely on the specific type of device under consideration. In general, accumulation of material within these controls reduces their pollutant removal efficiency until they are roughly half full, at which time little additional removal occurs. These inlets retain sediment and floatables including oils, which must be removed periodically.

These devices should be frequently monitored during their first year of operation to determine the rate at which material accumulates. This is highly dependent on the location of the control and the nature of the watershed. The California Department of Transportation (2004) found that up to 85% of the material collected in a device they monitored was composed of vegetated material. Consequently, there may be substantial seasonal variation in the rate at which material accumulates, with much higher rates recorded in the fall when trees lose their leaves.

TABLE 11.7 Vegetation management with trash and minor debris removal for dry extended detention ponds (WERF, 2005).

Description: Mow grounds; cut small woody vegetation to prevent unwanted tree growth. Walk or drive site; pick up obvious litter; informal inspection: check outfalls for blockage and notify maintenance staff if major problems observed.

Frequency		
Default	**Once per year**	Self-explanatory.
High	Every 4 to 6 weeks	Done for aesthetics, esp. for BMPs with high public visibility; not required in low rainfall areas (except possibly trash control component). Commercial areas often maintain on same schedule as rest of grounds.
Medium	Once or twice per year	Typical frequency. Aesthetics still is impetus; depends on community expectations, rainfall level, plant growth rate.
Low	Every 3 years, limited area mowed, plants selected for slow growth	Minimum required to ensure woody plants do not take over embankment and outfall areas. Can mow perimeter, embankment, and access points only if desired. Use of native plants can improve appearance. May have to target "problem ponds" for more frequent maintenance.
Time required		
Default	**4 hours**	Assumes small (2 person) crew. Larger crew could maintain an "average" sized facility more quickly. Each agency strikes its own balance.
Range	2 to 5 hours per crew per facility	Depends greatly on size of control & level of maintenance, distance and speed of travel between sites, and size and equipment of crew. Large equipment may slow transport between sites. Supervisor spends fraction of time at each site.
Labor		
Default	**2 persons**	Calculate cost by multiplying number of persons times local wage rate(s). If contracted, use lump sum.
Range	1 to 5 workers plus supervisor	Depends on equipment used and level of maintenance. Large one-person mowers used by some; minimal maintenance site requires much less labor than manicured site.
Equipment and materials		
Default	**Truck, trailer, tractor with mower, miscellaneous landscaping tools.**	Determines equipment cost. Select an hourly expense.
Typical	See above; equipment varies.	Greatly varies on size of BMPs, budget, and level of maintenance desired. Some agencies much more tolerant of plant growth on site.
Options	Public crew vs contracted services	Market-driven factors determine choice. Both in-house labor and subcontracted labor used by agencies interviewed.

3.3   Filter Maintenance

3.3.1   Media Filters

Media filters are often perceived as a relatively high maintenance type of stormwater control; however, review of maintenance records often shows this is not the case (Caltrans, 2004). The main focus of filter maintenance is preservation of the hydraulic conductivity of the filter bed; however, a functioning filter is one that removes and accumulates particulates and, as such, clogging is a typical part of its life cycle and is something that can only be avoided with frequent maintenance. As with other stormwater controls, maintenance activities can be divided into routine and intermittent categories as follows:

- Routine maintenance—inspection, reporting, and information management; vegetation management; trash and minor debris removal; and vector control; and

- Intermittent maintenance—media replacement; structural repairs; and sediment removal.

3.3.1.1   Inspection, Reporting, and Information Management

Sand filters are one of the easiest controls to inspect because most failures are associated with clogging of the filter media. Consequently, the most obvious indicator of needed maintenance is standing water in the filter more than 72 hours after the last rain event. In many instances, standing water in a sand filter can be observed without ever leaving the vehicle, which is a substantial advantage for overworked maintenance crews.

Items to assess in each inspection include

- Whether standing water is present on the filter more than 72 hours after the last rain event;

- Whether litter and debris are obstructing inlet and outlet elements;

- If erosion is occurring in areas inside and downstream of the control (these should be identified and repaired or revegetated immediately);

- Whether damage has occurred to structural elements of the system (pipes, concrete drainage structures, retaining walls, etc.); and

- Whether trees and root systems are present that could grow in cracks, joints, or embankments that can cause structural damage.

Mowing contractors or crews should report problems as they see them, which provides additional inspection capability.

Table 11.8 provides a list of estimated resource requirements for inspections. Default values are included in boldface type for use in the WLC model in Chapter 12. It is important to note that local data, where available, are preferable to that of nationwide averages or literature values.

3.3.1.2 Vegetation Management

Vegetation management for media filters is similar to that of dry basin systems in that the grounds are typically vegetated with grass and must be periodically mowed for aesthetic purposes and to prevent takeover of woody vegetation (see Table 11.7 for guidance on the vegetation management program appropriate for media filters).

3.3.1.3 Trash and Minor Debris Removal

Trash and minor debris removal requirements for media filters are similar to that of dry basins. The primary location for accumulation of trash is on the riser pipe used to separate the pretreatment sedimentation basin from the filter itself (referred to as *full sedimentation*) or along the gabion used in combined systems (referred to as *partial sedimentation* in the Austin, Texas, terminology). Grass clippings, having relatively neutral buoyancy, are particularly prone to accumulate on the riser. Clogging of the filter bed itself with trash (as opposed to sediment) is not typically observed. Table 11.7 addresses trash and litter removal of vegetative systems; this applies to sand filters as well.

3.3.1.4 Intermittent Maintenance

Most media filters consist of about 30 to 45 cm (12 to 18 in.) of sand or occasionally sand augmented with organic matter. The sand specifications may follow the City of Austin's recommendations for the use of "concrete" sand, which is the American Society for Testing and Materials C-33 specification for fine aggregate. This material generally has a substantial fine fraction, so material filtered out of the runoff is typically retained in the top 5 to 10 cm (2 to 4 in.) of media. As material is retained, the hydraulic conductivity is reduced and water begins to pond over the filter bed for longer periods of time. Once this drain time reaches a few days, algae will start to grow on the filter surface and total clogging rapidly follows. Removal of the top 5 to 10 cm (2 to 4 in.) of filter media will generally restore much of the lost permeability. When the total filter media thickness is reduced to less than 30 cm (12 in.), then all of the remaining sand should be removed and replaced.

TABLE 11.8 Summary method to estimate costs for inspection, reporting, and information management for media filters (WERF, 2005).

Description: Visit site; review comprehensive checklist of items; note and refer problems to maintenance staff; document findings in database.

Frequency

Default	**Every year**	Self-explanatory.
High	Twice per year and following large rainfall events	Work crews sometimes asked to do informal inspections; formal inspections typically every year.
Medium	Every year	Typical frequency, especially for agencies with large numbers of BMPs.
Low	No scheduled inspections; respond to citizen complaints	Not recommended. Need more timely observations.

Time required

Default	**2 hours**	Includes recording field data into computer database.
Range	1 to 3 hours	Depends on distance and speed of travel between sites, level of detail of reporting required.

Labor

Default	**1 person**	Calculate cost by multiplying number of persons times local wage rate(s).
Range	1 to 2 persons	Typically one person. Some agencies prefer two.

Skill level

Default	**Skilled Professional**	Determines wage level.
Range	High school trainee to graduate student to skilled professional	Dictated by budget; higher turnover typically for lower paid employees; depends on complexity of BMPs.

Equipment and materials

Default	**Vehicle; field data form; computer database**	Determines equipment cost. Select an hourly expense.
Range	See above; also digital camera and Global Position System devices to record and track control locations.	Depends on level of sophistication desired.

The interval between surface restorations of the filter bed is highly dependent on sediment loading from the watershed. If the catchment area contains active construction sites, then the filter can be expected to clog almost immediately. In stabilized watersheds, the period between this maintenance activity might be 3 to 5 years or more based on a visual assessment of standing water in the basin. For smaller systems (those serving a few hectares [<10 ac]), removal of the filter media can be accomplished with a small crew using hand tools. If the filter is pumped dry and the surface is allowed to dry, it will often form a crust that is easy to remove. Complete removal and replacement of the filter media can be expected at approximately 10-year intervals. These activities are summarized in Table 11.9. Used filter media are typically disposed of at municipal landfills; however, concentrations of mobile pollutants are typically low enough that the material can be used as fill if there is a convenient location.

Occasionally, structural repairs will also be required of the filter system. Many designs recommend including cleanout access for the underdrain system. Vandals often break them off if they protrude far enough above the level of the media. This allows runoff to enter the underdrain without filtering; as such, they must be repaired as soon as possible.

Sediment removal is typically performed with other maintenance functions. In the filter basin, most of the sediment is associated with the upper layer of media and is removed when media are removed or replaced. Sediment may accumulate at the inlet to the facility and should be removed periodically to prevent standing water.

3.3.2 Bioretention Filters

Bioretention filter systems (sometimes known as *rain gardens*) are a relatively new stormwater treatment technology; most systems have been built in the last 10 years or less. The bioretention design concept originated in Prince George's County (where the design was first developed), and has radiated out somewhat in the Mid-Atlantic states and Pacific Northwest. Numerous communities in other states are now considering use of bioretention filters, but applications are more sporadic. Maintenance history for the systems is, therefore, limited. Information on long-term maintenance (life span of materials, refurbishment costs, etc.) does not yet exist.

By design, bioretention filters tend to be small-scale, distributed systems, typically serving less than 1 ha (1 ac) of contributing drainage area. Routine care is similar to site landscaping (weeding, mulching, and tending to plants) and not as large-scale and specialized as that required for larger wet and dry basins. Most bioretention

TABLE 11.9 Filter maintenance for media filters (WERF, 2005).

Description: Replace surface layer of filter media from basin and haul away to disposal site.

Frequency

Default	**Every 3 years**	Local conditions (drainage area stability, soils, etc.) will dictate frequency; need to establish long-term averages based on local experience. Each filter will have its own periodicity.
High	Every 1 to 2 years	Watersheds with unstabilized channels or construction activity
Medium	Every 3 years	Frequency observed in previous sand filter studies
Low	Every 7 years	Very stable watershed

Time required

Default	**2 days**	Actual figure will greatly depend on facility size, quantity of media, and other factors.
Range	2 to 5 days	Depends greatly on size and accessibility, quantity of media, weather, location of disposal site, etc. Long-term averages should be established based on local data.

Labor

Default	**2.5 persons**	Calculate cost by multiplying number of persons times local wage rate(s). If contracted, use lump sum.
Range	2 to 5 workers plus supervisor	Depends on equipment used and size & complexity of projects.

Equipment and materials

Default	**Pickup truck, trailer, miscellaneous hand tools.**	Assume control with adequate access (i.e., does not have to be provided to maintain).
Typical	See above. May use excavator for large projects and/or for difficult access.	Dependent on size of controls, equipment available, and facility design. Controls with no provision for maintenance will require ad hoc measures to remove media, raising costs and project lengths.

Description: replace entire media bed

Default	**Every 10 years**	Local conditions (drainage area stability, soils, etc.) will dictate frequency; need to establish long-term averages based on local experience. Each filter will have its own periodicity.
High	Every 3 years	Watersheds with unstabilized channels or construction activity.
Medium	Every 10 years	Frequency observed in previous sand filter studies.
Low	Every 15 years	Very stable watershed.

Time required

Default	**5 days**	Actual figure will greatly depend on facility size, quantity of media, and other factors.
Range	4 to 7 days	Depends greatly on size and accessibility, quantity of media, weather, location of disposal site, etc. Long-term averages should be established based on local data.

Labor

Default	**2.5 persons**	Calculate cost by multiplying number of persons times local wage rate(s). If contracted, use lump sum.
Range	2 to 5 workers plus supervisor	Depends on equipment used and size & complexity of projects.

Equipment and materials

Default	**Bobcat, dump truck, pickup truck, trailer, miscellaneous hand tools.**	Assume control with adequate access (i.e., does not have to be provided to maintain).
Typical	See above. May use excavator for large projects and/or for difficult access.	Dependent on size of BMPs, equipment available, and facility design. Controls with no provision for maintenance will require ad hoc measures to remove media, raising costs and project lengths.

systems currently in use are privately owned and maintained. These are typically inspected but not maintained by public agencies. Facilities directly maintained by public agencies are primarily demonstration projects. Bioretention filter designs are similar to those of traditional sand filters (with some notable differences such as media characteristics and the presence of vegetation); therefore, the longer maintenance history for sand filters may help in understanding what is in store for bioretention care and upkeep.

The small scale of bioretention filter facilities is perceived by agencies as both a maintenance challenge and advantage. Many agencies, including those that have had direct experience with installations and those that have not, were concerned that a large number of small installations would result in systems that were difficult to track, inspect, and ensure correct functionality. However, an unanticipated benefit of the systems is that their small size and familiar design elements make their maintenance more equivalent to that of traditional landscaped areas. As such, smaller landscaping companies and even homeowners could take on the work to care for them. A significant issue with larger basin controls is that only relatively few, specialized contractors can or are willing to maintain them, which increases costs.

The following are sets of maintenance categories for bioretention filters, divided between routine and intermittent maintenance:

- Routine maintenance—inspection, reporting, and information management; vegetation management; trash and minor debris removal; and mulch removal and replacement; and
- Intermittent maintenance—woody vegetation removal; structural repairs; animal control; and sediment removal.

These events are discussed by subcategory in this section. Estimates of best practices levels of maintenance are presented for typical applications. Minimum levels and other options are also discussed, where appropriate. For each maintenance task where data are available, costs are tracked per event and on an annualized basis. Conclusions presented in this section are drawn from these quantitative data and from qualitative insights from interviews with agency representatives.

3.3.2.1 *Inspection, Reporting, and Information Management*
Routine maintenance of bioretention filter facilities should include a semiannual health evaluation of trees and shrubs and subsequent removal of any dead or diseased vegetation, weeds, or invasive species. Bioretention facilities are susceptible

to invasion by aggressive plant species such as cattails, which increase the chances of standing water and subsequent vector production if not routinely maintained; as such, their presence should be noted and they should be removed.

Routine inspections for areas of standing water within the control and corrective measures to restore proper infiltration rates are necessary to prevent the creation of mosquito and other vector habitats. In addition, erosion areas inside the facility should be identified

Table 11.2 presented a typical inspection program and resource needs for swales that are appropriate for other small-scale vegetated facilities. Bioretention filter facilities are designed to collect water and could, if not draining properly, experience prolonged ponding of water and subsequent mosquito problems. However, bioretention system design typically calls for maximum water depths of less than 150 mm (6 in.), with infiltration times of less than 72 hours. Moreover, use of a thick mulch layer on top of the soil media and an underdrain further diminish chances of having ponded water. Site inspections during construction would need to ensure that the actual level of ponding provided by the inflow and outflow structures maintained these shallow ponding levels.

3.3.2.2 *Vegetation Management*

Vegetation management constitutes the dominant maintenance activity for bioretention filters in terms of labor, equipment, and overall cost. In many ways, it can be conducted as would the standard practice for landscaped areas such as ornamental gardens and parkland. Plantings have to be periodically pruned and replaced and the underlying mulch layer also must be replaced (typically at least once a year). The inlet and outlet points must be checked (most efficient by those maintaining the vegetation and not a separate inspection) and cleared of debris and plant growth.

Much maintenance takes place on a schedule dictated by aesthetic concerns rather than for water quality function. In commercial complexes, routine care of bioretention units under landscaping contracts is not distinguished from that of the surrounding lawn and garden areas because the goal of bioretention is to integrate these facilities to residential and commercial developments and take the place of conventional landscaping. Generally, landscaping companies do not charge more to maintain sites with bioretention filters than sites without them. Bioretention maintenance costs, like swales, appear to be the same or similar to those for landscaping done whether the water quality feature is there or not. Use of native plants may help lower costs by minimizing the use of irrigated water and also provide a more natural habitat. The frequency and scale of vegetation management (labor, equipment, etc.) for bioretention filters is similar to that of swales (see Table 11.3).

3.3.2.3 Trash and Minor Debris Removal

Trash and minor debris removal for bioretention facilities is typically done by landscaping crews during the normal course of their work. Cost data were not available distinguishing between landscaping and litter pickup. Trash and litter removal from bioretention facilities tend to follow the same schedule and costs of those for vegetative management programs (see Table 11.3).

3.3.2.4 Intermittent Maintenance

The frequency and scale of corrective maintenance (labor, equipment, etc.) for bioretention filters are similar to that of swales (see Table 11.4). A maintenance history for periodic corrective maintenance is limited because many facilities have not been in place for that long.

Bioretention facilities can have some structural components such as concrete inflow splitter boxes and outfall structures. These are typically small in scale and resemble curb, gutter, and drainage pipe infrastructure, which is routinely maintained by municipal public works crews (i.e., specialized skills are not required).

Bioretention plants require the same type of care as do typical landscapes, with the notable difference that they have the advantages and disadvantages of being down-slope of their contributing drainage area. As such, bioretention areas remain much wetter than other landscaped areas. This leads to a reduced need for irrigation, but it also means that the plants receive a concentrated dose of whatever pollutants are contained in the runoff. Thus, in many areas, plantings have had to be replaced after winter storms have delivered waters heavily laden with road salt. Acute (e.g., chemical spills and dumping) and persistent (e.g., routine washoff of hydrocarbons) toxic inputs would also affect plantings and potentially require new plants (and even soil remediation). These issues, which apply to all vegetated controls, can be mitigated in part by the use of mesic plants and by including pretreatment in the design.

In Prince George's County, virtually all bioretention filter systems are privately maintained. The facilities are small and do not require specialized equipment to maintain vegetation and scarify surface or even to remove sediment. The following guidelines from Prince Georges County can be applied in most any location:

- Ensure mulch is in place and sufficiently deep (75 mm [3 in.]). Replace mulch every 6 months, although other jurisdictions do this much more infrequently (e.g., 1 to 3 years);
- Water plants if stressed from heat or lack of rainfall (as needed);

- Prune plants per standard practice for landscaping and replace dead plants (as needed);

- Weed the bed to control growth of unwanted plants (monthly); and

- Water in the facility should infiltrate the system within 12 hours or less. If longer, the underdrain may be clogged. Unclog the underdrain using the cleanout pipe per standard plumbing practices (as needed). (In addition, experiment with puncturing the filter fabric before requiring re-excavation and replacement of the soil media.)

In practice, private property owners do an uneven job of maintaining bioretention systems for which they are responsible. An oft-cited advantage of bioretention filter systems is that they can be maintained "just like a garden," implying that ordinary, unsophisticated skills and techniques are all that is necessary; however, many systems go unmaintained. Some owners are not aware that these facilities exist on their property and mow down the plants and establish turf grasses to blend the area in with the lawn. (This occurs in spite of requirements that all homeowners with bioretention systems be given a pamphlet explaining the purpose and care of these systems.) Other owners simply do no maintenance at all. Additional problems can occur when the basins are too sparsely planted or plants are ignored and allowed to die-off. This allows for non-native plants to invade and establish themselves.

Fortunately, most neglected systems still perform their function at some level, allowing water to infiltrate to the soil. The idea was that bioretention units would all be maintained by property owners; however, to help ensure that these early systems functioned properly, Prince Georges County has continued to play a direct role in assisting to maintain them when necessary.

Bioretention filter facilities, like infiltration trenches, are subject to failure if the surface or subsurface media become clogged with sediment and if the systems are designed to rely on infiltration to drain the basin. The main threat comes during construction itself, when the site is disturbed and sediment loads are high. Proper construction sequencing, inspection, and control during this phase are essential. Generally, bioretention guidelines specify that no water be allowed to enter the bioretention basin until site vegetation is stabilized and impervious surfaces are completely installed. Prevention of clogging using construction sedimentation controls and a proper soil media mixture is obviously preferable to addressing system blockage after the fact. In addition, it is good practice to fence off these future infiltration areas and not allow equipment or staging to be performed there. One of the objectives of providing a top layer of mulch is to reduce the potential for clogging with sediment. Similar to sand filters, once clogged it is likely that much of the permeability can be restored by removing and replacing just the mulch and the upper 10 cm (4 in.) of media.

The frequency and scale of sediment removal for bioretention facilities is similar to that of swales in terms of labor, materials, and equipment. In many instances, the small scale of bioretention facilities makes it possible to have sediment buildup removed by hand tools (shovels, wheelbarrows, etc.). As with most BMPs, sediment tends to fall out right at the inflow point; given that many bioretention filter systems have a simple curb cut or storm drain inlet for an inflow structure, this area is relatively straightforward to maintain. For larger systems, backhoes and like equipment are probably sufficient.

3.3.3 Inlet Baskets

Baskets used as inlet inserts are one of the more problematic maintenance controls. Previous studies (Caltrans, 2004) have documented a variety of issues regarding their operation. A particular issue with inlet baskets is runoff bypassing the filter tray. This occurs in three situations. The first is screening of the surface of the filter by trash, leaves, or other debris, which causes runoff to be diverted over the filter and into bypass areas, even at low flows. A second potential problem is that devices that retain any substantial amount of water can pull away from the edge of the inlet (especially at low flowrates), allowing runoff to pass between the filter tray and the edge of the inlet. A final issue is that, because some models are relatively narrow, in high-intensity events the runoff can enter the inlet with such velocity that much of it passes over the filter and into the bypass opening. These are all factors that should be evaluated at each inspection.

Maintenance of drain inlet baskets depends on the rate at which pollutants and debris accumulate in the device, storage capacity, and requirements for proper operation. Because the area available for filtering is relatively small and debris can accumulate quite rapidly, weekly inspections are recommended. At the time these inspections are being conducted, all loose debris obstructing the filter trays should be removed. (During the Caltrans study, removal of this material was required during every storm to ensure that runoff did not bypass the system.)

Based on the level of maintenance required in the Caltrans study, recommended future maintenance activities include the following:

- Perform inspections and maintenance weekly, which includes inspections for trash and debris, structural integrity, and sediment accumulation;

- Inspect the structural integrity at the beginning and end of the wet season; and

- Renew the insert or medium annually at the end of the wet season or per manufacturer's direction.

Inspections and removal of accumulated debris is not a time-consuming operation and will likely take less than an hour, on average, if there are a number of inlet inserts in close proximity; as such, drive time may not be a factor. It is estimated that about 25 hours per year will be required to maintain each inlet (Caltrans, 2004). The cost of replacement filters is dependent on the type of device selected.

3.3.4   Landscaped Roofs

Maintenance of landscaped roofs is inseparable from their design; in other words, they should be designed with maintenance in mind (Tolderlund, 2010; Weiler and Scholz-Barth, 2009). Maintenance activities for landscaped roofs include one-time activities during establishment of the roof, periodic activities over the life of the roof, and intermittent activities (Snodgrass and McIntyre, 2010), typically to replace the roof membrane or correct problems. In many cases, maintenance activities are conducted by the installer as a service maintenance agreement.

The establishment period of the roof is critical for vegetation health and can last up to 2 years, depending on the geographic location. The roof should be designed to include provisions for this initial irrigation need. If the plants are selected properly in accordance with local climate and building conditions, there should be minimal need for periodic irrigation, except in cases of extreme drought. Proper choice of plants also improves fire resistance during a drought. It is important to note that these plants may not be native to the area because the environment of a landscaped roof has its own micro-climate; for example, the conditions of a poor soil in a wind-swept roof atop a tall building may be akin to an alpine desert, which dictates the choice of plants. Consultation with a horticulturalist specialized in landscaped roofs is vital to reduce maintenance needs through proper plant selection.

The option of a temporary irrigation system for the initial establishment period needs to be weighed against a permanent drip irrigation system that may be useful for extreme drought events. The size of the roof is also a factor; for a very large landscaped roof, an irrigation system that is only in service during a drought may be more cost-effective and reliable than deploying an emergency system when irrigation is required.

The application of fertilizer is a source of debate among the industry (Luckett, 2009). Fertilizers may become a source of nutrients in the landscaped roof effluent; on the other hand, the growth medium in extensive landscaped roofs is a very thin engineered layer with low organic content, and there may be instances when even the hardiest plants require some fertilization. If so, the maintenance plan for a landscaped roof needs to contain adequate provisions such that only slow-release fertilizers are allowed. If needed, another stormwater control may be installed downstream of the landscaped roof to treat potential nutrients in the effluent.

Semiannual inspections should be conducted to assess the health of the vegetation and conduct normal landscaping activities such as pruning, plant replacement, disease control, debris removal, and weeding. Vegetation-free zones must be allowed around the entire perimeter of the green roof to allow access for inspections and maintenance and as a fire barrier. Penetrations through the landscaped roof's membrane should also have this provision, for example vents, drains, and utility conduits. The integrity of the membrane is essential for the landscaped roof's performance; therefore, these areas should be inspected 3 times a year (Tolderlund, 2010). The irrigation system should be checked twice annually in places where freezing may occur (Snodgrass and McIntyre, 2010) and it should be flushed before the first winter freeze (Tolderlund, 2010). The drainage system should be inspected to identify blockage, damaged pipe and other components, and leaks around framing or flashing (Weiler and Scholz-Barth, 2009).

3.4   Infiltrator Maintenance

3.4.1   Infiltration Trench

Infiltration trench systems are small-scale controls, typically serving under 1 ha (1 ac) of drainage area, that capture and infiltrate a design volume of runoff for treatment in the underlying soil. Infiltration trenches were first widely used in Maryland and the Washington, D.C., area in the mid-1980s, and were thought to be a breakthrough technology in that they provided water quality benefits (reproducing the predevelopment hydrologic cycle) in an era in which flood detention was the predominant practice, offering only benefits for large storms (for flood control, not water quality). The trenches worked well at first, confirming hopes that runoff from small storms could be almost completely mitigated; however, as detailed in Chapter 9, there were some performance issues related to clogging that discouraged their application (Galli, 1992). Analysts speculated that the underlying geotextile fabric was the main problem, clogging with sediment fines and preventing passage of water. News spread quickly of these failures, sharply discouraging their potential use and popularity in other areas of the country.

Few agencies oversee communities that now use these systems. For example, the collective national experience led the influential UDFCD to reject all use of infiltration trenches. Specifically, UDFCD explains that it tries to encourage solutions that can be maintained at the surface and does not require that the system be entirely removed and rebuilt to continue to function over the long term.

Not all agencies have completely abandoned this technology and some agencies believe that the early designs were flawed. Early designs did not include monitoring wells, which allowed no way of checking to see if they were working (i.e., infiltrating water), nor were designers required to conduct soil and geotechnical tests prior to designing these systems (many were built in unsuitable clayey soils).

The following is a set of maintenance categories for infiltration trenches, divided between routine and intermittent maintenance:

- Routine maintenance—inspection, reporting, and information management; and trash and minor debris removal; and

- Intermittent maintenance—sediment removal.

These events are discussed by subcategory in this section. Estimates of best practices levels of maintenance are presented for typical applications. Minimum levels and other options are also discussed, where appropriate. Conclusions presented in this section were drawn from this quantitative data and from qualitative insights from interviews with agency representatives.

3.4.1.1 Inspection, Reporting, and Information Management

Because of the increased potential to fail, infiltration trenches should be inspected annually. These inspections should occur more than 3 days following a rain event to see if standing water remains within the trench. Table 11.2 presented the range of inspection program options found for swales and other small-scale facilities, including infiltration trenches. Many agencies interviewed reported that *no inspection or maintenance of any kind* was being done for infiltration trenches, most of which were installed many years ago. Almost all agencies have had to focus their limited staff and resources on larger and more publicly visible basins, frequently responding to complaints rather than categorically checking all facilities. Infiltration trenches are small-scale and disbursed, and many agencies have been unable to keep track of their locations. Most are on private property and many are unknown even to their owners.

3.4.1.2 Trash and Minor Sediment and Debris Removal

Trash and minor debris removal from infiltration trenches is ideally done by landscaping crews during the normal course of their work in areas surrounding trenches. For this reason, it is critical that landscaping crews understand that they must not allow grass clippings and other vegetative debris to collect on top of, or in the flow path of, the infiltration trench. Table 11.10 summarizes actions taken by agencies interviewed about infiltration trenches.

3.4.1.3 Sediment Removal

Removal of sediment from infiltration trenches essentially requires the excavation and removal of rock filter media and filter fabric and their replacement with new, clean materials. This type of substantial rehabilitation costs an equivalent amount to the installation of the system in the first place. In instances where clogging is a problem and underlying soils are judged not to be to blame, attention should be focused on the contributing drainage area. If this area is exporting significant amounts of sediment and can be reasonably stabilized, less maintenance may have to be performed on the trench.

Table 11.11 presents sediment removal components for infiltration trenches.

3.4.2   Infiltration Basin

Maintenance requirements for infiltration basins are similar to those of dry basins (see Section 3.2.2 for information on types and frequencies of maintenance activities). The significant difference between the two types of controls is that the hydraulic conductivity of underlying soils must not be reduced by compaction with heavy equipment or introduction of fine-grained materials to the basin. A second prominent difference is that infiltration basins may not have outlets to maintain if they are constructed off-line.

3.4.3   Pervious Pavement

Although pervious pavement systems have been in use for some time in the United States, their application still remains fairly limited. Concern over system failures, the same perception problem that plagues infiltration trenches, has limited their acceptance by regulatory agencies. Pervious pavement has a significant advantage over infiltration trenches in that the surface area for infiltration is typically much larger per unit of water quality volume (particularly if only the rainfall on the parking surface is infiltrated), thus placing a reduced burden on soil infiltration capacity.

Most pervious pavement installations are on private property and many are not inspected by agency personnel. With few publicly built and maintained pervious pavement systems, the familiarity of agency representatives is limited. Known

TABLE 11.10 Trash and minor sediment and debris removal for infiltration trenches (WERF, 2005).

Description: walk site; pick up obvious litter; informal inspection: notify maintenance staff if significant problems observed.

Frequency

Default	**Once per year**	Self-explanatory.
High	Every 4 to 6 weeks	Done for aesthetics, especially for BMP's with high public visibility. Commercial areas often maintain on same schedule as rest of grounds.
Medium	Once or twice per year	Typical frequency. Aesthetics still is impetus; depends on community expectations.
Low	No maintenance (Assume minimum every 3 years for planning purposes)	Many systems are not maintained at any level. Trash and debris may be an indicator of larger problems with sedimentation and should be removed.

Time required

Default	**1 hour**	Most infiltration trenches are small; most of the time spent will be driving in between sites.
Range	0.5 to 2 hours	Depends greatly on size of control and level of maintenance, distance and speed of travel between sites, and size and equipment of crew. Large equipment may slow transport between sites. Supervisor spends fraction of time at each site.

Labor

Default	**1 person**	Calculate cost by multiplying number of persons times local wage rate(s). If contracted, use lump sum.
Range	1 to 2 workers plus supervisor	Small facilities typically require small crew to maintain.

Equipment and materials

Default	**Truck.**	Determines equipment cost. Select an hourly expense.
Typical	Truck.	Also need trash bags, etc.
Options	Public crew vs contracted services	Market-driven factors determine choice. Both inhouse labor and subcontracted labor used by agencies interviewed.

TABLE 11.11 Sediment removal for infiltration trenches (WERF, 2005).

Description: remove existing rock media and built-up sediment from control and haul away sediment to disposal site. Install new rock media.

Frequency

Default	**Every 5 years**	Local conditions (drainage area stability, soils, etc.) will dictate frequency; need to establish long-term averages based on local experience. Five years is likely maximum given high failure rate within 5 years.
High	Every 1 to 2 years	Recommended level in some maintenance guidelines; small number of agencies use this frequency in practice. Caltrans requires annual sediment inspection and removal.
Medium	Every 3 to 5 years	More typical frequency. Montgomery County estimates sediment removal every 5 years.
Low	No maintenance (Assume minimum every 5 years for planning purposes)	Most systems have received no maintenance to date; not an acceptable long-term strategy: high percentage of all systems fail within 5 years and need to be restored by removing sediment and replacing media to function.

Time required

Default	**3 days**	Actual figure will greatly depend on facility size, quantity of sediment, and other factors. Three days assumes 1 day to excavate; 1 day to replace media; 1 day to seed, stabilize, and restore site per Montgomery County experience.
Range	2 to 4 days	Depends greatly on size and accessibility of controls, quantity of sediment, weather, location of disposal site, etc. Long-term averages should be established based on local data.

Labor

Default	**Five persons**	Calculate cost by multiplying number of persons times local wage rate(s). If contracted, use lump sum.
Range	Approximately five workers plus supervisor	Depends on equipment used and size & complexity of projects.

Equipment and materials

Default	**Backhoe; dump truck; miscellaneous hand tools**	Assume control with adequate access (i.e., does not have to be provided to maintain).
Typical	Backhoe; dump truck; miscellaneous hand tools	Dependent on size of control, equipment available, and facility design.
Options	Public crew vs contracted services	Market-driven factors determine choice.

examples of failures are recalled more readily than successes. Much of the debate in the United States has, therefore, been between pervious system venders and skeptical agency staff. Further complicating things is that there are many different types of pervious pavement systems, each with their own strengths and weaknesses (e.g., pervious asphalt, monolithically poured pervious concrete, grass pavers, gravel pavers, and modular block pervious pavement systems).

Routine maintenance of pervious pavement consists of inspections, street sweeping or vacuuming, and minor trash and debris removal. Intermittent maintenance is comprised of structural repairs and sediment removal.

3.4.3.1 Inspection, Reporting, and Information Management

Few agencies actually inspect pervious pavement systems; instead, most leave responsibility for their function with their private owners because of budget constraints. An inspection protocol used by Montgomery County (Harper, personal communication) for infiltration trenches states that each system should be viewed 3 days after a rainfall to check for clogging. Many problems, such as a landscape contractor storing soil on the pervious pavement, would be difficult to identify during inspections; citizen complaints or similar information might be a better source of information for these sporadic types of problems. The inspector should also include a check to see that the pervious material is still in place and not paved over by an impervious surface.

3.4.3.2 Street Vacuuming and Trash and Minor Debris Removal

It is recommended that pervious pavement surfaces be vacuumed twice per year; however, this is likely more often than occurs in standard practice. Indeed, many systems have been in place for years with no maintenance of any kind. Planted areas and landscaping activities near the pavement should be maintained to prevent deposition of soil or organic materials (e.g., leaves) on the surface of the pavement as this can be pulverized by vehicle tires and washed into the pavement by runoff. Table 11.12 presents some guidelines on street sweeping and trash and debris removal practices.

3.4.3.3 Intermittent Facility Maintenance

As with all pavement surfaces, pervious pavement systems must be periodically repaired because of wear from vehicles and aging of materials; however, these systems require that care be taken in replacing pervious material with similar pervious material. Areas of less than 1 m² (1 yd²) can be patched with conventional pavement with minimal effects on system performance by drilling holes through the pavement (WERF, 2005). Agency representatives interviewed noted examples where entire

TABLE 11.12   Street sweeping and trash and minor debris removal practices for pervious pavement (WERF, 2005).

Description: walk site; pick up obvious litter; informal inspection: notify maintenance staff if significant problems observed; remove sediment with vacuum sweeper.		
Frequency		
Default	**Once per year**	Self-explanatory.
High	Every 4 to 6 weeks	Done for aesthetics (e.g., at high-use commercial sites).
Medium	Once or twice per year	Standard level of vacuuming specified.
Low	No maintenance (Assume minimum every 3 years for planning purposes)	Many systems are not vacuumed; risks diminished performance and need for significant repair and expense.
Estimated cost		
Default		Data not available from agencies.
High		Data not available from agencies.
Medium		Data not available from agencies.
Low		Many systems have received no maintenance to date, but will likely compromise long-term function of system.
Options	Public crew vs contracted services	Market-driven factors determine choice. Both inhouse labor and subcontracted labor used by agencies interviewed.

pervious pavement systems had been inadvertently paved over with conventional pavement, thereby sealing them off. Montgomery County requires that signs be posted warning to not resurface. Table 11.13 presents guidelines on repairing minor structural damage to pervious pavement systems.

Sediment is best removed from pervious pavement systems during routine vacuuming and maintenance (see Section 3.4.3.2). Once clogged, it is necessary to remove the top layer of pavement, excavate the substrate, and replace it with clean media. The bottom interface can also be scarified to improve infiltration. This type of substantial rehabilitation costs an equivalent amount to installation of the system in the first place. Table 11.14 presents guidelines on the restoration of porous pavement systems following long-term sedimentation.

TABLE 11.13 Intermittent facility maintenance: structural repairs for pervious pavement (WERF, 2005).

Description: periodic repair of pavement surface damaged by traffic wear, soil movement, etc.

Frequency

Default	N/A: Variable. As required based on inspection findings (and budget)	Wide variety of pavement types, traffic patterns, and climate and soil conditions make general predictions difficult.

Time required

N/A	Wide variation	Varies with project size and complexity from 1 hour to several days or more.

Labor

Default	N/A: Inherently variable	Crew size varies by agency and project. Local wage rate(s) determine labor cost.
Range	3 to 6 workers plus supervisor	Depends on equipment used and level of maintenance.

Equipment and materials

Default	N/A: Inherently variable	Equipment and materials vary by agency and project.
Typical	Front-end loader, backhoe, dump truck, trailer for vehicles, miscellaneous hand tools, replacement components.	Varies with project size and complexity.

Estimated cost

Default		Data not available from agencies.
High		Data not available from agencies.
Medium		Data not available from agencies.
Low		Many systems have received no maintenance to date; but some level of problems must be anticipated and budgeted for.
Options	Public crew vs contracted services	Market-driven factors determine choice. Most agencies used inhouse labor.

TABLE 11.14   Sediment removal for pervious pavement (WERF, 2005).

Description: remove sediment from control and haul away sediment to disposal site.

Frequency

Default	**Every 15 years**	Use as placeholder to establish cost. Local conditions (landscaping practices, soils, etc.) and system type will dictate frequency; need to establish long-term averages based on local experience.
Range	0 to 20 years	Many systems not maintained. Favorable soils will help life span of system prior to needing sediment removal. Landscaping practices (keeping sediment off pavement) and traffic wear are main factors in frequency of sediment removal required.

3.5 Catch Basin Cleaning

Many municipalities, especially those with combined sewer systems, have catch basins that maintain a permanent pool of water. These inlets retain sediment and floatables, which must be periodically removed. As material accumulates in the catch basin, pollutant retention decreases. According to Aronson et al. (1983), catch basins should be cleaned at least once or twice per year. It is also a good idea to inspect and clean all catch basins that serve as a tributary to a wet basin or wetland when that facility is cleaned to reduce sediment loading to the forebay.

One study of catch basins in Alameda County, California, found that increasing the maintenance frequency from once per year to twice per year could increase the total sediment removed by catch basins on an annual basis (Mineart and Singh, 1994). The study found that annual sediment removed per inlet was 25 kg (54 lb) for annual cleaning, 32 kg (70 lb) for semiannual and quarterly cleaning, and 73 kg (160 lb) for monthly cleaning.

Although catch basins are relatively inexpensive to install, the real cost is associated with long-term maintenance cost. An eductor truck (or Vactor truck), the most common method of catch basin cleaning, can cost up to $250,000 (U.S. dollars). Typical trucks can store between 10 and 15 m³ (10 and 15 cu yd) of material, which is enough storage for three to five catch basins (WERF, 2005). Typically, using a crew of two, the average catch basin takes 30 minutes to clean. Severely polluted catch basins, which typically result from illegal dumping, may take several days of repeated cleaning.

4.0 CONCLUSIONS

This chapter identified maintenance practices required for a variety of stormwater controls and presented some guidelines on the potential costs of these activities. An emphasis has been placed on how vegetation management often dominates the effort required and how this can vary substantially depending on the expectations of nearby residents. Rough cost estimates have also been developed for various levels of maintenance to reflect the wide variety of practices observed in the United States. Chapter 12 will use these estimates along with capital cost estimates to provide guidance on the expected whole life costs of various practices. As will be demonstrated, these maintenance costs can far exceed capital costs for certain types of facilities. Consequently, it is critical to develop a mechanism for funding future maintenance so that stormwater controls can provide real water quality benefits over the life of the facilities.

5.0 REFERENCES

Aronson, G.; Watson, D.; Pisaro, W. (1983) *Evaluation of Catch Basin Performance for Urban Stormwater Pollution Control*; EPA-600/2–83-043; U.S. Environmental Protection Agency: Washington, D.C.

California Department of Transportation (2004) *BMP Retrofit Pilot Program, Final Report*; CTSW-RT-01–050; California Department of Transportation: Sacramento, California.

CH2M HILL (2001) Stormwater System Maintenance Cost Estimates. Prepared for the Montgomery County Department of Environmental Protection, Rockville, Maryland.

Galli, J. (1992) *Analysis of Urban BMP Performance and Longevity in Prince George's County, Maryland*; Metropolitan Washington Council of Governments: Washington, D.C.

Harper, D. Montgomery County Department of Environmental Protection. Personal communication.

Kulzer, L. Seattle Public Utilities. Personal communication.

Liptan, T. Portland Bureau of Environmental Services. Personal communication.

Luckett, K. (2009) *Green Roof Construction and Maintenance*; McGraw-Hill: New York,196 pp.

Mineart, P.; Singh, S. (1994) *Storm Inlet Pilot Study;* Woodward-Clyde Consultants; Alameda County Urban Runoff Clean Water Program: Oakland, California.

Serdar, D. (1993) *Contaminants in Vactor Truck Wastes,* Prepared for the Washington State Department of Ecology. http://www.ecy.wa.gov/pubs/93e49.pdf (Nov 8, 2007).

Snodgrass, E.; McIntyre, L. (2010) The Green Roof Manual: A Professional Guide to Design, Installation, and Maintenance; Timber Press: Portland, Oregon, 295 pp.

Tolderlund, L. (2010) *Design Guidelines and Maintenance Manual for Green Roofs in the Semi-Arid and Arid West;* University of Colorado, Denver, Colorado, 59 pp.

Water Environment Research Foundation (2005) *Performance and Whole Life Costs of Best Management Practices and Sustainable Urban Drainage Systems;* Project 01-CTS-21Ta; Water Environment Research Foundation: Alexandria, Virginia.

Weiler, S.; Scholz-Barth, K. (2009) *Green Roof Systems: A Guide to the Planning, Design and Construction of Building Over Structure;* Wiley & Sons: Hoboken, New Jersey, 313 pp.

Chapter 12

Whole Life Cost of Stormwater Controls

(continued)

1.0   WHOLE LIFE COST MODEL

The information presented in this chapter is based largely on the cost analysis pre-sented in the Water Environment Research Foundation (WERF) report, *Performance and Whole Life Costs of Best Management Practices and Sustainable Urban Drainage Systems* (WERF, 2005). This work has been extended for this manual by developing similar cost estimates for additional stormwater controls that were not the subject of the earlier study.

Whole life costing (also known as *life cycle cost analysis*) is about identifying future costs and referring them back to present-day costs using standard accounting techniques such as present value. Present value is defined here as the value of a stream of benefits or costs when discounted back to the present time. It can be thought of as the sum of money that needs to be spent today to meet all future costs as they arise throughout the life cycle of a facility. The formula for calculating the present value (PV) is

$$PV = \sum_{t=0}^{t=N} \frac{C_t}{\left(1+\dfrac{r}{100}\right)^t} \tag{12.1}$$

where

N = time horizon in years;
C_t = total monetary costs in year t;
r = discount rate (%).

For public agencies, the proper discount rate is the interest rate that the Federal Reserve Bank charges on loans to institutions that borrow money from it, and is generally close to the interest rate that one would receive on short-term deposits. In these calculations, the underlying objective is to determine how much money would have to be deposited in an interest-bearing account to pay for all future capital and maintenance costs. Consequently, the present value is sensitive to the assumed discount rates, assumptions of future costs, and the timing of these costs.

In the greater sense, the present value also includes the values of benefits that arise from implementation of stormwater controls. These benefits might include increased energy efficiency, reduced stormwater user fees, improved aesthetics, and reduced urban heat island effects. Many of these benefits are difficult to quantify; consequently, this analysis focuses on out-of-pocket expenses associated with each of the stormwater management facilities.

Benefits of developing an accurate whole life cost include the following:

- Improved understanding of long-term investment requirements in addition to capital costs;
- More cost-effective project choices for stormwater control selection;

- Explicit assessment and management of long-term financial risk when integrated with a planned maintenance program; and

- Better understanding of the future financial liabilities when considering acceptance of responsibility for a system.

All expenditures incurred by the drainage system owner or operator, whether they are termed *operational* or *capital*, result from the requirement to manage surface water runoff. Adopting a long-term approach complements the fact that most drainage assets have a relatively long, useful life, provided appropriate management and maintenance are performed.

There are a series of stages in the life cycle of a drainage asset. A conceptual diagram of these stages is shown in Figure 12.1. These stages represent "cost elements" and can be defined as

- Acquisition, which may include feasibility studies, commissioning, conceptual design, preliminary design, detailed design and development, and construction (or purchase of a proprietary device);

- Use and maintenance; and

- Disposal and decommissioning.

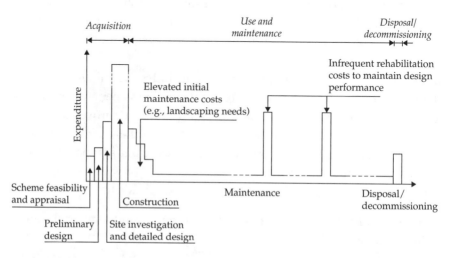

FIGURE 12.1   Life cycle stages and associated costs (adapted from WERF, 2005).

Discounting techniques are applied to future costs using an appropriate discount rate to consider the time value of money. Figure 12.2 shows the present value cash flows for two facilities with different capital and maintenance cost streams over a 25-year period assuming a discount rate of 3.5%. Scheme 1 has lower capital costs but assumes higher annual maintenance and full rehabilitation after 20 years. Scheme 2 has high initial capital costs and low recurrent costs. This example illustrates that a stormwater control that is initially $50,000 (U.S. dollars) less expensive to construct (scheme 1) actually is slightly more expensive over the life of the facility because of higher maintenance costs. Consequently, it is vital to evaluate potential stormwater control options on their life cycle cost rather than on just construction costs when considering the financial aspects of their implementation.

2.0 CAPITAL COSTS

2.1 Approach

The following approach has been developed for use in determining reasonable cost estimates for stormwater controls:

- Review and summarize cost estimates from literature;
- Review and summarize real incurred construction costs;

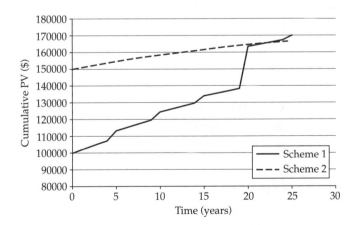

FIGURE 12.2 Cumulative discounted costs for two stormwater controls.

- Review and summarize unit construction activity costs from standard civil engineering price guides;

- Develop costing models to facilitate generic stormwater control cost estimation; and

- Compare actual and predicted costs.

2.2 Cost Components

The model presents an estimate of average or likely costs for an assumed set of conditions and characteristics, but these should be reviewed and adjusted for all site-specific applications. Costs can be highly variable and will depend, to a certain extent, on the size of the system being considered. Economies of scale can be realized as system size increases because of the existence of significant fixed initial costs such as mobilization of staff and equipment and travel.

Most U.S. cost studies assess only part of the cost of constructing a stormwater management system, typically excluding permitting fees, engineering design, and contingency or unexpected costs. In general, these costs are expressed as a fraction of construction costs (e.g., 30%). These costs are generally only estimates and are based on the experience of designers.

The cost of land varies regionally and often depends on surrounding land use. Many suburban jurisdictions require open-space allocations within the developed site, reducing the effective cost of land for the control to zero for certain types of facilities. On the other hand, the cost of land may far outweigh construction and design costs in dense urban settings.

2.3 Capital Cost Influences

Actual capital costs for controls depend on numerous factors. Many of these factors are site-specific and, therefore, are difficult to estimate. Consequently, locally derived cost estimates are more useful than generic estimates made using national data. The following subcategories in this section provide brief descriptions of some significant factors affecting costs.

2.3.1 Project Scale and Unit Costs

Stormwater controls can be built at much lower costs as part of a larger project rather than as stand-alone projects. Larger projects offer better economies of scale and do not have as large of a fraction of total cost for mobilization and project initiation.

It is more cost-effective to grade in extra basins or swales when a much larger development site is already being graded. Similarly, wet basins and dry basins generally have lower unit costs as facility size increases.

2.3.2   Retrofits Versus New Construction

Most cost studies have looked at the cost of building a new system on previously undeveloped land. However, many of the systems, especially those built by public agencies, are constructed as retrofits to a previously developed area lacking sufficient stormwater controls. These two scenarios represent different costs, with retrofit being much higher because of utility relocation and road realignment. Moreover, some retrofits are built into existing public land or easements (e.g., within a flood control basin), while others require that the land be purchased and may have higher costs to get the water to drain to the facility because many sites are not in optimal hydraulic locations due to constraints imposed by prior development. Some proactive communities have mandates to retrofit existing developed areas and not just to provide controls for new developments. Higher costs should be expected for these retrofit projects.

2.3.3   Regulatory Requirements

Each jurisdiction has varying requirements for water quantity and water quality control volumes and flowrates, and for structure components such as inflow structures, splitter boxes, and fencing. Some of the required structural components can be simple and inexpensive, while other jurisdictions may require designs that are complex and costly.

2.3.4   Public Versus Private Design and Construction

Costs vary depending on whether a public or a private entity pays for the work. Typically, public projects are more expensive because of greater supervision and restrictions. For instance, public projects are often subject to bidding laws and other regulatory requirements depending on funding sources. Public projects are more likely to take additional precautions for the long-term success of a project. In contrast, developers often turn over responsibility of the constructed project to the new owners and, therefore, may not worry about long-term viability of the stormwater controls. It is much easier to get information on public projects because the costs become public record. Private developers are generally reluctant to reveal what it costs to build their projects to avoid divulging private information that they perceive as giving them a competitive edge.

2.3.5 Flexibility in Site Selection and Site Suitability

Stormwater controls cost can vary considerably based on local conditions. In a site with favorable grading, a basin may require almost no excavation, which substantially lowers the cost. Another location with a similar capture volume may require blasting through hard rock and a long distance haul to a spoils site. Some projects are required by applicable rules and regulations and do not have the flexibility to choose a more cost-effective site.

2.3.6 Partnerships with Others

Some agencies have begun to seek partnerships with other entities (e.g., private developers or other agencies) to build stormwater controls with a better economy of scale and thus reduced cost. For instance, the Texas Department of Transportation and the City of Austin, Texas, have collaborated on the construction of controls to treat runoff from both a highway and adjacent commercial land use.

2.3.7 Level of Experience of Both Agency and Contractors

Some regions in the United States have required construction of stormwater controls for more than 20 years. In these areas, local contractors adapt to the market and learn the skills needed to build controls. The steps involved are known and predictable. Local agency staff will know how to help guide regulations and make design suggestions to facilitate better, more cost-effective projects. In an area in which one or more control technologies are a recent introduction, contractors will be unfamiliar with the expectations and effort required and will raise their prices to guard against the potential risk. Inexperienced agency staff will likewise not be confident or knowledgeable enough to suggest cost-reducing changes in rules and designs.

2.3.8 State of the Economy at the Time of Construction

Another consideration is the strength of a local economy when a control is bid and built. If projects are hard to obtain, more contractors will seek a project, placing downward pressure on the cost. If work is plentiful for contractors, the project may be less desirable and the cost may rise.

2.3.9 Water Quantity Design Criteria

Water quantity design criteria vary regionally and by jurisdiction. These criteria determine discharge rates and volumes of attenuation storage that are required, with greater treatment requirements increasing project costs.

2.3.10 Water Quality Design Criteria

Water quality design criteria vary by jurisdiction. These criteria determine construction methods, design requirements, and postconstruction controls. For instance, the design may be influenced by the volume of permanent storage required for water quality treatment, which affects the cost for excavation.

2.3.11 Geography

The geographic location of the project may influence the design rainfall and rainfall runoff characteristics of a site, which will in turn affect drainage system component sizing.

2.3.12 Land Allocation and Costs

Land may be allocated for the control alone or may include an amenity area, areas dedicated to extracted sediment dewatering, vegetation harvesting, access for maintenance purposes, and so on. The cost of land is extremely variable, both regionally and depending on surrounding land use. Through careful design and use of open space allocations, the effective cost of land allocated to surface water drainage can be reduced significantly. On the other hand, the cost of land may far outweigh construction and design costs for some controls in dense urban settings. For this reason, some underground controls that are relatively more expensive to construct may be attractive in such situations, provided that subsurface conditions are appropriate. Land costs may include both purchase and legal costs.

2.3.13 Soil Type and Groundwater Vulnerability

Soil type and groundwater vulnerability dictate whether infiltration methods can be used to control excess runoff volumes on-site or whether additional storage and attenuation will be required. The soil type also dictates the level of erosion protection and grass reinforcement required, and may influence plant selection.

2.3.14 Material Availability

Many stormwater control components require granular fill as the attenuation and filtering media; these costs will vary depending on the distance of the site from a potential source. Topsoil costs will also depend on source locations. Other market factors such as fuel costs to transport materials may greatly alter costs within a short period of time.

2.3.15 Planting

The availability of suitable plants and required level of planting planned for a particular control component will have a significant influence on landscape costs, which can be substantial. In addition, landscape contractors are often required to provide a warranty for the plantings for some period. This warranty typically escalates costs because a mortality rate of 20 to 25% for plantings is typically assumed.

2.3.16 Opportunity Costs

The installation of a particular stormwater control should consider the effect on the usability of the site. For example, permeable pavement allows full use of a parking lot serving an office or retail building. If parking space needs to be reduced to accommodate another type of stormwater control (e.g., a basin), the minimum parking regulations may force a reduction in the building floor space allowed, which affects the profitability of the project and even the tax revenue for the municipality. It should be noted that many such regulations require much more parking than is actually needed for adequate operation of a commercial or industrial site.

3.0 CAPITAL COSTS FOR VARIOUS STORMWATER CONTROLS

This section describes the capital costs in 2004 associated with each of the types of stormwater management facilities. These costs will then be combined with operations and maintenance costs and used to determine the whole life cost and present value of each of the stormwater controls.

3.1 Basin Capital Cost

3.1.1 Wet Basins and Wetlands

The following methods, which range in complexity and accuracy, can be used to estimate capital costs for wet basins:

- Estimate cost by contributing-area size using reported cost ranges or unit costs,
- Correlate basin volume or drainage area size with actual costs to create a regression formula, and
- Build engineering estimates using more detailed system components.

3.1.1.1 Simple Cost Ranges Based on Drainage Area

At the most basic level, several agencies have estimated capital costs using a range of costs per treated area of drainage area. These estimates are derived by taking an average of all costs per treated acre of known projects. Montgomery County, Maryland, has extensive experience with retrofitting basins. Its staff now estimate that the costs of about 80% of these facilities range from $2,500 to $7,500 (U.S. dollars) per hectare ($1,000 to 3,000 per acre) treated for retrofits to existing stormwater basins (e.g., flood control facilities) and from $7,500 to $22,500 per hectare ($3,000 to 5,000 per acre) for retrofits to new sites (with no preexisting infrastructure). These costs include utility conflict costs (Harper, 2004).

A study conducted by the Washington State Department of Transportation estimated wet basin costs at $37,500 per *impervious* hectare ($15,000 per acre) treated; additional costs were added for traffic control (15%), mobilization (10%), sales tax (8.6%), and civil engineering and contingency (50%). These methods do not recognize cost efficiencies that might be possible for large-scale projects, but they are general enough for certain planning purposes that do not require a level of detail beyond which the data can support.

3.1.1.2 Regression Relationships Using Existing Data

The following studies have developed relationships between size and cost for a number of control types, including wet basins: Wiegand et al. (1986), Southeastern Wisconsin Regional Planning Commission (SWRPC) (1991), Young et al. (1996), Brown and Schueler (1997), and U.S. Environmental Protection Agency (EPA) (1999). With the exception of SWRPC, all of these studies draw largely upon the same or modified versions of the same data sets.

Capital cost data for 23 wet basins were also evaluated for the California Department of Transportation (Caltrans) (2004). These data were compiled from the Center for Watershed Protection, with additional U.S. data obtained during the Caltrans study. Figure 12.3 shows there can be significant uncertainty in estimating capital costs solely as a function of facility size (as reflected by drainage area). Costs are adjusted for region using city cost indexes in *Heavy Construction Cost Data 2000* (R.S. Means, 1999), and date using the Construction Cost Index History from Engineering News Record (2004).

The data show a reasonable and predictable relationship between facility size (as reflected by drainage area) and cost. Similar relationships were found in all of the aforementioned studies of wet basins. However, the great variation in regional costs of stormwater controls makes this exercise of a more general interest. A stormwater manager in an area with limited experience with structural controls might use these relationships to better determine an approximate range of costs for future systems,

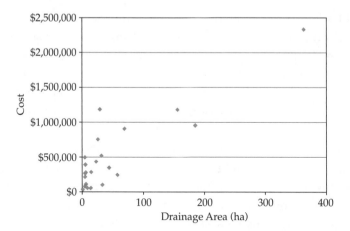

FIGURE 12.3 Relationship between drainage area and capital cost for wet basins (WERF, 2005).

giving insight into whether bid costs for a facility appeared too high. However, once data are available locally, they should be preferred over generic, regional, and national information.

3.1.1.3 Engineering Estimates

An additional approach to estimating costs is an engineering estimate. With this method, a spreadsheet is typically used to estimate subcomponent costs, which are then summed to yield a total cost. Many of the items (e.g., clearing and grubbing, excavation, etc.) are standard construction practices and should be familiar to agencies and contractors alike, even in areas that do not yet have specific stormwater control experience. However, specialized features like outflow structures and aquatic plantings will not be as familiar and may cost more in initial projects until the contracting community becomes comfortable with what is expected. This method has the advantage of reflecting local costs from the outset, which can be adjusted over time as new information is collected. Items (and units) that must be considered include

- Clearing and grubbing (area);
- Excavation and embankment (volume);
- Sediment and trash pretreatment structure (length);
- Overflow structure of concrete or rock rip-rap (volume);

- Dam and embankment (volume);

- Impermeable liner (area);

- Water's edge vegetation (area);

- Wetlands vegetation (area);

- Revegetation and erosion controls (length or area);

- Project management;

- Permitting and construction inspection;

- Engineering;

- Land acquisition; and

- Contingency (e.g., 30%).

3.1.2 Dry Basins

Figure 12.4 presents the relationship between cost and total volume for dry basins. Costs for these controls consist of some sites constructed as retrofit projects by Caltrans (2004), while others include both new and retrofit projects compiled by Caltrans (2001) from a variety of sources. Some of the costs from Caltrans are associated with facilities constructed as retrofits to the existing drainage system and located adjacent to major highways. These facilities are among the most expensive.

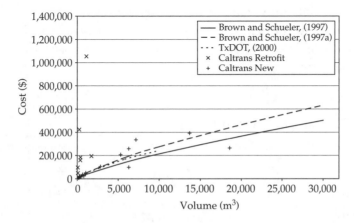

FIGURE 12.4 Dry basin capital costs (WERF, 2005).

3.2 Infiltrator Capital Costs

3.2.1 Infiltration Trench

Limited data are available for estimating infiltration trench capital costs. Infiltration trenches are somewhat expensive, compared to other stormwater practices, in terms of cost per area treated. Typical construction costs, including contingency and design costs, are about $180 to $300 (U.S. dollars) per cubic meter of stormwater treated (Brown and Schueler, 1997; SWRPC, 1991; U.S. EPA, 1999). Actual construction costs may be much higher. The average construction cost of two infiltration trenches installed by Caltrans in southern California (Caltrans, 2004) was about $1,800 per cubic meter; however, these were constructed as retrofit installations.

3.2.2 Infiltration Basin

Infiltration basins are similar to dry basins. For example, their construction requires excavation of an area to capture the required water quality volume and some engineered structure to bypass runoff that exceeds this volume. The main additional cost would be for soil permeability analysis and potential soil amendment to improve infiltration capacity. Consequently, the reader should refer to Figure 12.4 to see what the potential capital cost might be.

3.2.3 Pervious Pavement

Capital cost data are available, but generally not through agencies. The source of most cost data is from private companies who manufacture the components and/or design the installations. There are a wide variety of products available for numerous applications (e.g., light-duty traffic vs heavy use, asphalt vs concrete, and monolithically poured vs modular block) and an equally wide variety of costs. The Low Impact Development Center (2008) researched pervious pavement costs; these costs are summarized in Table 12.1.

TABLE 12.1 Pervious pavement costs.

Paver system	Cost per square meter (installed)
Asphalt	$5 to $10
Pervious concrete	$20 to $60
Grass/gravel pavers	$15 to $57
Interlocking concrete paving blocks	$50 to $100

An important consideration related to the selection of pervious pavement for a parking lot or other setting is that a parking lot will be needed whether pervious or not. Consequently, one should consider only the net cost attributable to the water quality component. Users should also keep in mind that a more accurate price comparison would involve costs of the full stormwater management and paving components. For example, a grass and gravel paver and pervious concrete representative stated that when impervious paving costs for drains, reinforced concrete pipes, catch basins, outfalls, and stormwater connects are totaled, asphalt or conventional concrete cost between $95 and $115 (U.S. dollars) per square meter, compared to a pervious system at $45 to $65 per square meter (Low Impact Development Center, 2008). These savings in capital costs may be offset over the life of the facility because of increased maintenance and more frequent replacement.

3.3   Capital Costs of Vegetated Swales and Strips

The SWRPC (1991) reported that costs may vary from $28 to $164 (U.S. dollars) per linear meter ($8 to $50 per linear foot) depending on swale depth and bottom width. These cost estimates include activities such as clearing, grubbing, leveling, filling, and sodding. On the other hand, cost for retrofitting an existing site may be cost prohibitive. The California Department of Transportation (2004) documented a median construction cost of six retrofit projects at about $1,300 per meter at sites that did not previously have swales. Site-specific considerations and local costs for labor and materials will also affect costs.

As with permeable pavement, the cost of a swale should be compared to the cost of the conventional drainage system. Engineered swales are a much less expensive option for stormwater conveyance than the curb and gutter systems they replace. Curbs, gutters, and associated underground storm sewers frequently cost twice as much as the cost of a grass swale (CWP, 1998). Consequently, use of swales can reduce the overall capital cost of a project and provide a water quality benefit.

3.4   Filter Capital Costs

3.4.1   Media Filter

Capital costs have been compiled for a number of installations of Austin sand filters that were constructed in the Austin, Texas, area where contractors are familiar with the facilities. The costs are related to water quality volume in Figure 12.5, where y is the capital cost and x equals the water quality volume. An important qualification is

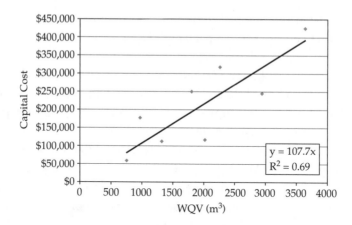

FIGURE 12.5   Capital cost for Austin sand filters.

that these costs are for construction only and do not include design, permitting, land costs, or any other related activities.

3.4.2   Bioretention Filter

Construction costs for bioretention filters have been studied in the past. Young et al. (1996), Brown and Schueler (1997), and the U.S. Environmental Protection Agency (1999) all include cost predictors for this control type. The Low Impact Development Center (2004) offers the following cost summary:

"A general rule of thumb is that residential rain gardens average about $3 to $40 per square meter [of control footprint], depending on soil conditions and the density and types of plants used. Commercial, industrial and institutional site costs can range between $100 to $400 per square meter, based on the need for control structures, curbing, storm drains and underdrains"

Bioretention filter costs vary considerably depending on whether or not an underdrain system is used and whether the system is installed along with many systems under one contract or simply as a stand-alone system (Low Impact Development Center, 2004).

Like swales, these systems are comprised of well-known construction materials and techniques. A list of cost elements includes

- Excavation (volume);
- Geotextile fabric (area);
- Perforated poly(vinyl chloride) underdrain pipe (150-mm in length);

- Poly(vinyl chloride) cleanouts (150-mm each);

- Gravel for underdrain (volume);

- Mulch (volume);

- Overflow storm drain inlet (each);

- Poly(vinyl chloride) outflow pipe from overflow structure (length);

- Project management;

- Permitting and construction inspection;

- Engineering;

- Land acquisition; and

- Contingency (e.g., 30%).

4.0 MAINTENANCE COSTS FOR VARIOUS STORMWATER CONTROLS

4.1 Factors Affecting Cost Estimates

In general, estimates of maintenance costs have a substantial amount of uncertainty associated with them. Reasons for this include

- Stormwater agencies generally do not track expenses for specific activities at individual controls;

- In many areas, stormwater controls are maintained by private entities that are unable or unwilling to provide maintenance costs;

- There is substantial regional variation in the amount of maintenance that actually occurs;

- Climatic variations can have a substantial effect on the frequency of many activities;

- Watershed characteristics (especially the amount of unstabilized areas) can have a significant effect on the frequency of sediment removal and other tasks; and

- Labor rates vary substantially across the United States.

Consequently, the reader is advised not to put too much weight on the absolute value of the costs presented here. Instead, the main benefit is a comparison of the relative costs of a variety of stormwater treatment options. To develop more site-specific maintenance cost estimates for a particular location, WERF (2005) provides a set of spreadsheets for several common treatment controls that allow the user to generate their own estimates of maintenance, capital, and whole life costs for these controls.

4.2 Vegetated Swales and Strips

Various maintenance activities and their frequency for swales and buffer strips were described in Chapter 11. Estimated costs were developed for low, medium, and high levels of maintenance assuming a swale treating runoff from a 0.8-ha catchment by WERF (2005). At the low maintenance level, routine maintenance was assumed to cost $150 (U.S. dollars) per year (inspections, vegetation management, and minor trash and debris removal). Intermittent maintenance, which consists of significant sediment removal, was estimated to occur every 10 years at a cost of $960 in addition to the annual cost for that year.

The medium level of maintenance (primarily more frequent mowing) was estimated to result in annual costs for routine activities of $527 per year. Intermittent corrective maintenance was assumed to occur every 4 years at a cost of $1440 in addition to the routine costs for that year. At the high level of maintenance, annual costs for routine activities were estimated to be $6,020 per year (monthly mowing accounting for the bulk of the cost). Corrective maintenance was assumed to occur every 2 years at $1440 in addition to routine costs.

4.3 Basins

4.3.1 Wet Basins and Wetlands

Based on the maintenance activities and frequencies identified in Chapter 11, cost estimates were developed by WERF (2005) for wet basins and wetlands sized to treat runoff from an 8-ha catchment. Routine annual costs are estimated to be $1,750 (U.S. dollars) per year for the low level of maintenance, which consists of vegetation management, minor trash and debris removal, and miscellaneous activities. Minor sediment removal is assumed every 20 years (about $6,000 in addition to other activities) and major sediment removal and dewatering every 30 years (about $170,000).

A moderate level of maintenance results in an estimated annual cost of about $3,000 per year, which differs from the low level of maintenance by having more intensive vegetation management. Sediment removal from the forebay is assumed to occur at 8-year intervals ($4,000). Major sediment removal is assumed to occur every 20 years at a cost of about $120,000. Sediment removal costs are less when activities are scheduled more frequently because it is assumed that less sediment will have accumulated.

Finally, a high level of maintenance is estimated to incur a little more than $20,000 per year in routine annual maintenance, of which the vast majority is vegetation management and trash and debris removal. This may seem high; however, basins sited to provide a significant amenity value can easily reach this figure. The City of Austin, for example, pays $35,000 per year to control aquatic plants and trash in its Central Market wet basin (located in a heavily populated and frequented commercial and multifamily area), and this activity is driven primarily by aesthetic concerns. Costs for sediment removal from the forebay and main basin are assumed to occur at the same intervals and incur the same costs as the medium level of maintenance.

4.3.2 Dry Basins

Maintenance activities and frequencies identified in Chapter 11 for dry basins were used to estimate costs for low, medium, and high levels of maintenance using the cost spreadsheets developed by WERF (2005). Annual costs for routine maintenance were estimated to be only $150 (U.S. dollars) per year, mainly because it was assumed that vegetation management occurred only once every 3 years. Intermittent maintenance, excluding sediment removal, was assumed to occur every other year with an associated cost of $1,000. Major sediment removal was assumed at 20-year intervals at a cost of about $27,000. This is much less than the cost of sediment removal from wet basins because the logistics are much easier and sediment dewatering is not required.

The medium level of maintenance incurs costs of about $2,100 per year, which includes more vegetation management (twice a year) as well as costs for miscellaneous repairs. Major sediment removal was assumed at 10-year intervals at a cost of $13,500 (less sediment accumulation than the low maintenance schedule). At the high level of maintenance, annual costs are approximately $9,500 per year, which is primarily the result of monthly vegetation management. Sediment removal is assumed at 6-year intervals at a cost of about $10,000.

4.4 Swirl Concentrators and Vaults

Maintenance of swirl concentrators and vaults can involve substantial costs. An eductor truck, the most common method of cleaning below-grade concentrators and vaults, can cost up to $250,000 (U.S. dollars). Typical trucks can store between 7 and 11 m^3 (10 and 15 cu yd) of material, which is enough storage for three to five smaller devices. Typically, using a crew of two, a small vault takes 30 minutes to clean. Severely clogged vaults may require several days of repeated cleaning. If a private contractor is used to perform the cleaning, then $0.13 per liter ($0.50 per gallon) is a rough estimate of the cost to remove and dispose this material based on experience in Houston,

Texas. Because of the limited disposal cost, the reader should contact local resources if more accurate information is required. This cost can be substantially higher if the device contains any significant amount of oil or other hazardous substances.

4.5 Media Filters

Estimated costs for low, medium, and high levels of maintenance were developed for the activities identified in Chapter 11 for a media filter serving 8 ha. Annual maintenance cost for the low level is about $2,000 (U.S. dollars) per year. These costs cover inspections, vegetation management, sand replacement every 6 years, and miscellaneous activities. In addition, major sediment removal was assumed to occur at 20-year intervals at a cost of about $21,500.

A medium level of maintenance was estimated to have annual costs of $3,600 per year. The increase, compared to the low level, was largely the result of assuming more frequent vegetation management (twice a year) and more frequent sand replacement (every 3 years). Intermittent maintenance included major sediment removal at 10-year intervals at a cost of $21,500. At the high level of maintenance, annual costs were calculated at about $7,800 per year, which is higher primarily because of the assumption of monthly vegetation management. Intermittent sediment removal was assumed to occur at 6-year intervals at a cost equal to that of the medium level of maintenance.

4.6 Bioretention Filters

Costs for three levels of maintenance activities were developed based on the material presented in Chapter 11 for a bioretention facility serving an 8-ha catchment. At a low level of maintenance, annual costs for routine activities (e.g., vegetation management) were calculated to be about $300 per year. In addition, major corrective maintenance was assumed to occur at 12-year intervals and to cost approximately $3,400. Corrective maintenance would include removal of all vegetation and replacement of rehabilitation of the filtration media.

At the medium level of maintenance, vegetation management is assumed to occur annually (rather than at the 3-year intervals assumed for the low level), which drives the annual cost for routine maintenance to $1,000 per year. Major corrective maintenance is assumed at 8-year intervals at a cost of $4,800. The cost for a high level of maintenance is driven by much more frequent vegetation management (monthly) and calculated to cost about $11,800 year. Corrective maintenance is assumed at 4-year intervals at the same cost associated with a medium level of maintenance.

5.0 WHOLE LIFE COST SUMMARY

Whole life costs have been estimated for a variety of controls to provide guidance on the ultimate cost of various pollutant reduction strategies. The capital costs are based on values presented earlier in this chapter. For each type of facility, cost implications of three levels of maintenance have been provided. These maintenance activities, frequencies, and costs are based on information provided in Chapter 11. A discount rate of 4% was selected to calculate present value of future expenditures over a 50-year life.

5.1 Vegetated Swales and Strips

Two options exist for calculating the whole life cost of swales and strips. A conventional analysis can be performed that values the cost of land acquisition, grading, vegetation establishment, and maintenance similar to other controls. Alternatively, the cost of a swale can be considered relative to the value of a conventional drainage system, which leads to the conclusion that the swales are effectively free because some type of system is required for drainage purposes.

Consider the case of swales implemented in a residential subdivision. Swales are one option that a developer can consider for creating a stormwater drainage system in lieu of curbs, gutters, and buried pipe. The cost of this type of system is substantially less than the conventional alternative. In general, swales would be incorporated to an easement in the front yard of every residence and no additional land would be required to be purchased by the developer. The land developer incurs no additional cost for selecting the swale option and, in fact, saves money. Although one might consider the opportunity cost (e.g., the lost opportunity to use that portion of the property for some other purpose) for the future homeowner, given the typical size of a residential lot in the United States, this cost is minimal.

The remaining cost is for maintenance and rehabilitation. In the residential scenario, the swale is incorporated to each front yard and routine maintenance, consisting of vegetation management, is performed by the homeowner. The cost of routine maintenance is thus negligible from the perspective of the municipal or other regulatory agency, which is an attractive feature. Work done by the homeowner can be considered a cost; however, the area occupied by the swale would still need to be mowed and otherwise maintained, whether the swale was present or not. Therefore, the homeowner incurs no significant additional cost for maintaining this area. In the long term, the swale will have to be regraded to prevent standing water (particularly in culverts), ensure sheet flow, and to remove accumulated sediment; this cost likely will be borne by the municipality or other responsible entity (e.g., homeowner association), rather than by the homeowner directly.

A similar case can be made that vegetated strips in many configurations also have no cost associated with water quality benefits. Consider the case of highways, in particular. One element of highway design is to provide a "clear recovery zone" adjacent to the roadway. The purpose of this zone is to provide motorists with the opportunity to recover from evasive maneuvers without rolling over or hitting a fixed object. These zones typically consist of vegetated areas adjacent to the shoulder with relatively low slopes up to about 10-m (30-ft) wide. These are precisely the design criteria to optimize the water quality benefit of vegetated strips. Highway departments across the United States have implemented this configuration for many years prior to the advent of water quality concerns and requirements for stormwater treatment. It is only recently that the water quality benefits of these areas have been recognized. Therefore, highway agencies provide areas that provide water quality benefits, but are selected for reasons of safety and highway drainage. These areas are routinely mowed for aesthetic reasons or to provide clear lines of sight; these activities are consistent with maintenance needed for water quality benefits.

This same type of argument can also be made for vegetated strips implemented in other situations. Many municipalities have requirements for landscaping and developers often include some green space around parking areas or buildings even when

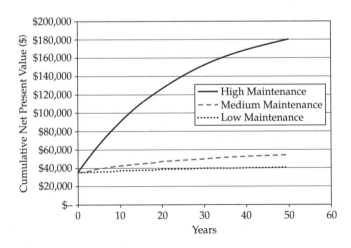

FIGURE 12.6   Whole life cost of a vegetated swale and strip for a 0.8-ha drainage area at a 4% discount rate.

landscaping is not a specific requirement. Vegetated strips can easily be created in these areas to manage runoff from roofs, parking lots, and other impervious surfaces.

A conventional estimate for whole life costs of swales has also been made. The assumption in this instance is that the swale is treating and conveying the runoff from a 0.8-ha (2-ac) catchment. The capital cost was estimated using a cost per area of the catchment. The costs for low-, medium-, and high-maintenance options are shown in Figure 12.6. The primary difference in the three scenarios is the frequency of mowing and vegetation management, which increases from once every 3 years (low maintenance) to annually to monthly (high maintenance) depending on the level of maintenance selected.

5.2 Basins

Whole life cost estimates were developed for wet basins, wetlands, and dry basins. Each estimate was based on common assumptions for drainage area and water quality. The catchment area was assumed to be 8 ha (20 ac) and the water quality volume was assumed to be about 820 m³ (29 000 cu ft). The base cost of the facility is determined using a relationship between drainage area and facility cost (about $41,000 [U.S. dollars] per hectare [$16,500 per acre], including design). This base cost has been increased to include a cleanout of construction-generated sediment in the watershed (assuming new development, not retrofit). Cost estimates were done for high, medium, and low levels of maintenance, which were described in Chapter 11. The discount rate for calculating present value was 4%.

5.2.1 Wet Basins and Wetlands

An estimate of the whole life cost of wet basins and wetlands was developed based on the general configuration described previously. The same costs are assumed for both types of facilities because there is little available information to distinguish between the two at this time. Major sediment removal is assumed to occur at a 20-year interval for the high and medium levels of maintenance, while the low level assumed maintenance at 30-year intervals, with an appropriate increase in the amount of sediment removed because of the longer period of time for accumulation. The cost of this major activity results in step increases in cost shown in Figure 12.7. As can be seen in the graph, this activity does not result in much difference in the ultimate cost of the three scenarios. Instead, the difference is mainly a function of how intensively the facility is maintained. The high level of maintenance assumes monthly mowing and trash and litter removal, which is appropriate for a high-visibility location. In addition, it is

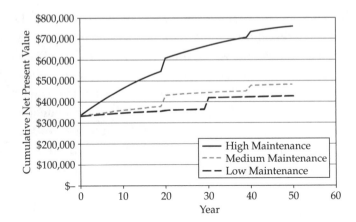

FIGURE 12.7   Whole life cost of wetlands and wet basins for an 8-ha drainage area.

assumed that some activities are carried out annually to address pests such as mosquitoes or beavers. Routine mowing and litter removal is assumed to occur twice yearly for the medium-level case, while the low-maintenance evaluation assumes that this is only done once per year.

It should be noted that the higher cost associated with a higher level of maintenance has little or no effect on pollutant removal; instead, this is primarily an issue of aesthetics and public expectations. The performance of a wet basin may be slightly compromised by the deferred sediment removal in the low-maintenance case. Normalized by water quality volume, the whole life cost for low, medium, and high-maintenance options are $500 (U.S. dollars), $600, and $900 per cubic meter. The important finding is that maintenance costs make up almost 50% of the whole life cost when basins are implemented in high-visibility locations, where aesthetics are at a premium.

5.2.2   Dry Basins

Dry basins have much in common with wet basins and wetlands in terms of construction costs; the primary difference lies in required maintenance activities. These activities tend to be easier and less expensive because there is little or no standing water in the facility. The initial capital cost shown in Figure 12.8 is based on the relationship between drainage area and facility cost (about $30,000 [U.S. dollars] per hectare [$12,000 per acre], including design).

The higher cost associated with a high maintenance facility is mainly attributable to the more frequent vegetation management (monthly vs biannually for the medium maintenance level).

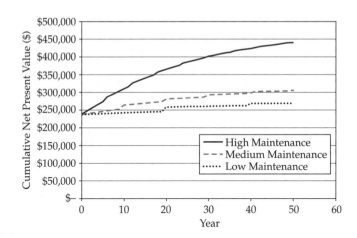

FIGURE 12.8   Whole life cost of dry basin for an 8-ha drainage area.

5.3   Filters

5.3.1   Media Filter

The capital cost for a sand filter was based on the same assumptions used for basins; that is, the catchment area was assumed to be 8 ha (20 ac) and the water quality volume was assumed to be approximately 820 m³ (29 000 cu ft). The base cost of the facility is based on the relationship between drainage area and facility cost (about $39,000 per hectare [$15,500 per acre], including design). Estimated whole life costs for sand filters are presented in Figure 12.9. Like many other controls, the largest expense for sand filters is vegetation management in the sedimentation basin and surrounding area. This is followed closely by the cost to rehabilitate and replace filter media. Occasionally, sand filters are constructed in concrete boxes in space-constrained areas. In this instance, capital costs are much higher; however, the maintenance cost may be substantially lower because there is less grass to mow. The cost differences in the three scenarios are primarily a function of assumptions about frequency of mowing, sand replacement, and rehabilitation.

5.3.2   Bioretention Filter

The whole life cost for the bioretention filters assumes a catchment of 0.8 ha (2.0 ac), a water quality volume of about 80 m³ (2900 cu ft), and a maximum ponding depth of 150 mm (6 in.). The capital cost was estimated to be $200 (U.S. dollars per square meter ($20 per square foot), with an additional $30,000 in engineering and planning.

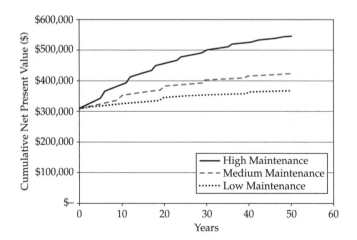

FIGURE 12.9   Austin sand filter whole life costs for an 8-ha drainage area.

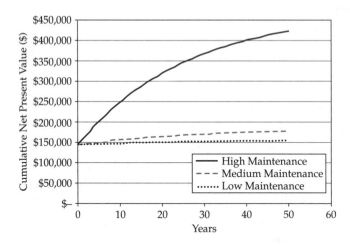

FIGURE 12.10   Whole life cost for bioretention filters for a 0.8-ha drainage area.

Estimated whole life costs for bioretention facilities are presented in Figure 12.10. The primary maintenance cost was associated with vegetation management. The frequency of this activity was assumed to be similar to swales, but with a greater cost because many bioretention facilities would require weeding, mulch replacement, and other activities beyond the mowing required for most swales.

5.4   Infiltrator Facilities

5.4.1   Infiltration Trench

The whole life cost for an infiltration trench is shown in Figure 12.11. Infiltration basin sizing is based on a drainage area of 0.8 ha (2 ac) and a water quality volume of about 80 m³ (2900 cu ft). A construction cost of $400 (U.S dollars) per cubic meter of runoff captured was assumed. Little routine maintenance is expected in this type of facility (mainly litter and debris removal); as such, the whole life cost driver is the frequency with which the trench must be rehabilitated. For the low-, medium-, and high-maintenance scenarios, intervals of 4, 8, and 12 years, respectively, were assumed. It is assumed that this cost is essentially the same as the original construction cost.

5.4.2   Infiltration Basin

The whole life cost graph for infiltration basins is presented in Figure 12.12. The sizing of the infiltration basin was based on the same water quality volume used for sand filters, wet basins, and dry basins. The fundamental assumption in the whole life cost estimate for infiltration basins is that capital cost and routine maintenance are essentially the same as those for a dry basin. The one area that distinguishes the two is that an infiltration basin can incur much higher costs associated with maintaining sufficient infiltration rates. In addition to sediment removal, this may require additional activities to remove and replace clogged soils on the floor of the basin. The

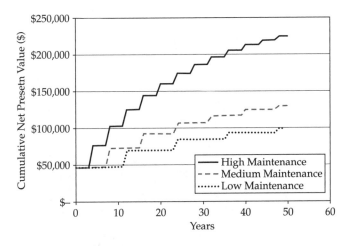

FIGURE 12.11   Whole life cost of an infiltration trench.

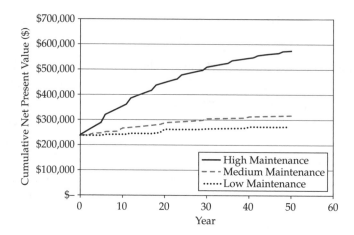

FIGURE 12.12   Whole life cost of an infiltration basin.

frequency of this activity is largely dependent on the initial soil texture and the rate at which sediment accumulates in the basin.

5.4.3   Pervious Pavement

The whole life cost shown for pervious pavement in Figure 12.13 assumes that the paving material is asphalt and the size of the lot is 0.8 ha (2 ac). In addition, because the parking lot or other surfaces would presumably be constructed at the same size

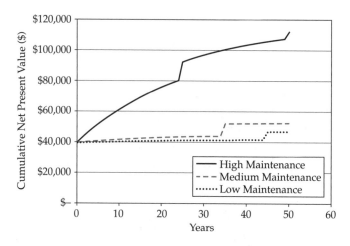

FIGURE 12.13   Whole life cost of a pervious asphalt parking lot.

and in the same location as a conventional surface, only the incremental cost difference between a conventional pavement and pervious pavement is used to calculate the initial capital cost, which is about $3.23 (U.S. dollars) per square meter ($0.30 per square foot). The large difference in whole life cost is attributable to the assumption of monthly sweeping and litter removal for the high-maintenance scenario vs annually for the medium-maintenance scenario and once every 3 years for the low-maintenance scenario. In addition, the pavement is assumed to need replacement more frequently (every 25 years vs 35 and 40 years) at a cost equal to the original construction cost.

6.0 WHOLE LIFE COST COMPARISON

Some of the stormwater controls considered in this chapter are appropriate for relatively large drainage areas, while others are small-scale systems that are used to treat individual tracts. To facilitate a cost comparison, the whole life cost for each system for each of the maintenance scenarios was normalized based on the equivalent water quality volume. These are presented in Table 12.2. One important caveat is that, for some of these controls (e.g., swales and strips), water quality benefits can effectively be considered free when compared to conventional drainage systems and when the maintenance is performed by the property owner.

Another important lesson from this exercise is that a bare-bone, marginal maintenance program (e.g., inspections every 3 years and little vegetation management) does not save that much money compared to a maintenance program at the medium level.

TABLE 12.2 Whole life cost comparison.

Stormwater control	Whole life cost ($/m³)		
	Low maintenance	Medium maintenance	High maintenance
Swales/strip	500	660	2200
Wet basins/wetlands	520	600	925
Dry basins	330	375	575
Sand filter	450	520	670
Bioretention	1900	2200	5100
Infiltration trench	1200	1600	2700
Infiltration basin	330	400	700
Permeable pavement	570	640	1400

High-level maintenance costs for most controls are driven by aesthetics more than performance requirements. The one exception is infiltration trenches, where the maintenance cost is driven by assumptions about how long they can perform without clogging.

7.0 EFFECT OF STORMWATER SYSTEMS ON WHOLE LIFE COST

Stormwater systems are commonly recommended for stormwater management because they can provide different unit processes for pollutant removal, additional area for ancillary infiltration, and a robustness and redundancy to the system. Installation of controls in a series has little effect on their capital cost, but can influence maintenance costs substantially. Use of stormwater systems tends to transfer the maintenance costs associated with sediment removal from the last facility to those earlier in the system. This can have substantial benefits when the last facility has a tendency to clog (e.g., filters and infiltration devices) or contains saturated sediment (e.g., basins and wetlands). It is much easier to remove sediment from swales and buffer strips, for instance, than to replace filter media, dredge basins, or rehabilitate infiltration facilities. The exact value of this benefit is difficult to estimate precisely because it is largely a function of the sediment load to the stormwater control.

8.0 REFERENCES

Brown, W.; Schueler, T. (1997) *The Economics of Stormwater BMPs in the Mid-Atlantic Region;* Prepared for the Chesapeake Research Consortium, Edgewater, Maryland; Center for Watershed Protection: Ellicott City, Maryland.

California Department of Transportation (2004) *BMP Retrofit Pilot Program Final Report.* http://www.dot.ca.gov/hq/env/stormwater/special/newsetup/_pdfs/new_technology/CTSW-RT-01–050.pdf (accessed Oct 5, 2010).

California Department of Transportation (2001) *Third Party Best Management Practice Retrofit Pilot Study Cost Review,* Appendix to BMP Retrofit Final Report. http://www.dot.ca.gov/hq/env/stormwater/special/newsetup/_pdfs/new_technology/CTSW-RT-01–050/AppendixC/ThirdPartyCost.pdf (accessed Sept 2011).

Center for Watershed Protection (1998) *Costs and Benefits of Storm Water BMPs: Final Report;* Center for Watershed Protection: Ellicott City, Maryland.

Engineering News Record (2004) Construction Cost Index History (1908–2004). http://enr.construction.com/features/conEco/costIndexes/constIndexHist.asp (accessed June 29, 2004).

Harper, D. (2004) Montgomery County, Maryland, Department of Environmental Protection. Personal Communication.

Low Impact Development Center (2004) Bioretention Costs. http://www.lid-stormwater.net/bio_costs.htm (accessed June 28, 2004).

Low Impact Development Center (2008) Permeable Paver Costs. http://www.lid-stormwater.net/permpaver_costs.htm (accessed Dec 5, 2008).

R.S. Means Company Inc. (1999) *Heavy Construction Cost Data 2000,* 14th ed.; R.S. Means Company Inc.: Kingston, Massachusetts.

Southeastern Wisconsin Regional Planning Commission (1991) *Costs of Urban Nonpoint Source Water Pollution Control Measures;* Technical Report No. 31; Southeastern Wisconsin Regional Planning Commission: Waukesha, Wisconsin.

U.S. Environmental Protection Agency (1999) Stormwater Technology Fact Sheet, Infiltration Trench. http://www.epa.gov/owm/mtb/infltrenc.pdf (accessed Dec 4, 2007).

Water Environment Research Foundation (2005) *Performance and Whole Life Costs of Best Management Practices and Sustainable Urban Drainage Systems;* Project 01-CTS-21Ta; Water Environment Research Foundation: Alexandria, Virginia.

Wiegand, C.; Schueler, T.; Chittenden, W.; Jellick, D. (1986) *Cost of Urban Runoff Controls, Urban Runoff Quality Impact and Quality Enhancement Technology;* American Society of Civil Engineers: New York; pp 366–382.

Young, G. K.; Stein, S.; Cole, P.; Kammer, T.; Graziano, F.; Bank, F. (1996) *Evaluation and Management of Highway Runoff Water Quality;* Publication No. FHWA-PD-96-032; U.S. Department of Transportation, Federal Highway Administration, Office of Environment and Planning: Washington, D.C.

Chapter 13

Performance Assessment

(continued)

(continued)

1.0 INTRODUCTION

This chapter presents methods to evaluate the performance of stormwater controls with respect to the goals defined in Chapter 3. The emphasis of the chapter is on sampling and statistical methods for data evaluation. Aspects of performance other than hydrologic and water quality benefits are not discussed in this chapter, although these factors are also essential to effective stormwater management systems. Operators of stormwater controls should examine their perceived value by the public relative to such factors as appearance, active and passive recreational opportunities, wildlife habitat, property value enhancement, and other social and environmental objectives.

Selection of appropriate stormwater management technologies for a particular site requires a thorough understanding of the relative ability of various controls (e.g., wet basins, swales, wetlands, sand filters) to reduce runoff volume and peak flows, and to improve the quality of stormwater runoff. As a result, regulatory and environmental agencies have taken interest in the development of accurate and comparable methods of control performance assessment. Many studies have been completed that have assessed the ability of stormwater treatment controls to reduce pollutant concentrations and loadings in stormwater system discharges. However, in attempting to review and summarize information gathered from these individual control evaluations, it is apparent that inconsistent study methods, terminology, lack of associated design information, and absence of reporting protocols make wide-scale assessments difficult, if not impossible.

To further complicate this issue, the most common control performance measure used today is "percent removal" of pollutants. However, multiple studies have determined that percent removal, particularly when based on concentration, is a highly problematic method for assessing performance and has resulted in some significant errors in control performance reporting (Strecker et al., 2001; Urbonas, 2000; Winer, 2000; U.S. EPA, 2002c). If relatively clean water is entering a control, then there is limited performance potential that can be achieved by the control. Controls that treat the dirtiest water (e.g., runoff with relatively high pollutant concentrations) are likely to achieve higher percent removals. As a result, percent removal may be more dependent on influent concentrations than control performance. Despite their popular use and pervasiveness as a regulatory goal, percent removals are no longer recommended as performance descriptors for stormwater controls.

This chapter describes several effective and widely agreed upon methods for assessing control performance. Sections 2.0 and 3.0 present an outline for developing and implementing an assessment plan. Goals, objectives, and performance criteria should be established early in a monitoring program, and typical examples of each are discussed in Section 4. A wide variety of assessment methods are presented in Section 5.0, including relevant statistical methods useful in the evaluation of control performance, as well as important guidelines for their application. These tools can be used to determine the ability of a control to reduce runoff volumes and improve effluent quality. Sections 6.0, 7.0, and 8.0 describe data needs, execution of the monitoring program, and considerations for reporting results, respectively. The chapter concludes with Section 10.0, which provides three examples of application of the statistical methods presented to a given influent and effluent data set for assessing control performance.

To better clarify terminology used to describe the level of treatment achieved and how well a device, system, or practice meets its goals, the following definitions of terms often used in control literature are provided:

- *Control*—a device, practice, or method for removing, reducing, retarding, or preventing targeted stormwater runoff quantity, constituents, pollutants, and contaminants from reaching receiving waters;

- Control system—a control system includes the control and any related bypass or overflow. For example, the efficiency (see definition of term below) can be determined for an off-line wet basin either by itself (as a control) or for the control system (control including bypass flows);

- Performance—a measure of how well a control meets its goals for stormwater that flows through or is processed by it;

- Effectiveness—a measure of how well a control system meets its goals for all stormwater flows reaching the control site, including flow bypasses; and

- Efficiency—a measure of how well a control or control system removes pollutants.

The reader should note that *performance* and *effectiveness* can be expressed in terms of pollutant removal, effluent quality, and/or how well increased flows caused by urbanization are mitigated.

1.1   General Overview

In an effort to develop a set of consistent protocols for assessing control performance, Urbonas (1995) and Strecker (1994) summarized relevant information that should be collected and reported. In addition to considering sampling and analysis methods, they specified collection of data with respect to the physical, climatic, and geological parameters that likely affect the effectiveness and performance of a control. These protocols have recently been applied to existing control data, which are continually compiled and loaded into the International Stormwater Best Management Practices Database (www.bmpdatabase.org). An initial assessment of the results of the analyses of the database has been completed (Strecker et al., 2001). Additional data continue to be incorporated to the International Best Management Practices Database, especially from performance of green infrastructure stormwater controls (Clary et al., 2011). A summary of recent findings is published by the Water Environment Research Foundation (2011). A detailed guidance document on control monitoring is *Urban Stormwater BMP Performance Monitoring: A Guidance Manual for Meeting the National Stormwater BMP Database Requirements* (U.S. EPA, 2002c), available for download at www.bmpdatabase.org. In addition, documents that summarize control efficiency information include the *National Pollutant Removal Performance Database for Stormwater BMPs* (Center for Watershed Protection, 2007); the Terrene Institute's report, *The Use of Wetlands for Controlling Stormwater Pollution* (Strecker et al., 1992); and Minton (2011).

Significant findings of the U.S. EPA control database effort to date include methodology to best assess control pollutant removal performance for most pollutants (Strecker et al., 2001). Effective assessment required determination of the following:

- How much of the runoff that occurs is and is not treated by the control? In other words, what is the amount of flow not bypassed or exceeding control effective treatment rates?

- How much stormwater runoff is prevented, particularly via evapotranspiration and/or infiltration (e.g., hydrological source control)?

- Of the runoff treated, what is the effluent quality as determined by statistical characterization?

1.1.1 Hydrologic Improvement

A key consideration in assessing overall success of a control is the evaluation of the technology's ability to capture runoff for treatment. The capture efficiency of a control indicates the portion of flow that is treated and the portion of flow bypassed without treatment. This is an important assessment criterion, as a control with a high pollutant removal efficiency will have little effect if it can capture only a small percentage of the total attainable stormwater runoff. In general, capture efficiency is taken to be a function of a control's volume and outlet structure.

Capture efficiencies will likely vary for the duration of a storm event, between storm events, and seasonally and annually. This may have serious treatment implications, particularly in light of the first flush theory, which suggests that runoff occurring early in an event has a higher concentration of pollutants than runoff occurring at the tail end of an event. As a result, control capture efficiency should be considered for a variety of conditions and durations.

One of the goals of implementing stormwater controls is to improve local hydrology. Of particular interest is whether some controls may be more beneficial than others in terms of reducing runoff volume (i.e., HSC). For example, a wet basin might not significantly decrease the volume of runoff, but a biofilter, given its contact with drier soils and resulting evapotranspiration and/or infiltration, might substantially decrease runoff volumes. Much of the premise of low-impact development is based on reducing runoff volumes. However, accurately measuring flow during storm conditions is difficult. Programs to monitor and assess control performance should include consideration of the following parameters:

- Peak-flow reduction caused by evapotranspiration;

- Volume reduction caused by infiltration and groundwater recharge; and

- Changes in the time series distribution of flow.

The most common tool that is used to evaluate the effect of controls on hydrology is a hydrograph, which is a graphical presentation of flow over time. A hydrograph depicting influent and effluent flows allows for evaluation of the change in peak runoff, total volume, and the overall distribution (i.e., timing) of stormwater flows.

1.1.2   Water Quality Improvement

The analysis of control water quality performance data should consist of a comprehensive evaluation of effluent vs influent water quality. Specifically, *pollutant removal efficiency* refers to the pollutant reduction from the inflow to the outflow of a system. The two most common water quality parameters considered are event mean concentration (EMC) efficiency and mass or load efficiency. Event mean concentration is generally considered the most useful measure of stormwater runoff water quality and is particularly well-suited for wet weather flows. Collection of EMC data has been the primary focus of the International Stormwater Best Management Practices Database (U.S. EPA, 2002c). However, for waterbodies regulated under total maximum daily load (TMDL) standards, pollutant loads are the central focus of control studies. Load measures are well-suited for dry weather flows, which can contribute substantially to long-term loading. As a general rule, the concentration-based technique often results in slightly lower performance efficiencies than the mass-based technique because concentration-based techniques do not include the effect of influent volume reduction that can be removed through storage, infiltration, reuse, or evaporation–transpiration.

Historically, the ability of a control to remove pollutants has been quantified as a percent reduction in concentration or load. However, recent studies indicate that this measure is sometimes heavily dependent on influent concentration rather than control performance. For example, Schueler (1996) noted that the effluent generated by most controls is limited to an "irreducible concentration" such that effluent water quality cannot be improved beyond this point. As a result, pollutant removal efficiencies tend to be low when influent concentrations are low, and the percent removal measure mistakenly suggests poor performance in such instances.

As an alternative to the percent removal method, pollutant removal efficiencies can be evaluated using several statistical models that are appropriate when the only input data that are available are storm event mean influent and effluent concentrations. The following methods for evaluating control performance using EMC data are summarized in documentation for the U.S. EPA (2002c) control database:

- Efficiency ratio;

- Summation of loads;

- Regression of loads;

- Event mean concentration;

- Efficiency of individual storm;

- Irreducible concentration and achievable efficiency;

- Percent removal relative to water quality standards;

- Lines of comparative performance;

- Multivariate and nonlinear models; and

- Effluent probability method (EPM).

Of these methods, Strecker et al. (2001) recommend only EPM for control performance analysis. Characterization of effluent quality is one feature of EPM, discussed further below. The other methods of evaluation are either not recommended or recommended only in conjunction with a more comprehensive statistical analysis. This chapter presents both the EPM method and several qualitative and quantitative (statistical) methods to enhance assessment of control performance concentration and load data.

1.2 Practical Considerations

Based on the *National Pollutant Removal Performance Database, Version 3.0* (CWP, 2007), which consists of 166 individual control performance studies, the following are key issues concerning the evaluation of control performance:

- Limited data—control research is still a relatively young field and studies are limited, especially for certain categories of controls. Users should understand that these performance results represent an analysis of currently available research; further research will likely lead to revised numbers. As the number of studies increase, so will the confidence with which control performance can be reported.

- Range of data—across the various categories of controls, the range of data for a particular pollutant can be quite high. That is, there is a large difference between the lowest and highest removal efficiency reported. The greater the range, the less confidence there is in the median removal efficiency. Also, further work is necessary to identify factors that lead to either poor or good performance.

- Factors that affect performance—related to the preceding point about data ranges, there are many factors that affect control performance, including

  - Number of storms sampled;

  - Incoming pollutant concentrations;

  - Manner in which pollutant removal efficiency is computed;

  - Monitoring technique used;

  - Internal geometry and storage volume provided by the practice design;

  - Sediment and water column interactions;

  - Regional differences in soil type;

  - Rainfall, flowrate, and particle sizes of the influent (runoff entering the control);

  - Latitude;

  - Size and land use of the contributing catchment;

  - Vegetation characteristics;

  - Historic maintenance and operation; and

  - Standard instrumental and procedural laboratory errors.

- Control age—data used to determine general removal capabilities are based on "best condition" values. In particular, most of the studies focused on controls that were constructed within 3 years of monitoring (Winer, 2000).

- Volume reduction—several categories of controls can be quite effective at reducing the overall volume of runoff. Volume reduction controls have a filtering, infiltration, biological uptake or storage and reuse component that permanently removes some volume of runoff from the outflow. Controls that reduce volume are also reducing pollutant loads, although a concentration-in vs concentration-out study would not account for this unless it is time-series correlated. For this reason, the removal efficiency of these types of controls may be under-reported, especially when a concentration-in vs concentration-out study approach was used.

Additional sources of relevant practical information related to evaluation of control performance include literature from the following: Federal Highway Administration

(2000), U.S. EPA (2002c; 2004); California Department of Transportation (Caltrans) (2003); Technology Acceptance Reciprocity Partnership (2001); and Washington State Department of Ecology (2002).

2.0 OVERVIEW OF ASSESSMENT PLAN DEVELOPMENT

Development of a control performance assessment plan sets the foundation for a successful monitoring project. The following is an ordered summary of key tasks that should be addressed when developing an assessment plan. Each of these tasks is discussed in detail in successive sections, particularly Section 4.0 through Section 7.0.

2.1 Formulate Objectives Based on Goals

Once project goals have been established, relevant objectives should be developed that will provide direction for the project. Objectives need not only pertain to control performance, but may reflect other successes, such as meeting specified constraints (e.g., limitations of time and resources) or providing educational opportunities to benefit the public.

2.2 Formulate Criteria or Metrics for Satisfying the Objectives

Criteria and metrics are used to determine the extent to which a project successfully meets specified objectives. Criteria should be selected such that results are unambiguous and provide clear evidence as to whether or not the project has succeeded. If an objective is worded well, the appropriate criterion or metric may be clear. For other objectives, more specific (mathematical) definitions of metrics will be required.

2.3 Establish Assessment Method and Tools

The next step in the planning process is to determine how control performance will be assessed based on available knowledge, tools, and information. The application of some tools and methods may be constrained by limitations of time, resources, data, staff expertise, and/or technology. In general, it will be difficult to select specific statistical methods for data analysis until a general evaluation and characterization of the collected data can be performed.

2.4 Establish Data Needs

To generate meaningful results, valid and relevant data must be collected for analysis. In particular, the amount and quality of collected data must be sufficient to support the evaluation process.

2.5 Develop Monitoring Plan to Collect Data

A final, important task is to develop a comprehensive monitoring plan to guide the process of collecting data on-site. Specific measurements, frequency and timing of collection, necessary equipment and personnel, and a consistent and orderly method of data recording should be specified during the planning process.

3.0 OVERVIEW OF ASSESSMENT PLAN IMPLEMENTATION

The manner of execution of a stormwater control assessment plan should be considered well in advance of the project. Specifically, the processes of data collection, data evaluation and validation, data analysis, and reporting should be outlined and appropriate methods selected. A more detailed discussion of implementation tasks is presented in Section 8.0 ("Implementation of the Plan") and Section 9.0 ("Reporting Stormwater Control Performance").

3.1 Collect Data

Standardized test methods and procedures should be used to collect stormwater control data when possible. Standardized methods have been developed by technology-specific expert committees and have undergone thorough peer-review processes. Various nationally recognized agencies have developed applicable data collection standards for both water quality and flow measurements, including the American Society for Testing and Materials, the American Society of Civil Engineers, U.S. EPA, the American Water Works Association (AWWA), NSF International, and the American Public Health Association (APHA) (see Section 7.3.3 for further discussion of data collection standards [APHA et al., 1998; ASTM, 1997]. In the event that standardized methods cannot be applied, evidence assuring data quality should be produced and submitted in support of a proposed alternative method.

3.2   Evaluate Data for Quality and Usefulness

Before collected data can be used to generate results and conclusions of significance, they should be evaluated for quality and usefulness. The process of reviewing the quality of data is called *data validation*. This is typically followed by an initial statistical analysis. This procedure can verify that there are enough data of sufficient quality to complete the analysis and guide the selection of appropriate statistical methods, if necessary.

3.3   Apply Data to Assess Performance

Following the validation and initial evaluation of collected data, tools that have been selected to produce meaningful results and answer key questions should be applied (e.g., statistical methods, computer models, etc.). Results of the data analysis can then be compared to the criteria and metrics established during the planning process to produce meaningful conclusions regarding control performance.

3.4   Reporting

Results of a control performance assessment program should be documented and presented in a formal report. While a comprehensive, final report should be produced at the completion of the monitoring program, production of regular progress reports throughout the program should also be considered. Monitoring regularity and program objectives should dictate the frequency of progress reports.

4.0   FORMULATING OBJECTIVES AND ASSESSMENT CRITERIA OR METRICS

The initial steps for assessing performance of stormwater controls are the formulation of objectives and assessment criteria or metrics. These two elements are derived from the performance goals established during the selection and design phase. They provide the framework for defining analysis methods, information needs, and evaluation. These are considered fundamental steps for developing an efficient plan to assess performance of stormwater controls (FHWA, 2000).

Performance goals define the overall purpose of the stormwater control. They include a number of categories that address effectiveness, efficiency, operations, management, regulations, and research targets. Table 13.1 provides a list of goals commonly associated with stormwater controls (U.S. EPA, 2002c). However, goals

TABLE 13.1   Typical performance goals for stormwater controls (source: Table 2.1, U.S. EPA [2002c]).

Category	Goal
Hydraulics	• Improve flow characteristics upstream and/or downstream of the stormwater control.
Hydrology	• Flood mitigation, improve runoff characteristics (peak shaving).
Water quality	• Reduce downstream pollutant loads and concentrations of pollutants.
Treatment	• Achieves desired pollutant concentration in outflow.
Water quality	• Reduce downstream pollutant loads and concentrations of pollutants. • Achieve desired pollutant concentration in outflow.
Source control	• Removal of litter and debris.
Regulatory	• Compliance with NPDES permit. • Meet local, state, or federal water quality criteria.
Implementation feasibility	• For nonstructural controls, ability to function within management and oversight structure.
Cost	• Capital, operation, and maintenance costs.
Aesthetic	• Improve appearance of site.
Maintenance	• Operate within maintenance and repair schedule and requirements. • Ability of system to be retrofitted, modified, or expanded.
Longevity	• Long-term functionality.
Resources	• Improve downstream aquatic environment and erosion control. • Improve wildlife habitat. • Multiple-use functionality.
Safety, risk and Liability	• Function without significant risk or liability. • Ability to function with minimal environmental risk downstream.
Public perception	• Information is available to clarify public understanding of runoff quality, quantity, and effects on receiving waters.

are often too broad or vague to develop an assessment process that will demonstrate attainment of the goals. Therefore, the goals need to be broken down into objectives that address specific issues associated with a particular stormwater control or management program. At least one objective should be formulated for each goal, but multiple objectives are often required. Objectives should be as specific as possible to the control type and its location.

Criteria and metrics define how monitoring will address an objective. Depending on how the objective is worded, the criterion or metric may be clear. For other objectives, specific questions may need to be formulated that, when answered, will address the objective.

4.1 Considerations for Evaluating Stormwater Control Performance

Assessing performance of a stormwater control can be approached a number of different ways depending on established project goals (U.S. EPA, 2002c). This section presents several elements that should be considered during the planning stage.

4.1.1 Information Requirements

One consideration is the amount of information required given the great temporal (including seasonal) and spatial variability of stormwater flows and pollutant concentrations (U.S. EPA, 2002c). Stormwater at a given location varies greatly during a single runoff event and from event to event. Consequently, a large data set is required to accurately characterize stormwater at a given site (U.S. EPA, 2002c). Collecting enough information to address the objectives and goals with a high level of statistical confidence generally requires a relatively long time or application at several sites. A study lasting several monitoring seasons is not uncommon.

4.1.2 Background Information

Background information is essential to formulating appropriate goals and objectives (U.S. EPA, 2004). A background review can

- Provide related information available from existing studies on the same stormwater controls carried out by others;
- Identify specific data gaps that need to be filled through additional studies; and
- Identify successes and/or failures in implementing monitoring programs, obtaining meaningful results, and achieving project goals.

A starting point for background information is the International Stormwater Best Management Practices Database.

4.1.3 Physical Layout

The physical layout of the stormwater runoff system can help define some of the objectives. Physical attributes of the stormwater control structure to consider include bypasses and overflows, stormwater controls constructed in a series, and how the controls will be operated (U.S. EPA, 2002c).

4.1.4   Study Period

The period of time used to assess performance is an important factor (U.S. EPA, 2002c). Consideration of seasonal changes and acute vs chronic effects should be included when developing objectives.

4.2   Implication of Stormwater Control Types

The performance assessment of stormwater controls should also consider the types and designs of controls that can be implemented. U.S. EPA (2002c) recommends classifying stormwater controls according to one of the following four distinct categories for purposes of comparison:

- Stormwater controls with well-defined inlets and outlets whose primary treatment depends on extended detention storage of stormwater (e.g., wet basins and dry basins, wetland basins, and underground vaults);

- Stormwater controls with well-defined inlets and outlets that do not depend on significant storage of water (e.g., sand filters, swales, buffers, and flow-through controls);

- Stormwater controls that do not have a well-defined inlet and/or outlet (e.g., full retention, infiltration, porous pavement, and grass swales where inflow is overland flow along the length of the swale); and

- Widely distributed (scattered) and nonstructural stormwater controls (e.g., catch basin retrofits, education programs, and source control programs).

The performance of stormwater controls with defined inlets and outlets can be assessed using influent and effluent information. Controls with extended storage need to be considered separately from flow-through controls because performance goals for detention units include hydraulic and hydrologic considerations such as flood control, whereas flow-through units do not (U.S. EPA, 2002c).

The performance of stormwater controls without defined inlets or outlets typically need to be assessed using information collected before and after the controls was installed, or from paired sites.

Widely distributed and nonstructural controls are typically assessed using information derived from the watershed where the controls are located. Watershed approaches are applied when the objectives relate to how controls affect the receiving environment. They are often used when it is too difficult or costly to monitor a large number of individual controls or during evaluation of the effectiveness of nonstructural controls, such as street sweeping and public outreach programs. Watershed approaches include upstream and downstream, before and after controls were deployed, and paired watershed.

Factors to consider with a watershed approach include the following:

- The effects of specific controls cannot be isolated;

- Watershed monitoring may produce a more accurate measure of the true performance of stormwater controls in minimizing the effects of urban runoff on receiving waters (U.S. EPA, 2004);

- The effects of stormwater management programs may be obscured because receiving waters are influenced by many other stressors or the total pollutant load from stormwater (or change in the load from stormwater controls) may be too small to detect (U.S. EPA, 2002c);

- Watershed monitoring can be applied to pipe systems or "sewersheds" in addition to instream locations (U.S. EPA, 2004);

- Before and after monitoring obviously requires data collection prior to implementation of the stormwater control or controls to establish baseline conditions. Monitoring prior to implementation should also be conducted for pair monitoring to establish similarities and differences between the two watersheds;

- Studies have found that a minimum of 2 to 3 years is recommended for watershed monitoring programs (FHWA, 2000); and

- Watershed monitoring may not always be a viable option because watersheds do not typically follow political boundaries and, therefore, involvement of all necessary governing agencies may not be possible.

There are several additional factors that need to be considered when assessing the performance of nonstructural stormwater controls. Tailor and Wong (2002a; 2002b) discuss how information useful for assessing performance is difficult to compile because

- Nonstructural controls rely on behavioral change and behavioral changes are difficult to measure;

- The effects cannot be isolated for direct measurement; and

- Nonstructural control programs are strongly pressured to report only positive results.

Several approaches are recommended for compiling required information that is qualitative and quantitative in nature. Qualitative information can involve public awareness of target issues and levels of participation. Quantitative approaches include direct measurement of items removed from stormwater such as litter or sediment, modeling the entire system, or long-term trend monitoring of a downstream point (U.S. EPA, 2004).

4.3 Typical Objectives

Table 13.2 presents examples of objectives formulated from stormwater control performance goals listed in Table 13.1. Performance assessments are typically based on one or more of these objectives (U.S. EPA, 2002c). Objectives shown in the table do not represent the entire set of potential objectives. Site-specific conditions may require others to be formulated and applied or for these to be revised. The more specifically an objective relates to the site, the better defined the data needs are.

4.4 Examples of Criteria or Metrics

Table 13.2 also presents examples of criteria and metrics formulated from stormwater control performance objectives. The criteria or metrics shown in the table represent a small portion of those that can be considered. Moreover, they should be modified to include site-specific conditions and key parameters of interest.

TABLE 13.2   Examples of objectives and criteria or metrics associated with performance goals.

Category	Goal

Hydraulics	• Improve flow characteristics upstream and/or downstream of the stormwater control.
	  - **Change in the downstream flowrate from baseline conditions.**
	    a. Statistical difference in downstream flowrate distribution.

Hydrology	• Flood mitigation, improve runoff characteristics (peak attenuation).
	  - **Peak outflow rate during various runoff events.**
	    a. Outflow rate distribution.

Water quality	• Reduce downstream pollutant loads and concentrations of pollutants.
	  - **Change in water quality from baseline conditions.**
	    a. Statistical difference in downstream water quality concentrations.
	    b. Statistical difference in downstream pollutant loads.

(continued)

TABLE 13.2   (continued)

Category	Goal
Treatment	• Achieves desired pollutant concentration in outflow.
	- **Degree of treatment provided under typical operating conditions.**
	a. Statistical difference in influent and effluent concentrations.
	b. Percent difference in event influent and effluent concentrations.
	- **Variation in effectiveness from pollutant to pollutant.**
	a. Statistical difference in percent differences between influent and effluent concentrations.
	- **Effect of various influent concentrations on overall treatment effectiveness.**
	a. Distribution of influent and effluent concentrations for pollutants of concern.
	- **Effect of storm characteristics on overall treatment effectiveness.**
	a. Comparison of percent difference between influent and effluent for different rainfall totals.
	- **Effect of design variables on treatment performance?**
	a. Distribution of influent and effluent concentrations of pollutants of concern.
Source control	• Removal of litter and debris.
	- **Amount of litter and debris is collected in areas with clean neighborhood programs.**
	a. Mass of collected litter and debris.
Regulatory	• Compliance with NPDES permit.
	- **Change in water quality from baseline conditions.**
	a. Statistical difference in downstream water quality concentrations
	• Meet local, state, or federal water quality criteria.
	- **Comparison of downstream water quality to criteria?**
	a. Statistical difference of downstream concentrations and a standard or objective.
	b. Percent exceedance.
Implementation feasibility	• Ability to function as designed.
	- **Comparison of the control's efficiency, performance, and effectiveness compared to other controls.**
	a. Statistical difference in effluent quality among different controls.
	b. Statistical difference in percent difference in influent and effluent quality among different controls.

(continued)

Cost
- • Capital, operation, and maintenance costs.
  - **Life cycle costs (labor and materials).**
    - a. Annual operating and maintenance costs.

Aesthetic
- • Improve appearance of site.
  - **Public's perception of the amount of trash present downstream.**
    - a. Visual appearance.

Maintenance
- • Operate within maintenance and repair schedule and requirements.
  - **Variation in treatment effectiveness with different operational and maintenance approaches?**
    - a. Statistical difference in percent difference between influent and effluent and effluent levels for different approaches.
- • Ability of system to be retrofitted, modified, or expanded.

Longevity
- • Long-term functionality.
  - **Effectiveness improves, decays, or remains stable over time.**
    - a. Statistical difference in the percent difference between influent and effluent for different time periods.
    - b. Trend of effluent levels.

Resources
- • Improve downstream aquatic environment and erosion control.
  - **Change in the biological community from baseline conditions.**
    - a. Change in macroinvertebrate species and populations.
- • Improve wildlife habitat.
  - **Change in the downstream flowrate.**
    - a. Statistical difference in downstream flowrate distribution.
- • Multiple use functionality.
  - **Comparison of downstream water quality to established criteria for various designated uses.**
    - a. Percent exceedance.

Safety, risk, and liability
- • Function without significant risk or liability.
  - **Drainage time of the facility within the allotted period of time.**
    - a. Standing water levels over time.
- • Ability to function with minimal environmental risk downstream.
  - **Presence of streambank erosion in downstream areas.**
    - a. Loss of material.

Public perception
- • Information is available to clarify public understanding of runoff quality, quantity, and effects on receiving waters.
  - **Public events the program has participated in.**
    - a. Number of events.

5.0 ASSESSMENT METHODS

Once control performance data have been collected and validated, an analysis must be conducted to produce useful results. Care should be taken to select the most appropriate evaluation method given the characteristics of the data set. It is recommended that the designer first examine data qualitatively, via, for example, a scatter plot or standard parallel probability plot. Doing so will help to characterize the data set and will also allow one to determine if influent and effluent values are statistically different from one another.

Appropriate statistical methods can then be applied to determine the statistical significance of differences in influent and effluent parameter values. As mentioned, nine of 10 methods reviewed by the U.S. EPA study team were unable to produce a comprehensive analysis of control performance. In this section, several alternative statistical tools are presented along with guidelines for their applicability. In addition, qualitative methods for control performance data evaluation are presented, including EPM recommended by U.S. EPA.

5.1 Qualitative Methods

In addition to quantitative methods for control performance analysis, useful qualitative evaluation techniques also exist. For example, both scatter plots are graphic displays that can be used to provide an initial overview of a data set, while probability plots allow for a more detailed evaluation. Alternatively, qualitative tools such as box-and-whisker plots can be used to summarize the statistical characterization achieved by the application of quantitative methods. Each of these qualitative tools is described in further detail in this section.

5.1.1 Scatter Plot

A scatter plot is a basic tool that can summarize the relationship between two variables. This diagram consists of a collection of data points plotted on a Cartesian coordinate system. Each point contains X–Y data that are paired values from two variables. The independent variable is typically plotted on the horizontal axis, and the dependent variable, if any, on the vertical axis. A sample scatter plot is shown in Figure 13.1. If neither variable is dependent, the scatter plot reveals correlation between the two variables, but not causation. Using an example can help in understanding the difference between cause and correlation. As the implementation of land treatment (such as implementation of controls) occurs in a watershed, improvements in water quality are observed. However, an association between control

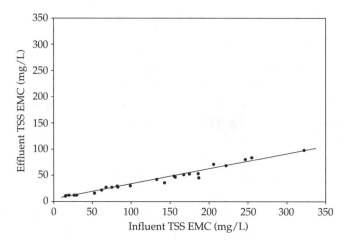

FIGURE 13.1   Sample scatter plot.

implementation and water quality improvements by itself is not sufficient to infer a cause-and-effect relationship. Other factors that are not related to control implementation may be causing the changes in water quality, such as changes in land use or rainfall. If, however, the association is consistent and responsive and has a mechanistic basis, it may be inferred as a cause-and-effect relationship.

Scatter plots allow one to describe the nature of the correlation between two variables as linear, nonlinear, or null. If the correlation is linear, the relationship can further be described as positive or negative. The visual display can be enhanced by generating a best-fit line and determining the regression equation that describes that line. If the best-fit line is a horizontal line, the relationship is null.

With respect to controls, scatter plots can be essential to determining whether or not the data have a linear relationship. In addition, scatter plots are particularly useful for evaluating data quality. Points that appear to fall far from the best-fit line are potential outliers. It should be noted that the scatter plot will show only one point for each unique X–Y pair. If the data set contains multiple identical pairs, there will be fewer data points than pairs of raw scores.

5.1.2   *Box-and-Whisker Plot*

Box-and-whisker plots (also known as box plots, candlestick charts, etc.) are often used to provide a graphical summary of the statistical characteristics of a data set. However, use of box-and-whisker plots does not require any assumptions on the statistical distribution of the data set of interest. Although these diagrams may not convey all of the information necessary to evaluate control performance, they are useful for a basic understanding of control behavior. A sample box-and-whisker plot is shown in Figure 13.2.

The various components of the box-and-whisker plot represent different statistics and, when observed together, can depict more general characteristics of the data set. For example, the box-and-whisker plot indicates the range of values in a data set via "whiskers," which represent minimum and maximum values. Similarly, the spread (also known as dispersion) of the data is depicted by the box, the ends of which represent the first and third quartiles. The mean or median of the data set is typically represented by a line within the box, as shown in Figure 13.2.

The box plot diagram can also provide a visual indication of variance, skewness, and potential outliers. For example, as a rule of thumb, equal variance can be assumed if the box length for each group is less than 3 times the length of the shortest box. The difference between box lengths in Figure 13.2 indicates these two data sets do not have equal variance.

5.1.3 Effluent Probability Method

The EPM evaluates control performance by providing a visual comparison of influent and effluent water quality. In this method, pollutant concentrations are plotted on probability plots such that probability curves are produced for parameters of interest (e.g., suspended solids, dissolved solids, chemical oxygen demand, etc.). The EPM

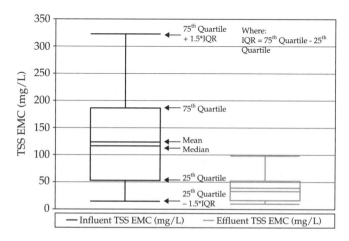

FIGURE 13.2 Sample box-and-whisker plot.

plots include influent and effluent EMC data for all storms, and EMP curves are typically plotted on a standard parallel probability plot (see Figure 13.3). If data are not typically distributed (see Section 5.2.1, "Normal Distribution and Normality Tests"), they should be log-transformed, although other transforms should be explored if this transformation does not produce a normal distribution. The designer should keep in mind that normal distribution is indicated by a straight line on normal probability paper, and that two data sets have equal variances when they have parallel plots on probability paper. It should be emphasized that the EPM does not compare corresponding pairs of influent and effluent data for individual storms.

By comparing the concentrations of various pollutants in the influent and effluent side by side, pollutant reduction can be determined visually. In particular, EPM curves reveal the range of influent concentrations, if any, over which a particular control is most effective. This is a distinct advantage over the percent removal approach. In fact, U.S. EPA (2002c) recommends the EPM method of control evaluation above all others, and suggests that "curves of this type are the single most instructive piece of information that can result from a BMP evaluation study" (U.S. EPA, 2002c). The manual goes so far as to recommend the EPM approach as an industry standard rating curve for stormwater control evaluation.

Many agencies "approve" stormwater controls based on their performance so that they can be used in land development projects. To support this function, a procedure needs to be defined to define an acceptable level of performance. Especially

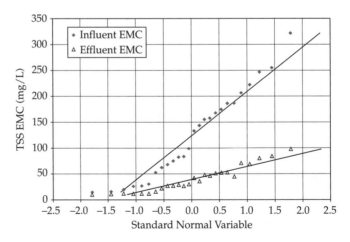

FIGURE 13.3 Sample probability plot.

for manufactured treatment devices, using the EPM alone leads to ambiguous determination of meeting a predefined metric. While an excellent tool for a researcher to reach a conclusion about the degree of effectiveness, for approval process, the EPM alone does not provide all that is needed.

5.2 Quantitative Methods

Application of statistical methods to control performance data can prove to be difficult because these data sets tend to be highly variable with a low population, and they are rarely normally distributed (Lenhart, 2007a). Nevertheless, several basic statistical tools can be applied to generate useful information, including the following:

- Descriptive statistics of influent and effluent EMCs
  - Mean, median, standard deviation and the coefficient of variation and
  - Determined for both arithmetic and log-transformed data sets;
- Percentiles for influent and effluent EMCs
  - Cumulative distribution functions (CDFs) and
  - Probability plots;
- Percent difference in influent and effluent percentiles (10th and 90th);
- Confidence interval about the mean and median EMC values
  - Useful for estimating the minimum and maximum possible removal efficiency; and
- Parametric and nonparametric analyses of variance.

Many of these statistics require simple, straightforward calculations. However, a more detailed explanation of the difference between influent and effluent flow requires application of more advanced procedures including regression and analysis of variance (ANOVA). Both of these methods are described here.

The designer should keep in mind that, in some instances, a data set may need to be transformed before application of statistical methods. The Nationwide Urban Runoff Program (NURP) evaluated 2300 stormwater events between 1978 and 1982, concluding that EMCs of stormwater pollutants are best described by lognormal distributions. However, more recent data indicate that the lognormal distribution does not accurately describe all stormwater constituents (Behera et al., 2000; Van Buren et al., 1997).

An ANOVA is a method for assigning portions of the observed variance in a data set to different explanatory variables. Analysis of variance is closely related to regression, but is used to detect differences in the average values of dependent variables. Analysis of variance methods can be categorized as either parametric or nonparametric, and both parametric and nonparametric ANOVA statistical methods can be used to evaluate control performance data sets. Although parametric techniques are favored, these techniques can only be applied when certain conditions are met. To determine which type can be applied most effectively, the data set must be tested for the following characteristics: normality, equal variance, and independence. Application of most parametric tests assumes that these conditions are true. Many methods exist for testing these assumptions, and several are described in this section.

5.2.1 Normal Distribution and Normality Tests

Whether or not a data set is normally distributed will affect selection of statistical methods that can be applied. Normal distribution, also known as the Gaussian distribution, is a continuous probability distribution in which the middle score has the highest frequency, while the highest and lowest scores have low frequencies. As a result, the probability density curve of normally distributed data is symmetrical and closely resembles a bell (it is often called a "bell curve"). A particular distribution is defined by the mean, μ, and variance, σ^2, of the data set (e.g., the "standard" normal distribution is the distribution with a mean of zero and a variance of one). Multiple statistical tests are dependent on the assumption of normality.

There are several normality tests that can be applied to a data set to determine whether or not a random variable is normally distributed, including the Kolmogorov–Smirnov (K–S), Chi-squared, Shapiro–Wilk, and Anderson–Darling tests. Also known as *goodness-of-fit tests*, these methods generate a statistic that can be compared to a critical statistic, which is a function of the sample size and desired level of significance. These tests are discussed in more detail later in this section.

Alternatively, for some tests, a P value is generated. The P value reveals the probability that a randomly selected sample from a normally distributed population will deviate from the normal distribution as much as or more than a random sample from the data set in question. If the P value is small, typically less than 0.05, then the null hypothesis (normality) is rejected and one can conclude that the data set is not normally distributed.

5.2.1.1 Probability Plot

As an alternative to formal normality tests, a probability plot can be used to visually evaluate the data set for characteristics of normality. Probability plots are presented on special probability paper where the top horizontal axis depicts the nonexceedance probability, while the bottom horizontal axis shows the exceedance probability (i.e., the probability that the value will be exceeded). In addition, the horizontal axis is scaled according to the distribution of interest. The ordinate scale on a normal probability plot is stretched at both ends. As a result, data with a normal cumulative distribution will plot as a straight line. A sample normal probability plot is shown in Figure 13.4.

To evaluate the observed data, each data value must be assigned a "plotting position." Assuming that successive values are independent, the data are rank-ordered from largest to smallest and the exceedance probability for each value is calculated using one of several formulas. The most commonly used formula in water resources analysis is the Weibull formula, given by

$$\frac{m}{n+1}$$

The data are then plotted according to resulting positions. The set is normally distributed if the plot produces a relatively straight line. In addition, the mean of the data set can be determined as the value corresponding to the 50th percentile. The standard deviation can be estimated as the difference between the 50th- and 84th-percentile values or, similarly, the difference between the 16th- and 50th-percentile values.

If the data do not appear to be normally distributed (i.e., they do not plot as a straight line), potential transformations should be explored. For example, evidence

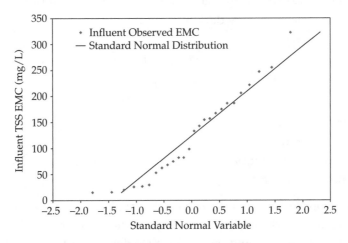

Figure 13.4 Normal probability plot (created using data from Ridder et al. [2002]).

indicates that water quality data are often log-normally distributed between the 10th and 90th percentiles. Log-normal probability paper exists that is identical to normal probability paper, except that it features a logarithmic scale rather than an arithmetic scale. A log-normal data set will plot as a straight line on log-normal probability paper. Other common transformation operations include taking the square root, square, or inverse of the original data values.

Although somewhat subjective, probability plots can prove useful in evaluating normality, particularly for small sample sizes. When the data appear to be normally distributed, probability plots should be supplemented with formal statistical tests. Several of these tests are presented here. In addition to detecting normality and determining useful statistics like the mean and standard deviation, probability plots can be used to observe abnormalities in variance and outliers in the data set.

5.2.1.2 Chi-Square (χ^2) Test

The chi-square test for goodness-of-fit, sometimes known as *Pearson's chi-square test*, can be applied to data sets with a relatively large sample size. This method tests the null hypothesis that the frequency of observed events follows a given frequency distribution, and, in this instance, the normal distribution.

To apply the test, the observed data must first be separated into distinct, non-overlapping intervals, similar to the bins of a histogram. Although not required, each interval typically has the same range. The numadata points that would lie in each interval if the data set were normally distributed (i.e., the expected frequency value) can then be calculated for each interval based on the mean, standard deviation, and sample size, n, of the data set. The chi-square statistic, χ^2, is then given by eq 13.1, as follows:

$$\chi^2 = \sum_{i=1}^{k} \frac{(O_i - E_i)^2}{E_i} \tag{13.1}$$

where

    i = a particular interval;
    O_i = the observed frequency;
    E_i = the expected frequency assuming a normal distribution; and
    k = the number of intervals.

The null hypothesis is rejected if the calculated chi-square is greater than the critical chi-square, χ_c^2, which is provided in published reference tables as a function of desired significance level and the appropriate degrees of freedom. A significance level of 5% ($\alpha = 0.05$) is typically used. The number of degrees of freedom is equal to

k-1-p, where p is the number of independently estimated parameters. In this instance, two parameters were estimated, the mean and standard deviation, so $p = 2$. When χ^2 exceeds χ_c^2, the null hypothesis is rejected, indicating that the frequency distributions are not the same and the observed data are not normally distributed.

The chi-square test is not particularly sensitive or powerful relative to other goodness-of-fit tests. The test performs best with relatively large data sets and, in particular, when there are more than five observations in each interval.

5.2.1.3 Kolmogorov–Smirnov Test

The K–S test is a goodness-of-fit test used to determine whether a data set of interest has a particular, specified distribution. When used as a normality test, the proposed null hypothesis is that the observed data set is normally distributed. Deviations between the theoretical (in this instance, normal) cumulative distribution function, $F(x)$, and the observed cumulative distribution are given as eq 13.2, as follows:

$$F^*(x^i) = i/n \tag{13.2}$$

where x^i is the ith largest observed value in the random sample of size n. The K–S statistic, D, quantifies the discrepancy between the two cumulative distributions as eq 13.3, as follows:

$$D = \max_{i=1,n} \left| F^*(x^i) - F(x^i) \right| \tag{13.3}$$

The K–S statistic, D, is then the maximum absolute difference between the normal and observed cumulative probability distributions. Application of the K–S goodness-of-fit test is concluded by comparing the calculated value, D, to the critical statistic, $d_{n,\alpha}$ (see Figure 13.5). The latter can be referenced in various publications as a function of the sample size and level of significance. The null hypothesis is rejected if D is greater than d, indicating that the observed data set does not have a normal distribution.

The K–S test should only be applied to data sets with a sample size of 50 or more. The K–S test tends to be more sensitive near the center of the distribution than at the tails. However, the K–S test is more efficient than the chi-square test for small samples. The Shapiro–Wilk and Anderson–Darling tests are considered more powerful normality tests.

5.2.1.4 Shapiro–Wilk Test

The Shapiro–Wilk test was first published in 1965 for the purpose of determining whether or not a sample comes from a normal distribution, as is posed by the null

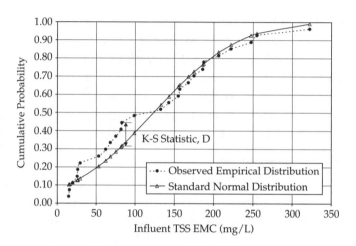

FIGURE 13.5 Kolmogorov–Smirnov test.

hypothesis. To apply the Shapiro–Wilk test, sample data should first be ordered, smallest to largest. Next, a weighted sum of the differences between the most extreme observations should be calculated as eq 13.4, as follows:

$$b = \sum_{i=1}^{k} a_{n-i+1}(x_{n-i+1} - x_{(i)}) = \sum_{i=1}^{k} b_i \tag{13.4}$$

where

$x_{(i)}$ = the ith smallest number in the sample and

k = the greatest integer less than or equal to $n/2$.

The constant a_i can be referenced in various statistics texts including *Statistical Procedures for Analysis of Environmental Monitoring Data and Risk Assessment* (McBean and Rovers, 1998), as a function of the sample size, n. The test statistic, W, is then given by eq 13.5, as follows:

$$W = \left\{ \frac{b}{S\sqrt{n-1}} \right\}^2 \tag{13.5}$$

The null hypothesis is rejected if the value of W is less than the critical statistic, W_c, indicating that the observed data set is not normally distributed. The critical statistic, W_c, is given by reference tables for the appropriate sample size, n, and desired significance level.

The Shapiro–Wilk goodness-of-fit test is a highly regarded normality test. It performs particularly well on small sample sizes and is recognized for its ability to effectively evaluate the tails or ends of a sample distribution.

5.2.1.5 Anderson–Darling Test

The Anderson–Darling test is a particularly powerful normality test as it can be applied to small sample sizes ($n \leq 25$). However, the test may fail with large sample sizes. The Anderson–Darling test determines whether a sample comes from a particular distribution, in this instance, a normal distribution. It is known as an empirical distribution function (EDF) test (i.e., a distance test) and the A^2 statistic is one of the most powerful EDF tools for detecting departures from normality. The test requires that the mean and standard deviation of the sample be calculated, and that the sample values be sorted from high to low. The sample values, X_i, are then standardized, Y_i, as eq 13.6, as follows:

$$Y_i = \frac{X_i - \overline{X}}{s} \tag{13.6}$$

A^2 is then calculated as eq 13.7, as follows:

$$A^2 = -n - \frac{1}{n} \sum_{i=1}^{n} (2i-1) \left\{ \ln\left[\Phi\left(Y_i\right)\right] + \ln\left[1 - \Phi\left(Y_{n+1-i}\right)\right] \right\} \tag{13.7}$$

where Φ is the standard normal CDF of the data set. An adjustment for sample size can then be applied as eq 13.8, as follows:

$$A^{2*} = A^2 \left(1 + \frac{0.75}{n} + \frac{2.25}{n^2} \right) \tag{13.8}$$

The normality hypothesis is rejected at the 5% level if A^{2*} is greater than 0.752.

5.2.2 Equality of Variance

Another assumption necessary for the application of parametric methods is equality of variance, also known as *homoscedasticity*. This condition is satisfied when the variances (i.e., the square of the deviation from the mean or, more commonly, the square of the standard deviation) are equal across samples. This condition can be tested by the F test, Bartlett's test, or Levene's test. In addition, a box plot can be used to determine qualitatively whether or not variances are equal.

5.2.2.1 F Test

An *F* test is used to determine whether two samples have different variances. The *F* statistic is calculated as eq 13.9, as follows

$$Fstatistic = \frac{s_1^2}{s_2^2}$$

(13.9)

where s_1^2 and s_2^2 are the sample variances for samples 1 and 2, respectively. It is important to note that $s_1^2 > s_2^2$. The more this ratio deviates from 1, the stronger the evidence for unequal population variances. The hypothesis that the two standard deviations are equal is rejected if the calculated *F* statistic is larger than $F(\alpha/2, df_1, df_2)$, in which α is the significance level and df_1, and df_2 are the degrees of freedom for sample 1 and sample 2, respectively.

5.2.2.2 Bartlett's Test

Bartlett's test is used to determine whether or not a group of samples have equal variances. It assumes that the data set is normally distributed, and it is particularly sensitive to non-normality. It may also reject equality of variances if the data set has a long-tailed distribution.

Given *k* groups with n_i data points for the ith group, the sample variances for each group are given by eq 13.10, as follows:

$$S_i^2 = \frac{\sum_{j=1}^{n_i} \left(x_{ij} - \bar{x}_i \right)^2}{n_i - 1}$$

(13.10)

For each variance, the number of degrees of freedom is given by $f_i = n_i - 1$. The value, *f*, can be calculated as the total sample size minus the number of groups, as seen in eq 13.11, as follows:

$$f = \sum_{i=1}^{k} f_i = \left(\sum_{i=1}^{k} n_i \right) - k$$

(13.11)

The weighted variance across all groups (i.e., the pooled variance), S_P^2, is given by eq 13.12, as follows:

$$S_P^2 = \frac{1}{f} \sum_{i=1}^{k} f_i S_i^2$$

(13.12)

The test statistic, χ^2, is then given by eq 13.13, as follows:

$$\chi^2 = f \ln\left(S_p^{\,2}\right) = \sum_{i=1}^{k} f_i \ln(S_i^2) \qquad (13.13)$$

The calculated chi-square statistic can then be compared to the critical chi-square value of $\chi_c^{\,2}$, with $k - 1$ deg of freedom and the desired significance level, as provided by a reference table. The null hypothesis is rejected if the statistic is greater than the critical value, and the variances are taken to be unequal at the specified level of significance.

5.2.2.3 Levene's Test

Unlike Bartlett's test, Levene's test is not sensitive to non-normality. The absolute values of the data set residuals can be calculated by eq 13.14, as follows:

$$Z_{ij} = \left| x_{ij} - \overline{x_i} \right| \qquad (13.14)$$

where
  x_{ij} = the jth value of the ith group; and
  $\overline{x_i}$ = the mean of the ith group.

A one-way ANOVA is then applied to the Z_{ij} values. An ANOVA is a method for assigning portions of the observed variance in a data set to different explanatory variables. The ANOVA method is discussed in further detail in Section 5.3.

The null hypothesis that the standard deviation of the observed data set is equal to that of a normally distributed data set is rejected if the F test is significant, that is, if the calculated F statistic exceeds the critical value of F.

5.3 Parametric Analysis of Variance

The parametric ANOVA is generally preferred over nonparametric analyses. However, its application is limited to data sets that are characterized by normality and equal variances. This method is based on various parameters that are functions of the mean, standard deviation and sample size of the two data sets being compared. When more than two data sets are evaluated (e.g., to compare the performance of multiple controls), the data produced in a one-way ANOVA can be summarized in a table of the format shown in Table 13.3.

A parametric ANOVA analysis is typically completed with an F test (discussed previously). The null hypothesis is rejected if the F test is significant, that is, if the

TABLE 13.3   Analysis of variance summary.

Source of variation	Sum of squares (SS)	Degrees of freedom	Mean squares (MS)	F
Regression (between groups)	$\sum (\overline{x_i} - \overline{x})^2$	P-1	$\dfrac{SS_{between}}{(P-1)}$	$F = \dfrac{Ms_{between}}{MS_{within}}$
Residual (within groups)	$\sum \sum (\overline{x_i} - \overline{x})^2$	N-P	$\dfrac{SS_{within}}{(N-P)}$	
Total	$\sum_{i=1}^{p} \sum_{j=1}^{n_i} (x_{ij} - \overline{x})^2$	N-1		

calculated F statistic exceeds the critical value of F. The nonparametric complement to the parametric ANOVA of multiple data sets is the Kruskal–Wallis H test, which is discussed in Section 5.4.2.

5.3.1   Regression Analysis

A regression analysis is typically used to evaluate data trends and can help determine the degree to which a dependent variable relies on an independent variable. For the special case of control performance assessment, regression analysis can reveal the extent to which effluent concentrations are dependent on influent concentrations, or some alternative driver. In this method, paired influent and effluent data are evaluated to produce a linear relationship for each control type. Barrett (2004) proposed a regression methodology specifically for application to control performance analysis. In this method, a linear regression analysis is performed and then tested for statistical significance using the t statistic. The results of the regression are then used to calibrate the coefficients of a predictive linear equation that describes the relationship between effluent EMCs and the independent variable of interest.

The strength of the linear relationship between two variables is quantified in the sample estimate of the correlation coefficient, r. This is a unitless factor that can range in value from -1.0 to 1.0, where values from -1.0 to 0.0 represent a negative relationship and values from 0.0 to 1.0 represent a positive relationship. Larger absolute values of r indicate a stronger degree of linear relationship. The correlation coefficient, r, can be calculated as eq 13.15, as follows:

$$r = \frac{\sum\limits_{i=1}^{n}\left(x_i - \bar{x}\right)\left(y_i - \bar{y}\right)}{\left[\sum\left(x_i - \bar{x}\right)^2\right]^{\frac{1}{2}}\left[\sum\left(y_i - \bar{y}\right)^2\right]^{\frac{1}{2}}} \tag{13.15}$$

Once the linear regression analysis is complete, the results are tested for statistical significance. Assuming normal distribution, the correlation coefficient, r, can be used to produce a t statistic as eq 13.16, as follows:

$$t^* = r\frac{\sqrt{n-2}}{\sqrt{1-r^2}} \tag{13.16}$$

The calculated statistic can then be compared to the critical value, t_c, as given by the reference for tables for n - 2 deg of freedom and the desired level of significance. If t^* is greater than t_c, the null hypothesis that the degree of linear relationship between the influent and effluent concentrations is significant (as given by the correlation coefficient, r) is rejected. According to Barrett (2004), if the linear relationship is not statistically significant at the 90% confidence level, then effluent quality should be considered a constant value.

A linear equation that describes the relationship between the dependent variable (typically effluent concentration), y, and independent variable (typically influent concentration), x, can be developed in the form, $y = a + bx$, where

$$b = \frac{\sum\left(x_i - \bar{x}\right)\left(y_i - \bar{y}\right)}{\sum\left(x_i - \bar{x}\right)^2} = \frac{S_{xy}}{S_{xx}} \text{ and } a = \bar{y} - b\bar{x}.$$

Given influent quality and control type, effluent quality can then be predicted from the following relationship in eq 13.17, as follows:

$$C_{eff} = aC_{inf} + b \tag{13.17}$$

where
   C_{eff} = predicted effluent EMC;
   C_{inf} = influent EMC;
      a = slope of the regression line; and
      b = y-intercept.

In some instances, b is representative of the irreducible concentration, as introduced by Schueler (1996). As the influent concentration approaches zero, the effluent concentration approaches b. This is representative of observed physical behavior in which low influent concentrations lead to either a marginal reduction (i.e., a lower percent reduction than observed when given higher influent concentrations) or an increased concentration in effluent flows, as described by Minton (2011). Similarly, the often used percent removal technique is captured in the term $(1 - a)$. This generalization holds for large influent concentrations, where $C_{inf} \cong aC_{eff}$.

The uncertainty in the average predicted effluent concentration (i.e., the control performance over many storms for a given influent concentration) is calculated according to

$$\pm t_{0.05} s \sqrt{\frac{1}{n} + \frac{\left(X - \overline{X}\right)^2}{\sum_{i=1}^{n}\left(X_i - \overline{X}\right)^2}} \tag{13.18}$$

Where

t = the value of the t statistic for the appropriate degrees of freedom $(n - 2)$;
s = standard error of the regression;
n = the number of paired data points;
X = average influent EMC at which the confidence interval is calculated;
$\overline{X}$ = the mean of observed influent EMCs from monitoring data; and
X_i = the individual observed influent EMCs from monitoring data.

When added to and subtracted from the values that compose the linear regression line, the result of this calculation provides confidence limits for the regression line. The "true" effluent EMC will lie within the bounds of the upper and lower limit with 90% certainty.

Similarly, the uncertainty associated with predicting the effluent concentration associated with a single storm event is given as eq 13.19, as follows:

$$\pm t_{0.05} s \sqrt{1 + \frac{1}{n} + \frac{\left(X - \overline{X}\right)^2}{\sum_{i=1}^{n}\left(X_i - \overline{X}\right)^2}} \tag{13.19}$$

The parameters of a linear regression line are not dependent on the distribution of paired influent and effluent data, so no transformation is required prior to application. However, to generate useful confidence intervals for the predicted and average observed data, the residuals resulting from the regression must be normally distributed and random. Outliers should be evaluated for their effect on the regression analysis. Outliers that strongly skew the results should be considered for removal. In addition, when applying Barrett's linear regression method, the designer should keep in mind that the regression analysis will more heavily weight paired values with high concentrations than other data.

Also keep in mind that load reductions can be determined from water quality data and volume reduction as Equation 13.20:

$$L_r = 1 - \left[\frac{C_{eff}}{C_{inf}} (1-I) \right] \tag{13.20}$$

where L_r is the load reduction and I is the fraction of runoff lost to infiltration and evapotranspiration in the control (Barrett, 2004).

5.3.2 T Test

The t test is a parametric statistic and perhaps one of the simplest analyses. Prior to applying the t test, the designer should verify that data do not violate any of the following assumptions underlying the test:

- Test data represent a random sample from the population under study;
- Distribution of the mean of the sample is normal based on one or more of the analyses described in Section 5.2.1; and
- The variances of the different groups studied are similar.

If data violate one or more of these assumptions, a Type I error (i.e., false positive) may be being committed more or less often than the alpha probability that is being set (either .01 or .05). This bias may undermine the value of the t test, and therefore, the study results.

Paired sample t tests compare means where the two groups are correlated, as in before–after, repeated measures, matched-pairs, or case-control studies. The procedure applied to the data is different from the independent sample t test, but interpretation of output is otherwise the same.

Considering a random sample of n pairs, $(x_1, y_1), (x_2, y_2), (x_3, y_3), \ldots\ldots, (x_n, y_n)$, the paired-sample t test is conducted using the following steps:

- Calculate the differences, $d_i = (x_i - y_i)$;
- Determine mean and variance of d_i, $\bar{d}$, and S^2;

- Test the null hypothesis that the mean of $\bar{d} = 0$ by calculating the following statistic, which follows a T distribution with $n - 1$ deg of freedom if the null hypothesis is true for eq 13.21, as follows:

$$t = \frac{\bar{d} - 0}{S / \sqrt{n}} \qquad (13.21)$$

Compare to the critical t statistic if $n < 30$ or the z statistic if $n \geq 30$, where critical t statistic or z statistic are tabular values that define the region of acceptance and the region of rejection for the null hypothesis.

5.4   Nonparametric Methods

Parametric methods cannot be applied when the assumptions of normality and equal variances do not hold. In contrast, nonparametric tests make no assumptions about the distribution of the data set and pendent samples from continuous populations. Nonparametric methods differ in that they evaluate the ranks of data instead of actual data values. For a given data set, nonparametric analysis of rank is a direct parallel to a parametric analysis of values. However, nonparametric methods use only a portion of available information, and they are generally less efficient than their parametric equivalents. Nevertheless, nonparametric tests require less difficult calculations and are just as powerful, if not more so, as parametric tests.

5.4.1   Wilcoxon Matched Pairs Test

The Wilcoxon paired-sample test is the nonparametric equivalent of the paired-sample t test. As mentioned earlier, the paired t test relies on the assumption that the mean of the difference between observations is normally distributed. The Wilcoxon paired-sample test is applicable whenever the paired-sample t test is applicable, but especially when it cannot be assumed that the differences are from a normal distribution.

This test uses the differences between the pairs of measurements, just like the paired t test. Again, the actual differences are replaced by ranks. Then, the sum of the ranks of the positive differences is compared to the sum for the negative differences. If the null hypothesis were true, these two sums would be approximately equal. To decide if there is a large enough difference between the two sums, a value of the Wilcoxon T statistic is calculated and a table is used to find the critical value. Considering a random sample of n pairs, $(x_1, y_1), (x_2, y_2), (x_3, y_3), \ldots \ldots, (x_n, y_n)$, the Wilcoxon paired-sample test is conducted using the following steps:

- Calculate the differences as $d_i = (x_i - y_i)$;
- Rank them from smallest to largest by absolute values, that is, $|d_i|$;
- Add all the ranks associated with positive differences, giving the T^+ statistic;
- Add all the ranks associated with negative differences, giving the T^- statistic;
- Determine the Wilcoxon T statistic = min (T^+, T^-); and
- Compare to the critical value of T, T_c.

Application of the Wilcoxon paired-sample test is demonstrated in examples 1 through 3 presented in Section 10.0.

When the number of nonzero differences is large, say over 30, we can use a normal approximation to the Wilcoxon T statistic. The formulae for the mean (μ) and variance (σ^2) of the T statistic, when the null hypothesis of zero difference is true, are as follows:

$$\mu = \frac{n(n+1)}{4}, \quad \text{and} \tag{13.22}$$

$$\sigma^2 = \frac{n(n+1)(2n+1)}{24} \tag{13.23}$$

The test statistic (z) is given as follows:

$$z = \frac{T - \mu}{\sigma} \tag{13.24}$$

This statistic can be used to determine the corresponding p value using the standardized normal distribution.

5.4.2 Kruskal–Wallis H Test

The Kruskal–Wallis test is a nonparametric equivalent to the one-way ANOVA test and is an extension of the U test. As a multiple-comparison procedure, it can be applied to three or more groups. This test evaluates whether or not k independent samples come from the same continuous distribution by comparing their means. The H test does not depend on any assumptions regarding data set distribution, and it is readily applied when data or residuals are significantly different from normal. Application of the Kruskal–Wallis test requires there be at least three groups with at least three observations (i.e., a minimum sample size of three) in each group.

To apply the Kruskal–Wallis H test, the entire data set (all values in all groups) is ranked from lowest to highest. For each group, R_{ij} is the rank of the jth observation in the ith group. Then, the sum of the ranks for each group is calculated in addition to the average rank within each group. The average rank for each group is $\overline{R}_i = R_i / n_i$, where R_i is the sum of ranks for the ith group. The average rank of the overall data set is then determined, and the H statistic is then given by eq 13.25, as follows:

$$H = \frac{12}{N(N+1)}\left[\frac{R_1^2}{n_1} + \frac{R_2^2}{n^2} + ... + \frac{R_k^2}{n_k}\right] - 3(N+1) \tag{13.25}$$

where n_i is the number of observations in each group. When the sample size, n, is greater than 5 for all groups and the null hypothesis holds, the H statistic can be approximated by the chi-square distribution. As such, the null hypothesis that the sample means are equivalent is rejected if H is greater than the critical chi-square value, χ^2, given $k - 1$ deg of freedom. Additional steps can then be take to determine which of the groups differs significantly from the theoretical or control group.

5.4.3   Performance Expectation Functions

Performance expectation functions offer a simplified approach to evaluation of stormwater controls against predefined expectations, typically from a regulatory agency (Lenhart, 2007b). This methodology is useful in evaluating stormwater controls for agency "approval" as accepted devices.

An agency may issue minimum requirements in terms of effluent concentrations, percent removal, load reductions, or a combination of all. An example is requiring a constant maximum effluent concentration for influent concentrations below a given threshold and a percent removal for greater influent concentrations. This set of criteria recognizes that stormwater controls often yield a constant effluent concentration up to some influent concentration, after which the effluent concentration increases with the influent concentration. By using percent removal, the agency is implicitly stating that the increase is linear. Figure 13.6 shows an example of PEFs corresponding to criteria that require an effluent concentration of 20 mg/L for influent concentrations up to 100 mg/L and an 80% removal for greater influent concentrations.

The nonparametric sign test or the Wilcoxon Matched Pairs Test can be used with PEFs to determine whether the difference between actual and expected performance are significant. A negative difference between actual and expected effluent concentrations means that the control is overperforming and vice versa. For the sign test, the null hypothesis is that, in a pair of actual and expected performances, one is equally likely to be larger than the other; that is, the probability of actual concentration being greater than the expected concentration is 0.5. To test the hypothesis, the signs of the

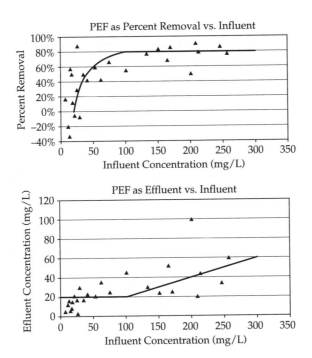

FIGURE 13.6 Examples of a PEF expressed in terms of percent removal and effluent concentration (Lenhart, 2007b).

concentration differences are evaluated. Zero-concentration differences are excluded. The number of pairs with a positive difference follows a binomial distribution and the binomial test is used to calculate significance. Two alternative hypotheses are tested: that the probability of overperforming is greater than 0.5 or less than 0.5. If the sample is large, the binomial distribution can be approximated by a normal distribution (Siegel, 1956).

6.0 DATA AND INFORMATIONAL NEEDS

The data or informational needs required to assess the performance of a given storm-water control are derived from the goals, objectives, criteria or metrics, and assessment methods discussed in Sections 4.0 and 5.0. Because there are a wide variety of data and information that can be used to assess the performance of a control, the goals, objectives, criteria or metrics, and assessment methods should be well-defined and site-specific as possible to hone in on an appropriate set of needs (U.S. EPA, 2004). Broad or vaguely defined objectives can often lead to identifying a large number of parameters or information that, in turn, can be expensive and time-consuming to compile without providing any real insight to the performance of the control.

This section reviews the considerations and process for identifying data and informational needs. Considerations include types of data and information typically included in assessing stormwater control performance. The process of identifying data and information needs includes selecting key parameters of interests, establishing data quality objectives and minimum amount of data, compiling existing data, and defining gaps in required data and information.

6.1 Types of Parameters

Parameters associated with assessing stormwater control performance have been divided into six general categories. They include (1) hydrological and hydraulic, (2) chemical, (3) physical (4), biological, (5) qualitative, and (6) other relevant factors. U.S. EPA (2004), in *The Use of Best Management Practices (BMPs) in Urban Watersheds*, provides a detailed discussion of all categories except qualitative parameters. Each category is summarized in this section.

6.1.1 *Hydrologic and Hydraulic*

Hydrologic and hydraulic parameters are key components of assessing the performance of stormwater controls because controls are either commonly designed to mitigate the effects of stormwater runoff or the level of water quality treatment is affected by flows passing through. Hydrologic and hydraulic parameters associated with stormwater controls include precipitation (volume, intensity, duration, type, and antecedent conditions) and flow (type, volume, flowrate, level, velocity, and duration). Additional parameters include bypass or overflow volumes, infiltration, groundwater inflows, dry weather flows, and evaporation. Flow measurements are required for some water quality sampling and to generate loads. The U.S. Geological Survey report, *Basic Requirements for Collecting, Documenting, and Reporting Precipitation and Stormwater—Flow Measurements*, prepared by Church et al. (1999), is another guidance source on collecting hydrologic and hydraulic data associated with stormwater.

6.1.2 *Chemical*

Chemical parameters commonly associated with stormwater controls include pH, conductivity, dissolved oxygen, salinity, organic carbon, hardness, suspended solids, nutrients (total and dissolved), and, to a lesser extent, minerals, pesticides and herbicides, oil and grease, polycyclic aromatic hydrocarbons, and organics (volatiles and semivolatiles). Chemical parameters are expressed as concentrations or loads when multiplied with flow data. They provide specific information about the water quality passing through stormwater controls. Comparing inflow levels to outflow levels is a common assessment to evaluate control performance. Effects on receiving waters can also be identified.

Chemical levels in stormwater are highly variable during an individual event, from event to event, and from different locations. Generating a representative characterization often requires a series of samples collected over the course of an individual event, from a series of events, and, perhaps, from different locations (U.S. EPA, 2002c). Cumulative or chronic effects caused by low levels are not readily observed when monitoring chemical parameters alone and, perhaps, from two or more locations. When reviewing chemical data, it is important to understand the analytical procedures, standard instrumental error, and issues surrounding subsampling error and hold times.

6.1.3   Physical

Physical parameters most commonly associated with stormwater controls are turbidity and temperature. Both these parameters can be applied similarly to chemical parameters for assessing the performance of a stormwater control.

Particle-size distribution, settling velocity distribution, and accumulated sediments are physical parameters associated with stormwater controls designed to remove sediment. Gross solids, such as litter, trash, and other debris, represent a parameter that can be applied, especially when improvement in aesthetic quality is a goal. Physical changes to the receiving water channel caused by stormwater such as streambank erosion and channel down-cutting are considered physical parameters that can be applied to assess performance. U.S. EPA's *Rapid Bioassessment Protocols for Use in Streams and Wadeable Rivers: Periphyton, Benthic Macroinvertebrates and Fish* has a physical habitat assessment component that includes streambank and channel changes to the receiving water channel over time (U.S. EPA, 1999b).

6.1.4   Biological

Biological parameters can be divided into the following two groups: organisms associated with pollution and ecological effects on receiving waters. Organisms associated with pollution include bacteria, viruses, and pathogens. Typically, indicator organisms of total coliform; fecal coliform; *Escherichia coli;* and, to a lesser extent, *Enterococcus* are applied because they are included in most National Pollutant Discharge Elimination

System (NPDES) permits and state water standards for public health. Results can be applied similar to chemical parameters for assessing the performance of a stormwater control or evaluating downstream effects.

Parameters associated with ecological effects on receiving waters include toxicity testing of the stormwater control effluent and instream indices. Toxicity results of influent and effluent can be compared to assess performance or effluent results can be assessed alone. Toxicity testing involves monitoring mortality rates, growth rates, and other changes in behavior or overall health of sample test species (U.S. EPA, 2002).

Instream indices typically involve assessment of one or more of the biota communities that include fish, invertebrates, and/or plants (U.S. EPA, 2002a). They are most often applied to assess stormwater management programs being conducted on a watershed basis. Performances of stormwater controls implemented in the watershed can be assessed by observing changes in population, diversity, and mass of the biota of interest. Instream indices are not appropriate for assessing individual stormwater controls, watershed-based control programs if the total contribution of the controls is minor compared to other loadings, or effects of individual storms.

6.1.5   Qualitative

The final category of parameters, qualitative parameters, typically includes a measure of public outreach, public involvement, public perception, behavioral changes, or level of participation. Assessing the performance of nonstructural controls often relies on qualitative parameters. Improving aesthetics has a public perception component. Tracking the areas and frequency where street sweeping and drain inlet cleaning are performed are other qualitative parameters that can also be combined with physical parameters such as mass of sediment and gross solids removed.

6.1.6   Other Relevant Factors

There are a number of other factors that can also influence the overall performance of a stormwater control. These factors have been grouped into the following categories (U.S. EPA, 2002c):

- Stormwater control design;
- Test site characteristics;
- Watershed condition and characteristics;
- Monitoring station characteristics; and
- Maintenance and operations.

These factors should be documented for all performance assessment studies. They are also useful to effectively compare the results of performance studies for different control types, conditions, locations, operating methods, and study methods.

Some factors apply to all stormwater controls, while others are unique to specific controls. U.S. EPA (2002c) included detailed tables listing factors useful for assessing the performance of many of the more common control types. Additional factors include age and maintenance practices (U.S. EPA, 2004).

Operations and maintenance of stormwater controls have a direct effect on performance of stormwater controls. Detention time, bypassing, and the control of erosion, vegetation height, trash, and sediment buildup may directly affect performance.

6.2   Parameters of interest

Well-defined objectives, along with their associated assessment criteria and metrics, should identify the parameters of interest. The parameters will come from one or more of the five aforementioned categories. Any number of potential parameters can be identified for assessing the performance of stormwater controls. Further refinement of the objectives or assessment criteria and metrics to identify specific parameters can be performed by applying the following considerations (U.S. EPA, 2002c):

- Regulatory or court-ordered legal requirements;
- Applicable surface water quality standards for receiving waters;
- Beneficial uses or impairments of receiving waters;
- Prevailing land use type or types;
- Parameters particularly useful for evaluating the type of stormwater control being assessed;
- Typically monitored constituents; and
- Existing data to identify parameters that show up above levels of concern or those that rarely are detected, which can be eliminated from consideration.

6.3   Estimating Minimal Amount of Information

Estimating the appropriate amount of information required to assess the performance of a stormwater control is important because the amount of information needed has a direct effect on resources required to compile or collect it. Available resources in terms of funding and staff for these tasks are typically limited. Estimating the amount of data or information required is a good approach for prioritizing program objectives. The limited resources can then be allocated to those objectives that are considered to provide the least cost benefit.

The basis for most statistical methods discussed in Section 5.0 is the application of a statistically valid data set. The nature of stormwater, with its high variability in both quantity and quality, often requires a substantial amount of data to obtain a statistically valid representation of stormwater at a given location. Consequently, data compilation and collection tasks can be expensive and time-consuming (U.S. EPA, 2002c).

A power analysis is a statistical analysis available to estimate the number of data needed to achieve a statistically valid data set. U.S. EPA (2002c) provides a detailed summary of this method and other supporting information, in the section on sampling frequency. Working closely with a statistician familiar with this analysis is recommended.

Performing a power analysis requires that the following elements be estimated for each parameter of interest:

- Variability in the data set;

- Confidence level;

- Statistical power or probability of detecting a difference; and

- Magnitude of detectable change.

Estimating the number of data needed using the power analysis can be applied to chemical parameters, hydraulic and hydrologic parameters, and those physical and biological parameters that can be assessed similar to chemical parameters such as dissolved oxygen concentrations and bacteria levels. The analysis is not appropriate for instream indices, physical parameters associated with the amount of sediment and gross solids, and qualitative parameters. These parameters typically require fewer data because they are not affected by stormwater variability, but track long-term trends.

6.4 Existing Data

A review of existing data or studies can provide useful information. Existing data can be used to estimate the variability required for the power analysis as discussed earlier. Similar studies may also provide an indication of the number of data required to satisfy the objectives.

Completed studies may provide compatible results. However, careful review of all aspects of the previous study must be performed to ensure that the studies are compatible and the results can be extrapolated. Design elements, study goals and objectives, watershed and environmental characteristics, monitoring methods, analytical data quality, operations, and assessment methods should be included in the review. The International Stormwater Best Management Practices Database is a good place to start because its purpose is to provide this range of information for various stormwater control performance studies (U.S. EPA, 2002c).

Existing data from the same catchment area may be able to supplement data needs and reduce the number of new data. Care must be taken to ensure the data are totally compatible with the data quality objectives and needs of the new study. Extrapolating any data collected during an earlier time period or location always introduces some degree of uncertainty. An important consideration in any performance assessment is minimizing uncertainty.

6.5 Identifying Data Gaps

Data gaps are identified by comparing data needs to any existing data or studies. It is unlikely that exiting data sets will be appropriate to supplement the data needs of an individual control. However, locating compatible studies is possible as more studies that assess the performance of stormwater controls are conducted using similar methods and documenting all relevant information. These studies may provide sufficient information to satisfy one or more of the goals or objectives of a new study and eliminate the need for the associated data.

7.0 PERFORMANCE ASSESSMENT PLAN

The next phase translates established objectives, criteria and metrics, statistical analyses, and data needs and gaps into a plan that can be implemented. Issues that need to be defined include

- Required and available resources;
- Data quality objectives;
- Collection approaches and protocols including methods, location, and frequency;
- Identification and selection of equipment and materials;

- Quality assurance and quality control (QA/QC) initiatives;

- Data management and analyses; and

- Method quality objectives, which encompass QA/QC.

The designer should pay particular attention to the planning phase because data collection in the form of field monitoring is generally expensive because it requires considerable resources and time to complete. It is important to note that time and money can be easily wasted when a plan is poorly designed, which results in poor quality data or an incomplete data set. These situations can lead to erroneous performance assessments (U.S. EPA, 2004; 2002c).

7.1 Available Resources

Successful plans need to balance the scope for collecting and analyzing information with available resources (U.S. EPA, 2002c). This balance needs to be evaluated early on by comparing informational and monitoring requirements to an estimate of the general costs, staffing needs, and schedule. If available resources are not sufficient to meet the proposed objectives and required informational needs, selected objectives and or a portion of the scope should be scaled back, additional resources added, or some combination of the both until the scope is commensurate with resources.

A general scope can be formulated by looking at informational requirements that have been established and dividing the requirements into field efforts and literature reviews. Field efforts can be further divided into either event-based efforts, such as effluent concentrations, or watershed trends, such as fish populations or public perception.

7.1.1 Cost

Cost estimates can be developed based on each type of effort for collecting required information. Literature reviews are primarily a labor task with, some costs for acquiring relevant reports. Costs for event-based and trend field monitoring include

- Developing a sampling plan document;

- Site selection;

- Equipment purchase;

- Equipment installation;

- Monitoring including qualitative surveys or event-based sampling;

- Laboratory analyses;

- Equipment maintenance;

- Data management and validation; and

- Costs for equipment and bottle cleaning, field vehicles and travel, shipping of samples, and miscellaneous field supplies such as gloves and ice.

Event-based monitoring may have multiple events in a year or season, whereas trend monitoring may only be performed on an annual basis or less. Trend monitoring should be done at the same time each year or under the same hydrologic characteristics, if possible, to prevent bias in the study.

Total cost estimates are then compared to available funds. The more detailed the breakdown in costs, the easier it will be to identify specific elements with the highest costs such as labor for monitoring or laboratory analyses.

7.1.2   Personnel Resources

U.S. EPA (2002c) also recommends assessing available resources in terms of personnel. This includes staff size, technical background, physical condition, and ability (and willingness) to respond to events with little advance notice or after hours. Available staff resources may be a limiting factor to the scope of a performance assessment program, just as funding can be. Supplementing staff resources with outside personnel is an option; however, the costs of this will need to be included.

7.1.3   Schedule

Planning should consider a schedule for collecting required data. Data can come from a few sites, but this approach may take several seasons to complete. Or, data can come from a larger number of similar sites, which may reduce the collection period for completing the data set to one or two seasons. Objectives sometimes include geographic and temporal aspects that fix the number of test sites or the length of the study period. A short schedule often requires higher costs for 1 to 2 years, whereas a long schedule will allow the costs to spread out over several years to collect the same set of data.

7.1.4   Additional Considerations

7.1.4.1   Analytical Reporting Limits

When applying water quality to assess performance, running analytical methods with low reporting limits to minimize the number of nondetect results can be expensive. Low reporting limits may require use of specialty analytical equipment and laboratories and/or additional QA/QC to define the precision and accuracy of results. Identifying a typical concentration in stormwater for a given parameter will help determine an acceptable reporting limit.

7.1.4.2 Representing Quality

A decision needs to be made on how to represent water quality if it is being applied. Water quality can be represented in terms of a concentration, an EMC, and load (U.S. EPA, 2002c). Each one is described here along with its effect on costs.

7.1.4.2.1 Concentration

Concentrations represent a measure at a point in time. A single measure is often not considered representative of stormwater quality because of high variability during an event and among different events (U.S. EPA, 2002c). A large data set is required to statistically characterize the quality of stormwater when based on single concentrations. However, collecting a single measurement or sample during an event is often the least-expensive option.

If a series of discrete samples are collected at specific times during an event, they can be analyzed individually and the results used to define temporal variations during an event (U.S. EPA, 2002c). This information is used to identify first flush phenomena or peak concentrations that may exert an acute toxic effect. Laboratory costs of analyzing individual samples from each site for each event can quickly add up and make this option the most expensive to consider. For example, if 16 samples are collected during an event at one station, 16 samples would be analyzed for all the parameters of interest. Available funding typically limits the number of samples that can be analyzed. One option is to analyze selected individual samples for one or two parameters while a single composite sample is developed and analyzed for a majority of the parameters of interest. Another method to reduce cost is to inspect the individual sample bottles for visual cues (i.e., clear water on the falling limb of the hydrograph), then composite the aliquots into bigger samples for analysis. If the aliquots are flow weighted, the EMC for the entire storm can be calculated, while also having information on intrastorm concentrations.

7.1.4.2.2 Event Mean Concentration

Event mean concentration is a statistical term used to represent the average concentration of a given parameter for an entire runoff event. Event mean concentrations can be represented by combining the results of a series of discrete samples collected at various times over the duration of the runoff event. Or, a single composite sample can be developed from a series of samples and this composite sample analyzed. In either case, individual results or samples must be combined on a flow-proportioned basis.

Event mean concentration data often provide the most useful means for quantifying the level of pollution resulting from a runoff event (U.S. EPA, 2002c). Analyzing a single flow-proportional composite sample limits laboratory costs, often making the use of EMCs the most cost-effective expression of quality. Applying EMCs requires flow data be collected or generated at the site during each of the monitored events. Additional capital costs and some labor will be required to monitor or model the flow. Still, EMC is the expression recommended by developers of the International Stormwater Best Management Practices Database to represent stormwater quality (U.S. EPA, 2002c).

7.1.4.2.3 Load

Loads represent the mass of pollutant, typically expressed by weight (kilograms or pounds) or rate (pounds per day or kilogram per minute). Loads or loading are calculated by the combination of a concentration and associated flow volume or flowrate. The combination of EMC results with event flow volume represent an estimate of the total pollutant load for a runoff event. Accurate flow measurements or flow modeling results are essential for load determination (U.S. EPA, 2002c).

Loads are often used to assess the long-term effect of a stormwater control on the receiving environment, whereas concentrations are used for short-term or event-based assessments. Loads can be the central issue in stormwater control studies when receiving waterbodies are regulated under the TMDL program (U.S. EPA, 2002c). Dry weather loads can also contribute substantially to long-term loading.

Selecting EMCs to represent water quality will typically provide data for calculating total loads on an event basis and no additional data need to be collected. Modeling is typically used to estimate loads on an annual basis.

7.1.4.3 Sampling: Manual Versus Automatic

All sampling has some manual component involved. However, with water quality sampling and flow monitoring, automatic equipment is available that can reduce the amount of manual labor. Automated monitoring systems are comprised of electromechanical devices that can be operated automatically (i.e., an on-site operator is not needed).

There is a trade-off, however. Automatic equipment can have relatively high capital costs, along with some maintenance costs. Manual sampling can be considered for events that can be scheduled and/or only involve collecting one to three samples and measurements at a few sites. Automatic equipment should be considered if the water quality data will be represented by EMCs, which rely on multiple samples and flow data collected over the duration of a given event, or if the program is focused on wet weather events. Manual sampling will be labor-intensive, whereas automatic sampling will include higher capital costs and some labor.

7.2 Plan Optimization

The next step is to optimize the plan based on estimated costs, available funding and personnel, and schedule, with some consideration paid to analytical reporting limits, representation of water quality, and use of manual or automatic sampling techniques. The goal of this step is to develop a design for generating information and data needed to address the objectives by generating either the most resource-effective data collection process that is sufficient to fulfill study objectives or a data collection process that maximizes the amount of information available for synthesis and analysis within a fixed budget (U.S. EPA, 2006).

Not having limitations to complete the ideal study is rare. Collecting enough information and data to answer questions regarding stormwater control performance with a high level of confidence is generally expensive and time-consuming (U.S. EPA, 2002c). Consequently, plans will often have to be revised.

Reductions in scope should be done in a careful manner based on an analysis of the effects on the plan's ability to address study objectives. Reducing the number of stations may eliminate critical characteristics needed to assess performance or reducing the number of data will produce unreliable results on a statistical basis. The approach for reducing scope is a judgment call based on how well each approach provides answers to study objectives. Generally, producing reliable results in a relatively narrow application is preferred to widespread, but less reliable results. Strategies to reduce the scope and its associated costs include the following:

- Eliminate low-priority objectives and their associated information needs;

- Reduce the number of parameters of interest;

- Phase the study over several years, implementing just a portion each year (U.S. EPA, 2002c);

- Pool resources with other local or regional agencies with similar studies (U.S. EPA, 2002c);

- Switch to monitoring that requires fewer data such as source identification, sediment sampling, biological sampling, and/or visual surveys (U.S. EPA, 2002c);

- Incorporate simple, screening-type monitoring programs (U.S. EPA, 2002c);

- Extrapolate data from existing studies or perform detailed literature reviews to help address some objectives;

- Incorporate modeling to predict performance and reduce data needs (U.S. EPA, 2004). Use of modeling may limit usability of the data depending on the validity of the assumptions made, the accuracy of the model itself, and accuracy of the information input to the model (U.S. EPA, 2002c);

- Incorporate bench-scale experiments to test many different approaches and pilot test only the approach that shows the most promise; and

- Do not perform the study until adequate resources are available.

Several iterations may be required before an acceptable plan is developed. The final plan should be capable of providing information to reliably answer the remaining study objectives.

7.3 Defining Plan Elements

Once the scope has been established, the following elements need to be defined to complete the plan:

- Data quality objectives (DQOs);
- Monitoring locations;
- Equipment and methods;
- Procedures;
- Quality assurance and quality control; and
- Health and safety.

7.3.1 Data Quality Objectives

Data quality objectives establish acceptable quality for collected data required to support the specified objectives of the performance assessment study. Data quality objectives specify the level of error considered to be acceptable in the data along with the acceptable ranges of field sampling and laboratory performance (Caltrans, 2003). Data quality objectives are represented in terms of precision, accuracy, completeness, representativeness, and analytical reporting limits (U.S. EPA, 1994c). Data quality objectives are typically numeric. The Caltrans (2003) comprehensive monitoring protocols guidance manual provides detailed guidance on the development of DQOs, typical values, and their application in the data validation process that is used by Caltrans in their stormwater monitoring programs.

The central goal for the collection of information and data is for the results to be scientifically defensible and fulfill program objectives. This goal is best achieved through scientific design of the program and sound technical planning (Caltrans, 2003).

7.3.2   Monitoring Locations

Monitoring locations are identified primarily from the data needs for conducting the performance study. Typical locations include upstream, downstream, intermediate, overflows and bypasses, and intra. Locations also include areas for monitoring precipitation and groundwater.

7.3.2.1 Upstream

Monitoring stations established upstream of a stormwater control or stormwater control program can give results that reveal conditions before they are affected by the control or, in the case of receiving waters, discharge from the control. Upstream conditions can be indicative of conditions that would be observed if no control or control program were implemented (U.S. EPA, 2002c).

7.3.2.2 Downstream

Monitoring stations established downstream of a stormwater control or stormwater control program are used to indicate the change in the conditions achieved by the control(s). Downstream locations include the effluent of a structural control or the section of the receiving water downstream of the treated discharge or watershed.

7.3.2.3 Intermediate

Intermediate monitoring stations located in the interior of stormwater controls or within treatment train systems are useful for investigating how various sections of the control are working and establishing intermediate characteristics (U.S. EPA, 2002c).

7.3.2.4 Overflows and Bypasses

Monitoring stations established at overflow and bypass points are used to indicate the volume, quality, or load that is not completely treated by the control. Bypasses and overflows can have a substantial effect on the treatment efficiency of an overall system and, therefore, need to be considered (U.S. EPA, 2002c). Their behavior is different. A bypass is the intentional process to route flows in excess of the design flow around the device to prevent scour and other damage to the device or ancillary elements. An overflow occurs when the device malfunctions and cannot treat flows up to the design flow. To calculate the efficiency of a device, overflows should be measured and their concentration should be sampled or the inflow concentration should be applied to them. If a bypass occurs, it should not be part of the device efficiency evaluation because the stormwater controls were not designed to treat it. However, to estimate the load on receiving waters, the bypass should be sampled (or its concentration assumed to be that of the influent).

7.3.2.5 Intra
Intra monitoring locations typically apply to nonstructural stormwater control monitoring and reference a geographic area of interest where a control program or survey may be conducted. The monitoring location is the study area or some representative portion.

7.3.2.6 Precipitation
Rainfall gauges should be established within the study drainage area or watershed. Multiple locations may be required depending on the size of the area or watersheds because rainfall can vary substantially from site to site. Use of local or regional precipitation recording networks should be incorporated to the monitoring program.

7.3.2.7 Groundwater
Groundwater can be monitored at stormwater controls if groundwater can be affected such as at infiltration basins. Monitoring stations should be located sufficiently downgradient from the control (U.S. EPA, 2002c).

7.3.2.8 Site Selection
Once the number and type of monitoring sites have been defined based on the established scope to collect required information, actual sites need to be selected. There are a number of factors that need to be considered to ensure selection of the most appropriate monitoring sites. These factors include

- Representativeness;
- Personnel safety;
- Site access;
- Equipment security;
- Flow measurement capability;
- Electrical power and telephone;

- Outside sources of runoff;

- Control effectiveness; and

- Site visit.

Not all of these factors may be appropriate for all monitoring studies or individual locations. Each of these elements is discussed in detail in Section 3 of *Comprehensive Monitoring Protocols Guidance Manual: Stormwater Quality Monitoring Protocols, Particle/ Sediment Monitoring Protocols, Gross Solids Monitoring Protocols, Toxicity Monitoring Protocols, and Caltrans Data Reporting Protocols* (Caltrans, 2003).

In *Urban Stormwater BMP Performance Monitoring: A Guidance Manual for Meeting the National Stormwater BMP Database Requirements,* U.S. EPA (2002c) considers the location of a permanent sampling station as a critical factor in a monitoring network that collects water quality data. Section 3.2.1 of the publication includes a number of criteria for selecting monitoring sites.

Selecting areas or populations for nonstructural stormwater control programs is discussed in *Techniques for Tracking, Evaluating, and Reporting the Implementation of Nonpoint Source Control Measures:* Urban (U.S. EPA, 2001) and in two papers by Tailor and Wong (2002a; 2002b).

7.3.3 Methods and Equipment

Methods for the collection of required data and information need to be defined along with equipment that will be used in the field. A variety of methods and equipment can be applied. Parameters that are typically associated with stormwater (hydraulic and hydrology, chemical, physical, biological, and qualitative) each have methods that have been developed, along with associated equipment. Standardized methods commonly used in the measurement of flow data and pollutant concentrations include

- American Society for Testing and Materials flow measurement methods;

- American Society of Civil Engineers hydraulic flow estimation methods; and

- U.S. EPA test methods for water constituent analysis.

Additional standard methods have been established by other nationally recognized organizations such as AWWA, NSF International, and APHA *Standard Methods.*

In the event that standardized methods cannot be applied, evidence assuring data quality should be produced and submitted in support of a proposed alternative method. The DQOs selected for the study can also define which methods to apply to maximize the amount of usable data. A unique sampling plan appropriate for the tests' unique conditions should be developed. Standard methods documented in the literature should be applied whenever possible. Regardless of the method selected, the standard method that is typically used for the particular field where technology is applied should be noted.

7.3.3.1 Hydraulic and Hydrology Parameters

The primary hydraulic and hydrologic parameters are flowrate, water level, and precipitation. Methods and equipment that can be considered for each are summarized here.

7.3.3.1.1 Flow

Generating accurate flow and level measurements can be a difficult task (Caltrans, 2003). Flow data are an important component of assessing stormwater control performance (U.S. EPA, 2002c). The method and equipment must be carefully selected to ensure the DQOs are met. Research on flow measurement techniques and considerations is recommended before implementing a monitoring program. For additional information, the reader is referred to the following documents:

- *Basic Requirements for Collecting, Documenting, and Reporting Precipitation and Stormwater-Flow Measurements* (Church et al., 1999);

- *Isco Open Channel Flow Measurement Handbook* (Grant and Dawson, 1997); and

- *Urban Stormwater BMP Performance Monitoring: A Guidance Manual for Meeting the National Stormwater BMP Database Requirements* (U.S. EPA, 2002c).

Flows can be measured using a variety of methods. In the aforementioned publication, U.S. EPA (2002c) lists seven methods along with a detailed summary of each. These methods can be applied at natural waterbodies, drainage systems, and stormwater control structures. The method selected will depend on conditions at a given site; no one approach is suited to all conditions (Caltrans, 2003).

Flows may be measured manually or with automated equipment. Manual methods include the volume-based bucket and stop watch method, the velocity-based float method, or various depth–discharge-based methods (Caltrans, 2003). Manual sampling is performed when only a few instantaneous measurements are sufficient or when other parameters are being manually collected at the same time. Manual sampling is also applied in the development of a stage-discharge relationship or the calibration of automatic flow monitoring equipment.

Automated flow measurements can be made with either an electronic depth measurement matched to a stage-discharge relationship or area and velocity measurement devices. Automatic equipment is often applied to stormwater programs because they can measure flowrates or levels at defined intervals (every minute, 30 minutes, or hour) for extended periods of time (days, weeks, or months). This high frequency allows changes in flowrates or levels that occur over the course of a runoff event to be captured in addition to long-term trends.

Manual flow monitoring equipment can include bucket and stop watch, a float, a staff gauge, and/or a velocity meter. Most automatic methods rely on a primary flow device (e.g., flumes, weirs, nozzles, pipe, or natural constriction), where a stage-discharge relationship can be established. A secondary device is applied to measure level (e.g., bubblers, pressure transducers, and ultrasonic devices). Automated area-velocity meters can have applications in conduits with defined consistent cross sections, such as circular pipes or channels that are rectangular, trapezoidal, or U-shaped. A data logger is also required to collect and store the data. Commercial equipment is readily available for a wide range of applications.

It is important to mention that, when a stormwater control is monitored to determine whether it is an acceptable device, the monitoring program should cover the entire range of flows that the control is designed to treat. The control should not be approved to treat up to the maximum design flow if the monitoring events did not test that capability.

7.3.3.1.2 Water Level

Because water level is an integral element in the measurement of flowrates, many of the same methods and equipment apply if only the water level is being monitored. Water level is often monitored in stormwater controls that include basins. Maximum depth, draw-down rates, and storage duration can all be monitored by measuring standing water levels. Staff gauges or automated level devices (e.g., bubblers, pressure transducers, and ultrasonic devices) coupled with data loggers represent typical equipment.

7.3.3.1.3 Precipitation

Measuring precipitation requires use of a gauge. The electronic "tipping bucket" gauge is recommended whenever possible because of the improved accuracy and electronic recordability of the data when coupled with a data logger (Caltrans, 2003). This type of gauge generates a contact closure every time the bucket fills and tips. The closure sends a signal to the data logger where it is recorded. The data logger calculates the total volume of precipitation that occurred at a defined interval (15 minutes, 30 minutes, and hourly) for extended periods of time (days, weeks, or months).

Use of a portable, direct-reading gauge is an option when automated sampling stations are not installed at the site. This type of gauge measures total amounts for the event unless field personnel will be present on-site to take periodic readings. Readings must be taken prior to and directly after an event to maximize accuracy of the measurement.

Precipitation gauges can be adapted to measure snow in terms of rainfall equivalent. Regional precipitation networks can be used to supplement the database, especially for large watershed projects. However, regional or distant gauges are not acceptable to use for a smaller watershed study of a singular control. Local storm activity typically has no relation of depth or intensity to distant rain gauges.

7.3.3.2 Chemical

Samples of stormwater are analyzed by laboratories for the chemical parameters of interest. Samples can be collected to represent a point in time (referred to as a *grab sample*) or a period of time (referred to as a *composite sample*) (Caltrans, 2003). A grab sample is essentially a one-time collection, whereas a composite sample is comprised of some number of individual sample aliquots mixed together.

Grab and composite samples can be collected using either manual or automated means. A monitoring program may require a combination of sample types (grab and composite) and techniques (manual and automated) based on the data needs, DQOs, and available resources. In most instances, automated composite sampling is the recommended sample collection method, with manual grab sampling as required for certain constituents (Caltrans, 2003).

Grab samples are required for monitoring parameters that transform rapidly, require special preservation, or adhere to bottles, such as oil and grease, petroleum hydrocarbons, ammonia, and volatile organics. Grab samples are most often collected using manual methods.

Composite samples may be collected using either manual or automatic methods. Automated sampling is generally the most cost effective method of composite sample collection, particularly for large-scale programs when either a large number of sampling sites are monitored or numerous sampling events are conducted (Caltrans, 2003). The manual method may be warranted when the sampling program is to be of limited scope or duration or where installation of automated sampling equipment is economically or logistically infeasible (Caltrans, 2003).

In addition to sample collection methods, methods for analyzing the samples need to be established. These analytical methods should be based on reporting limits and other DQOs for the project (Caltrans, 2003).

Resources for analytical methods include

- *Standard Methods for the Examination of Water and Wastewater* (APHA et al., 1998); and

- *Methods and Guidance for Analysis of Water* (U.S. EPA, 1999a).

Although alternative analytical methodologies can be considered to meet data quality objectives, they need to be thoroughly documented and clearly identified when reporting results. Methods may be updated and new methods developed that may improve data quality at similar or lower prices (U.S. EPA, 2002c).

Manual equipment can include sample bottles along with hand-operated items such as bailers, grab poles, or other items designed to lower an appropriate sample container into the runoff flow. All grab sampling equipment that directly contacts the sample during or after collection must be made of chemical-resistant materials that will not affect the quality of the sample.

Equipment for sample collection includes an automatic sampler. Automatic samplers are programmed to collect samples based on the objectives of the study. For example, if flow-weighted sampling is planned, the automatic sampler must be programmed to collect a sample when it receives a trigger from a connected flow meter. Commercial equipment is readily available with a wide range of programming options for sample collection.

Electronic equipment is available to measure certain chemical parameters in situ. Chemical parameters include temperature, turbidity, pH, electrical and specific conductivity, dissolved oxygen, salinity, nitrate, and ammonia (U.S. EPA, 2002c). This equipment applies electronic sensors and data loggers for near-continuous measurements, such as every minute over several days or weeks. Use of this electronic equipment has limitations and, therefore, its application should be researched thoroughly (Caltrans, 2003).

7.3.3.3 Physical

Turbidity can be collected as a grab or composite sample using either manual or automatic methods. Standard methods are defined for its analysis. Electronic in situ equipment for near-continuous measurement and portable meters are available to measure samples in the field. The other common physical parameter, temperature, needs to be measured in situ using electronic equipment or manually using a portable electronic meter or thermometer.

Samples for particle-size distribution and settling velocity distribution can be collected as a grab or composite sample using chemical sampling methods (manual and automatic) and equipment. Sampling and analyzing accumulated sediments should apply standard methods developed for sediment sampling (ASTM, 1997). Manual sampling is performed using standard equipment to collect a sample of sediment profile for analysis.

Sampling gross solids requires manual labor to remove the solids from the stormwater control or to collect them in the receiving environment. The samples represent composite samples either for a single runoff event or for a period of time with multiple events. Methods for analyzing the sample need to be defined based on study objectives and can include wet weight, dry weight, and content.

7.3.3.4 Biological

Manual grab sampling is the only cost-effective method for biological organisms such as bacteria because the sample has to be collected directly from the flow steam into a sterilized container. Toxicity samples can be collected as a grab or composite sample using chemical sampling methods (manual and automatic) and equipment.

Surveying biota communities in the receiving water is performed by experienced staff in the field. U.S. EPA's *Rapid Bioassessment Protocols for Use in Streams and Wadeable Rivers: Periphyton, Benthic Macroinvertebrates and Fish* provides standard methods and equipment for performing an assessment (U.S. EPA, 1999b). Manual sampling is typically performed with specially designed equipment for the collection of various types of biota. Analyses of the samples may involve types and populations, age, weight, visual abnormalities, and chemical content.

7.3.3.5 Qualitative

Methods for compiling or collecting qualitative information will vary with the program and desired information. Surveys are common methods (Tailor and Wong 2002a; 2002b). Proven methods for monitoring public opinion or levels of participation should be applied. An educational element should be included so the target audience will understand the purpose of the stormwater control and the survey.

Qualitative monitoring also includes visual observations of the control during an actual runoff event. These observations can provide valuable information toward understanding recorded data, analytical results from the collected samples, or equipment failures. Simply relying on the data may not provide the complete picture on how an individual control or monitoring station is operating.

7.3.3.6 Operations and Maintenance

Operations and maintenance activities are often monitored because of their direct effect on performance. Stormwater controls should be operated to maximize treatment efficiency within design specifications. Maintenance is conducted to keep the control aesthetic in proper working order. Routine maintenance may include erosion and structural repair, debris and litter removal, sediment removal and disposal, mowing to control vegetation and woody growth, nuisance control, and vector management.

The establishment of maintenance indicator thresholds is an effective tool for ensuring consistency in operations. Maintenance activities are conducted when a field measurement exceeds an indicator such as the depth of sediment, height of vegetation, and time period when standing water is present.

Monitoring operations and management activities includes documenting

- Field measurements;
- Photographs;
- List of specific maintenance activities performed;
- Start, end, and total time and resources used for each activity;
- Status of completion of each activity; and
- General site observations and comments.

Cost is another important element of monitoring operations and maintenance. Monitoring costs is important for evaluating the cost benefit of a control, budgeting future control operations and maintenance cost expenditures, tracking the level of effort during the year to determine when peak staff effort is required, identifying opportunities to adjust maintenance activities, and estimating future life cycle costs for potential installations.

7.3.4   Quality Assurance and Quality Control

Quality assurance and quality control is an important component to any performance assessment study to ensure results have reliable quality. The QA/QC procedures need to be established for the field, laboratory, and assessment based on specific DQOs. Acceptable levels of variance and error should be included (U.S. EPA, 2004).

Field QA/QC initiatives include

- Standard operating procedures so the collection of measurements, samples, and information is performed consistently. Applying standard procedures maximizes comparability of results among sites and events;

- Standard operating procedures for equipment cleaning, calibration, and maintenance;

- Established sample bottle type, preservative, holding time, and minimum volume for each parameter;

- Collection of field blanks to identify contamination and field replicates to assess variability attributable to collection, handling, shipment, storage and/ or laboratory handling and analysis, along with the schedule for collecting each of these samples;

- Coverage represented by the sample in terms of percent of the runoff event, study area, or target population; and

- Chain of custody procedures that emphasize accurate sample labeling and documentation.

Laboratory QA/QC initiatives include (U.S. EPA, 2002c)

- Control samples such as method blanks (contamination), laboratory replicates (precision), matrix spikes (accuracy), and external reference standards (accuracy), along with the frequency at which these tests will be performed;

- Laboratory performance standards (e.g., detection limits, practical quantitation limits, objectives for precision, accuracy, and completeness);

- Data reporting requirements, including schedule;

- Data validation procedures;

- Corrective action procedures; and

- Random audits.

Assessment QA/QC initiatives include

- Use of data identified with quality issues, outliers, and nondetected results; and

- Effects of data distribution (i.e., normality) on appropriate statistical analyses.

7.3.5   Validation and Management

All data and information compiled for a study should be carefully reviewed to determine whether the project's DQOs have been met. Procedures validating the data and information need to be established. Procedures also need to be established for managing the information because assessment studies can generate a considerable amount of information in a wide variety of forms.

The initial screening identifies and corrects, when possible, inadvertent documentation or process errors introduced by the field crew or laboratory.

The information and data are then evaluated for the level of quality. For analytical data, results are compared to holding times, conformity to reporting-limit requests, analytical precision, analytical accuracy, and possible contamination during sampling and analysis. Data evaluation results in rejection, qualification, and narrative discussion of data points or the data as a whole. U.S. EPA guidelines for data validation (U.S. EPA 1994a; 1994b) are recommended as a guide for qualifying data (U.S. EPA, 2002c).

Qualification of data or information, other than rejection, does not necessarily exclude their use in the assessment process. The data user decides whether or not to use qualified information based on specifics of the application (Caltrans, 2003).

A process for managing information generated during an assessment study is crucial because a mixed hard copy and electronic set of information will need to be organized and stored so it can be easily accessed (U.S. EPA, 2002c). Planning should establish

- A central file and filing procedures for hard copy documents and
- A database to accommodate digital information such as results of laboratory analyses, field measurements, maps, and spreadsheets.

Reporting protocols also need to be established. A uniform system for reporting is useful to interpret information and effectively compare the performance of different stormwater controls under a variety of conditions. The protocols established for the International Stormwater Best Management Practices Database is a good reference. This database has identified a number of fields that should be reported during each stormwater control performance study including test-site location, watershed characteristics, climatic data, control design and layout, monitoring instrumentation, and monitoring data for precipitation, flow, and water quality (U.S. EPA, 2002c).

7.3.6   Health and Safety

Health and safety of field personnel should be considered throughout the development of any program that involves field activities. Monitoring locations and methods should be selected that have the lowest potential for health and safety problems. Some potential considerations include

- Wet weather conditions;
- Hot or cold temperatures;

- Physical obstructions to the site;
- Traffic hazards;
- Confined spaces;
- Working around waterbodies;
- Flooding and fast-moving water;
- Poor visibility;
- Slippery conditions;
- Contact with biological hazards such as animals, insects, bacteria, and garbage;
- Contact with hazardous materials;
- Contact with human hazards; and
- Lifting and carrying heavy and bulky pieces of equipment or filled sample coolers.

Based on the hazard assessment, appropriate equipment and procedures need to be identified to protect field personnel. Adjusting monitoring locations and/or methods may be necessary to minimize the risk of health and safety problems. Hazards and steps to reduce any negative effect should be described in a health and safety plan (Caltrans, 2003).

7.3.7   Plan Documentation

The main product of the assessment planning phase is a document that lays out all the details of the elements discussed in Section 7.0. Such a document will serve as a guide for all personnel involved, while maximizing consistency between team members (U.S. EPA, 2002b). Thorough review by team members, especially in terms of quality assurance, is highly recommended before implementation.

This document is referred to as a *quality assurance project plan* (QAPP) by U.S. EPA. A good source of guidance regarding the preparation of a QAPP is U.S. EPA's *Guidance for Quality Assurance Project Plans* (U.S. EPA, 2002b). A similar document is often referred to as a *sampling and analysis plan*. The following are typical topics covered in such plans:

- Project overview and description;
- Monitoring sites;

- Analytical constituents;

- Data quality objectives;

- Field equipment maintenance;

- Monitoring preparation and logistics;

- Sample collection, preservation, and delivery;

- Quality assurance and quality control;

- Laboratory sample preparation and analytical methods;

- Data management and reporting procedures;

- Data analysis procedures; and

- Health and safety plan.

Several of the listed topics were not included in the discussions. The Federal Highway Administration (2000), U.S. EPA (2002c), and Caltrans (2003) provide detailed discussions on all these topics. These references can be helpful to formulate project- and site-specific details for the study plan.

8.0 PLAN IMPLEMENTATION

Implementation of the plan involves using it to (1) collect new information and data and (2) compile all available information and data into accessible formats for use in the evaluation phase. Implementation includes the following actions:

- Training;

- Site preparation;

- Pre-event preparation;

- Event monitoring;

- Validation of collected information and data; and

- Plan assessment.

8.1 Training

Training of team members is required for all planned field activities to maximize the collected information and samples that meet information requirements and DQOs of the study. Familiarity with requirements of the monitoring plan (e.g., QAPP or

sampling and analysis plan) and competence in the techniques and protocols specified in the plan are essential while protecting the health and safety of the team members (Caltrans, 2003).

8.2 Site Preparation

Activities associated with site preparation include

- Acquiring permission to use the site;
- Acquiring necessary equipment;
- Installing equipment;
- Testing and calibrating equipment; and
- Modifying site features to provide safe access and security.

All equipment should be installed, tested, and calibrated based on manufacturer specifications. U.S. EPA (2002c), Caltrans (2003), Grant and Dawson (1997), and Church
et al. (1999) provide detailed instructions for installing the general categories of equipment used at automatic flow monitoring and water quality sampling stations.

8.3 Pre-Event Preparation

Activities associated with pre-event preparation include

- Compiling supplies and sample containers;
- Sample container cleaning;
- Weather tracking;
- Storm selection criteria;
- Storm action levels;
- Communications; and
- Laboratory coordination.

Detailed discussions of these activities are presented in *Comprehensive Monitoring
Protocols Guidance Manual: Stormwater Quality Monitoring Protocols, Particle/Sediment
Monitoring Protocols, Gross Solids Monitoring Protocols, Toxicity Monitoring Protocols,
and Caltrans Data Reporting Protocols* (Caltrans, 2003).

For monitoring performed in response to precipitation events, the weather needs
to be tracked to identify candidate events. Caltrans (2003) provides a good discussion

on weather tracking and available resources. Arrival date and time and the potential amount are two crucial pieces of information needed to determine if field teams will be deployed.

Communications are required during preparation activities, personnel notification of storm action level changes, monitoring, and when coordinating activities following an event. Communications with laboratory and emergency personnel may also be required.

8.4   Event Monitoring

Activities associated with event monitoring include

- Mobilization of field crews;
- Checking equipment;
- Setting up automated equipment;
- Weather tracking;
- Collecting manual samples;
- Servicing automated stations;
- Sample representativeness evaluation;
- Sample handling, delivery, and documentation; and
- Data collection and handling.

Caltrans (2003) also provides detailed descriptions of each of these activities. Although the focus is on water quality monitoring, these elements can apply to all field activities for collecting samples, data, and information.

All sampling should be performed in accordance to standard procedures documented in the monitoring plan. Field forms developed for the study should be used to document any measurements or information.

Immediately following a monitoring event, samples or information collected should be compared to the project criteria and guidelines established for representativeness. If the minimum acceptable storm and sampling DQO criteria are not met (i.e., antecedent conditions, rainfall depth, minimum number of sample aliquots, storm coverage, and sample volume), the sample or information may be rejected. Some of these factors are guidelines or criteria, depending on the application. For example, the antecedent condition is a guideline so that a relatively short deviation from the minimum would still qualify the sampling event if it met all the other DQOs.

Antecedent conditions do not really affect the controls performance but can have an effect on pollutant concentrations. If the purpose of the monitoring program is to evaluate the characteristics of a watershed instead, then the antecedent conditions would be more important and should be treated as part of the criteria. Samples not meeting the criteria are generally not sent to the laboratory for analysis. The intent of this step is to prevent analysis of samples whose results would later be rejected during the data validation phase. Samples with low volumes can be sent to a laboratory, but the requested analyses need to be prioritized in case there is not enough sample volume to complete all of them.

Proper handling, documentation, and delivery of samples to the laboratory are important elements of quality assurance (Caltrans, 2003). Samples must be carefully handled to prevent breakage, loss, contamination, missed holding times, and tampering. Samples should be properly labeled and documented on chain-of-custody forms. Shipping containers must be properly labeled and the shipper should be made aware that samples have required arrival times to the laboratory.

All data and information collected in the field (e.g., electronic data, manual measurements, field form entries, survey notes, and photographs) need to be carefully handled to prevent loss. This information should be reviewed, identified, labeled, and then uploaded to a database or placed in the study file.

8.5   Validation of Collected Information and Data

All data and information generated during field activities should be validated. The quality or adequacy of results should be defined before interpretation begins. Standard procedures should have been defined during the planning phase.

If laboratory and field performance objectives were achieved, no further actions are needed. If performance objectives were not achieved, a review of procedures should be performed and adjustments made to prevent further noncompliance.

8.6   Plan Assessment

Implementation status of the monitoring plan should be reviewed periodically in terms of amount of information collected, its quality, costs to date, labor requirements, the number of monitoring attempts and successes, and adherence to the schedule to determine if any adjustments need to be made. Depending on any identified issues, adjustments can be made in sites, equipment, procedures, parameters, training, or staff to correct any deficiencies. Care must be exercised to avoid introducing changes that interrupt the continuity of monitoring, making information and data collected at different times in the study incompatible.

9.0 REPORTING STORMWATER CONTROL PERFORMANCE

Results of a control performance assessment program should be documented and presented in at least one formal report. While a comprehensive, final report should be produced at the completion of the monitoring program, producing regular progress reports throughout the program should also be considered. Monitoring regularity and program objectives should dictate the frequency of progress reports, although quarterly or semiannual production is common.

9.1 Useful Graphical Presentations

Presentation of results is a key component of an effective control performance assessment report. As discussed in Section 4.0, several graphical methods exist that are useful for the evaluation and presentation of control performance data. Some of these methods include

- Time series scatter plots;
- Box-and-whisker plots; and
- Normal probability plots.

The scatter plot is a basic tool that can summarize the relationship between two variables. In addition, scatter plots are particularly useful for evaluating data quality. Points that appear to fall far from the best-fit line are potential outliers. In addition, the scatter plot can reveal useful information regarding the change in influent and effluent pollutant concentrations over time. This is particularly useful in situations where the reduction of peak effluent concentration is more important than the reduction of EMC.

Box-and-whisker plots are a concise way of summarizing a comprehensive statistical analysis of control performance data. Box plots depict the range and dispersion of a data set and reveal the minimum, maximum, lower and upper quartiles (Q1 and Q3), and the mean and/or median of a data set. The box plot diagram can also provide a visual indication of variance, skewness, and potential outliers.

U.S. EPA (2002c) recommends EPM of control performance evaluation above all others, and suggests that "curves of this type are the single most instructive piece of information that can result from a BMP evaluation study" (U.S. EPA, 2002c). The manual goes so far as to recommend the EPM approach as an industry-standard rating curve for stormwater control evaluation (U.S. EPA, 2002c). By comparing the concentrations of various pollutants in the influent and effluent side by side, pollutant reduction can be determined visually. In particular, EPM curves reveal the range of influent concentrations, if any, over which a particular control is most effective. One potential limitation of EPM plots is that they do not show paired influent and effluent concentrations, such as values corresponding to a given storm event.

9.2 Typical Discussion Points

In addition to presentation of formal methodology and analysis, a comprehensive report should include discussion of the following:

- Data qualifications (i.e., any concerns regarding quality, validity, potential outliers, interesting distributions, etc.);
- Hydrologic, anthropogenic, and environmental context for performance observations (e.g., seasonal performance changes);
- Unexpected results;
- Proposed explanations of performance variations;
- Planning and implementation challenges; and
- Recommendations for future study.

While the majority of an assessment report should be scientific and objective, the discussion section of a report should include hypothesis, opinions, and explanations. The most important function of this section is to provide a context for the results of the control performance assessment program. In particular, this section should describe the environmental, hydrologic, and/or man-made conditions that may have favorably or adversely affected control performance and led to unexpected results.

In addition, the discussion section may be the best place to present a summary of any problems or issues that may have arisen during the planning, implementation, and analysis portions of the assessment program. Alternative methods should be proposed if necessary. It may also be particularly useful to discuss the most significant challenges to the program and how they were or were not overcome.

9.3   Data Reporting Formats

Progress reports should include a summary of the following information for the reporting period:

- Accomplished work;
- Results and findings;
- Changes in program;
- Contact with the public, NGO's, and government agencies; and
- Anticipated activity for the following reporting period.

In addition to the aforementioned points, final or year-end (for long-term programs) reports should include the following information:

- Program summary;
- Objectives;
- Site description and background;
- Description of monitoring program
    - Selected parameters for performance evaluation,
    - Selected analytical methods, and
    - Method reporting limits;
- Monitoring station descriptions;
- Description of sample methods and equipment
    - Equipment calibration,
    - Equipment inspections,
    - Sampling frequency, and
    - Sampling conditions;
- Data validation and results
    - Precipitation data,
    - Influent and effluent hydrographs, and
    - Water quality data.
- Discussion;

- Summary and conclusions;
- Recommendations for management; and
- Complete data set (appendix).

In the set of protocols for reporting control monitoring results in the International Stormwater Best Management Practices Database (www.bmpdatabase.org), required data parameters include test site location, watershed characteristics, climatic data, control design and layout, monitoring instrumentation, and monitoring data for precipitation, flow, and water quality. The group provides examples and templates for reporting results to meet the minimum requirements for acceptance in the International Stormwater Best Management Practices Database. Requirements vary for each type of control and forms are categorized accordingly.

10.0 STATISTICAL ANALYSIS

This chapter has reviewed a variety of methods for evaluating control performance data. This section concludes the chapter with three examples of data analysis. In each of these examples, the methods previously described are applied in a step-by-step fashion to actual EMC and load data collected from specified sources.

10.1 Example 1

Control performance data evaluated in example 1 were collected in 2002 and their source is a Stormwater Management Inc. (SMI) research and development study (Ridder et al., 2002). Relevant documentation entitled, "Influence of Analytical Method, Data Summarization Method, and Particle Size on Total Suspended Solids (TSS) Removal Efficiency," was first presented in 2002 at the 9th International conference on Urban Drainage in Portland, Oregon (Ridder et al., 2002). This particular study monitored the performance of a filtration-based stormwater control, known specifically as The Stormwater Management StormFilter®. The criterion of interest was the ability of the control to remove total suspended solids (TSS) under controlled conditions. The performance data, as indicated by influent and effluent EMC of TSS (mg/L), are shown in order of increasing influent in Table 13.4.

10.1.1 Qualitative Assessment

Data analysis begins with a qualitative assessment, which will characterize the data set. Specifically, graphical displays of data reveal data distribution, the magnitude of

TABLE 13.4   Example 1: SMI performance data (in order of increasing influent TSS EMC) (data source: Ridder et al. [2002]).

Influent TSS EMC (mg/L)	Effluent TSS EMC (mg/L)	Difference $(TSS_{in} - TSS_{out})$ (mg/L)
15	10	5
16	11	5
20	12	8
26	12	14
27	12	15
30	12	18
53	16	37
62	22	40
68	27	41
75	27	48
82	29	53
83	27	56
99	30	69
133	42	91
143	36	107
155	48	107
157	46	111
168	51	117
175	52	123
186	53	133
187	45	142
206	71	135
222	68	154
247	80	167
255	84	171
322	98	224

the difference between influent and effluent concentrations, and outliers. Common tools for this assessment include scatter plots, box-and-whisker plots, and probability plots.

A scatter plot of data set 1 was presented in Figure 13.1. The independent variable, influent EMC, is plotted on the horizontal access, while effluent EMC, which may or may not be dependent on influent EMC, is plotted on the vertical axis. A best-fit line was sketched through the data points. The proximity of all points to this line suggests that the data are well approximated by a linear relationship. The line's upward slope from left to right indicates a positive relationship (i.e., as influent EMC increases, effluent EMC also increases). No outliers are apparent.

A box-and-whisker plot of data set 1 was presented in Figure 13.2. The range of influent data is much larger than that of effluent data. The minimums of each set are similar, suggesting that the control may have a limited effect on influent EMCs that are already extremely low. However, other important statistics such as mean, median, first quartile, and third quartile have much higher values for the influent data set than for the effluent data set. In sum, the effluent TSS EMC data feature a limited range and reduced values compared to the influent TSS EMC.

Finally, a probability plot of data set 1 was presented in Figure 13.3. The influent and effluent data both show good agreement with the straight lines, indicating that both have relatively normal distributions. The lines are not parallel, which suggests that variances of the influent and effluent data may differ notably.

10.1.2 Quantitative Assessment

To begin a quantitative assessment, the designer should start by calculating some simple descriptive statistics such as the sample size, minimum, maximum, mean, median, standard deviation, standard error, and covariance for both the influent and effluent concentrations and for a data set consisting of the values of the difference between paired influent and effluent concentrations (see Table 13.5). Several of these statistics will be necessary for the application of statistical methods.

10.1.2.1 Testing Assumptions

Next, assumptions of normality and equal variances should be tested to determine which methods (i.e., parametric or nonparametric) will be applicable.

10.1.2.1.1 Normality

The probability plot suggested that the influent and effluent data are normally distributed. However, a more quantitative analysis should be performed to verify that

TABLE 13.5 · Example 1: Summary statistics.

	Influent TSS EMC	Effluent TSS EMC	Difference $(TSS_{in} - TSS_{out})$
Sample size, n	26	26	26
Minimum, mg/L	15	10	5
Maximum, mg/L	322	98	224
Mean, mg/L	123.54	39.27	84.27
Median, mg/L	116	33	80
Standard Deviation	85.64	25.07	61.09
Standard error	16.80	4.92	11.98
Covariance	0.693	0.638	0.725

TABLE 13.6 Example 1: Test for normality of distribution of influent EMC data (significance level = 0.05).

Procedure	Test value	p Value	Conclusion
Shapiro–Wilk test	0.939	0.128	Fail to reject the H_0 that the distribution is normally distributed[a].
Anderson–Darling test	0.490	0.202	Fail to reject the H_0 that the distribution is normally distributed[a].
Kolmogorov–Smirnov test[b]	0.144	NA	Fail to reject the H_0 that the distribution is normally distributed.
Chi-square test	5.274	0.153	Fail to reject the H_0 that the distribution is normally distributed.

[a]Based on approximate p values.
[b]The critical value for the K–S test given a sample size of 26 is ~0.26.

this is the case. The values of the difference between paired influent and effluent data should also be evaluated for normality. The results of application of the Shapiro–Wilk, Anderson–Darling, Kolmogorov–Smirnov, and chi-squared methods to these three data sets are presented in tabular format in Tables 13.6, 13.7, and 13.8.

The results of each test are easily summarized and presented by calculating a p value. The p value is the probability of calculating a test statistic for a truly normally distributed population that is as extreme as the value actually obtained for the observed data set. When the p value is small (i.e., smaller than or equal to a specified

TABLE 13.7 Example 1: Test for normality of distribution of effluent EMC data (significance level = 0.05).

Procedure	Test value	p value	Conclusion
Shapiro–Wilk test	0.916	0.037	Reject the H_0.
Anderson–Darling test	0.668	0.072	Fail to reject the H_0 that the distribution is normally distributed[a].
Kolmogorov–Smirnov test[b]	0.144	NA	Fail to reject the H_0 that the distribution is normally distributed.
Chi-square test	5.923	0.115	Fail to reject the H_0 that the distribution is normally distributed.

[a]Based on approximate p values.
[b]The critical value for the K–S test given a sample size of 26 is ~0.26.

TABLE 13.8 Example 1: Test for normality of distribution of differences (significance level = 0.05).

Procedure	Test value	p value	Conclusion
Shapiro–Wilk test	0.94	0.128	Fail to reject the H_0 that the distribution is normally distributed[a].
Anderson–Darling test	0.52	0.166	Fail to reject the H_0 that the distribution is normally distributed[a].
Kolmogorov–Smirnov test[b]	0.14	NA	Fail to reject the H_0 that the distribution is normally distributed.
Chi–square test	9.23	0.026	Reject the H_0.

[a]Based on approximate p values.
[b]The critical value for the K–S test given a sample size of 26 is ~0.26.

significance level), the null hypothesis is rejected. In such an instance, because there is little chance that the test statistic representing a normally distributed data set would be as extreme as the statistic calculated for the observed data set, the observed data set is not likely to be normally distributed. For the examples presented here, conclusions are based on the 95% confidence level. The calculated p value must then be 5% (0.05) or lower to reject the null hypothesis.

When applied to influent data, all four tests fail to reject the null hypothesis at the 95% confidence level. This indicates that the influent data are acceptably normally distributed. When the same tests are applied to effluent data, only the Shapiro–Wilk test rejects the null hypothesis. The resulting p value is 0.04, which indicates the test is close to not rejecting the null hypothesis. Given this and the three supporting tests, one might conclude that the effluent data are acceptably normally distributed. Similarly, when applied to the values of the difference between paired influent and effluent EMCs, only the chi-square test rejects the null hypothesis that the data are normally distributed. This may be attributed to the sensitivity of the chi-square test to variability in the tails (upper and lower extremes) of a data set. Again, one might conclude that the differences are acceptably normally distributed.

10.1.2.1.2   Variance

Next, the designer should test the assumption that the influent and effluent data sets feature a similar degree of variance. The null hypothesis that the variances are equal has been evaluated with an F test and Bartlett's test, and the results are presented in Tables 13.9 and 13.10.

Both the F test and Bartlett's test rejected the null hypothesis with 95% confidence, leading to the conclusion that the two data sets do not have equal variance.

10.1.2.1.3   Correlation

During the qualitative analysis, a scatter plot revealed that the paired influent and effluent concentrations of data set 1 appear to be well-approximated by a linear trend line. The strength of that relationship is quantified by determining the level of correlation between the data sets. In fact, a correlation analysis of the paired influent and effluent data reveals that the two data sets are highly correlated, with a correlation coefficient, r, equal to 0.99 (a perfect correlation is indicated by $r = \pm 1.0$).

TABLE 13.9 F test.

F value	9.9
p value	1.03E-07
F critical	1.96
Conclusion	Reject H_0

TABLE 13.10   Bartlett's test.

p value	3.76E-08
Conclusion	Reject H_0

10.1.2.2   Difference between Influent and Effluent

Once assumptions regarding characteristics of the data have been tested, the appropriate parametric or nonparametric statistical method for assessing the difference between the two data sets can be selected. Although data from data set 1 were found to be acceptably normally distributed, the influent and effluent data have different variances. In this instance, nonparametric methods are more appropriate than parametric methods. However, it is important to remember that one parametric method, the *t* test, is not particularly sensitive to unequal variances. As such, the results of both a *t* test and a Wilcoxon test are presented here for comparison.

A *t* test will reveal whether or not the difference between influent and effluent concentrations is significant at the 95% confidence level. The test is applied to the set of values representing the difference between paired influent and effluent data (see Table 13.11). The proposed null hypothesis is that the mean of this data set is zero, that is, that the average difference between influent and effluent concentrations is zero.

The calculated *t* statistic for the observed data is larger than the critical value of *t*. As a result, the *p* value is less than the specified significance level, 0.05. The null hypothesis that the average difference between influent and effluent means is equal to zero can be rejected with 95% confidence. There is a nonzero difference between influent and effluent concentrations that is statistically significant.

Application of the Wilcoxon test to the data yields similar results (see Table 13.12). The null hypothesis that the average difference between influent and effluent concentrations is zero is once again rejected with 95% confidence.

10.1.2.3 Conclusions

For example 1, both the influent and effluent data are acceptably normally distributed, but have unequal variances. The difference between influent and effluent TSS

TABLE 13.11   Example 1: *T* test.

Parameter	Value
T statistic	7.03
Degrees of freedom	25
Significance level	0.05
Critical value of *t* statistic	2.06
p value	1.13E-07

TABLE 13.12   Example 1: Wilcoxon test results.

Parameter	Value
Sample size, n	26
Mean	175.5
Standard Deviation	39.37
Z statistic	−4.46
p value	4.15E-06

concentrations is different from zero with 95% confidence, as indicated by both the t test and Wilcoxon test. As a result, it can be concluded that the control does have a notable effect on the quality of stormwater runoff. In addition, according to the correlation coefficient, nearly all of the variation in effluent values can be explained by variation in influent values. This indicates that effluent EMC is heavily dependent on influent EMC, and an accurate predictive equation can be generated to determine effluent EMC from influent EMC.

10.2 Example 2

Example 2 is an analysis of observations at a bioretention area in Louisburg, North Carolina, taken from May through December of 2004. The performance data consist of influent and effluent total Kjeldahl nitrogen (TKN) concentrations for various sample dates.

For several dates when no sample concentration was collected, the average seasonal concentration was substituted. This is one option for increasing the size of the data set to match other data sets related to the site. However, it may introduce a bias that will carry through all the statistical tests. Only including actual results is another option. However, this may limit the size of the data set and, in turn, may limit confidence in resulting statistics.

The data (see Table 13.13) were presented in a master's thesis entitled "The Performance of Bioretention Areas in North Carolina: A Study of Water Quality, Water Quantity, and Soil Media" (Sharkey, 2006).

10.2.1 Qualitative Assessment

A scatter plot of data set 2 is presented in Figure 13.7. The independent variable, influent EMC, is plotted on the horizontal axis, while effluent EMC, which may or may

TABLE **13.13**   Example 2: Observed TKN influent and effluent concentrations at Louisburg, North Carolina, bioretention site (data source: Figure 5.9, Sharkey [2006]).

Influent TKN concentration (mg/L)	Effluent TKN concentration (mg/L)	Difference in concentrations (TKN_{in} - TKN_{out}) (mg/L)
0.85	0.92	0.07
1.73	1.22	−0.51
1.73	1.22	−0.51
3.7	1.22	−2.48
1.73	1.22	−0.51
1.73	1.22	−0.51
1.6	1.4	−0.2
1.73	1.22	−0.51
1.73	1.22	−0.51
1.73	1.22	−0.51
1.1	2.4	1.3
1.73	1.22	−0.51
1.73	1.22	−0.51
1.73	1.22	−0.51
1.73	1.22	−0.51
1.1	1.3	0.2
1.73	1.2	−0.53
1.73	1.22	−0.51
1.3	0.93	−0.37
2.4	0.85	−1.55
1.73	1.22	−0.51
1.73	1.22	−0.51
1.6	1.4	−0.2
1.9	0.71	−1.19
1.3	0.95	−0.35
0.68	0.29	−0.39
0.26	0.32	0.06
1.39	0.51	−0.88
1.39	0.51	−0.88
1.39	0.51	−0.88

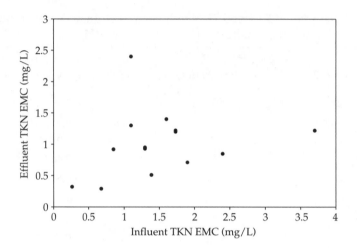

FIGURE 13.7   Example 2: Scatter plot.

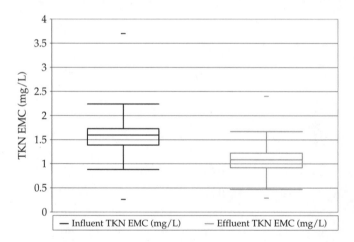

FIGURE 13.8   Example 2: Box-and-whisker plot.

not be dependent on influent EMC, is plotted on the vertical axis. A best-fit line is not readily apparent, and none was sketched through the data points. This indicates that the data are not well-approximated by a linear relationship.

A box-and-whisker plot of data set 2 is presented in Figure 13.8. Although the data within one standard deviation of the mean of each set are similarly dispersed, the total range of influent data is larger than that of the effluent data. While the minimums of each set are similar, the effluent minimum appears to be slightly higher than the influent. Other important statistics such as mean, median, first quartile, and third quartile have higher values for the influent data set than for the effluent data set. In sum, the effluent TKN EMC values are reduced compared to the influent TKN EMC. The pronounced difference in the upper extremes suggests that the control produced substantial reduction in this region, while the similarity of the minimum values suggest a minimal and, in some instances, negative effect to extremely low influent concentrations.

A probability plot of data set 2 was presented in Figure 13.9. Values of the smallest halves of the influent data and effluent data both show reasonable agreement with best-fit lines; however, the overall data set of each does not. The influent and effluent data sets are not likely normally distributed.

Because of this poor fit, influent and effluent data sets were transformed by taking the natural log of each value. The results were then plotted and are shown in Figure 13.10. However, this transformation does not appear to substantially improve the fit of the data to the linear trend line. Therefore, the data are not likely lognormally distributed.

10.2.2 Quantitative Assessment

A summary of the basic descriptive statistics for influent and effluent EMC data and for the values of the difference between influent–effluent pairs is presented in

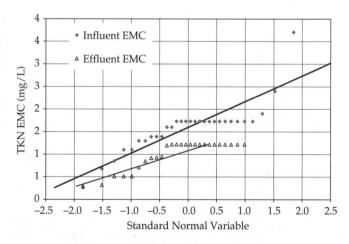

FIGURE 13.9 Example 2: Normal probability plot.

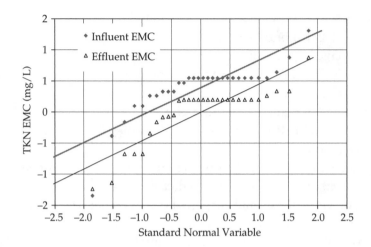

FIGURE 13.10   Example 2: Log-normal probability plot.

TABLE 13.14   Example 2: Summary statistics.

	Influent TKN EMC	Effluent TKN EMC	Difference in TKN EMC (TKN$_{in}$ - TKN$_{out}$)
Sample size, n	30	30	30
Minimum, mg/L	0.26	0.29	-1.3
Maximum, mg/L	3.7	2.4	2.48
Mean, mg/L	1.60	1.08	0.51
Median, mg/L	1.73	1.22	0.51
Standard Deviation	0.57	0.40	0.60
Standard error	0.10	0.07	0.11
Covariance	0.357	0.373	1.173

Table 13.14. Several of these measures will be necessary for the application of statistical tests.

10.2.2.1 Testing Assumptions

The probability plot was inconclusive as to whether or not the influent and effluent data are normally distributed. As such, a more quantitative analysis should now be performed. The results of application of the Shapiro–Wilk, Anderson–Darling,

TABLE 13.15 Test for normality of distribution for influent EMC (mg/L) (significance level = 0.05).

Procedure	Test value	p value	Conclusion
Shapiro–Wilk test	0.788	4.02E-05	Reject the H_0 that the distribution is normally distributed[a].
Anderson–Darling test	2.498	1.78E-06	Reject the H_0 that the distribution is normally distributed[a].
Kolmogorov–Smirnov test[b]	0.308	NA	Reject the H_0 that the distribution is normally distributed.
Chi-square test	38.8	1.91E-08	Reject the H_0 that the distribution is normally distributed.

[a]Based on approximate p values.
[b]The critical value for the K-S test given a sample size of 30 is ~0.24.

TABLE 13.16 Test for normality of distribution for effluent EMC (mg/L) (significance level = 0.05).

Procedure	Test value	p value	Conclusion
Shapiro–Wilk test	0.812	1.07E-04	Reject the H_0 that the distribution is normally distributed[a].
Anderson–Darling test	2.497	1.79E-06	Reject the H_0 that the distribution is normally distributed[a].
Kolmogorov–Smirnov test[b]	0.280	NA	Reject the H_0 that the distribution is normally distributed.
Chi-square test	32.60	3.91E-07	Reject the H_0 that the distribution is normally distributed.

[a]Based on approximate p values.
[b]The critical value for the K–S test given a sample size of 30 is ~0.24.

Kolmogorov–Smirnov, and chi-squared methods are presented in tabular format in Tables 13.15, 13.16, and 13.17.

Results for all tests necessitate the conclusion that neither the influent, effluent, or paired differences are normally distributed at the 95% confidence level. As a result, parametric tests cannot be applied to this data set unless a proper transformation, probably using a Box-Cox method (Weisberg, 2005), resulting in a normal

TABLE 13.17 Test for normality of distribution for difference between influent–effluent pairs (significance level = 0.05).

Procedure	Test value	p value	Conclusion
Shapiro–Wilk test	0.807	8.89E-05	Reject the H_0 that the distribution is normally distributed[a].
Anderson–Darling test	2.551	1.31E-06	Reject the H_0 that the distribution is normally distributed[a].
Kolmogorov–Smirnov test[b]	0.289	NA	Reject the H_0 that the distribution is normally distributed.
Chi-square test	38.6	2.11E-08	Reject the H_0 that the distribution is normally distributed.

[a]Based on approximate p values.
[b]The critical value for the K–S test given a sample size of 30 is ~0.24.

distribution is determined and applied. As a result, nonparametric equivalents should be substituted.

Next, the assumption that the influent and effluent data sets feature a similar degree of variance should be tested. The null hypothesis that the variances are equal has been evaluated with an F Test and Bartlett's test, and the results are presented in Tables 13.18 and 13.19.

The F test rejected the null hypothesis with 95% confidence; however, Bartlett's test failed to do so. These tests are inconclusive but, because it has already been determined that the data are not normally distributed, this does not affect selection of parametric or nonparametric analysis methods.

10.2.2.2 *Difference between Influent and Effluent*

Data set 2 was found to be non-normally distributed and, as such, a nonparametric method should be applied. In this instance, results of only the Wilcoxon test are presented.

Application of the Wilcoxon method tests the proposed null hypothesis that the mean of the differences data set is zero, that is, that the average difference between influent and effluent concentrations is zero. According to the Wilcoxon test (see Table 13.20), the null hypothesis that the average difference between influent and effluent concentrations is zero is rejected with 95% confidence.

10.2.2.3 *Conclusions*

The TKN EMC data evaluated in example 2 are non-normally distributed such that nonparametric evaluation methods are required. The difference between influent and

TABLE 13.18 F test.

F value	2.2
p value	0.020
F critical	1.96
Conclusion	Reject H_0

TABLE 13.19   Bartlett's test.

p value	0.069
Conclusion	Fail to reject H_0

TABLE 13.20   Example 2: Wilcoxon test results.

Parameter	Value
Sample size, n	30
Mean	232.5
Standard Deviation	48.62
Z statistic	-4.14
p value	1.70E-05

effluent TKN concentrations is different from zero with 95% confidence, as indicated by the Wilcoxon test. As a result, it can be concluded that the control does have a notable effect on the quality of stormwater runoff.

10.3 Example 3

Like the previous problem, example 3 is an analysis of observations at the bioretention area in Louisburg, North Carolina, from May through December of 2004. However, in this instance, the performance data (see Table 13.21) consist of influent and effluent TKN *load* data for various sample dates, rather than concentrations. The load values were calculated by combining the previously presented concentration data with associated flowrates. Once again, for dates when no sample was collected, the average seasonal load was substituted. The caveats of this substitution were explained in Example 2.

TABLE **13.21**   Example 3: Observed TKN load at Louisburg, North Carolina, bioretention site (data source: Figure 5.9, Sharkey [2006]).

Influent load (mg)	Effluent load (mg)	Difference in load (mg)
14	2	12
337	83	254
48	11	37
8	0	8
53	12	41
20	0	20
78	19	59
77	21	56
50	11	39
100	15	85
193	133	60
74	13	61
15	7	8
212	61	151
29	3	26
465	316	149
63	40	23
17	0	17
267	115	152
213	50	163
77	21	56
126	69	57
40	10	30
306	109	197
89	21	68
91	16	75
21	11	10
91	16	75
82	11	71
67	8	59

10.3.1 Qualitative Assessment

A scatter plot of data set 3 is presented in Figure 13.11. Influent load is plotted on the vertical axis, while effluent load is plotted on the horizontal axis. A best-fit line was sketched through the data points. The line's upward slope from left to right indicates a positive relationship, that is, as influent load increases, effluent load also increases. The proximity of most points to the line suggests that the data may be well-approximated by a linear relationship. However, it should be noted that the points are not evenly dispersed; there is a large cluster of data points at the lower extreme, while substantial scatter characterizes larger values.

A box-and-whisker plot of data set 3 is presented Figure 13.12. The range of influent data is much larger than that of the effluent data. Important statistics such as mean, median, first quartile, and third quartile have much higher values for the influent data set than for the effluent data set. The effluent TKN load has a limited range and values are reduced compared to the influent TKN load.

Finally, a probability plot of data set 3 is presented in Figure 13.13. These data exhibit particularly poor agreement with the best-fit lines. The data are not likely normally distributed and should be transformed prior to applying statistical methods.

Because of this poor fit, the data set was transformed by taking the natural log of each value. Results were then plotted and are shown in Figure 13.14. This transformation substantially improves the fit of the data to linear trend lines. Influent and

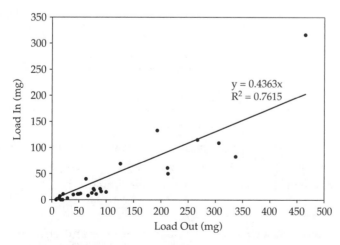

FIGURE 13.11 Example 3: Scatter plot.

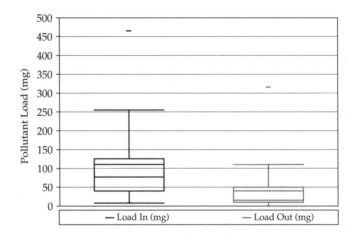

FIGURE 13.12   Example 3: Box-and-whisker plot.

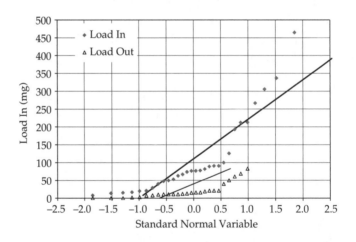

FIGURE 13.13   Example 3: Normal probability plot.

effluent data both show good agreement with straight lines, indicating that both are log-normally distributed. In addition, the lines are close to parallel, indicating that the variances of the influent and effluent data are similar.

10.3.2 Quantitative Assessment

A summary of basic descriptive statistics for influent and effluent load data and for the values of the differences between influent–effluent pairs is presented in

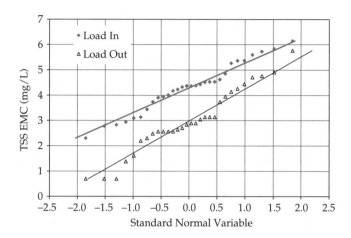

FIGURE 13.14 Example 3: Log-normal probability plot.

TABLE 13.22 Example 3: Summary statistics.

	Influent load	Effluent load	Difference in load
Sample size, n	30	30	30
Minimum, mg	2.30	0.69	0.37
Maximum, mg	6.15	5.76	2.40
Mean, mg	4.29	2.98	1.31
Median, mg	4.37	2.86	1.37
Standard Deviation	0.98	1.27	0.53
Standard error	0.18	0.23	0.10
Covariance	0.228	0.426	0.402

Table 13.22. Several of these measures will be necessary when applying statistical tests to the data set.

10.3.2.1 Testing Assumptions

During the qualitative assessment, probability plots suggested that the influent and effluent data are log-normally distributed. A more quantitative assessment can be applied to both the original and transformed data set to verify that this is the case. Results of application of the Shapiro–Wilk, Anderson–Darling, Kolmogorov–Smirnov,

TABLE 13.23   Example 3: Test for normality of distribution of original influent load data (significance level = 0.05).

Procedure	Test value	p value	Conclusion
Shapiro–Wilk test	0.792	4.63E-05	Reject the H_0 that the distribution is normally distributed[a].
Anderson–Darling test	2.30	5.49E-06	Reject the H_0 that the distribution is normally distributed[a].
Kolmogorov–Smirnov test[b]	0.272	NA	Reject the H_0 that the distribution is normally distributed.
Chi-square test	28.8	2.47E-06	Reject the H_0 that the distribution is normally distributed.

[a]Based on approximate p values.
[b]The critical value for the K–S test given a sample size of 30 is ~0.24.

TABLE 13.24   Example 3: Test for normality of distribution of original effluent load data (significance level = 0.05).

Procedure	Test value	p value	Conclusion
Shapiro–Wilk test	0.607	8.98E-08	Reject the H_0 that the distribution is normally distributed[a].
Anderson–Darling test	3.837	8.16E-10	Reject the H_0 that the distribution is normally distributed[a].
Kolmogorov–Smirnov test[b]	0.318	NA	Reject the H_0 that the distribution is normally distributed.
Chi-square test	17.6	0.001	Reject the H_0 that the distribution is normally distributed.

[a]Based on approximate p values.
[b]The critical value for the K–S test given a sample size of 30 is ~0.24.

and chi-squared to the original influent and effluent load data are presented in tabular format in Tables 13.23 and 13.24.

The results for all tests necessitate the conclusion that neither the influent nor effluent data are normally distributed at the 95% confidence level. However, the same tests produce different results when applied to log-transformed influent, effluent, and differences between paired load data (see Tables 13.25, 13.26, and 13.27).

Table 13.25   Example 3: test for normality of distribution of transformed influent load data (significance level = 0.05).

Procedure	Test value	p value	Conclusion
Shapiro–Wilk test	0.972	0.593	Fail to reject the H_0 that the distribution is normally distributed[a].
Anderson–Darling test	0.353	0.441	Fail to reject the H_0 that the distribution is normally distributed[a].
Kolmogorov–Smirnov test[b]	0.103	NA	Fail to reject the H_0 that the distribution is normally distributed.
Chi-square test	13.4	.004	Reject the H_0 that the distribution is normally distributed.

[a]Based on approximate p values.
[b]The critical value for the K–S test given a sample size of 30 is ~0.24.

Table 13.26   Example 3: test for normality of distribution of transformed effluent load data (significance level = 0.05).

Procedure	Test value	p value	Conclusion
Shapiro–Wilk test	0.961	0.319	Fail to reject the H_0 that the distribution is normally distributed[a].
Anderson–Darling test	0.504	0.188	Fail to reject the H_0 that the distribution is normally distributed[a].
Kolmogorov–Smirnov test[b]	0.151	NA	Fail to reject the H_0 that the distribution is normally distributed.
Chi-square test	12.8	0.005	Reject the H_0 that the distribution is normally distributed.

[a]Based on approximate p values.
[b]The critical value for the K–S test given a sample size of 30 is ~0.24.

In this instance, with the exception of the chi-square method, the tests fail to reject the null hypothesis that the transformed data are normally distributed. Once again, the rejection of the null hypothesis by the chi-square test may be explained by the sensitivity of the test to variation in the tails of the data. Thus, it can be concluded with 95% confidence that the influent, effluent, and differences between pairs are log-normally distributed data sets.

TABLE 13.27   Example 3: Test for normality of distribution of differences between transformed influent–effluent pairs (significance level = 0.05).

Procedure	Test value	p value	Conclusion
Shapiro–Wilk test	0.95	0.21	Fail to reject the H_0 that the distribution is normally distributed[a].
Anderson–Darling test	0.60	0.11	Fail to reject the H_0 that the distribution is normally distributed[a].
Kolmogorov–Smirnov test[b]	0.17	NA	Fail to reject the H_0 that the distribution is normally distributed.
Chi-square test	9.00	0.029	Reject the H_0 that the distribution is normally distributed.

[a]Based on approximate p values.
[b]The critical value for the K–S test given a sample size of 30 is ~0.24.

TABLE 13.28   Example 3: F test (transformed data).

F value	2.1
p value	0.03
F critical	1.96
Conclusion	Reject H_0

TABLE 13.29   Example 3: Bartlett's test (transformed data).

p value	0.17
Conclusion	Fails to reject H_0

10.3.2.1.1 Variance

Next, the assumption that the transformed influent and effluent data sets feature a similar degree of variance should be tested. The null hypothesis that the variances are equal has been evaluated with an F test and Bartlett's test and the results are presented in Tables 13.28 and 13.29.

The F test rejected the null hypothesis with 95% confidence; however, Bartlett's test failed to do so. These tests are inconclusive and, therefore, further analysis should be considered.

10.3.2.1.2 Correlation and Prediction

During the qualitative analysis, a scatter plot provided inconclusive evidence as to whether or not the paired influent and effluent load of data set 3 are well-approximated by a linear trend line. However, because it has been confirmed that the data are log-normally distributed, of most interest is whether or not the *transformed* data are well-approximated by a linear relationship. This question can be answered by determining the strength of the linear relationship. A correlation analysis of the transformed, paired influent and effluent data reveals that the two data sets are highly correlated, with a correlation coefficient, *r*, which is equal to 0.92.

This knowledge can be used to develop a linear trend line that accurately describes the relationship between influent and effluent load (see Figure 13.15). In addition, confidence intervals can be determined that will indicate the most likely range of effluent load data that will result from a given influent load after treatment by this particular control.

10.3.2.2 Difference between Influent and Effluent

Data set 3 was found to be log-normally distributed, but tests for equal variance were inconclusive. In addition to a nonparametric test, a parametric method that is insensitive to the condition of equal variances is applied to the transformed data set. Results of a *t* test and a Wilcoxon test are presented here.

A *t* test will reveal whether or not the difference between influent and effluent concentrations is significant at the 95% confidence level. The test is applied to the set of values representing the difference between transformed, paired influent and effluent data (see Table 13.30). The proposed null hypothesis is that the mean of this data

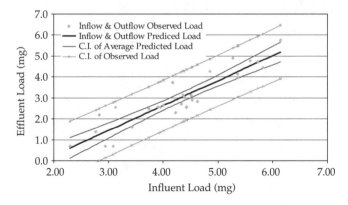

FIGURE 13.15 Example 3: Linear trend line and confidence intervals.

set is zero, that is, that the average difference between influent and effluent concentrations is zero.

The calculated t statistic for the observed data is larger than the critical value of t, and the p value is less than the specified significance level, 0.05. As a result, the null hypothesis that the average difference between influent and effluent means is equal to zero can be rejected with 95% confidence.

Application of the Wilcoxon test to the data yields similar results (see Table 13.31). The null hypothesis that the average difference between influent and effluent concentrations is zero is once again rejected with 95% confidence.

10.3.2.3 Conclusions

For example 3, it was determined that the influent, effluent, and difference between pairs of TKN loads are log-normally distributed data sets. The tests for equal variance were inconclusive. The difference between influent and effluent TKN concentrations is nonzero with 95% confidence, as indicated by the t test and Wilcoxon test. As a result, it can be concluded that the control has a notable effect on the quality of stormwater runoff. In addition, according to the correlation coefficient and regression

TABLE 13.30   Example 3: t test.

Parameter	Value
t statistic	13.62
Degrees of freedom	29
Significance level	0.05
Critical value of t statistic	2.05
p value	1.96E-14

TABLE 13.31   Example 3: Wilcoxon test results.

Parameter	Value
Sample size, n	30
Mean	232.5
Standard deviation	48.62
Z statistic	−4.78
p value	8.67E-07

analysis, the majority of the variation in effluent values can be explained by variation in influent values. This indicates that effluent load is largely dependent on influent load, and an accurate predictive equation can be generated to determine effluent load from influent load. This is in contrast to example 2, where a similar predictive equation could not be generated to relate influent EMC values to effluent EMC values.

The examples presented here represent a small sample of the wide variety of data that may be collected to analyze control performance in the real world. Data sets may vary in size, distribution, range, variance, and so on. It is clear that analysis methods should be chosen carefully and according to the characteristics of the data set. Even so, results may prove inconclusive and necessitate more indepth analysis. It is also clear that concentration and load data, even when they describe a single control's performance given identical events, may result in different conclusions.

11.0 REFERENCES

American Public Health Association; American Water Works Association; Water Environment Federation (1998) *Standard Methods for the Examination of Water and Wastewater,* 20th ed.; American Public Health Association: Washington, D.C.

American Society for Testing and Materials (1997) *Standard Guide for Monitoring Sediment in Watersheds;* ASTM-D-6145–97; American Society for Testing and Materials: West Conshohocken, Pennsylvania.

Barrett, M. (2004) Performance Comparison of Structural Stormwater BMPs. *Water Environ. Res.,* **76,** 85.

Behera, P. K.; Li, J. L.; Adams, B. (2000) Characterization of Urban Runoff Quality: A Toronto Case Study. In *Applied Modeling of Urban Water Systems,* Volume 8; James, W., Ed.; Computational Hydraulics International: Guelph, Ontario, Canada.

California Department of Transportation (2003) *Comprehensive Monitoring Protocols Guidance Manual: Stormwater Quality Monitoring Protocols, Particle/Sediment Monitoring Protocols, Gross Solids Monitoring Protocols, Toxicity Monitoring Protocols, and Caltrans Data Reporting Protocols;* California Department of Transportation: Sacramento, California.

Center for Watershed Protection (2007) *National Pollutant Removal Performance Database, Version 3.0;* Center for Watershed Protection: Ellicott City, Maryland.

Church, P. E.; Granto, G. E.; Owens, O. W. (1999) *Basic Requirements for Collecting, Documenting, and Reporting Precipitation and Stormwater-Flow Measurements;* USGS Open-File Report 99–25; U.S. Geological Survey: Northborough, Massachusetts.

Clary, J.; Quigley, M.; Poresky, A.; Earles, A.; Strecker, E.; Leisenring, M.; Jones, J. (2011) Integration of Low-Impact Development into the International Stormwater BMP Database. *J. Irrig. Drainage Eng., Special Issue: Urban Storm-Water Management in the 21st Century,* **137** (3), 190–198.

Federal Highway Administration (2000) *Stormwater Best Management Practices in an Ultra-Urban Setting: Selection and Monitoring;* FHWA-EP-00–002; U.S. Department of Transportation, Federal Highway Administration: Washington, D.C. http://www.fhwa.dot.gov/environment/ultraurb/index.htm (accessed Jan 2011).

Grant, D. M.; Dawson, B. D. (1997) *Isco Open Channel Flow Measurement Handbook,* 5th ed.; Isco, Inc.: Lincoln, Nebraska.

International Stormwater BMP Database. http://www.bmpdatabase.org (accessed Jan 2011).

Lenhart, J. (2007a) Evaluating BMP's Programs, Success and Issues; Queensland Stormwater Industry Association, Annual State Conference; Sunshine Coast, Australia; Keynote: Lenhart, J. Evaluating BMP's Programs, Success and Issues; CONTECH Stormwater Solutions, Portland, Oregon. http://www.stormwater360.co.nz/images/lenhart%20bmp%20evaluation%20sia.pdf (accessed Feb 2008).

Lenhart, J. (2007b) BMP Performance Expectation Functions—A Simple Method for Evaluating Stormwater Treatment BMP Performance Data. *Proceedings of the 9th Biennial Conference on Stormwater Research & Watershed Management,* University of Central Florida, May, Orlando, Florida.

McBean, E. A.; Rovers, F. A. (1998) *Statistical Procedures for Analysis of Environmental Monitoring Data and Risk Assessment,* Volume 3; Prentice Hall: Upper Saddle River, New Jersey.

Minton, G. R. (2011) *Stormwater Treatment—Biological, Chemical and Engineering Principles,* 3rd ed.; Resource Planning Associates: Seattle, Washington.

Ridder, S. A.; Darcy, S. I.; Calvert, P. P.; Lenhart, J. H. (2002) Influence of Analytical Method, Data Summarization Method, and Particle Size on Total Suspended

Solids (TSS) Removal Efficiency. In *Global Solutions for Urban Drainage;* 9ICUD 2002; American Society of Civil Engineers: Reston, Virginia.

Schueler, T. (1996) Irreducible Pollutant Concentrations Discharged from Urban BMP's. *Watershed Protection Tech.,* **2** (2), 75.

Sharkey, L. J. (2006) *The Performance of Bioretention Areas in North Carolina: A Study of Water Quality, Water Quantity, and Soil Media.* Master's Thesis, North Carolina State University, Department of Biological and Agricultural Engineering, Raleigh, North Carolina.

Siegel, S. (1956) *Nonparametric Statistics for the Behavioral Sciences;* McGraw-Hill: New York.

Strecker, E. W. (1994) Constituents and Methods for Assessing BMPs. In *Proceedings of the Engineering Foundation Conference on Storm Water Monitoring;* Crested Butte, Colorado; Aug 7–12.

Strecker, E. W.; Kersnar, J. M.; Driscoll, E. D.; Horner, R. R. (1992) *The Use of Wetlands for Controlling Storm Water Pollution;* The Terrene Institute: Washington, D.C.

Strecker, E. W.; Quigley, M. M.; Urbonas, B. R.; Jones, J. E.; Clary, J. K. (2001) Determining Urban Storm Water BMP Effectiveness. *J. Water Resour. Plann. Manage.,* **127** (3), 144.

Tailor, A.; Wong, T. (2002a) *Non-Structural Stormwater Quality Best Management Practices—A Literature Review of Their Value and Life-Cycle Costs;* EPA Victoria Technical Report 02/13; Cooperative Research Center for Catchment Hydrology: Victoria, Australia. http://www.catchment.crc.org.au/pdfs/Technical200213.pdf (accessed Jan 2011).

Tailor, A.; Wong, T. (2002b) *Non-Structural Stormwater Quality Best Management Practices—An Overview of their Use, Value, Cost and Evaluation;* EPA Victoria Technical Report 02/11; Cooperative Research Centre for Catchment Hydrology: Victoria, Australia. http://www.catchment.crc.org.au/pdfs/technical200211.pdf (accessed Jan 2011).

Technology Acceptance Reciprocity Partnership (2001) *The TARP Protocol for Stormwater Best Management Practice Demonstrations.* http://www.state.nj.us/dep/stormwater/docs/tarp_stormwater_protocol.pdf (accessed July 14, 2011).

Urbonas, B. R. (2000) Assessment of Stormwater Best Management Practice Effectiveness. In *Innovative Urban Wet-Weather Flow Management Systems;*

Field, R., Heaney, J. P., Pitt, R., Eds.; Technomic Publishing Co., Inc.: Lancaster, Pennsylvania; pp 255– 300.

Urbonas, B. R. (1995) Recommended Parameters to Report with BMP Monitoring Data. *J. Water Resour. Plann. Manage.*, **121** (1), 23.

U.S. Environmental Protection Agency (1994a) *Laboratory Data Validation: Functional Guidelines for Evaluating Inorganics Analyses*; U.S. Environmental Protection Agency, Data Review Workgroup: Washington, D.C.

U.S. Environmental Protection Agency (1994b) *Laboratory Data Validation: Functional Guidelines for Evaluating Organics Analyses*; U.S. Environmental Protection Agency, Data Review Workgroup: Washington, D.C.

U.S. Environmental Protection Agency (1994c) *Guidance for the Data Quality Objectives Process*; EPA-QA/G-4; U.S. Environmental Protection Agency: Washington, D.C.

U.S. Environmental Protection Agency (1999a) *Methods and Guidance for Analysis of Water* [CD-ROM]; Version 2.0; EPA-821/C-99–004; U.S. Environmental Protection Agency: Washington, D.C.

U.S. Environmental Protection Agency (1999b) *Rapid Bioassessment Protocols for Use in Streams and Wadeable Rivers: Periphyton, Benthic Macroinvertebrates and Fish*, 2nd ed.; EPA-841/B-99–002; U.S. Environmental Protection Agency, Office of Water: Washington, D.C.

U.S. Environmental Protection Agency (2001) *Techniques for Tracking, Evaluating, and Reporting the Implementation of Nonpoint Source Control Measures: Urban*; EPA-841/B-00–007; U.S. Environmental Protection Agency, Office of Water: Washington, D.C.

U.S. Environmental Protection Agency (2002) *Guidelines Establishing Test Procedures for the Analysis of Pollutants; Whole Effluent Toxicity Test Methods; Final Rule.* http://www.epa.gov/fedrgstr/EPA-WATER/2002/November/Day-19/w29072.htm (accessed July 15, 2011).

U.S. Environmental Protection Agency (2002a) *Environmental Monitoring and Assessment Program—Research Strategy*; EPA-620/R-02–002; U.S. Environmental Protection Agency, Office of Research and Development, National Health and Environmental Effects Research Laboratory: Research Triangle Park, North Carolina.

U.S. Environmental Protection Agency (2002b) *Guidance for Quality Assurance Project Plans;* EPA-240/R-02–009; U.S. Environmental Protection Agency, Office of Environmental Information: Washington, D.C.

U.S. Environmental Protection Agency (2002c) *Urban Stormwater BMP Performance Monitoring: A Guidance Manual for Meeting the National Stormwater BMP Database Requirements;* EPA-821/B-02–001; U.S. Environmental Protection Agency, Office of Water: Washington, D.C.

U.S. Environmental Protection Agency (2004) *The Use of Best Management Practices (BMPs) in Urban Watersheds;* EPA-600/R-04–184; U.S. Environmental Protection Agency, Office of Research and Development: Washington, D.C.

U.S. Environmental Protection Agency (2006) *Guidance on Systematic Planning Using the Data Quality Objectives Process;* EPA-240/B-06–001; U.S. Environmental Protection Agency, Office of Environmental Information: Washington, D.C.

Van Buren, M. A.; Watt, W. E.; Marsalek, J. (1997) Applications of the Log-Normal and Normal Distributions to Stormwater Quality Parameters. *Water Res.,* **31** (1), 95.

Washington State Department of Ecology (2002) Guidance for Evaluating Emerging Stormwater Treatment Technologies, Technology Assessment Protocol-Ecology (TAPE). http://www.ecy.wa.gov/biblio/0210037.html (accessed July 14, 2011).

Water Environment Research Foundation (2011) *Research Digest: International Stormwater Best Management Practices (BMP) Database Pollutant Category Technical Summaries.* Prepared by Wright Water Engineers and Geosyntec Consultants for Water Environment Research Foundation, Federal Highway Administration, Environmental and Water Resources Institute of the American Society of Civil Engineers, July.

Weisberg, S. (2005) *Applied Linear Regression,* 3rd ed.; Wiley & Sons: Hoboken, New Jersey.

Winer, R. (2000) *National Pollutant Removal Performance Database for Stormwater Treatment Practices,* 2nd ed.; U.S. Environmental Protection Agency, Office of Science and Technology; Center for Watershed Protection: Ellicott City, Maryland; p 29.

Chapter 14

Analytical Tools for Simulation of Stormwater Controls

(continued)

(continued)

1.0 INTRODUCTION—MODELING NEEDS

As described in earlier chapters, numerous stormwater control technologies exist with varying levels of capital and operation and maintenance costs and associated performances. Some of these controls can function in a series or as integrated units to reduce the peak flow or volume of stormwater and pollutant loads and help in achieving desired volumetric and water quality targets. With hundreds of millions of dollars (U.S. dollars) at stake to comply with regulatory requirements for municipal separate storm sewer systems (U.S. EPA, 2010), it is important for municipal, industrial, and watershed agencies to screen and select site-specific and feasible stormwater controls that will attain and continue to achieve technical and regulatory requirements in a cost-effective manner.

One can choose to implement such controls, monitor their actual performance, and make determinations along the way on additional controls necessary to achieve desired goals. This trial-and-error process involves significant investment of resources and a long time frame to realize benefits. Alternatively, analytical tools can help in a priori and cost-effective evaluation of the necessary control elements.

Analytical tools (or models) can simulate physical processes of rainfall, evapotranspiration, infiltration to groundwater, and overland sheet-flow processes from individual urban land areas to outfalls, and eventually to receiving waters. In addition to characterizing reductions in volume and peak runoff rates, the accumulation and wash-off of various pollutants and fate and transport processes like settling, filtration, and decay can be simulated to quantify load reductions.

The models allow decision-makers to represent hydrologic and water quality processes and to quantify potential benefits associated with a single or combination of stormwater controls. Knowing the life cycle costs from other installations in the region or around the country, one can evaluate the cost implications of various systems of controls that can all achieve the same pollution reduction goal. This assessment will help in selecting a suitable, cost-effective, and feasible set of controls that an engineer can pursue for final design and implementation. Several such models have been developed in the public and commercial domain (Rangarajan, 2005).

Models are generally designed to characterize stormwater control performances to answer the following questions (Brown and Huber, 2004; Strecker et al., 2001):

- How much catchment runoff is reduced by a control measure (e.g., through infiltration or evapotranspiration)?

- Of the runoff not reduced, how much can be detained in temporary storage?

- What portion of the runoff is treated and how much is bypassed?

- What are the quality characteristics of the treated effluent?

- How much downstream flow management is provided by a stormwater control or system of controls if the goal is to mitigate downstream flooding or geomorphological effects?

Answering these questions provides an understanding of the physical, chemical, and biological processes that occur within stormwater controls. The hydrologic and water quality-related unit processes are briefly described in the next section, followed by a discussion on models pertinent to unit operations (that may include one or more unit processes to achieve a desired goal). Guidance for reviewing available public and commercial domain models is provided subsequently, along with an example case study. Discussions on model calibration and application are provided in the last few sections of this chapter, supported by two watershed-scale case studies.

2.0 MODELING PROCESSES IN STORMWATER CONTROLS

Traditionally, stormwater controls have been designed to reduce peak or volumetric runoff in urban watershed, with the intent of minimizing flooding, erosion, or combined sewer overflows, as an example. Since the early 1990s, water quality and geomorphological goals have necessitated practitioners to go farther than traditional design standards. Modeling stormwater controls in this modern context requires simulation of unit processes that represent the various physical, chemical, and biological processes. It is important to recognize that the unit process representation requires extensive data on stormwater treatability and site and design descriptions. Most controls are modeled by a heuristic combination of unit process simulation and empirical performance measures (Huber et al., 2006). Representation of the unit processes is discussed in the following subsections, to complement their descriptions in earlier chapters of this manual. Hydrologic and hydraulic quantity-based processes are discussed first, followed by water quality processes.

2.1 Modeling of Hydrologic and Hydraulic Processes

2.1.1 Evapotranspiration

Evaporation and transpiration together, known as *evapotranspiration*, can represent a significant hydrologic loss depending on prevailing temperatures and vegetation types. Pan evaporation studies are recommended to develop site-specific data. Because evapotranspiration exhibits significant temporal variability, pan evaporation data collected at nearby meteorological stations by the National Oceanic and Atmospheric Administration can be used to develop representative evapotranspiration values on an hourly or daily time scale for an urban watershed.

Often, evapotranspiration is defined in terms of a potential evapotranspiration (PET), which is the loss rate that occurs under specified, standard vegetative conditions and under an unlimited supply of water in the soil. A common method for PET estimation is the Penman–Monteith equation (Allen et al., 1998), which is shown in eq 14.1, as follows:

$$PET = 0.408D\left(R_n - G_s\right) + ku_2\left(\frac{900}{T+273}\right)\left(\frac{e_s - e_a}{D + k(1 + 0.34u_2)}\right) \qquad (14.1)$$

where

PET = potential evapotranspiration in mm/d;

T and u_2 = air temperature and wind speed in °C and meters per second, respectively, at a height of 2 m above the water surface;

e_s and e_a = saturated vapor pressure and the vapor pressure of air, respectively, in kPa (i.e., kN/m²);

D = slope of the saturated vapor pressure curve ($\partial e_s / \partial T$);

k = psychometric constant approximately equal to 0.0668 kPa/°C;

R_n = the solar radiation influx; and

G_s = sensible heat flux to the underlying soil or water, both expressed in MJ/m²/d.

The PET value derived for the water surface must be translated appropriately, using a pan coefficient, for specific land-cover categories such as synthetic lawns, dense vegetation, large tree canopies, and agricultural areas.

Evaporation is considered for both impervious areas (roads, walkways, driveways, building roofs, and paved surfaces) and pervious areas (covered with soil or vegetation such as turf). Evapotranspiration can be considered as unimportant when performing evaluations on an individual, large storm basis to support designs. However, it is important for long-term simulations to accurately characterize the effects of antecedent soil and plant moisture conditions on the resulting runoff. Additional information on evapotranspiration is presented in Chapter 3.

2.1.2   Infiltration

Infiltration represents a dominant hydrologic loss in urban systems, and its rate is dependent on soil characteristics, rainfall intensity, and availability of moisture at the ground surface. The Horton or Green–Ampt infiltration equations are typically used to characterize this loss in pervious areas. Impervious areas are assumed to have no infiltration. Horton's equation is empirical, but the Green–Ampt equation has a combination of empirical and physically based parameters such as infiltration capacity, maximum infiltration volume, average capillary suction, initial moisture deficit, and saturated hydraulic conductivity. The Green–Ampt equation can be used if sufficient experimental data are available or can be collected to support the parameter characterization. Otherwise, the simple Horton's equation can be used.

The simpler form of Horton's equation is given as

$$f_p = f_c + \left(f_o - f_c \right) e^{kt} \tag{14.2}$$

where

f_p = the infiltration rate at any time t;

f_c = the minimum (or ultimate) infiltration rate;

f_o = the maximum (or initial) infiltration rate;

t = time from beginning of consecutive infiltration; and

k = the decay coefficient.

Infiltration capacity will be recovered during subsequent dry periods. The time for full recovery of f_o must be specified such that if back-to-back storms occur, only a partial recovery takes place until the second storm is accounted for and the losses are computed accordingly.

Infiltrometer studies can be performed to characterize site-specific infiltration values, especially if the native soil is disturbed and compacted. This process is particularly important for highly urbanized watersheds that experience frequent new development or redevelopment. Otherwise, the values can be assumed based on the native soil conditions in pervious areas and adjusted during model calibration. Huber and Dickinson (1988) and Pitt and Voorhees (2000) reviewed initial values that can be chosen based on the hydrologic soil classification.

2.1.3   Depression Storage

Depression storage is an initial loss in both impervious and pervious areas, which can represent the potholes and other surface depressions on the ground. Overland runoff can occur only after filling in these depressions and when the water held is lost through evaporation subsequent to a wet weather period. Detention storage is the buildup of small depths of water necessary to initiate the runoff process. Practical measurement of depression and detention storage components is extremely difficult and, therefore, a lumped depression storage parameter is often used in urban hydrology models to characterize this loss.

Typical depression storage values are from 0.2 to 1.3 mm (0.01 to 0.05 in.) for impervious areas and can be much higher (e.g., 5 to 10 mm [0.2 to 0.4 in.]) for pervious areas (James et al., 1999; Walker, 2007).

The three hydrologic losses discussed previously (i.e., evaporation and transpiration, infiltration, and depression storage) determine the overall volume of overland runoff generated from a drainage area (see Figure 14.1). In terms of model calibration for these losses, the depression storage can be estimated from runoff responses for smaller storms with total rain volumes of approximately 6 mm (0.25 in.) or less. A combination of depression storage and evapotranspiration is dominant in this

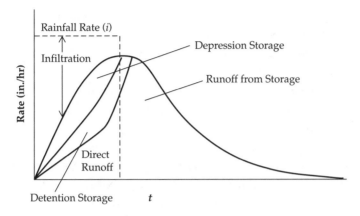

FIGURE 14.1   Typical distribution of flow caused by a storm.

rainfall range for impervious areas. Similarly, the extent of infiltration and evapo-transpiration can be estimated based on runoff responses for moderate storms ranging from, for example, 6 to 19 mm (0.25 to 0.75 in.). Depending on rainfall intensity, all the losses can play a role in this rainfall range for pervious areas.

2.1.4   Flow Routing

Many stormwater controls involve storage elements and outlet controls that route inflow hydrographs to meet the flow or water quality-based goals. The peak flow and volume of the inflow hydrograph and the characteristics of channel and storage elements govern attenuation that occurs within these controls.

2.1.4.1 Peak Inflow Computation

The dominant approach used in the design of urban storm drainage systems for small catchments is the Rational Method, shown in eq 14.3, as follows:

$$Q = C i A \qquad (14.3)$$

where
   C = the runoff coefficient,
   i = the rainfall intensity, and
   A = the catchment area.

   This empirical formulation linearly correlates the rainfall to runoff using a runoff coefficient, which is a collective function representing the influence of physical characteristics such as land use, soil type, and ground slope. Consequently, it demands considerable judgment and experience in parameter selection. It is applicable for small drainage areas of less than 20 ha (50 ac), and is generally used for sewer sizing. Average rainfall intensity for a storm duration equivalent to the time of concentration for the drainage area should be used as i.

The time of concentration (T_c) is critical for proper application of this method to sewer sizing. Bedient et al. (2007) define T_c as the travel time of a wave to move hydraulically from the most distant point in a catchment to its outlet. As sewers are designed at a block level in urban areas, the T_c is typically 5 to 10 minutes. Several empirical equations including the Federal Aviation Administration, Kirpich, and Kerby equations can be found in the literature (e.g., Nicklow et al. [2006]). A compilation with examples is available at http://www.lmnoeng.com/Hydrology/TimeConc.htm.

If the time of concentration time increases, the rainfall intensity decreases in accordance with the following equation:

$$i = \frac{a}{(c + T_c^b)}$$

(14.4)

where

T_c = the time of concentration and

a, b, and c = regression parameters derived from the intensity-duration-frequency characteristics for a specific geographic region.

The expression in eq 14.4 is known as an intensity–frequency–duration curve. This method involves implicit flow routing by varying peak intensity with changes in the time of concentration.

Another common empirical formulation is the Natural Resources Conservation Service (NRCS) Technical Release 55 method for estimating peak runoff in small- to mid-sized catchments (USDA, 1986; 2009). The peak runoff is computed as follows:

$$Q_p = q_u \, A P_e \, F_p$$

(14.5)

where

Q_p = in cubic meters per second;

q_u = the unit peak discharge in cubic meters per second per centimeter of runoff over a 1-km² area;

A = in square kilometers;

P_e = the 24-hour effective rainfall in centimeters for a given return period; and

F_p = a dimensionless adjustment factor to account for ponds and swamps that are not in the primary flow path.

The unit peak discharge (q_u) is a function of the time of concentration and the initial abstraction (I_a) to rainfall (P) ratio. McCuen (1998) presents q_u in graphical form for the various synthetic unit hydrograph distributions developed by the Soil Conservation Service (SCS), namely, Type I, Type 1A, Type II, and Type III, for a given time of concentration and I_a/P ratio.

The depth of runoff, P_e, is determined by the curve number method as follows:

$$P_e = \frac{(P_{24} - 0.2 S_r)^2}{(P_{24} + 0.8 S_r)} \tag{14.6}$$

for $P_{24} > 0.2 \, S_r$, where P_{24} is the 24-hour rainfall in centimeters and S_r is the potential maximum retention of soil. This method is generally recommended for homogeneous catchments with curve numbers generally greater than 50 and also for small- to mid-sized basins. Details on the application of this method are described in *Urban Hydrology for Small Watersheds* (USDA, 1986).

Peak flow estimations of this type are typically used for sizing controls to achieve a postdevelopment peak flow control objective.

2.1.4.2 Continuous Flow Routing

Channel storage can be significant in large watersheds, resulting in a longer time of concentration. Modeling methodology should account for variations in land use (e.g., urbanization), soil types, and topography that influence the time of concentration. Field-data derived or synthetic unit hydrographs (e.g., NRCS triangular, Snyder's, Colorado unit hydrograph, and Santa Barbara unit hydrograph) can be used to generate continuous time series of runoff responses to given rainfall conditions. Alternatively, non-empirical, physically based hydrologic routing methods can be used. Some overland flow routing formulations implemented in various urban runoff models are listed in Table 14.1.

Models such as the U.S. Environmental Protection Agency's (U.S. EPA's) Stormwater Management Model (SWMM) have many synthetic and user-defined hydrograph functions to route flows to a sewer system (i.e., catch basin or manhole). The subcatchment width and Manning's roughness for both impervious and pervious surfaces need to be specified to enable routing.

After deriving the runoff considering hydrologic losses, flow routing through open channels, storage reservoirs, and closed conduits is performed using the principles of continuity and momentum. A number of simpler formulations, both empirically and physically based, can be used for flow routing. These formulations include

TABLE 14.1   Some overland flow routing methods in urban runoff models.

Method	Brief description
UHG	A linear conceptual model used to transform rainfall excess to a runoff hydrograph. A convolution approach is used to combine UHGs for the given storm inputs to develop direct runoff and then add the baseflow to generate the entire storm hydrograph.
Wallingford	The flow is routed using two equal linear reservoirs in series whose routing coefficient depends on rainfall intensity, contributing area, and surface slope.
Large catchment	The flow is routed using two equal linear reservoirs in a series whose routing coefficient depends on rainfall intensity, contributing area, and surface slope as in the Wallingford model. The time-step lag and routing multiplier are applied and are functions of subcatchment area, ground slope, and catchment length.
SPRINT	The flow is routed using a single linear reservoir whose routing coefficient depends on subcatchment area, ground slope, and percent imperviousness.
Desbordes	The flow is routed using a single linear reservoir, whose routing coefficient depends on subcatchment area, ground slope, percent imperviousness, catchment length, storm duration, and storm depth.
U.S. EPA's SWMM	The flow is routed using a single nonlinear reservoir model developed based on Manning's equation, whose routing coefficient depends on surface roughness, surface area, ground slope, and catchment width.

storage indication, Muskingum, Muskingum–Cunge, and Modified Att–Kin methods (Nicklow et al., 2006).

Simpler hydrology methods such as unit hydrographs are often linked with simple routing methods. An example is a lumped routing technique for urban sewer systems that simply adds the first segment's flow to the next segment's flow with the appropriate time of travel (i.e., L/V, where L is the sewer length and V is the design velocity). Mays (2001) presents this formulation in the following equation:

$$\sum Q_{ij} + Q_j - Q_0 = \frac{dS}{dt} \tag{14.7}$$

where

Q_{ij} = the inflow from the ith sewer into junction j;

Q_j = the direct inflow (runoff in storm sewers and runoff and sanitary flow in combined sewers) collected at the junction;

Q_o = the outflow from the junction into the downstream sewer; and

S = the water stored in the junction or manhole.

The Storage, Treatment, Overflow, Runoff Model (STORM) developed by the U.S. Army Corps of Engineers (1977) and the RAINMAN model developed by HydroQual, Inc. (McMillin and Omer, 2000) use the Rational Method to generate urban runoff and the aforementioned formulation (eq 14.7) to route the storm and combined flows through the network to their outfalls or the wastewater treatment plant.

Detailed models use more complex, fully dynamic governing equations for non-uniform and unsteady flow routing in open channels and closed conduits. The most common formulations used in commercial and public domain models are the Saint Venant's equations that are based on mass, energy, and momentum conservation.

Explicit and implicit (and hybrid) solution techniques are used to solve complex equations for determining the velocity and depth values at each time step of the simulation period. The computational effort needed for these models can be significantly larger than simple equations. However, complex formulations can be more appropriate when the system hydraulic conditions are critical in an urban drainage area or within a stormwater control. Examples of critical conditions are when the hydraulic residence time is limiting, surcharging occurs in sewers, and basement and surface flooding occurs in a drainage area or there is excessive loading on high-rate treatment systems.

2.2 Modeling of Water Quality Processes

The physical, chemical, and biological processes in stormwater controls can include sedimentation, filtration, oxidation, adsorption, volatilization, precipitation, nitrification, and microbial decomposition. These unit processes are described in Chapter 4. The potential modeling formulations discussed in Chapter 4 have been incorporated to some of the common models used for urban runoff characterization and stormwater controls.

3.0 CONCEPTUAL MODELS FOR STORMWATER CONTROLS

One or more of the aforementioned hydrologic and water quality processes can govern operations within each type of stormwater control. As described in Chapter 4, a *unit operation* is defined as a structure in which one or more unit processes occurs. The generic modeling formulations to characterize specific unit operations are discussed in this section.

3.1   Basins

Stormwater basins can be designed to meet flood control, channel protection, and pollutant removal goals. The lowest storage zone of a basin defines the required volume for treatment, the middle portion for channel protection, and the upper volume for mitigation of flooding events that occur infrequently. The flood mitigation volume is determined using an empirical or physically based hydrologic model for a selected design storm. The design level of protection typically depends on local regulations and can vary between 10 and 100 years. Hydraulic efficiency is a significant design consideration for water quality and channel protection volumes and is discussed in detail in Chapter 4.

Water quality treatment is achieved mostly through sedimentation. The designer should look at factors that affect ideal settling conditions in these basins. Dead zones, short-circuiting, turbulence, and uneven distribution of stormwater entering and leaving the basin can lead to complexities in characterizing the sedimentation process. Some basin-type controls such as wet vaults and swirl concentrators operate on complex hydrodynamics. In such instances, a more complex computational fluid dynamics (CFD) methodology can be used (Pathapati and Sansalone, 2007). It should be noted that data requirements to support model calibration and computational effort associated with CFD are enormous. Therefore, this methodology should be explored only when detailed evaluations are necessary and resources are available to perform them.

3.1.1   Wet and Dry Basins

Currently, in U.S. EPA's SWMM, for example, removal in wet basins can be modeled using a generic function in which removal can be a function of detention time, influent concentration, and other state variables. The Storage and Treatment (S&T) block of U.S. EPA's SWMM also allows routing and settling of particulates described by a settling velocity (or particle size and specific gravity) distribution. Modeling basins involves storage and release of excess stormwater capture volumes based on hydraulic controls (Urbonas and Stahre, 1993). The stored volume can also be subjected to the appropriate hydrologic losses including infiltration and evapotranspiration. Water quality unit processes currently available in U.S. EPA's SWMM and suggestions for further improvement are detailed in Chapter 4 of Huber et al. (2006).

One common heuristic solution to represent dynamic settling in dry basins is to use Fair and Geyer's (1954) "tanks in series" method for analysis of imperfect sedimentation basins for water and wastewater treatment, in which the captured fraction of particles that have settling velocity (v_s) is defined as follows:

$$R = \left(1 - \frac{C_{out}}{C_{in}} \right) = 1 - \left(1 + \frac{v_s}{NQ/A} \right)^{-N} \tag{14.8}$$

where

R = the fraction captured or retained in the basin,
C_{out} = the effluent event mean concentration (EMC),
C_{in} = the influent EMC,
Q = the basin outflow rate,
A = the basin surface area, and
N = the number of tanks in a series, which is an empirical measure of hydraulic efficiency.

Simulation of detention in dry basins involves modeling of the storage routing based on outlet characteristics. These controls are designed to drain slowly through a modified outlet configuration. U.S. EPA's SWMM is well-equipped to characterize the hydrologic and water quality processes of detention and extended detention. At a site scale, the HydroCAD or StormCAD models that use simple runoff generation and routing can also be used for the design of detention tanks.

3.1.2 Wetlands

Simulation of wetlands is similar to wet basins, with additional capabilities to provide treatment to stormwater by sedimentation and through additional biological and filtration mechanisms. These pollutant removal mechanisms are simulated with methods applicable to wet basins.

3.2 Gross Pollutant Traps

Mathematical formulations related to the design of gross pollutant traps are reviewed in Chapter 10. The analytical formulations in urban runoff models, including entry and exit losses, are typically used to represent hydraulic head losses that occur in these controls. The following equations present formulations proposed by Tchobanoglous and Burton (1991) for bar racks and fine screens:

Bar Racks
$$h_L = \frac{1}{0.7}\left(\frac{V^2 - v^2}{2g}\right)$$
(14.9)

Fine Screens
$$h_L = \frac{1}{2C_g}\left(\frac{Q}{A}\right)^2$$
(14.10)

One of the challenges associated with modeling the performance of these controls is the clogging of screens, nets, or hoods over time. For example, the State of New Jersey Department of Environmental Protection is one of the first regulatory agencies to require communities with combined sewers to install screens or nets for floatables and solids capture at outfalls. Because the required screen spacing was 12 mm (0.5 in.), these units often were reported to be clogged with significantly higher head losses and associated surcharging in the outfall sewers. In terms of modeling this maintenance-related issue, empirical or laboratory data are used to assume a level of clogging of the screen or bar openings, which ranges between 50 and 90%, and the head losses are recalculated using the aforementioned formulations. Imposing such head losses in a sewer hydraulic model can help decision-makers in assessing the potential consequences on hydraulic conditions and undertaking mitigation strategies.

3.3   Drain Inlet Inserts

Also known as *catch basin inserts*, drain inlet inserts are designed to be suspended from the storm drain inlet structure to provide a treatment mechanism such as filtration, sedimentation, or gravitational adsorption of oils. Two outlets are designed, one for treated stormwater and the second one for stormwater that exceeds the capacity of the device.

From a modeling perspective, there is almost no attenuation or losses related to flowrates. The treatment performance can be represented using a flow-splitter (one up to the design capacity of inserts and the second for the bypassed flow), and appropriate EMCs can be used to reflect pollutant removal.

3.4   Swales and Strips

Grass swales typically promote sedimentation of particles by slowing down flow velocities. They may enhance infiltration of runoff and associated dissolved pollutants. Appropriate modeling formulations for specific unit processes can be used when these controls are used.

In this manual, swales and strips are assumed to provide minimal filtration and infiltration, although some available models allow this functionality. For example, the Source Load and Management Model (SLAMM) calculates the performance of grass swales similar to other infiltration devices, by assuming $(Q_p/Q_r)(A_s/A_t)$ as indicative of swale infiltration (Pitt and Voorhees, 2000). Runoff volume reduction fraction is assumed to be $(Q_p/Q_r)(A_s/A_t)$, where, Q_p is the percolation volume rate of the device, Q_r is the runoff rate to the device, A_s is the area draining to the device, and A_t is the total study area. The water percolation rate in the swale is calculated by

$$Q_p = \text{(dynamic percolation rate) (percolation area)} \qquad (14.11)$$

where percolation area is swale length times the swale width. The dynamic percolation rate represents the rate at which water moves through a soil, typically measured in the lab and in the field in terms of number of minutes it takes for 1 cm of water percolation. This dynamic percolation rate is generally about half of the typically measured static infiltration rate (Wanielista et al., 1983).

3.5 Swirl Concentrators

As mentioned previously, the CFD tool is the most appropriate method of characterizing the performance of swirl concentrators or other separation units. If the units provide an appreciable storage, in addition to the removal of large debris and settleable solids, then the physical configurations in the Transport or Extran blocks and the removal equations in the S&T block of SWMM can be used to model these processes. Several researchers have explored the use of CFD (Pathapati and Sansalone, 2007) to manufactured stormwater control devices.

3.6 Vaults

Vaults are essentially multichambered storage elements that induce settling as the means of removing particulate pollutants and floatables. The constricted outlets cause a temporary rise in water level similar to wet basins. Internal baffling and other design features such as bypasses will influence the performance; therefore, as mentioned earlier, CFD modeling may be more appropriate if an accurate characterization is desired and resources are available for detailed data characterization and modeling.

In a simpler sense, removal can be characterized based on a modification of Stoke's law for determining settling velocities for various particle sizes. The S&T

block of U.S. EPA's SWMM, for example, can be used to characterize storage and settling processes within this unit operation.

3.7 Forebays

Large wet basins can be supplemented by sediment forebays that trap coarse sediments before runoff enters the primary pool, effectively enhancing solids removal and also reducing long-term operation and maintenance problems. In essence, the forebay acts as a high-rate pretreatment unit where larger particles settle. Stoke's law can be used for the design, and the performance related to the storage and removal processes can be modeled using the S&T block of U.S. EPA's SWMM.

3.8 Cisterns

Cisterns and rain barrels are common stormwater controls used in combined sewered communities to reduce the volume and peak runoff flowrate reaching the regulators that can induce sewer overflows during wet weather. These controls are also increasingly being used in MS4 communities to reduce the volume and peak runoff rates during rain events. Draining water between storm events to make the capacity available for the next event is a key to representing the performance of these controls. An important consideration is the effective tributary area (roofs) from which the cisterns and rain barrels capture runoff.

If the interest is only on assessing the performance of cisterns in reducing the volume and peak flowrates of combined wastewater, the storage volume of cisterns can be translated to an equivalent depression storage applied on smaller subcatchment areas. An algorithm built in SLAMM or a customized spreadsheet can be used to characterize the performance for a complete water balance analysis involving reuse of this water for irrigation and associated reduction in city water supply.

3.9 Filters

Filters typically have two chambers, including a pretreatment settling basin and a filter bed filled with sand or other absorptive filtering media such as peat, compost, manufactured materials, or combinations thereof. In terms of modeling, the first chamber can be represented as a wet or dry basin for reducing coarse solids and floatables, and the second one can be represented with pollutant removal mechanisms for metals, organics, and oil and grease.

3.10 Landscaped Roofs

As described in Chapter 4, landscaped roofs are essentially sorptive filters whose designs vary significantly with respect to the type and thickness of media and vegetation species. Infiltration, evapotranspiration, storage, and sorption are the unit processes that can occur within this unit operation. Based on the extensive or intensive nature of these roofs, these can be modeled as pervious areas with the appropriate infiltration and evapotranspiration parameters. Maximum detention capacity of these roofs (e.g., 50 mm for extensive roofs) can be represented as the maximum infiltration volume so that rainfall in excess of this volume is assumed to bypass the unit operation and appear as overflow into the roof drains.

3.11 Bioretention

This unit operation typically consists of a grass strip, sand bed, ponding area, organic or mulch layer, planting soil, internal water storage zone, underdrains, and plants. Infiltration, evapotranspiration, storage, and water quality mechanisms such as adsorption are typical unit processes that occur in these units; therefore, modeling can incorporate these processes using appropriate equations discussed earlier in this chapter and in Chapter 4. For example, Heasom et al. (2006) applied the Hydrologic Engineering Center's Hydrologic Modeling System (HEC-HMS) model to represent a site on the Villanova University campus, assessing a bioretention unit's performance using the Green–Ampt and kinematic wave methods and seasonally varying parameters.

3.12 Pervious Pavements

Pervious pavements allow water to infiltrate through them and enter a gravel storage layer underneath the surface pavement; infiltration may occur through the bottom of the layer. These unit processes can be modeled using the appropriate storage and infiltration functions commonly available in urban runoff models.

4.0 MODELING APPROACHES

Watershed models are used to characterize flows and pollutant loads generated from urban landscapes and often conveyed through sewers or open channels to receiving waters. Modeling approaches appropriate for the hydrologic and water quality processes described in earlier sections are discussed here.

4.1 Hydrologic Models

The primary factors that govern urban hydrologic processes are rainfall volume, intensity, and duration, along with the physiographic aspects including watershed size, shape, storage, soils, land use types, and storage and conveyance. Parameters representing individual hydrologic processes have been incorporated in various ways in the existing models. Significant categories of models are as follows:

- Lumped vs distributed—lumped models convert rainfall into runoff volumes by characterizing the response of an entire watershed at a single or limited number of outlet locations, and also model the various physical processes using one or few parameters (e.g., the Rational formula). Distributed parameter models describe the physical processes and mechanisms at finer spatial scales, such as small subwatersheds, or in highly urbanized watersheds with varied land uses, at a block or lot level of detail.

- Event vs continuous—event-based models can simulate runoff for single rainfall events; for example, the HEC-1 and TR-20 models that are designed to simulate single-storm responses (Bedient et al., 2007). Continuous models are designed to simulate the hydrologic process over a continuum of climatic inputs, accounting for the remnant effects of prior storm events on the urban watershed response. Models such as HEC-HMS and U.S. EPA's SWMM are designed to perform both single-storm and continuous simulations.

- Stochastic vs deterministic—if the models allow explicit representation of stochastic variability in inputs such as rainfall and watershed parameters, then modelers can simulate a range of scenarios and understand the consequent system behavior. Synthetic hydrologic techniques such as Monte Carlo simulators can help in this process. Deterministic models, on the other hand, generate the system responses using deterministic rainfall inputs and single-valued estimates of parameters.

- Analytical vs numerical—analytical models have a closed-form solution that yields a dependent variable such as flow or concentration as a function of other variables. Numerical models typically compute approximate solutions to differential or integral fundamental equations by discretizing the time and space domains.

Table 14.2, shows examples of models under the aforementioned categories (Bedient et al., 2007).

TABLE 14.2   Examples of models classified by type.

Model type	Example of model
Lumped parameter	Rational formula, WinTR-55
Distributed	HEC-HMS, TR-20, HSPF
Event	HEC-HMS, U.S. EPA's SWMM, SCS TR-20
Continuous	U.S. EPA's SWMM, HSPF, Loading Simulation Program in C++, STORM
Deterministic	HEC-HMS, U.S. EPA's SWMM, HSPF
Stochastic	Synthetic stream flows
Numerical	Kinematic or dynamic wave models
Analytical	Rational Method, Nash instantaneous Unit Hydrograph

4.2   Unit Process Models for Stormwater Controls

Similar to hydrologic models, the significant categories of models available for representing various unit processes within stormwater controls are the following (Huber et al., 2006):

- Empirical models with constant effectiveness—these models typically use EMCs or effectiveness ratios as primary pollution reduction parameters to relate the effluent to influent characteristics (Strecker et al., 2001). While this may be appropriate for determining the reduction in pollution for an event or annual basis, it may not indicate performance of a stormwater control over time or for events of varying intensity and volume. Because of the variability in storm characteristics and antecedent dry periods, EMC is often the method chosen for predicting the effectiveness of controls for sites lacking extensive data input required by the other modeling methods. The EMC or effectiveness ratio values can be derived based on data observed from other sites, supplemented with limited information available at a project location.

- Empirical models with variable effectiveness—these models use variable treatment performance of stormwater control practices based on variations in influent concentrations. As the influent concentration increases, higher removal efficiency is expected from most stormwater controls. Instead of a mechanistic or heuristic model or a simple model that uses constant removal efficiency, this model type uses an effluent EMC distribution. Current data available are insufficient to tie stormwater control design to effluent quality, and this method would be difficult to apply for modeling controls in a series. Again, monitoring data from other sites can be used to derive the variable effectiveness curves, supplemented with the limited information available at a project location.

- Regression models—regression models are useful in doing preliminary investigations into cause–effect relationships, but they should be restricted to functional forms of how the stormwater control should work (Huber, 2001). For example, the particle size and detention time can be regressed to develop performance efficiency for a wet basin. Extensive site-specific data involving multiple sites and events are needed to derive the appropriate regression parameters and their use for long-term performance evaluation of stormwater controls.

- Physically based simulation models—simulation models allow the explicit characterization of physical processes that happen within stormwater controls, and assessment of volumes treated and those bypassed or processed at rates that result in non-effective treatment. Performance evaluation of a stormwater control must consider how much of the rainfall record is treated or controlled. The dynamics of the filling and emptying of these controls are vital to understanding treatment efficiencies and runoff removal rates (Huber, 2001). Simulation models with varying levels of complexity are available in the public domain, and models with simple unit process representation are also being upgraded by numerous researchers to add complexities when data and computational resources are available. Again, extensive field monitoring data are needed for several events and every unit process to characterize appropriate physical model parameters.

Several factors can govern the selection of simple to complex simulation approaches. These are discussed in a later section.

4.3 Usefulness, Appropriateness, and Reasonableness

Analytical tools allow evaluation of site-specific rainfall and watershed conditions to assess volumes of water treated by stormwater controls and the associated extent of pollutant capture. In principle, an analytical model, if accurate, can provide all the information needed to evaluate a stormwater control or system of controls that would be too expensive to collect using only field monitoring. Models can be useful in helping decision-makers in the screening, planning, and designing of stormwater control practices.

Appropriateness refers to the specific functions intended and whether a model is capable of simulating those functions. For example, detailed modeling of a neighborhood where green infrastructure is being monitored may require specific spatial representation of all stormwater controls, as opposed to a lumped-parameter model. For a watershed simulation, explicit representation of every control is expensive and it may be appropriate to lump the effects of green infrastructure into parameters representative of their combined effects.

Reasonableness refers to the desired level of complexity and data availability to support a robust model development and application. Simple models such as empirical equations can just satisfy the intended function when there are limited data to support model development and also where screening-level solutions are sought. There is often some level of conservatism built into these models that can lead to increased design costs. Additional data must be acquired and the level of modeling detail be improved to refine screening-level solutions for long-term stormwater control planning. For projects that involve regulatory compliance and potential litigation, data collection and modeling scope can be significantly enhanced to represent the processes to the detailed extent possible.

4.4 Analytical and Empirical Equations

4.4.1 Urban Hydrology

The Rational formula, a commonly used empirical model, is designed for small catchment areas. The common design guidance involves calculation of peak flows using this method to size new sewers or upgrade existing sewers. Representation of smaller catchments allows a user to define highly varying runoff coefficients depending on land uses, ranging from 0.13 to 0.17 for lawns with permeable soil and flat slope to about 0.70 to 0.95 for dense downtown areas.

This empirical method has several drawbacks in terms of conceptual design and water quality. It assumes a linear rainfall–runoff relationship through the use of a constant *C*, which can lead to overestimation of flows for microstorms (i.e., storms that are smaller in volume, but more frequent) and underestimation of flowrates for larger rain volumes caused by inaccurate representation of hydrologic losses. It is still a valid design tool, however, because it is mostly applied at a small catchment level with shorter times of concentration for the design of open channels, culverts, and sewers or detention facilities in urban areas.

Figure 14.2 shows a rainfall–runoff response from a small catchment area with, for example, 60% imperviousness. While the Rational formula produces a linear

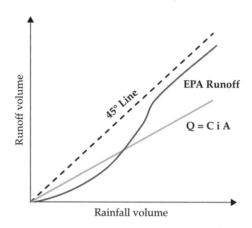

FIGURE 14.2 Comparison of the rainfall–runoff response from a small catchment area using the Rational formula and U.S. EPA's SWMM.

runoff response, a physically based rainfall–runoff model like U.S. EPA's SWMM can result in a lower runoff response because the losses are higher in the beginning. Once infiltration, evaporation, and depression storage losses are met, the resulting runoff can be higher than that given by the Rational Method. Depending on soil conditions and other factors that determine these losses, for example soil antecedent moisture, surface roughness, and slope, this approach can underestimate peak flows for storms with larger return intervals.

4.4.2   Water Quality

Several simple yet physically based equations for water quality processes exist. A common one is the Universal Soil Loss Equation (USLE) developed by the SCS for rural or mixed watersheds, primarily for the determination of long-term erosion rates. The general USLE equation is given as

$$A = RKLSCP \tag{14.12}$$

where

A = the potential long-term average annual soil loss per unit area per year,

R = the rainfall–runoff factor that depends on climatic regions,

K = the soil erodibility factor,

LS = the slope length-gradient factor;

C = the crop or vegetation and management factor that determines the relative effectiveness of management systems to prevent soil loss, and

P = the support practice factor that reflects the effects of practices that will reduce the amount and rate of the water runoff and thus reduce the amount of erosion.

This equation is built in comprehensive models such as Hydrological Simulation Program-Fortran (HSPF) and the Soil and Water Assessment Tool (SWAT), and also in simple spreadsheet models to compute pollutant loads on an annual or finer time scale. The equation was developed in English units; conversion to *Systeme Internationale* units is described by Foster et al. (1981).

Another example is the U.S. EPA model (Heaney et al., 1977) used to compute pollutant loads in urban runoff, expressed as

$$M = (\alpha \, or \, \beta) \, P f s \tag{14.13}$$

where

M = the amount of pollutant generated in pounds per acre per year (1 lb/ac = 1.12 kg/ha);

α or β = the loading factor corresponding to separately sewered or combined sewered drainage areas, respectively;

f = a population density function;

P = the mean annual rainfall; and

s = a street sweeping factor.

Heaney et al. (1977), for example, lists the loading factors for suspended solids corresponding to specific land uses, as shown in Table 14.3.

For residential areas, the value of f is

$$f = 0.142 + 0.134 \, (\rho_d)^{0.54} \tag{14.14}$$

Where ρ_d is the population density in persons per acre (1 ac = 0.405 ha) and, for commercial and industrial areas, f can be assumed to be 1.0. The street sweeping factor is

TABLE 14.3 Loading factors.

Loading factor	Land use type			
	Residential	Commercial	Industrial	Other
α	16.3	22.2	29.1	2.7
β	67.2	91.8	120.0	11.1

a function of the sweeping interval, N_s. If N_s is greater than 20 days, s can be taken as 1.0 and, if N_s is less than 20, then $s = N_s/20$.

Another commonly used empirical formulation for pollutant load estimation is the Metropolitan Washington Council of Government's equation that is generally applicable for drainage areas less than approximately 260 ha (Schueler, 1987). This is often referred to as the *Simple Method*, and was developed based on extensive data from the Washington, D.C., region and a Nationwide Urban Runoff Program (NURP) study (U.S. EPA, 1983). The pollutant load Y in pounds (1 lb = 0.454 kg) is expressed as

$$Y = 0.227 \, (P \, P_j \, R_v \, C_f \, A \,) \tag{14.15}$$

where

P = precipitation for the time interval being evaluated in inches (1 in. = 25.4 mm),
P_j = the fraction of precipitation events that produce runoff,
C_f = flow-weighted mean pollutant concentration (EMC) in mg/L,
A = the area in acres (1 ac = 0.405 ha); and
Rv = volumetric runoff coefficient that depends primarily on imperviousness of the land surface and can be approximated as

$$R_v = 0.05 + 0.009 \, p \tag{14.16}$$

where p is the percent of impervious area.

These analytical formulations, in spite of their simplicity, are still in common use because of the conservative assumptions and intuitive cause-and-effect relationships that are easy to explain to nontechnical audiences.

4.5   Spreadsheet Models

Spreadsheet models are often based on empirical or lumped-parameter equations, and are typically designed to perform flow volume and pollutant load calculations on a coarser time scale (e.g., annual, seasonal, or monthly). Also, reductions in pollutant loads are typically included as constant removal rates for the various parameters including nutrients, pathogens, solids, and metals. Because of their simpler formulations, these models are preferred by state and local agencies for simple pollutant estimation and tracking purposes. The following are a few example models:

- Spreadsheet Tool for Estimating Pollutant Loads, developed by U.S. EPA, provides a user-friendly interface to create a customized spreadsheet-based model. It computes watershed surface runoff; nutrient loads including nitrogen, phosphorus, and 5-day biological oxygen demand; and sediment delivery based on various land uses and management practices. The sediment load is calculated based on USLE and a sediment delivery ratio. Sediment and pollutant load reductions that result from the implementation of stormwater controls are computed using the prespecified removal rates.

- Region 5 Model, developed by the U.S. EPA Region 5, is an Excel workbook that provides a gross estimate of sediment and nutrient load reductions from an implementation of agricultural and urban stormwater controls. The algorithms for urban control practices are based on data and calculations developed by the Illinois Environmental Protection Agency. The Region 5 Model does not estimate pollutant load reductions for dissolved constituents.

- Poll-Track is a pollutant tracking tool in an Excel workbook for evaluating a range of stormwater controls needed to achieve a desired level of pollutant reduction. This model was developed by Rangarajan et al. (2008), as a back end to the ArcView-based Generalized Watershed Loading Functions (AVGWLF) model, for the drainage areas in the vicinity of Long Island Sound. However, it can easily be redesigned to process outputs from any simple to complex watershed model and in another geographical area. Costs and removal efficiencies for various stormwater controls have been included, which can be refined to reflect site-specific cost and efficiency factors and then evaluate controls necessary on an intra- or inter-watershed basis.

- Watershed Management Model (WMM) was developed by the Rouge River program in Michigan through funding from U.S. EPA. It was developed in MS-Access specifically to estimate annual and seasonal non-point-source pollutant loads from direct runoff on watersheds and sub-basins and was modified to address watershed management needs. The WMM estimates loads based on local hydrology and nonpoint EMCs.

- The Watershed Treatment Model (WTM) was developed by the Center for Watershed Protection (CWP). This spreadsheet model uses the Simple Method, and tracks pollutant sources and the effectiveness of various watershed treatment options in urban and urbanizing watersheds. It includes a series of spreadsheets that quantify the loads of several pollutants (including total coliform bacteria) based on land use, precipitation, and total coliform fate and transport information, where available. Although the WTM has several tiers of data specificity, loads can be estimated with simple land use data. The spreadsheets calculate a pollutant load on an annual basis by using a series of coefficients for runoff volume and pollutant loading derived from scientific literature.

While all of these spreadsheet models are inherently simple, they can be useful as screening or planning-level tools.

4.6 Models for Individual Controls

Most models are developed to characterize unit processes that can occur in one or more unit operations in terms of providing hydrologic and water quality benefits. For example, the hydrology models typically account for evapotranspiration, infiltration, depression storage, storage, and runoff so that the translation of rainfall into a resulting runoff can be performed accounting for the entire hydrologic cycle.

Models are rarely designed to represent one unit operation, for example, a tool only pertinent to the design of a dry basin. One such example is the Riparian Ecosystem Management Model (REMM) that was designed by the U.S. Department of Agriculture for modeling riparian buffers (Inamdar et al., 1998). Numerous process-based models specific to testing of manufactured stormwater controls or designing of specific controls have been developed by the academic and consulting communities. If there is interest in this type of control, it is recommended that a literature search or request for scientific information from vendors be obtained to understand the technical issues involved and characterize the unit process appropriately in a model.

4.7 Catchment Models

Some commonly used public-domain and university-developed models have been reviewed by Huber et al. (2006). The catchment models that have a long history of application for stormwater controls are briefly reviewed here.

4.7.1 Source Loading and Management Model

This model was developed to characterize the relationships between sources of urban runoff pollutants and runoff quality (Pitt et al., 1999; Pitt and Voorhees, 2000). It is strongly based on actual field observations and is mostly used as a planning tool. It is particularly suitable for characterizing a drainage area's responses to small storms that cause the most water quality effect on receiving streams. It can analyze an urban drainage area with up to six different land uses and 14 source-area types per land use. The implemented controls include catch basins, swales, infiltration devices, pervious pavement, wet basins, street sweeping, and user-defined devices. The SLAMM simulates runoff volume and pollutant loads for 10 standard and six user-defined pollutants, including particulate and filterable solids, phosphorus, total Kjeldahl nitrogen (TKN), chemical oxygen demand, chromium, copper, lead, zinc, ammonia, and fecal coliform bacteria.

4.7.2   Model for Urban Stormwater Improvement Conceptualization

The Model for Urban Stormwater Improvement Conceptualisation (MUSIC) is an integrated decision support system developed in Australia for urban catchment managers to facilitate cost-effective strategies for improved urban stormwater quality and aquatic ecosystem health at a regional, catchment, or subcatchment scale. The MUSIC (2010) the following:

- Rainfall–runoff model—a lumped model with an impervious area and two pervious areas to simulate stormwater controls at a finer temporal scale (e.g., 6 minutes);

- Stochastic pollutant generation—pollutant concentration time series are generated by a deterministic or stochastic algorithm, with the user-specifying EMCs and dry weather concentrations, along with standard deviations;

- Flow and pollutant routing—drainage links between the nodes in MUSIC allow for straight "pass-through" or user-specified routing (e.g., Muskingum–Cunge); and

- Stormwater controls—a universal stormwater treatment model (Wong et al., 2001), which uses a first-order kinetic decay algorithm (known as the "k-C^*" model) to model pollutant decay through a treatment measure.

4.7.3   Program for Predicting Polluting Particle Passage through Pits, Puddles, and Ponds (P8)

The Program for Predicting Polluting Particle Passage through Pits, Puddles, and Ponds (P8) is a model that has been applied in several U.S. case studies for predicting generation and transport of stormwater runoff pollutants in urban watersheds (Walker, 1990). Continuous water-balance and mass-balance calculations are performed on a user-defined system consisting of the following elements: (a) watersheds (non-point-source areas); (b) devices (runoff storage and treatment areas or stormwater controls); (c) particle classes; and (d) water quality components.

Simulations are driven by continuous hourly rainfall and daily air-temperature time series. Predicted water quality components include suspended solids (five size fractions), total phosphorus, TKN, copper, lead, zinc, and total hydrocarbons. Simulated stormwater control types include basins (wet and dry), infiltrators, swales, and strips.

4.7.4   Hydrologic Simulation Program-Fortran

One of the modules of the HSPF model, known as RCHRES, is used to simulate various processes that include hydraulic behavior, sediments, general quality constituents, and biochemical constituents in free-flowing channel reaches and well-mixed reservoirs. This module simulates certain stormwater controls such as basins (wet basins, wetlands, etc.) to mitigate the effects of runoff and associated water quality constituents. In its current development stage, the tool consists of open channels and flow control devices (weirs and orifices).

Although HSPF is well-known for large mixed land use watershed applications, this module enables the model's application to urban watersheds with sewer system networks and to areas with stormwater controls such as basins. Presently, the tool is not recommended for simulating infiltrators.

4.7.5   U.S Environmental Protection Agency's Stormwater Management Model

Some of the modeling formulations built into U.S. EPA's SWMM to simulate stormwater controls are listed in Table 14.4.

TABLE 14.4   U.S. EPA's SWMM capabilities to model stormwater controls.

Best management practices/ low-impact development option	SWMM suitability
Basins	Simulation of most storage options, with several options for hydraulic controls. Treatment by removal equations, first-order decay, or sedimentation. Removal in U.S. EPA's SWMM transport block channel and pipes by first order decay or sedimentation (constant settling velocity) or removal fraction applied to incoming loads.
Wetlands, bioretention	Simulation to the extent that wetland or bioretention behaves like a storage device.
Screening and filtration	Simulation by removal equations.
Chemical treatment	Simulation by removal equations.
Cisterns	Can divert water to storage, but cannot arbitrarily retrieve it.
Overland flow, swales, strips, infiltrators, pervious pavement	Simulation in runoff block only. Optional quality removal by first order decay or removal fraction applied to incoming load. Infiltrating water carries pollutants with it.

4.8 Model Reviews

Searching for an off-the-shelf model that can describe both hydrologic and water quality processes to characterize stormwater control effectiveness is challenging. Several model reviews and comparisons have been performed by federal and state agencies and research organizations. However, each of these reviews covered a broad range of issues that could overlap with stormwater control practices. A few of these reviews are highlighted here, along with brief descriptions of their study focus and associated Web links, where available (as of September 2010). Further guidance on model selection is provided in the following section. The reviews are as follows:

- The U.S. Department of Agriculture's NRCS provides a review of hydrologic and hydraulic modeling tools at

  www.wsi.nrcs.usda.gov/products/W2Q/H&H/Tools_Models/tool_mod.html;

- U.S. EPA's (1997) *Compendium of Tools for Watershed Assessment and TMDL Development* summarizes available techniques and models that assess and predict physical, chemical, and biological conditions in waterbodies. Specifically, it includes information regarding watershed- and field-scale loading models; receiving water models, including eutrophication and water quality models, toxics models, and hydrodynamic models; integrated modeling systems; and ecological techniques and models that can be used to assess and/or predict the status of habitat, single species, or biological community;

- *Water Quality Models: A Survey and Assessment* (Fitzpatrick et al., 2001) reviews the urban and rural watershed and hydrodynamic, water quality, and groundwater models available commercially and in the public domain. The review is a searchable database that allows a user to specify modeling needs (e.g., bacteria as the parameter of interest and lake as the waterbody of concern); the database provides a short list of models appropriate for these needs;

- *Evaluation of Chemical Bioaccumulation Models of Aquatic Ecosystems: Final Report* (Imhoff et al., 2004) evaluates chemical bioaccumulation models of aquatic ecosystems; and

- *A Critical Review of BMP Models and Guidance for Selection* (Rangarajan, 2005) discusses some general and specific criteria that guide a model selection process with respect to both urban and rural land uses. A comparison of commonly used stormwater control models is presented based on model selection criteria for a case study in Long Island Sound.

It should also be noted that significant research initiatives are being undertaken by university and federal researchers leading to the evolution of new models that can overcome limitations of existing ones. Therefore, reviews should be performed on a periodic basis (e.g., every 2 years) to compile up-to-date information to assist the professional community in making informed decisions.

It is also important to recognize that every project is unique in terms of designing a monitoring program and applying a mathematical modeling framework to support the selection of stormwater controls. The reviews previously performed by other professionals can minimize the reinventing process. However, project-specific issues will guide selection of a specific modeling framework. These issues are discussed in the next section.

5.0   SELECTION OF A STORMWATER CONTROL MODEL

The purpose of a model is to characterize existing system conditions to the best extent possible to then be used to predict responses for certain design storms or continuous hydrologic series to support decision-making on stormwater controls. To evaluate potential improvements, many alternatives may need to be evaluated and an appropriate design paradigm can help a decision-maker in evaluating these alternatives using a mathematical model.

A challenging task facing planners and designers of stormwater controls is the model selection process that identifies what models are available, how to select the most appropriate one, and what types of data are needed to support the model calibration and validation process.

Models applied and validated in other regions of the country or abroad can be reviewed to understand their applicability and pitfalls. Based on literature in the public domain, the designer can make an informed decision on a model or combination of models to suit the desired application.

Selection of specific models is dependent on various factors. Important criteria that can help in the choice of a model or a suite of models to meet study goals are described in the following sections along with some examples.

5.1 Modeling Objectives

The foremost use of a model is to assist a decision-maker in demonstrating that the adopted controls will help in achieving required regulatory compliance. For example, a municipality may need to evaluate a goal of 85% volumetric capture on an annual basis, which is presumed to achieve water quality protection in receiving waters. This municipality can choose to evaluate the effects of stormwater controls on the volume, peak flowrate, and frequency aspects of overflows from each outfall. On the other hand, if a demonstration approach is used for long-term control planning to address combined sewer overflows, overflow data need to be linked to a receiving water quality model to demonstrate compliance to the appropriate water quality standards.

A model needs to be developed such that its complexity level adequately reflects the maximum use of available data and the system dynamics to be simulated so that it meets the regulatory requirements to be addressed. As complexity increases, a greater number of parameters with large uncertainty ranges are introduced, which can result in greater difficulty to calibrate model parameters. Use of a complex model with a limited amount of data can result in overfitting of model predictions to the data without justifying the physical basis for certain model parameters. On the other hand, a simpler model may not allow specific physical conditions to be addressed and to comply with regulations. The level of detail included in a model must be reflective of the availability of sufficient data to support model calibration and also its intended use.

5.2 Hydrologic Processes

Most stormwater models can consider single storm events or continuous rainfall and simulate the physical processes of rainfall, soil infiltration loss to groundwater, and overland flow in a watershed. Flood control and channel protection goals may require hydrologic conditions that are generally extreme such as a 100-year storm to mitigate a possible, yet rare, runoff rate that can cause significant damages to property and human lives. Flood control involves design of facilities to attenuate peak flowrates to minimize potential flooding risks. Such controls operate on large spatial scales such as watersheds or significant sub-basins for flood and water quality analyses.

However, runoff volume, particularly on smaller spatial scales, is typically the most important hydrology variable in water quality studies. For example, erosion and benthic life impairment in urban streams can result from the runoff generated at the lot or sub-basin level and also from drainage areas adjacent to streambanks (Pitt, 1987).

Most existing stormwater models incorrectly predict flows associated with small rains (e.g., less than 12 mm) in urban areas (Pitt, 1987; Pitt and Voorhees, 2000). These storms occur frequently and, therefore, are important to characterize when runoff-associated water quality violations (e.g., pathogens) are of concern. Storms between 12 to 37 mm are responsible for about 75% of pollutant discharges. Rains greater than 37 mm are associated with drainage design and are only responsible for relatively small portions of annual pollutant discharges.

This interest in smaller storms may require a higher resolution modeling approach than the traditional site-scale models. The hydrology and data used for model calibration should be focused on smaller storms. Similarly, the fundamental hydrologic unit for this analysis can be small (e.g., roof, sidewalk, grass lawn, and driveway).

5.3 Model Scope

Models must be selected according to the problem that needs to be addressed. For example, the runoff from urban and agricultural watersheds with associated pollutants such as sediments, bacteria, and nutrients must be collected and routed through a flow network (e.g., pipes, open channels, creeks, and streams) before entering receiving waters. A few models include stream routing modules (e.g., U.S. EPA's SWMM, HSPF, and SWAT). Such routing techniques involve simulation of instream transport and pollutant transformation processes that are applicable depending on the nature of the receiving waterbody (e.g., estuary, lake, or a river). Most models consider sediment deposition and first order decay of pollutants, and only a few consider complex processes such as evapotranspiration and nutrient uptake in wetlands, nutrient cycling in water column and sediments, and resuspension of sediment and associated pollutants.

5.4 Intended Use

Models are typically used for the following three targeted uses: (a) engineering assessment or planning; (b) preliminary and/or final design; and (c) operational. Planning-level models are often used for a "big-picture" view of the entire rainfall–runoff process in a drainage area, component loads from the contributing pollution sources, and to identify tradeoffs among various stormwater controls to achieve an overall watershed planning objective. Such models use a longer temporal scale (monthly and annual), with fewer data requirements and lesser mathematical complexity than detailed models used for design. Almost all the spreadsheet models discussed earlier belong to this category.

Design-level models provide a detailed simulation of the system for specific events and a complete description of flow and pollutant routing from the contributing drainage areas to receiving waters. The recommended practice is to use event-based analysis for regulatory compliance by using models such as NRCS's WinTR-55 (USDA, 2009), but to focus on continuous simulation to represent the continuum in hydrology and water quality conditions accurately.

Finally, the operational models are finer-level representations of the controls, including factors that influence operation and maintenance needs and actual performance with respect to meeting the desired water quality goals. Projects involving litigation related to cost-sharing of pollution control programs often involve highly complex and finer-level details. Process-based models such as U.S. EPA's SWMM, HSPF, HEC-HMS, Hydrologic Engineering Center's River Analysis System (HEC-RAS), and SWAT can be used to develop both design and operational models, although the spatio-temporal resolution can be finer in operational models.

Postconstruction monitoring is a key component of operational models so that one can assess whether the controls are functioning as designed. If not, the specific unit processes can be refined based on postconstruction data and additional analyses can be pursued to enhance efficiency or introduce another unit process as appropriate.

5.5 Modeler Experience

Modeling of point and nonpoint sources of pollution is a crucial element that will lead to credible, scientifically defensible decisions concerning stormwater controls. It is not uncommon to see large-scale studies with limited budgets using a cookie-cutter approach to develop models with limited technical rigor. Resulting modeling efforts are often challenged by regulated parties for exactly the same reasons. In addition to time and budget resources, these complex modeling efforts require significant training and experience for successful performance.

Agencies that focus on a big-picture view of pollution reductions can use simple tools within their financial and resource limitations. On the other hand, projects that require detailed characterization and pinpointing sources for storm-water controls will need either inhouse or contractor support with the right combination of education and experience. Typically, 2 years of experience with design or involvement in a flow and water quality monitoring program and at least 5 years of experience in the direct construction and calibration of models (under the supervision of experienced professionals) is recommended for undertaking moderate-to-complex modeling studies. A broad understanding of flooding and water quality issues and underlying assumptions may be adequate for application of simple modeling tools.

With perceived financial and time constraints, it is not uncommon to see practitioners or regulatory agencies use models as "black box" tools. This is a serious concern among the modeling community; that is, that a user of model results should know the underlying mathematical formulations, and their limitations, before using them to develop guidance on watershed management efforts. The lead agency (municipal, state, or watershed management) should ensure that their modeling staff and contractor are fully aware of and that they also present the modeling assumptions to support screening, design, and operational-level decision-making.

Numerous technology-based training opportunities are offered by U.S. EPA and other university and consulting organizations. Similarly, there are certification programs offered to enhance modeling skills, understanding of basic equations, and quality control procedures (e.g., by the American Society of Civil Engineers [ASCE]). Internet listservs maintained by academic and federal organizations also exist for various models (e.g., U.S. EPA's Better Assessment Science Integrating Point and Nonpoint Sources [BASINS] and SWMM), where the user community shares their valuable experience with novice modelers. It is recommended that such training and learning opportunities be explored and guidance from experienced professionals be sought prior to undertaking, and during the course of, any modeling project.

5.6 Complexity

For each stormwater control, analytical or numerical algorithms can be either simple or complex in terms of characterizing runoff and water quality processes and, thereby, determining removal efficiencies. Most models use a buildup and wash-off (B&W) approach, USLE, or an export coefficient to characterize pollutant load generation. The B&W approach is comprehensive, requiring extensive field data to calibrate the load generation model. Dry periods between rainfall events must be monitored to characterize dry weather deposition rates for specific pollutants of concern and to study the effects of management practices such as street sweeping. The primary advantage of this method is that rates can be developed for specific land use types and management practices and can be applied for small drainage areas (e.g., lots and blocks). The USLE, on the other hand, is empirical but is based on long-term assessments of soil loss data for relatively large drainage areas (tens of hectares to square kilometers). This limits its use for specific rainfall events for small drainage areas.

Similarly, unit process equations can be simple to complex based on the selected model. An example characterization of swales in two urban models (Cannon, 2002) is discussed here to highlight the differences in flow and pollutant load generation so that watershed planners can choose an appropriate model to meet their specific needs.

In one of the urban stormwater control models, P8 (Walker, 1990), the methodology adopted to describe settling and decay in basins is also used for swales. Particle and pollutant removal are also calculated similarly, although runoff velocities in swales are calculated using Manning's equation. An added process modeled in swales is infiltration and the associated filtration. Therefore, surface water outflows from grass swales have reduced pollutant mass because of the reduction in water volume from infiltration. This model tracks particulate and dissolved pollutant loads to groundwater that may be useful if modeling stormwater control interactions with a shallow groundwater system.

As discussed earlier, SLAMM (Pitt et al., 1999; Pitt and Voorhees, 2000) calculates the performance of grass swales in a similar manner as other infiltration devices, that is, by assuming a runoff volume reduction fraction in the swale. The two urban stormwater control models use entirely different sets of input data and parameters to characterize flow and pollutant load generation. Depending on data availability and site-specific physical conditions, one can choose either of the model frameworks.

It should be recognized that all the models are mathematical abstractions of real-world processes. Several approximations are built into both simple and complex models; however, the degree of approximation can be different. A general rule of thumb is to start with a simple methodology and understand the big-picture view of the problem and potential remedies. More complexity can be added as needed, and when data and financial and technical resources become available to support this level of complexity, to screen and select the most appropriate remedy.

5.7   Spatial and Temporal Considerations

The spatial resolution can range from subwatershed to individual lots and blocks where stormwater controls can be installed and, similarly, the temporal resolution can range from annual to hourly and minute time steps. Selection of these resolutions is highly dependent on the study intent (planning, design, and operational), stormwater control targets (runoff volume, peak flow, and pollutant load), and data availability (pollutant accumulation in various land uses and fertilizer application in lawns and agricultural lands). For most planning-level studies, annual to daily time steps and general land use categories (low and medium density residential, industrial, and commercial) are adequate.

Another important aspect in stormwater control modeling is selection of design storms or continuous precipitation records for performance evaluation. Srivastava et al. (2003) evaluated pollutant loading and stormwater control performance evaluation based on a series of design storms and continuous records and found that continuous simulations provided smaller non-point-source pollutant loads. Similarly, short historic rainfall records may not have the extreme events useful for design. An important recommendation is to use a synergistic design storm and continuous simulation approach whenever resources permit.

5.8   Performance Considerations

Stormwater controls can be modeled as unit operations (see Sections 2.0 and 3.0) or as unit processes that occur within a control (see Chapter 4). If modeling the control by operations, a method for determining performance parameters such as EMCs or effectiveness ratios must be defined. Such parameters can be developed from reviews of literature including the International Stormwater Best Management Practices Database (www.bmpdatabase.org) and CWP's National Pollutant Removal Performance Database (Winer, 2000; CWP, 2007) and applying similar removal rates to the model. Modeling the controls by unit processes, on the other hand, requires extensive data input for site and design descriptions. Such an effort may require modelers to set up a series of processes in an urban runoff model and sequence them in accordance with those that occur in the real-world system of controls.

5.9   Preprocessing and Postprocessing Utilities

To increase functionality and facilitate usage of stormwater control models, model developers (e.g., U.S. EPA, consulting firms, and state agencies) have often created preprocessing and postprocessing utilities that help with input setup, model calculations, and output viewing. Most models use a geographic information system (GIS) as the data preparation and visualization platform and different programming platforms (e.g., C++ or Visual Basic) for preprocessing and postprocessing interfaces. Maidment (2002) reviews some recent and more efficient software platforms such as ArcHydro. U.S. EPA's BASINS and Region 4 toolbox are among the commonly used interfaces that offer numerous processing utilities.

In addition to providing flexibility to users, preprocessing and postprocessing utilities are aimed at developing information in a format that can easily be communicated to interested stakeholders and shared with watershed organizations and agricultural extension centers for technology transfer. Although the preprocessing and postprocessing utilities simplify the steps involved in constructing model inputs and analyzing results, the model algorithms should be given more importance than a sleek interface during a model selection process.

5.10   Guidance on Model Selection Using a Case Study

In general terms, the criteria described previously have been used to demonstrate selection of an appropriate model for a case study. The example is a pathogen total maximum daily load (TMDL) application in an urban and suburban watershed in the northern shore of Long Island, New York, concerning shellfish harvesting use protection in Mill Neck Creek and Oyster Bay Harbor shown in Figure 14.3 (NYSDEC, 2003).

The needs expressed by the stakeholders included (a) capability to compare model results to monitored data available in the creeks and harbor; (b) uncertainty and sensitivity analysis to consider variability in stormwater control performances and associated costs; and (c) ability to translate complex mathematical formulations to simple decision matrices that can be used during the public outreach and stakeholder buy-in process. A series of model capabilities or criteria required for developing TMDLs for pathogens in waterbodies closed to shellfish harvesting were

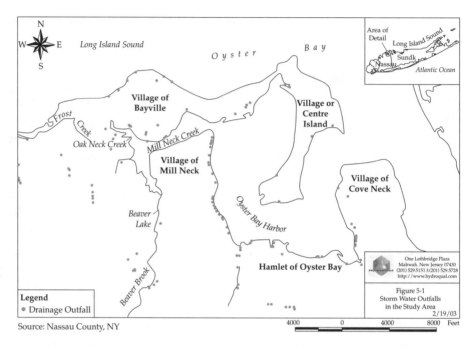

FIGURE 14.3   Mill Neck Creek and Oyster Bay Harbor with storm outfalls discharging to these waterbodies.

identified, and the models were screened and evaluated as to whether they met these criteria. The salient criteria used for reviewing the listed models include the following:

- Model availability, acceptance, and support—a thorough search and review was conducted to identify whether the models are proprietary or available in the public domain and generally accepted by the professional and regulatory community. Model user support mechanisms including live technical (phone and e-mail) availability and/or documentation were identified.

- Model uses—the model's capabilities in terms of its applications in planning, design, regulation, and operation and its applicability to different types of watersheds and waterbodies were identified.

- Resource requirements—an assessment of acceptable operating parameters (i.e., minimum computer configuration), data requirements, modeler expertise, and level of effort for using the model were conducted.

- Analysis levels—this criterion represents the range of model complexity (i.e., screening, intermediate, or detailed). The more complex models take into account additional processes and simulate a given process in a more detailed manner. Each model was reviewed to assess its capability for use with different analysis levels.

The specific urban watershed models evaluated are shown in Table 14.5. Subsequent to this comprehensive model review and consultations with various stakeholders, U.S. EPA's SWMM was chosen to characterize Mill Neck Creek and its tributaries. Continuous flow data were available in this creek and seasonal pathogen water quality data were available at several sections in the creek. The creek was tidally influenced, but the tidal flats limited the influence to during only high tide conditions. Most of the adjoining land use was suburban, with specific sources of pathogens including wastewater treatment plants, urban stormwater runoff (discharged through the outfalls shown as dots along the shoreline in Figure 14.3), mooring areas, and waterfowl. The hydrologic and water quality routines available within SWMM were deemed adequate to use the available data for characterizing existing conditions and also to evaluate conceptual stormwater controls to achieve the desired pathogen control goals in the creek and tributaries. Further discussion on the calibration and application of SWMM is provided in Section 8.0.

For Oyster Bay Harbor, however, there was no historical flow data available either at stormwater outfalls or in freshwater creeks to support quantification of pollutant loadings. Adequate ambient water quality data were available at stations within or adjacent to zones closed for shellfish harvesting. In order for the New York State Department of Environmental Conservation (NYSDEC) to develop targeted reductions in pathogen loads, the simpler WTM model was chosen.

The state used U.S. EPA's SWMM and WTM frameworks to develop target reductions and evaluated potential stormwater controls that would help achieve desired water quality standards in both Mill Neck Creek, and its tributaries, and Oyster Bay Harbor. Based on data available in receiving waters about loading from individual land uses (with almost no data available in upstream areas), decision-makers selected these two frameworks as screening-level approaches and to perform a sensitivity analysis to characterize the uncertainty. Once TMDL was established in 2003, there was ongoing work to refine the loading estimates in these waterbodies to support design and implementation of stormwater controls (Friends of the Bay and Town of Oyster Bay, 2009).

TABLE 14.5　Urban watershed models evaluated in the Mill Neck Creek and Oyster Bay Harbor project.

Models	Criteria	DR3M-QUAL	HEC HMS	HSPF/LSPC	INFOWORKS	KINEROS	LWWM	MIKEBASIN	MIKE URBAN	MIKE SHE	P8-UCM (P8)
Time scale	Event	×	×	×	×	×	×	×	×	×	
	Continuous	×	×	×	×	×	×	×	×	×	×
	Annual			×	×	×			×	×	
Pollutants	Sediment	×		×	×	×	×	×	×		×
	Nutrients	×		×	×		×	×	×	×	×
	Chemicals	×		×	×		×	×	×	×	×
Level of analysis	Screening		×	×	×	×	×	×	×	×	×
	Detailed planning	×	×	×	×	×	×	×	×	×	
Source release	Constant	×		×	×	×	×	×	×	×	×
	Time-varying	×	×	×	×	×	×	×	×		
	Single			×	×	×			×	×	
	Multiple			×	×	×	×	×	×	×	
Processes	Transport	×		×	×	×	×	×	×	×	×
	Transformations			×	×			×	×	×	
Input aids	GUIs		×	×	×		×	×	×	×	×
	Linkage to GIS		×	×	×		×	×	×	×	
Output aids	GUIs		×	×	×	×	×	×	×	×	×
	Linkage to GIS		×	×	×		×	×	×	×	
Stormwater control evaluation	Yes		×	×	×	×	×		×		×
	No	×						×		×	
Level of effort	Low	×						×		×	
	Medium		×	×	×	×	×	×	×	×	×
	High		×	×	×	×			×	×	
Data requirements	Low							×		×	
	Medium		×	×	×	×	×	×	×	×	×
	High	×	×	×	×	×			×		
Modeler expertise	Low	×						×		×	
	Medium		×	×	×	×	×	×	×	×	×
	High			×	×	×			×		
Model availability	Public domain	×	×	×		×	×				×
	Proprietary				×			×	×	×	

PRMS/ANNIE	Q-ILLUDAS	RRMP	RAINMAN	TR-55/20	WAM View	WMM	XP-SWMM	SITE MAP	SLAMM	STORM	EPA SWMM
×	×	×	×	×			×	×		×	×
×	×	×	×		×		×	×	×	×	×
					×	×	×				
×		×	×		×		×		×	×	×
	×	×	×		×	×	×	×	×	×	×
		×	×		×	×			×	×	×
		×	×	×		×	×	×	×	×	×
×					×	×	×				×
×	×	×	×		×	×	×	×	×	×	×
		×	×	×	×	×	×	×	×	×	×
	×				×		×				×
		×	×	×	×	×	×	×	×	×	×
					×		×				×
	×		×	×	×	×	×	×	×	×	×
×		×									
	×	×		×		×		×			
×			×		×		×	×	×	×	×
					×		×				×
	×	×		×		×					
			×		×		×	×	×		×
×					×		×		×	×	×
	×	×		×		×	×				
×			×		×	×	×	×	×	×	×
×					×	×			×		×
×		×		×		×				×	×
			×				×	×	×		

6.0 DATA NEEDS

6.1 National Data Sources

Characterization of pollutant loads from stormwater requires an understanding of the fate and transport of individual pollutants from contributing urban drainage areas. Depending on antecedent precipitation conditions, land uses, and management practices such as street cleaning and pet waste control, the accumulation and wash-off of pollutants can vary significantly. While it is important to conduct a local water quality monitoring program to enhance the understanding of system dynamics (see Chapter 13), similarities can be drawn from nationwide databases being compiled by various federal (e.g., U.S. EPA and the Federal Highway Administration [FHWA]), state (e.g., New Jersey, Florida, and California) and water organizations (e.g., Water Environment Research Foundation).

The most comprehensive database, NURP, was compiled by U.S. EPA and U.S. Geological Survey (USGS) on a nationwide basis (U.S. EPA, 1983). This program built on the Section 208 studies by characterizing the water quality of urban runoff and the potential for water quality effects in receiving waters. The overall objective was to develop a database that would assist U.S. EPA, states, and local governments in determining whether urban runoff was causing water quality problems. The NURP studies were performed cooperatively with 28 project sites across the United States. Each individual NURP project site also prepared a summary report. Most of these can be found on U.S. EPA Websites; a compilation of U.S. EPA and USGS NURP data sets can be downloaded at http://unix.eng.ua.edu/~awra/download.htm.

More recently, the University of Alabama and CWP have collected and evaluated stormwater data from a representative number of MS4 stormwater permit holders. This project, entitled the National Stormwater Quality Database (http://rpitt.eng.ua.edu/Research/ms4/Paper/recentpaper.htm), provides data both for developing pollutant loading assessments and water quality evaluations associated with compliance monitoring activities and determining the need for runoff monitoring as part of future stormwater permits (Pitt et al., 2003). In addition, CWP has compiled a National Pollutant Removal Performance Database consisting of 166 individual stormwater control performance studies published through 2006.

Another significant effort is the International Stormwater Best Management Practices Database, which began in 1996 under a cooperative agreement between ASCE and U.S. EPA and now has support and funding from a broad coalition of partners including WERF, ASCE's Environmental and Water Resources Institute, FHWA, and the American Public Works Association. The technical team leading this project is responsible for maintaining and operating the database clearinghouse and Web page, conducting analyses of newly submitted stormwater control data, conducting updated performance evaluations of the overall data set, and expanding the database to include low-impact development techniques.

These national databases can be consulted during the planning and design of stormwater controls to understand performance and associated costs. It is important to recognize that local factors such as climate, maintenance protocol and resources, labor market, and nature of pollutant types and loads can significantly affect the efficiencies and costs. For example, the University of New Hampshire Stormwater Center compiles fact sheets for numerous stormwater controls that provide design, cost, and performance information including the seasonality aspects such as effectiveness during cold months (http://www.unh.edu/unhsc/). In addition, numerous agencies including the States of New Jersey, New York, North Carolina, Washington, Florida, Texas, and California have conducted monitoring programs that provide useful data.

6.2 Quality Assurance Program Plans

Most watershed and water quality modeling projects require a quality assurance program plan (QAPP) for construction, maintenance, and long-term use of the developed models. Detailed protocol for development of a QAPP is given in U.S. EPA's (2002) Stormwater Permitting Memorandum from Robert Wayland in a TMDL Context; excerpts from this document are outlined in Table 14.6 for reference.

On projects supporting regulatory decision-making, the level of detail on model calibration in the QAPP should be sufficient to allow another modeler to duplicate the calibration method if the modeler is given access to the model and to actual data being used for calibration. Examples of QAPP elements for model calibration can include the following:

- Objectives of model calibration activities, including acceptance criteria;
- Frequency of model calibration activities;
- Details on the model calibration procedure;
- Method of acquiring input data;
- Types of output generated by model calibration;

TABLE 14.6 Quality assurance program plan requirements (U.S. EPA, 2002).

Section	Contents
Title page	Quality assurance program plan title; name of implementing organizations; effective date of the plan; and names, titles, signatures, and approval dates of appropriate approving officials (e.g., project managers, quality assurance managers, and state and U.S. EPA program officers).
Table of contents	Sections, figures, tables, references, and appendices.
Distribution list	Individuals and their organizations who need copies of the approved QAPP and any subsequent revisions, including all persons responsible for implementation (e.g., project managers), quality assurance managers, and representatives of all groups involved.
Project or task organization	Concise organizational chart showing the relationships and the lines of authority and communication among all project participants. Includes other model results users who may be outside the group that are developing and applying the model, but for whom the model outputs are intended.
Problem definition and background	Specific problem to be solved, decision to be made, or outcome to be achieved. Also includes sufficient background information to provide a historical, scientific, and regulatory perspective for this particular project.
Project or task description and schedule	Various tasks to be involved in model development and/or application effort, along with the general technical approach and the quality activities and procedures associated with these tasks
Quality objectives and criteria for model inputs and outputs	Definition of quality criteria that the expected components and outcomes of the modeling project need to achieve to meet the needs of the user. These criteria are specified within *performance or acceptance criteria that are developed in a systematic planning process* (these definitions are further discussed below).
Special training requirements and certification	Identifies and documents any specialized training requirements and technical expertise of the project team. Requirements can include expertise in certain scientific disciplines (e.g., statistics), code development or testing in a specific computer language, and data assessment, or experienceand in model development, evaluation, or application.
Documentation and records	Process and responsibilities for ensuring that appropriate project personnel have the most current approved version of QAPP, including version control, updates, distribution, and disposition. Itemize information and records that must be included in hard copy and any electronic forms. Records can include data from other sources, model input and output files, and results of model calibration and testing and archival process.
Model calibration	Tools affecting quality that must be controlled and, at specified periods, calibrated to maintain performance within specified limits. Describe or reference how calibration will be conducted. Identify the model and standards used for calibration. Indicate how records of calibration shall be maintained.

- Method of assessing the goodness-of-fit of the model calibration equation to calibration data;

- Method of incorporating variability and uncertainty in model calibration results; and

- Corrective action to be taken if acceptance criteria are not met.

Systematic planning identifies the expected outcome of a modeling project, its technical goals, cost and schedule, and the criteria for determining whether the inputs and outputs of the various intermediate stages, in addition to the project's final product, are acceptable. This is typically an iterative process involving at least modelers and users. On the other hand, the "performance criteria" are used to judge the adequacy of information that is newly collected or generated on a project, while "acceptance criteria" are used to judge the adequacy of existing information that is drawn from sources that are outside of the current project.

6.3 Additional Data Collection, Analysis, and Interpretation

Site-specific field data collection programs for flow and water quality conditions are discussed in Chapter 13. In addition to field monitoring data, several pieces of information need to be compiled and interpreted to support the characterization of existing systems and evaluation of benefits from certain stormwater controls. These are discussed in brief detail in the following sections.

6.3.1 Rainfall

Besides storms captured during a limited field monitoring program, long-term rainfall data from around the study area are necessary to develop appropriate design conditions (e.g., Driscoll et al. [1989]). To meet regulatory requirements for peak flow control and to ensure system performance for flood control or channel protection, a large design storm (e.g., 25- to 100-year return period) can be derived from rainfall records. Intensity–duration–frequency curves are available throughout the United States and can be used to derive design storms with desired recurrence intervals.

While a single storm with a certain recurrence interval is useful for design purposes, system performance must be evaluated with continuous rainfall records to characterize hydrologic and water quality conditions and potential improvements resulting from a selected set of stormwater controls. Practitioners conduct statistical analysis of long-term records to select an average hydrologic year (HydroQual, 2004) or use 20 to 50 years worth of long-term data as input and statistically analyze the model outputs to assess system performance.

6.3.2   Surface Slope and Roughness

Catchment slope and surface roughness determine the rate at which the runoff can travel toward a drainage point (i.e., catch basin or directly into a receiving water). Steep slopes and smooth surfaces lead to peaky runoff responses and, potentially, increased runoff volume because those surfaces will allow little opportunity for the rain to infiltrate.

Surface slopes are derived from comprehensive ground elevation survey data or from a digital elevation map. Conversely, surface roughness is based on soil and vegetation types in pervious areas and on the type of paving material in impervious areas (concrete or asphalt in roofs). If a digital map is not available to the desired accuracy, it is necessary to conduct aerial photography and remote sensing programs to develop elevation data for enhancing model accuracy. Techniques such as Light Detection and Ranging (LIDAR) can be used; LIDAR is a remote sensing system that can compile topographic data within 10 cm of horizontal accuracy, and is typically compiled along with low-altitude photography taken from an aircraft.

6.3.3   Imperviousness

The impervious cover is expressed in terms of a percent imperviousness for a given catchment area, which is one of the key parameters in quantifying an urban watershed's responses to various rainfall conditions. Pervious areas are complementary to this impervious cover. The connectivity of pervious and impervious covers is important in determining runoff responses from a catchment. For example, impervious areas such as rooftops may be connected to pervious areas like lawns or vegetated gardens. Runoff from such rooftops can be subjected to time delays, reductions in peak flowrates, or volume losses through infiltration.

A recent aerial photograph and ground cover characterization are necessary to support the development of this parameter (e.g., nationally available, comprehensive imagery data such as QuickBird taken in different seasons, or simple imagery that can be used to characterize the pervious areas and calculate the impervious areas as a complementary parameter). Various categories of land use, namely, low-, medium-, and high-density residential areas; commercial and industrial zones; and open spaces, parks, and agricultural areas, along with their impervious factors, can be assembled for inputting to the model.

Rapid urbanization is often associated with conversion of pervious areas into impervious cover. Specifically, some urban areas may have undergone significant construction activities in the last decade or so. Therefore, impervious fraction data should frequently be updated based on the level of urbanization. If significant changes in land use occur over 10 to 15 years and flow and water quality monitoring data are available for the entire period, it is recommended that the correlation between flow and water quality monitoring data and land use be reviewed carefully. A single land use pattern, when used to simulate this entire period of record, can lead to inappropriate selection of other model calibration parameters.

6.3.4 Water Quality Characterization

Collection and analysis of stormwater or combined wastewater water quality is essential to characterize pollutant loads from these discharges and quantify potential improvements from adoption of certain controls. Such information can be used to indicate potential exceedance of water quality criteria; identify potential effects on human health and aquatic life; and support the development of estuary, lake, and river water quality conditions.

Three distinct procedures have been used on several urban drainage and water quality modeling projects. These are

- Event mean concentrations, which are flow-weighted average concentrations for each parameter derived from the monitored wet weather events. Once the representative EMCs have been developed, they can be multiplied by flow-rates to derive pollutant loads. This procedure is applicable for both separately and combined sewered communities;

- Buildup and wash-off procedure that involves development of buildup (during dry weather) and wash-off (during rain events) estimates for various pollutants of concern in various land uses within urban watersheds. Atmospheric deposition and road surface accumulation in controlled areas have been monitored and regression equations and parameters have been developed in the literature (e.g., Clow and Campbell, 2008; Ollinger et al., 1993). Comprehensive models such as U.S. EPA's SWMM and HSPF incorporate B&W methodologies that can be parameterized for specific case studies. This procedure is also applicable for separately and combined sewered communities; and

- For combined sewered communities, the storm–sanitary splits in which the fractions of stormwater and sanitary flows in combined wastewater are determined using an urban runoff model, and appropriate concentrations for various water quality parameters in wastewater and stormwater can be applied to develop pollutant loads (Rangarajan et al., 2007). Water quality characterization of wastewater can be performed at wastewater treatment plant influent points or at upstream combined sewers if land use-specific water quality data are desired. For stormwater, however, a few outfalls that only carry stormwater need to be identified, and sampling needs to be performed at these outfalls to quantify concentrations for various parameters of concern. Alternatively, the samples can be collected at catch basins before runoff enters combined sewers.

Because sampling is typically not performed at all of the outfalls, care must be exercised to extend the concentration data developed at selected outfalls to a system-wide analysis. Frequently, the similarity in land uses between monitored and nonmonitored drainage areas can be used as guidance to assign concentrations for nonmonitored drainage areas. Typically, water quality monitoring performed at three to five outfalls in the system representing different land use combinations in their tributary areas can be used to appropriately develop concentrations (i.e., EMCs) for other nonmonitored areas.

Each of these three procedures has its own merits and drawbacks. Although the B&W procedure is cumbersome, it is comprehensive in terms of data needs and model parameters to be calibrated. The sanitary–split procedure involves fewer parameters, but data needs can be extensive depending on the level of detail sought in a specific municipal system. The EMC procedure is the simplest from a modeling perspective; however, data needs can be extensive because of significant variability that can be observed in water quality concentrations during and between rain events.

7.0 MODEL APPLICATION

7.1 Calibration Process

The purpose of a model is to characterize existing system conditions under a variety of rainfall conditions and to predict responses for certain design storms or long-term average hydrologic conditions for supporting screening and selection of stormwater controls. To evaluate potential improvements in the system, many alternatives may need to be evaluated. Therefore, model development and calibration should support this paradigm of assessing the performance of various alternatives relatively quickly. Several important steps in a model calibration and application process are discussed in this section.

7.1.1 Data Analysis

Model calibration and validation requires reliable flow monitoring data. The purpose of acquiring flow data is to use it to calibrate the appropriate hydrology-related unit processes. Flow meter data will need to be evaluated to assess whether the meters are providing reliable data and to note evidence of improper metering operations during the characterization of dry and wet weather conditions.

Proper quality control procedures need to be established to ensure that the data are truly representative of hydraulic conditions in the system. For example, Figure 14.4 shows a relationship between the depth and velocity in a closed pipe that appears to follow Manning's formula shown in black dotted lines.

7.1.2 Model Construction

The hydrologic and water quality-related elements of a model can be built based on climatic and physical databases. Some factors that can have effects on the overall schedule and accuracy of stormwater control modeling efforts are

- Availability of data on a system-wide basis at a finer temporal scale, which controls model accuracy;

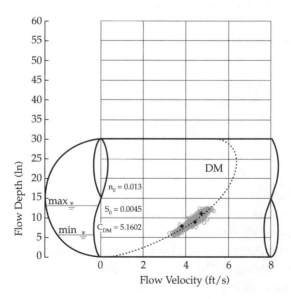

FIGURE 14.4 Flow data verified to follow Manning's depth and velocity relationship.

- Level of effort needed to set up input files;

- Delineation of subcatchments and selection of calibration parameters at a finer level, especially if monitoring data are primarily available in downstream portions of the system; and

- Computational effort to perform event-based and long-term rainfall simulations.

Geographic information system databases of soil, topography, land use, population, and aerial features can be used to develop initial values of hydrologic model parameters. Using these initial values and rainfall of specific storm events, hydrographs for a site can be developed for comparison with monitored data and calibration of appropriate parameters (Brown and Huber, 2004).

A key step in model construction is to establish linkage between hydrology and water quality. Most public-domain and commercial models already have established this linkage. For complex stormwater controls, it may be necessary to run control-specific models and generate input for an urban watershed model such as U.S. EPA's SWMM. For example, Huber et al. (2006) listed numerous improvements that can be performed to characterize certain stormwater controls in U.S. EPA's SWMM. Until these improvements are in place, modelers can choose to run process-specific models and generate inputs for the SWMM model.

7.1.3 Hydrologic and Hydraulic Model Calibration and Validation

The model calibration and validation process is defined as the accurate characterization of the appropriate hydrology and water quality processes in an urban drainage area so that potential improvements from a set of stormwater controls can be evaluated effectively. For the hydrology components, the goal will be to produce satisfactory comparisons with measured data in each land area contributing to a drainage system. Typically, a few wet weather events are chosen from the monitoring period to support model calibration. The hydrologic and hydraulic parameters must be characterized first, followed by the water quality processes.

For wet weather, typically two storms in the less than 6-mm range, two in the 12- to 20-mm range, and two more in the 25- to 75-mm range can be targeted to support the model calibration. One additional storm in each of these three ranges can be used to support model validation. The purpose of model validation using a data set independent from those used in model calibration is to avoid "overfitting" of models and enhance the robustness of the model by increasing its predictive ability.

Besides monitored events, it is common practice to apply the model to some historic large storms and compare it with available quantitative or anecdotal data to gain additional confidence about model performance. This is also an effective way of testing the robustness of model to predict system responses for storms that were not experienced during the limited monitoring program. In systems with combined sewers, the dry weather contributions from various drainage areas need to be determined and routed through the hydraulic elements (pumps and treatment plants) to ensure that system performance during dry weather is accurately captured. Once the dry and wet weather calibration is performed, model validation can begin with emulation of system responses for additional rain events from the monitoring period to independently confirm model performance.

When modeling combined sewer systems, calibration will first proceed with system performance characterization during dry weather. Typical parameters reviewed and adjusted, if needed, during this process, are sewer sedimentation documented during field inspections; Manning's roughness to reflect age and material of pipes; operation of pumps during dry weather; wastewater generation per capita; and diurnal, weekend vs weekday, and seasonal variations in base sanitary flows. The calibration process can then proceed with wet weather system performance; key calibration inputs and parameters are as follows:

- Precipitation—precipitation is the main external input to the hydrologic system and, because rainfall exhibits a highly varying spatio-temporal behavior, its representation at a finer detail helps in achieving a better model calibration process. Depending on the spatio-temporal resolution of available data, sensitivity analysis with different weighted-average precipitation data may be required to improve calibrations. Rain events to support model calibration can be chosen based on available rain gage data on a system-wide basis. For example, studies involving sewer or stormwater control design improvements will benefit from data at short time intervals, (e.g., 5 to 10 minutes). On the other hand, studies that focus on nutrient or sediment loads can use data at coarse intervals (e.g., 60 minutes).

- Runoff—runoff, or overland flow, is generated from the precipitation after losses from infiltration, evapotranspiration, and depression storage are subtracted. The primary variables affecting runoff routing are parameters such as slope, roughness, and hydraulic width.

- Evapotranspiration—as discussed previously, evapotranspiration can be a significant loss parameter depending on temperatures and seasonality in rainfall (e.g., thunderstorms in late summer) and can affect runoff generated from both pervious and impervious areas. Availability of site-specific evapotranspiration data may guide its representation in a model; however, at least monthly evapotranspiration values should be used by using data from adjacent areas if site-specific data were unavailable. This parameter is particularly important for continuous simulations.

- Infiltration—infiltration can be calculated using either the Horton or Green–Ampt methods. These can be calibration parameters, particularly if native soil has been subjected to compaction during construction in the vicinity. An impervious area is assumed to have no infiltration.

It is common practice to calibrate the hydraulic model to within 10% accuracy between monitored and modeled flow volumes at the calibration points. The peak flows can also be targeted for 15 to 20% calibration accuracy between the monitored and modeled values. The process of calibration is essentially an "optimization" process (i.e., minimizing the relative errors between measured and predicted values). As the calibration progresses from the upstream to the downstream end of the system, the relative error propagates. In regional and large-scale modeling studies, achieving overall calibration accuracy at most of the monitoring stations is appropriate.

After calibration is completed, a validation (also referred to as *verification* or *confirmation*) process can be used to test the model's ability to reproduce values comparable to monitored data without adjusting any parameters for an independent set of storm events. This process will provide a measure of the relative confidence in the model error for storms that were not used for model calibration. If this error is unacceptably high (e.g., greater than 20%), analysis should be conducted to determine the causes of the error. Model recalibration is often recommended in such instances.

The aforementioned discussion is more directly related to calibration and validation of a comprehensive urban drainage model such as U.S. EPA's SWMM. However, basic guidance for calibration is still valid for simpler models such as RAINMAN (McMillin and Omer, 2000) or for midrange to complex models such as AVGWLF (Rangarajan et al., 2008) and HSPF. Acceptable performance criteria need to be set a priori and a systematic parameter adjustment needs to be performed to ensure that the model, when calibrated, is useful for the intended application. Specific guidelines for modeling in sewers, which are generally applicable for both combined and separate stormwater systems, have been developed by several agencies (e.g., U.S. EPA [1999] and Wastewater Planning Users Group [WaPUG] [1998]).

7.1.4   *Water Quality Model Calibration*

Once hydrologic parameters appropriate for a study area and hydraulic conditions in the drainage system are established through model calibration, the next step is to calibrate water quality constituents. Simulation of urban runoff quality is extremely difficult and inexact (Huber and Dickinson, 1988). Primary reasons for this are the large uncertainty in representation of physical, chemical, and biological processes, and also the lack of extensive data to support a robust model calibration.

Measurement of hydrologic and hydraulic processes is much easier and far less expensive than a water quality process. Simple, automated instrumentation can be used to measure flows, water depths, and velocities to support the hydrologic and hydraulic model calibration. Water quality, however, demands manual and/or automated methods to collect samples and then to enumerate in a standard or certified laboratory. The availability of data to support water quality calibration is likely to be sparse.

Even if there are sampling data collected only at few outfalls (representing portions of the urban drainage area being studied), the calibration process should start with generation of pollutographs to identify any first flush effects. Parameters such as total suspended solids (TSS), biochemical oxygen demand, total nitrogen, total phosphorus, ammonia, and pathogens typically exhibit this behavior; however, nonstructural practices such as street sweeping can induce significant variability. Water quality sampling performed at selected outfalls should be analyzed to assess their data adequacy and accuracy. The data can also be used to assess the prestorm, first flush, peak flow, recovery, and poststorm water quality conditions in combined wastewater or stormwater for all the parameters of concern chosen in a study.

As discussed earlier, the B&W, sanitary–storm split or EMC procedures can be used for water quality characterization. Therefore, the compiled data can be processed to develop appropriate parameters, depending on the procedure being used.

The next step is to characterize the performance of individual stormwater controls in the modeling process. Depending on the unit processes or unit operations involved, modeling or calibration methodology will vary significantly. It is important to follow a methodology that will assist in evaluating stormwater control performance. For example, a characterization of suspended solids can be especially important or treatability data on settling velocities and/or particle size and specific gravity distributions (Huber et al., 2006). Such data can be essential to simulate a system of controls in which downstream performance depends on upstream performance. The information should be input and/or generated upstream to the model, which is a complex analysis that relates erosion, scour, deposition, and sediment transport, all of which are poorly represented in SWMM and in any alternative urban drainage model.

Again, the aforementioned discussion is more pertinent to a comprehensive model such as U.S. EPA's SWMM. The protocol, irrespective of a simple or complex model, should involve reviewing data to characterize the dominant processes, selection of appropriate parameters to represent involved fate and transport mechanisms, and performance of sensitivity analysis to enhance confidence for model application.

Similar to the guidelines for sewer modeling discussed previously, there are specific guidelines developed by several agencies for water quality modeling. Although these guidelines have been presented in a receiving water quality modeling context, the same guidelines can be applied to the water quality characterization in a stormwater control or system of controls. Two references that can provide guidelines for water quality calibration are studies by U.S. EPA (1999) and WaPUG (1998). Standard references such studies by Thomann and Mueller (1987) or Minton (2005) can also be reviewed to characterize individual unit processes and model them accordingly.

7.2 Guidance on Calibration Criteria

Several calibration criteria are used by practicing professionals to determine the adequacy of hydrologic and water quality models. Graphical comparison between simulated and observed data is a common method used to assess calibration adequacy. This is an effective visual method, particularly when there are sparse data available to support the model calibration. Figure 14.5 compares monitored and modeled total nitrogen loads as a time-series plot. If there are numerous concurrent modeled and monitored values, a correlogram around a 45-deg line is another effective way of assessing model performance. An example of a total nitrogen load correlogram is shown in Figure 14.6.

Besides graphical comparisons, several statistical or numerical criteria can be used to assess the adequacy of calibration. Some of these criteria are listed in the following equations.

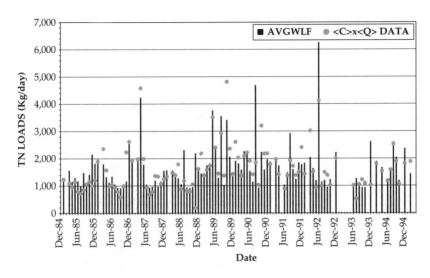

FIGURE 14.5 Monthly total nitrogen mass comparison for the Quinnipiac watershed.

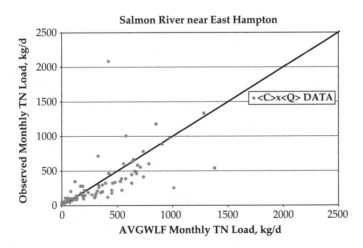

FIGURE 14.6 Modeled vs monitored data correlogram.

The mean error (e_1, also known as *bias*) and mean relative error (e_2) are described by

$$e_1 = \frac{1}{n}\sum (S_i - O_i)$$
(14.17)

$$e_2 = \frac{1}{n}\sum \frac{(S_i - O_i)}{O_i}$$
(14.18)

where

e = the error,

S_i and O_i = the simulated and observed values at time i, and

n = the sample size.

The first criterion represents magnitude of the average value of errors and the second represents the relative magnitude of average errors. It is desirable to make both of these two criteria approach zero during model calibration.

The first two criteria could be misleading if the sum of positive error is close to the sum of negative error. To provide more information, the absolute error (e_3) and root mean square error (e_4) can be used, as follows:

$$e_3 = \frac{1}{n}\sum |O_i - S_i|$$
(14.19)

$$e_4 = \sqrt{\frac{1}{n}\sum (O_i - S_i)^2}$$
(14.20)

It is desirable to make these two criteria as small as possible through the model calibration process. Another frequently used statistical measure is the Nash–Sutcliffe criterion. The predicted and measured values can be compared using the mean, percent error (*PE*), and Nash–Sutcliffe efficiency (*E*) equation (Nash and Sutcliffe, 1970), as follows:

$$PE = \left(X_{ci} - X_{mi} \right) * \frac{100}{X_{mi}}$$
(14.21)

$$E = 1 - \frac{\sum (X_{mi} - X_{ci})^2}{\sum (X_{mi} - X_m^-)^2} \quad \text{for all } i = 1, n$$
(14.22)

where

PE = percent error,

E = the model efficiency,

X_{mi} = the measured value,

X_{ci} = the predicted value, and

$\bar{X}_m$ = the average of measured values.

A value of $E = 1.0$ indicates a perfect prediction, while negative values indicate that the predictions are less reliable than if one had used the sample mean instead.

The aforementioned criteria should be treated strictly as calibration guidance. Visual comparisons of modeled and observed data should always accompany use of these numeric criteria. The amount and reliability of data available to support the model calibration and comparison of visual and statistical information between monitored and modeled values should guide the modeler in assessing its adequacy for further use in evaluating the effectiveness of stormwater controls.

7.3 Sensitivity and Uncertainty Analyses

Sensitivity analysis is used to examine variations in model predictions to changes in a particular input parameter. It serves the following two purposes: it points to which parameters have the most effect on various aspects of model output so that the user knows which ones to adjust during calibration and, once the model is calibrated and is being used to make predictive estimates, it is useful to be able to examine the effects of changes in parameter values, especially those that were used in the calibration process. It is important to establish an "expected" response range by varying the parameters within a range of error and document the effect on the outputs.

On the other hand, the model uncertainty is the difference between a value taken to be true and the estimated value that could be computed based on an assessment of the integrated effects of all possible sources of error (James, 2005). While common errors such as erroneous data entry and measurement errors in calibration data are recognized by modelers, there are other serious issues such as poor interpretation of results and uncertainty by model builders, users, and decision-makers alike.

James (2005) offers a simple procedure to conduct uncertainty analysis. It is summarized as follows:

- List and estimate all sources of uncertainty;
- Quantify input (e.g., rain) and output (e.g., runoff) uncertainties;

- Estimate independently measurement errors for those parameters that are measured;

- Quantify total uncertainty by sensitivity analysis for each parameter and subsystem; and

- Consider the remaining uncertainty to be model-structure uncertainty.

Irrespective of whether a simple or complex model is chosen for a study, the uncertainty analysis should be performed to assess the effects of variability in climatic inputs, such as rainfall, and the variability in physical, chemical, and biological processes in unit operations to develop their expected performance. The effectiveness of such operations should be expressed in terms of a range of variability rather than a single efficiency factor.

7.4   Single Events and Continuous Simulation

Continuous vs single-storm simulations have often sparked debates about which method is more appropriate or conservative from a design standpoint. Hydrologic and water quality processes do not end abruptly; for example, the infiltrated runoff can appear as baseflow in an urban stream along with the dissolved pollutants. Similarly, a wet basin or wetland may receive runoff from a second storm event while it is still handling the runoff from a preceding rain event.

In terms of an ecological or geomorphic standpoint, impairment can vary significantly based on the specific pollutant of concern. Bank erosion or sediment transport can occur during every rain event, but can exacerbate during larger storms. Bacterial impairment can sustain for a few days after rain events, whereas the nutrient or toxics-related impairments can prevail for a seasonal to multiyear timeframe. While practitioners have supported single-storm evaluations from a conservative or overdesign perspective, there is strong support for evaluation of system performance for continuous periods with varying rainfall patterns. It is important to recognize the effects of single-event and continuous simulation on the sizing of stormwater controls and to also study the effectiveness by accounting for deterioration in performance over time.

Farrell et al. (2001), for example, used a HSPF model in the Sixteen Mile Creek watershed in Metropolitan Toronto, Ontario, Canada, and compared the effect of using 12-hour SCS design hydrographs vs continuous simulation on the approximate size of detention facilities and outlet configurations. Most significant differences between the two designs were seen in terms of higher storage vs outflow and lower overall storage obtained using the continuous modeling approach. The authors also reported that the design event approach tended to overestimate antecedent moisture conditions, and that the stormwater controls designed based on design storms did not provide sufficient control for the more frequent storm events. Moreover, the design storm approach also was demonstrated to provide less effective designs of erosion control systems.

The design storm approach was further justified in the past, when numerical models used to require significant computational resources to solve underlying algorithms. Modern computers allow users to set up and perform simulations with long hydrologic records (e.g., 20 to 50 years) in a matter of minutes to hours. In complex urban or ultraurban watersheds, the connectivity of sewer networks can impose additional computational burden. Even in such circumstances, the user can attempt to simplify the network without compromising accuracy and perform continuous simulations with reasonable effort. Models such as RAINMAN (McMillin and Omer, 2000) or STORM (USACE, 1977), for example, can be applied in complex urban watersheds for long-term system performance assessment, although the hydrologic and hydraulic processes are rather simple in these models.

Continuous rainfall records, particularly if the record is short, may not include extreme events that are commonly used for sizing stormwater controls. In such instances, a general rule-of-thumb is to use both continuous simulation and design storms when time and financial resources permit.

7.5 Guidance for Performance Assessment of Individual Versus Integrated Controls

As cautioned in Chapter 4, the efficiency of individual vs integrated controls (i.e., multiple unit operations to achieve different goals, that is, pretreatment, adsorption, disinfection, etc.) can be very different. Individual operations are easier to model; for example, Stoke's law can be used to assess the performance of a dry basin. If a forebay is designed to enhance settling of larger particles and floatables, followed by a dry basin, then the particle-size distribution in the influent is much different from the stand-alone dry basin. The finer particles are more resistant to removal by gravity; therefore, the treatment efficiencies in these two are expected to be different.

Unit operations modeling should take into account this sequencing process and appropriately include the influent concentrations or pollutant loads to characterize the performance of individual stormwater controls. Equations 14.23 and 14.24, for example, are commonly used to calculate the efficiency of a system of controls *TR* (total removal) with two units in a series with removal efficiencies A and B, respectively, as follows:

$$TR = A + (1-A)*B \qquad (14.23)$$

$$TR = A + B - \frac{(A*B)}{100} \qquad (14.24)$$

where TR, A, and B are fractions in the first equation and percent in the second equation.

If the unit operations are to be accurately characterized by two different models, it is recommended that the output from the first unit operation model be provided as input to the next model. An example is the use of a swirl concentrator to capture coarser and medium-sized particles. This can be modeled using CFD or other appropriate techniques and the time sequence of remnant solids concentrations to be provided to a disinfection model. This model will then assess the kill of various pathogenic organisms based on the new particle-size distribution and dosage of disinfectant used. Model calibration should aim to capture the performance at the end of each unit operation so that the associated hydrologic and water quality benefits can be characterized accurately and linked to the next unit process in the overall modeling process.

The reader is cautioned again that percent removal efficiencies are not appropriate to characterize the performance of stormwater controls, as explained in Chapter 3. Nevertheless, many models still use this approach and the modeler needs to exercise careful judgment to select these efficiencies.

7.6 Modeling Operation and Maintenance of Stormwater Controls

As discussed in Chapter 11 ("Maintenance of Stormwater Controls"), the expense of maintaining controls is relatively small compared to the original construction cost. Improper maintenance decreases the efficiency of stormwater controls and can also detract from the aesthetic qualities of the practice. Because Chapter 11 covers regular and periodic maintenance requirements for various controls, only the relevant modeling aspect is discussed here.

An adjustment factor can be applied to unit operations to account for poor maintenance such as the inclusion of additional depth in large basins for accumulated sediment, conservative value for hydraulic conductivity in filters, and reduction of the observed or assumed infiltration rate for infiltrators. These corrections are highly dependent on the specific unit operation and unit processes involved and also are highly variable. One common sense based approach is to apply the factor on a sliding scale from full efficiency to the worst performance over the life cycle of a unit operation or over a scheduled maintenance period that a municipality uses for their planning process (e.g., 5 years).

Structural problems such as clogged or broken pipes and missing or broken parts (e.g., valves, seals, or malfunctioning control gates) can be explicitly included in the drainage system characterization; the effects can be demonstrated to decision-makers to highlight the importance of maintenance. This sensitivity analysis can also assist municipal agencies in designing the frequency and extent of inspections needed as part of their long-term implementation and performance tracking process.

7.7 Usefulness and Applicability

Models should be viewed as tools that can help decision-makers in evaluating modeling needs (e.g., performance goals) with the model's capabilities. The goal should be to ensure that the model is appropriate and that the algorithms represent unit operations involved or the model does not directly incorporate the necessary algorithms; however, there are equivalent or simpler algorithms that can help in representing the process to the best extent possible. The primary criteria that drive the selection and sizing of stormwater controls include how much water to treat, which pollutants to remove, and what is the desired performance target or goal. These are outlined as follows:

- Volume goal—the most common design goal is for a control to be sized such that a high fraction (e.g., 90%) of the stormwater occurring over time may be treated. The common approach is to gauge the volume target by specifying a storm runoff depth that defines either the volume or flowrate to be treated for volume- and flowrate-based systems, respectively;

- Targeted pollutants' goal—with many technologies being available, certain stormwater controls may be chosen for their effectiveness for targeted pollutants and sized to achieve their performance goal; and

- Performance targets or goals—these are becoming more common, differing with pollutant type and receiving water. An example of a common goal that might be characterized as "basic treatment" is 80% removal of TSS. Such goals need to specify a timeframe; an 80% removal for one single storm requires a different strategy than removing 80% of TSS annually. The goal can also be considered "technology" rather than "receiving-water-based," meaning that it is based on what technologies can achieve, rather than what is needed, to meet receiving water standards.

7.8   Cost Considerations

Selection of stormwater controls should account for both the capital (construction and land) and annual and seasonal operation and maintenance costs. Together, the whole life cycle costs discussed in Chapter 12 can be used to optimize the selection process and achieve intended goals. Summaries of costs for various stormwater controls can be seen in literature by Field et al. (2006) and WERF (2005a; 2005b). In translating these costs to local areas, it is recommended that additional research be undertaken at a specific urban watershed to review local labor and material costs and then use these in the decision-making process.

7.9   Selection of Controls in a Watershed Context

The Stormwater Phase I and II regulations require owners and operators of MS4 systems to obtain National Pollutant Discharge Elimination System (NPDES) permits. Unlike municipal and industrial wastewater treatment plants that discharge effluents at one or few outfalls, stormwater is a diffuse source that enters waterbodies through numerous outfalls. The urban stormwater discharges are considered "point sources" of pollution (U.S. EPA, 2002).

Stormwater is also governed by other regulatory mechanisms that address pollution controls on a watershed-wide basis such as TMDLs, the Safe Drinking Water Act, Beach Act, and Endangered Species Act. For example, many cities in California have been implementing end-of-pipe treatment systems for stormwater discharges to protect the quality of bathing beaches. Such programs require implementation of stormwater controls to achieve overall water quality improvement in a watershed. Recent regulatory tools such as watershed-based NPDES permitting and pollutant trading (point to point, point to nonpoint, or urban nonpoint to other nonpoint) are promising for municipalities to undertake controls in a watershed context (U.S. EPA, 2004; 2005; 2007).

Using watershed and source data inventories, watershed-based approaches present several ways to analyze data to identify implementation options that could form an NPDES watershed framework. The specific approach for a given watershed will depend on available data, the nature of water quality concerns, sources of pollutants or stressors, and the relationships among those sources.

From an analytical tool perspective, several public and commercial-domain decision support systems exist to facilitate watershed-based decision-making. These are discussed in the following section, along with the need to optimize selection of stormwater controls to achieve benefits in a cost-effective manner.

7.10 Role of Optimization and Decision Support Systems

The need for watershed-based controls for urban wet weather discharges requires the use of optimization and stormwater control placement strategies to cost-effectively plan the controls. The objective function can be to maximize pollutant reduction goals for a given budget or to achieve a desired target reduction goal at the least cost. Numerous decisions are involved in this process. In optimization modeling, "decision variables" have a specific meaning, which, in this instance, would be the stormwater control alternatives (and their sizes, locations, etc.) from which one can select the preferred solution based on the chosen objective function and constraints. Choices of an objective function and constraints are indeed decisions to be made by the decision-maker and defined upfront to guide the optimization process. Costs and performances can involve nonlinearity, thereby increasing the complexity of this decision-making process. Such decision variables can include

- Various stormwater controls along with their performances and costs;
- Interrelationships between specific controls when used in a system of controls;
- Performance indicators such as peak and volumetric flow reduction and removal of particulate and dissolved components of individual pollutants; and
- Water quality criterion (target reduction) for the pollutants of concern.

Simulation models, in conjunction with optimization routines, have been effective at helping decision-makers select stormwater controls. For example, Zhen et al. (2004) and Perez-Pedini et al. (2005) explored traditional and newer optimization techniques that have been used to design detention basins or similar stormwater controls to meet watershed-based pollutant removal goals at minimal cost. An example is a linear programming-based solver is implemented in the PRedICT tool developed by Evans et al. (2003), in which the output of the AVGWLF model is used in PRedICT to achieve the desired pollutant load reductions or optimize screening-level stormwater control strategies.

Traditional optimization methods have been applied in the past with simplifications to achieve desired computational efficiency. However, modern techniques allow decision-makers to include physical processes and optimization in a heuristic sense and arrive at possible solutions with relative ease. For example, genetic algorithms (e.g., Perez-Pedini et al. [2005]) have been interfaced with a simulation model to generate solutions and find an optimal set of stormwater controls. For ease of use, these algorithms can be implemented in spreadsheets to allow watershed planners to evaluate alternative controls. Tools can be used as decision support systems (DSS) to evaluate the effect of selecting alternatives based on model results. Although there are many such tools, only a few are mentioned in this section as examples. The PRedICT tool mentioned previously is a DSS for evaluating the implementation of both agricultural and nonagricultural pollution reduction strategies at the watershed level. This tool includes pollution reduction coefficients for nitrogen, phosphorus, and sediment, and also has built-in cost information for an assortment of stormwater controls and wastewater upgrades. Rangarajan et al. (2008) developed and tested Poll-Track, a DSS to screen and select initiatives for total nitrogen control in the vicinity of Long Island Sound. The first step was to calibrate and apply an AVGWLF model to the drainage areas. An interactive management tool developed in Microsoft Excel, with significant flexibility to modify the treatment performance and costs of controls, is the front end that allows decision-makers to evaluate stormwater control needs for current and future land uses. Although it has been designed to work with AVGWLF outputs, Poll-Track can be configured easily to use outputs from any public or commercial-domain models and for other geographical areas. An application of Poll-Track is described in Section 8.2.

8.0   CASE STUDIES

8.1   Site-Scale or Subwatershed Example

At a subwatershed level, the watershed model set up for the Mill Neck Creek example discussed earlier uses U.S. EPA's SWMM framework that characterizes the simple decay of a pollutant and evaluates instream concentrations. The model represents Mill Neck Creek as a series of hydrologically connected subwatersheds, as shown in Figure 14.7.

The SWMM was set up using data about watershed characteristics that influence runoff volume (e.g., land use distribution, percent imperviousness, surface roughness, evapotranspiration, infiltration, and depression storage). A representative baseflow was estimated from the January 1997 to March 2000 flow record available at the

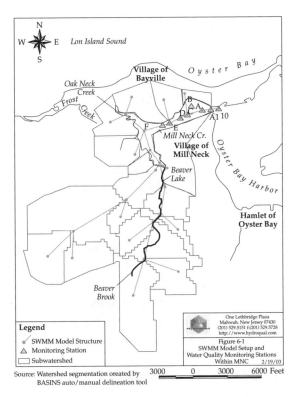

Legend

- SWMM Model Structure
- △ Monitoring Station
- ▢ Subwatershed

Source: Watershed segmentation created by
BASINS auto/manual delineation tool

One Lethbridge Plaza
Mahwah, New Jersey 07430
(201) 529.5151 f:(201) 529.5728
http://www.hydroqual.com

Figure 6-1
SWMM Model Setup and
Water Quality Monitoring Stations
Within MNC   2/19/03

3000   0   3000   6000 Feet

FIGURE 14.7   Subwatersheds in the Mill Neck Creek study.

USGS station and was used as constant baseflow in the continuous simulation period from 1997 to 2002. The percent imperviousness values were chosen based on land use classification, and aerial photographs of the study area were used to ensure that selected parameters were typical of local physiographic conditions.

The two graphs shown in Figure 14.6 correspond to the time-series comparison of flows and a probability of exceedance comparison of flows during the model calibration period. After calibrating hydrologic parameters, water quality was simulated by developing total coliform accumulation rates for each of the land uses. Concentrations for same land uses were varied to reflect differing numbers of wildlife and waterfowl and whether the houses were connected to a wastewater treatment plant or cesspools. In the model, total coliform loading was established as the relationship between total coliform buildup, which is a function of time between runoff-producing events, and the wash-off of the buildup. The coliform buildup was assumed to be linear, that is, it accumulates at a uniform rate and continues to accumulate at that rate (with no maximum) until some fraction is washed off during a storm event of sufficient intensity and duration. The uniform buildup rates for different land uses were adjusted to obtain a best fit for monitored data at the conditional stations within Mill Neck Creek and at the boundary station to Oyster Bay Harbor. Simulated total coliform concentrations have been compared to available monitored data, as shown in Figure 14.6.

Upon calibration of hydrologic and water quality conditions, the model was used to evaluate conceptual stormwater controls such as wetlands and disinfection. Percent removals for the unit processes were used to characterize potential reductions from these controls. The overall goal was to conceptualize screening-level controls and then follow with extensive monitoring to accurately characterize the various pathogen sources to support the final design of stormwater controls. For this adaptive implementation process, the modeling framework chosen here was adequate to support the screening-level analysis and also to have the flexibility to upgrade it for a detailed evaluation in the future. This scalability or adaptability aspect was viewed as a significant consideration by involved stakeholders. Work performed by NYSDEC (2003) is being used by the Friends of the Bay and the Town of Oyster Bay (2009) to plan and implement stormwater controls for pathogen removal.

8.2 Comprehensive Watershed-Scale Example

Detailed information on this case study can be found in studies by Rangarajan (2005) and Rangarajan et al. (2007; 2008). The Long Island Sound provides significant recreational and commercial value; unfortunately, a low dissolved oxygen condition (hypoxia) has affected the sound's water quality significantly in the past. The Long Island Sound TMDL required a 58.5% reduction in total nitrogen (identified to be the key pollutant) from point sources and a 10% reduction in urban and nonurban nonpoint sources from the inbasin drainage areas adjacent to the sound, as shown in Figure 14.8.

A brainstorming session held with the Long Island Sound Nonpoint Source and Watersheds Work Group identified the following key model requirements:

- Consider both urban and agricultural controls;
- Be in the public domain so that it can be distributed to individual municipalities, watershed agencies, State of Connecticut, and agricultural extension centers for future use;
- Interface easily with GIS databases to be able to evaluate nitrogen loads from past, current, and future land uses and subdivisions;

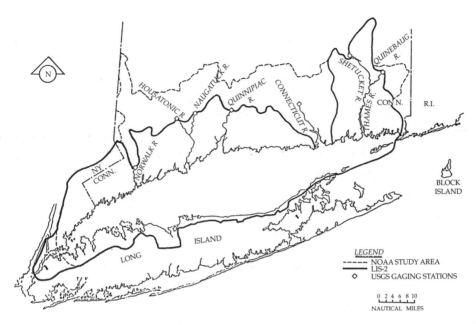

FIGURE 14.8   Inbasin drainage areas in the Long Island Sound.

- Allow the use of planning-level construction and maintenance costs and criteria (e.g., lot size, obstructions and access for construction of stormwater controls, and other local and state ordinances) that may guide screening and selection of controls;

- Provide flexibility to incorporate variability in stormwater control performances based on local geographic setting and weather conditions so the adequacy of stormwater controls to comply with the 10% reduction in nitrogen loads from urban and agricultural nonpoint sources of pollution can be assessed; and

- Incorporate treatment costs and nitrogen attenuation factors corresponding to the point sources so that cost-effective pollutant trading strategies between point and nonpoint sources can be evaluated in the future.

A comparison matrix of public domain and commercial stormwater control models was developed to support the model screening and selection process. The four models chosen for further discussion were AVGWLF, LIFE, MUSIC, and SLAMM.

Discussions were held with staff from U.S. EPA and the states of Connecticut and New York about the advantages and limitations of the models, and AVGWLF emerged as the preferred model.

A calibration strategy was used that compared AVGWLF predictions for flow and pollution load with the monitored streamflow data and predictions from an original study conducted by the Connecticut Department of Environmental Protection (CTDEP) that used an HSPF framework (AQUA TERRA and HydroQual, 2001). The calibration and validation periods of the CTDEP study (1986 to 1995) represented the most recent time period for which the required model input and execution data and calibration data were available and represented a wide range of hydrologic conditions. This entire 10-year data set was used for calibration of the AVGWLF model.

Application of the framework to one of the calibration watersheds, the Quinnipiac River, is reviewed here. Figure 14.5 shows the comparison of daily time series of stream flows. In general, the flows generated by AVGWLF matched well with the observed data.

Based on the generic hydrologic and pollutant-load parameters developed from the calibration watersheds, AVGWLF was applied to all other basins in Connecticut and New York. The simulation period was set the same as the calibration period, from April 1985 through March 1995, for calculation of flows and total nitrogen loads. The model outputs were then transferred to Poll-Track (Rangarajan et al., 2008), the management model developed to support watershed management efforts at a local watershed level. This watershed has significant point-source loads that are administered within the State of Connecticut's NPDES program. The remainder of nitrogen loads is contributed by a blend of urban land uses, septic systems, groundwater, and, to a smaller extent, by agricultural land uses. Scenario 1, shown in Table 14.7, lists existing baseline total nitrogen loads contributed by various point and nonpoint pollution sources in the Quinnipiac River watershed.

Scenario 2 lists total nitrogen loads with a selected set of stormwater controls, including nutrient management for agricultural land uses and constructed wetlands for urban land uses. Default values for costs and reduction efficiencies were used in this scenario. As shown in Table 14.7, reductions in total nitrogen loads from the adopted stormwater controls are listed in lines 12 to 22, and the effective reduction in the overall total nitrogen load with respect to the baseline scenario is 5.5%, as shown in line 33 for scenario 2. The total cost associated with this scenario is about $33.6 million (U.S. dollars).

TABLE 14.7 Example application of Poll-Track (lb × 0.4536 = kg).

Line no.	Quinnipiac River	Scenario			
		1	2	3	4
1	**Existing loads (lb)**				
2	Row crops	8726.9	8726.9	8726.9	8726.9
3	Hay/pasture	47 491.6	47 491.6	47 491.6	47 491.6
4	High-density urban	113 364.4	113 364.4	113 364.4	113 364.4
5	Low-density urban	97 542.3	97 542.3	97 542.3	97 542.3
6	Other	68 102.7	68 102.7	68 102.7	68 102.7
7	Streambank erosion	13 194.0	13 194.0	13 194.0	13 194.0
8	Groundwater/subsurface	440 179.0	440 179.0	440 179.0	440 179.0
9	Point-source discharges	1 161 504.9	1 161 504.9	1 161 504.9	1 161 504.9
10	Septic systems	143 081.9	143 081.9	143 081.9	143 081.9
11	**Total**	2 093 187.8	2 093 187.8	2 093 187.8	2 093 187.8
12	**Future loads (lb)**				
13	Row crops	8726.9	2604.5	2604.5	1881.2
14	Hay/pasture	47 491.6	22 480.6	22 480.6	15 334.6
15	High-density urban	113 364.4	72 593.8	72 593.8	53 407.6
16	Low-density urban	97 542.3	87 712.4	87 712.4	83 086.5
17	Other	68 102.7	68 102.7	68 102.7	68 102.7
18	Streambank erosion	13 194.0	13 194.0	13 194.0	13 194.0
19	Groundwater/subsurface	440 179.0	407 557.3	407 557.3	407 557.3
20	Point-source discharges	1 161 504.9	1 161 504.9	1 161 504.9	1 161 504.9
21	Septic systems	143 081.9	143 081.9	143 081.9	143 081.9
22	**Total**	2 093 187.7	1 978 832.0	1 978 832.0	1 947 150.7
23	**Percent load reduction**				
24	Row crops	0.0	70.2	70.2	78.4
25	Hay/pasture	0.0	52.7	52.7	67.7

(continued)

TABLE 14.7   Example application of Poll-Track (lb × 0.4536 = kg) (continued).

Line no.	Quinnipiac River	Scenario			
		1	2	3	4
26	High-density urban	0.0	36.0	36.0	52.9
27	Low-density urban	0.0	10.1	10.1	14.8
28	Other	0.0	0.0	0.0	0.0
29	Streambank erosion	0.0	0.0	0.0	0.0
30	Groundwater/subsurface	0.0	7.4	7.4	7.4
31	Point-source discharges	0.0	0.0	0.0	0.0
32	Septic systems	0.0	0.0	0.0	0.0
33	**Total**	0.0	5.5	5.5	7.0
34	**Costs**				
35	*Agricultural BMPs*				
36	BMP 1	0	20 000	20 000	20 000
37	BMP 2	0	0	0	0
38	BMP 3	0	0	0	0
39	BMP 4	0	0	0	0
40	BMP 5	0	0	0	0
41	BMP 6	0	1 122 000	2 244 000	1 122 000
42	BMP 7	0	0	0	0
43	Stream cost	0	3078	3078	3078
44	Total agricultural costs	0	1 145 078	2 267 078	1 145 078
45	*Urban BMPS*				
46	Detention basins	0	0	0	0
47	Constructed wetlands	0	32 500 000	65 000 000	32 500 000
48	Vegetated buffer strips	0	0	0	0
49	Total urban BMP costs	0	32 500 000	65 000 000	32 500 000
50					
51	**Total costs**	$0	$33,645,080	$67,267,080	$33,645,080

Scenarios 3 and 4 demonstrate how a user can conduct sensitivity analyses based on site-specific costs and removal efficiencies. Scenario 3 involves a simple doubling of costs for nutrient management and wetlands, while keeping the other stormwater control costs at default values. Total cost, for the same effective reduction of 5.5%, increases to about $67.2 million. Scenario 4, on the other hand, involves default cost values, but the reduction efficiencies for all of the stormwater controls adopted are increased and the effective reduction increases to 7.0%, with an associated total cost of $33.6 million.

It should be noted that this watershed-wide example also used constant percent removals for the various stormwater controls conceptualized for both urban and non-urban land uses. Large watershed-scale assessments like the aforementioned Long Island Sound case study can demand significant financial and computer resources if the unit processes are represented in the greatest detail possible. Decision support systems can allow users to represent stormwater controls at either coarse or moderate levels of detail so that the evaluations can be performed efficiently to support decision-making.

9.0 RECENT DEVELOPMENTS IN ANALYTICAL TOOLS

Common challenges and specific considerations pertinent to the selection and application of analytical tools have been discussed in this chapter. However, there are recent challenges or expectations from the user community that may influence the way in which these tools are applied for urban runoff management in the 21st century. These are briefly discussed in the following subsections.

9.1 Climate Change

The academic and federal communities have been augmenting models to meet recent challenges faced by urban watershed practitioners pertinent to climate change. Long-term variability in climatic conditions have been studied by researchers for decades; however, recent reports developed by New York City (http://www.nyc.gov/html/planyc2030/html/theplan/climate-change.shtml) and other significant metropolitan centers highlight the following potential issues:

- Sea-level rise that may affect stormwater controls located near the shoreline;

- Increase in peak intensity and/or volume of rainfall compared to historical data that were used for original sizing of stormwater controls; and

- Increase in air and water temperatures that can potentially influence the performance of controls such as wetlands

The primary challenge in evaluating potential effects of climate change has been the uncertainty related to translation of general circulation model (GCM) predictions to the scale of a local watershed. Downscaling of GCM outputs has been attempted by numerous researchers, and the comparison between various GCM models has been quite varied and baffling (IPCC, 2007; NYCDEP, 2008). Considering these uncertainties, a general recommendation is to conduct a range of sensitivity analysis for specific parameters that will be influenced by climate change (temperature, rainfall intensity, and sea level rise) and their effects on the quantity and quality aspects of individual stormwater controls. An adaptive design and implementation of stormwater controls may be necessary if the extant controls are inadequate to meet desired flood control and water quality objectives under future climate change conditions.

9.2 Sustainability

Peak flowrate and volume of runoff and water quality regulations have typically guided screening and implementation of stormwater controls in urban watersheds. Sustainability, although discussed in water resources literature since the early 1990s, has been emerging as new paradigm to guide stormwater management. The controls being envisioned should look at both today's regulatory requirements and the needs and long-term benefits of future generations. Pitt and Clark (2008) recently discussed this paradigm in terms of adaptability of modeling tools to account for watershed sustainability elements in stormwater controls.

A flaw of traditional stormwater management is that stormwater is viewed as a problem to be managed. Significant erosion, flooding, or water quality effects have supported this view of stormwater. Instead, if it is seen as part of the entire water cycle, then it becomes a resource to be used to the maximum extent possible at the place of origin and only excess flow during large storms remains as the problem to be managed. There is worldwide concern about the availability, quality, and affordability of water resources to meet the needs of future generations.

Stormwater reuse for purposes such as lawn or garden irrigation, cooling-water makeup, and toilet flushing reduce the demand for high-quality water treated for drinking water supply. Various agencies including the U.S. Green Building Council have developed guidelines for on-site use of stormwater to get sustainability credits for both new and redevelopments. Depending on climate conditions, stormwater controls should be chosen in a robust manner to maximize reuse during normal storms and to activate fail-safe mechanisms (e.g., a relief pipe at the bottom of a tank fitted with a sluice gate to be opened based on water level in the tank) to avoid flooding during extreme storms. In this context, analytical tools should be flexible to incorporate simple water balance (e.g., urban water cycle) methods to account for on-site stormwater reuse. Models such as SLAMM and U.S. EPA's SWMM can be easily adopted with extant system elements such as pumps, storage nodes, and real-time controls (e.g., heuristic operation rules) to account for stormwater reuse so that real-world processes associated with stormwater controls can realistically be represented and evaluated.

9.3 Integrated Urban Drainage Modeling

In ultraurban and suburban watersheds, stormwater generated at a block level is conveyed through sewers to receiving waters. When there are limitations in stormwater inlets or sewer capacities, stormwater generally runs on roadways following surface elevations. Models such as U.S. EPA's SWMM can be used to represent these limitations with the appropriate configuration of inlet constrictions or pipe sizes. Overland flow pathways can be represented in these models as quasi two-dimensional channels to be defined explicitly based on terrain slopes. Flood inundation occurrences in the United States and Europe have led to an increasing desire from decision-makers to model the sewer and overland pathway interactions and also to link with other influences, such as tides, to characterize the vulnerability of urban areas to flooding or risk during hurricanes.

Recent developments in the integration of sewer models with overland flood routing models can allow decision-makers to explicitly characterize interactions between sewer systems and overland flow pathways. Several university researchers and proprietary model developers have contributed to these developments. These are as follows:

- XP-SWMM 2D—an integrated XP-SWMM model with a DUFLOW two-dimensional routing model that uses shallow water equations for overland routing (XP-SWMM, 2011);

- WL Delft Hydraulics' SOBEK model (WL Delft, 2011);

- U.S. Army Corps of Engineers' interlinked HEC-HMS and HEC-RAS models (HEC, 2011);

- InfoWorks 2D—an integrated InfoWorks Collection System Model with a two-dimensional routing model (MWH Soft, 2011); and

- MIKE URBAN—an integrated urban catchment model developed by DHI (2011).

It should be noted that the computational needs associated with these models can grow exponentially compared to traditional application of urban drainage models in a one-dimensional context. However, flooding can result in significant financial and psychological effects on the public and may demand initiation of these comprehensive studies to support flood mitigation efforts, insurance assessments, and emergency management planning.

10.0 REFERENCES

Allen, R. G.; Pereira, L. S.; Raes, D.; Smith, M. (1998) Crop Evapotranspiration: Guidelines for Computing Crop Water Requirements; FAO Irrigation and Drainage Paper 56; Food and Agriculture Organization of the United Nations: Rome, Italy.

AQUA TERRA; HydroQual, Inc. (2001) Modeling Nutrient Loads to Long Island Sound from Connecticut Watersheds, and Impacts of Future Buildout and Management Scenarios; Connecticut Department of Environmental Protection, Bureau of Water Management: Hartford, Connecticut.

Bedient, P. B.; Huber, W. C.; Vieux, B. E. (2007) *Hydrology and Floodplain Analysis,* 4th ed.; Prentice-Hall: Upper Saddle River, New Jersey.

Brown, A.; Huber, W. C. (2004) Hydrologic Characteristics Simulation for BMP Performance Evaluation, Critical Transitions in Water and Environmental Resources Management. *Proceedings of the American Society of Civil Engineers and Environmental and Water Resources Institute World Water and Resources Conference;* Salt Lake City, Utah; June 27–July 1; pp 1–10.

Cannon, L. (2002) Urban BMPs and Their Modeling Formulations. M.S. Project Report, Department of Civil, Construction, and Environmental Engineering, Oregon State University, Corvallis, Oregon.

Center for Watershed Protection (2007) *National Pollutant Removal Performance Database for Stormwater Treatment Practices,* 3rd ed.; Center for Watershed Protection: Ellicott City, Maryland.

Clow, D. W.; Campbell, D. H. (2008) Atmospheric Deposition and Surface-Water Chemistry in Mount Rainier and North Cascades National Parks, U.S.A., Water Years 2000 and 2005–2006; U.S. Geological Survey Scientific Investigations Report 2008–5152; U.S. Geological Survey: Reston, Virginia.

DHI (2011) http://www.mikebydhi.com/Products/Cities/MIKEURBAN.aspx (accessed in Feb 2011).

Driscoll, E. D.; Palhegyi, G. E.; Strecker, E.; Shelley, P. E. (1989) *Analysis of Storm Event Characteristics for Selected Rainfall Gauges throughout the United States;* U.S. Environmental Protection Agency: Washington, D.C.

Evans, B. M.; Lehning, D. W.; Borisova, T.; Corradini, K. J.; Sheeder, S. A. (2003) *PRedICT Version 2.0 User's Guide for the Pollutant Reduction Impact Comparison Tool;* PennState: University Park, Pennsylvania.

Fair, M. F.; Geyer, J. C. (1954) *Water Supply and Waste-Water Disposal;* Wiley & Sons: New York.

Farrell, A. C.; Scheckenberger, R. B.; Guther, R. T. (2001) Chapter 7, A Case in Support of Continuous Modeling for Stormwater Management System Design. In *Monograph 9 on Models and Applications in Urban Water Systems;* James, W., Ed.; Computational Hydraulics International: Guelph, Ontario, Canada; pp 113–130.

Field, R.; Tafuri, A.; Muthukrishnan, S. (2006) *The Use of Best Management Practices (BMPs) in Urban Watersheds;* DEStech Publications: Lancaster, Pennsylvania; p 268.

Fitzpatrick, J. J.; Imhoff, J. C.; Burgess, E.; Brashear, R. (2001) *Water Quality Models: A Survey and Assessment;* Final Report for Project 99-WSM-5; Water Environment Research Foundation: Alexandria, Virginia.

Foster, G. R.; McCool, D. K.; Renard, K. G.; Modelhauer, W. C. (1981) Conversion of the Universal Soil Loss Equation to SI Metric Units. *J. Soil Water Conserv.,* **36** (6), 355.

Friends of the Bay; Town of Oyster Bay (2009) State of the Watershed Report for Oyster Bay/Cold Spring Harbor; Fuss & O'Neil, Inc.: Manchester, Connecticut.

Heaney, J. P.; Huber, W. C.; Medina, M. A.; Murphy, M. P.; Nix, S. J.; Hasan, S. M. (1977) *Nationwide Evaluation of Combined Sewer Overflows and Urban Stormwater Discharges, Volume II: Cost Assessment and Impacts;* EPA-600/2–77-064b; U.S. Environmental Protection Agency: Cincinnati, Ohio.

Heasom, W.; Traver, R. G.; Welker, A. (2006) Hydrologic Modeling of a Bioinfiltration Best Management Practice. *J. Am. Water Resour. Association,* **42** (5), 1329.

Huber, W. C. (2001) Wet-Weather Treatment Process Simulation Using SWMM. *Proceedings of Third International Conference on Watershed Management;* Taipei, Taiwan; Dec 11–14; National Taiwan University: Taipei, Taiwan; pp 253–264.

Huber W. C.; Cannon, L.; Stouder, M. (2006) *BMP Modeling Concepts and Simulation;* EPA-600/R-06–033; U.S. Environmental Protection Agency: Edison, New Jersey.

Huber, W. C.; Dickinson, R. E. (1988) *Storm Water Management Model, Version 4, User's Manual;* EPA-600/3–88-001a; (NTIS PB88–236641/AS); U.S. Environmental Protection Agency: Athens, Georgia; p 595.

Hydrologic Engineering Center (2011) http://www.hec.usace.army.mil/ *(accessed in Feb 2011).*

HydroQual, Inc. (2004) Analysis of Long-Term Rainfall Conditions in the New York City Metropolitan Area. Technical Memorandum; HydroQual, Inc.: Mahwah, New Jersey.

Imhoff, J. C.; Clough, J. S.; Park, R. A.; Stoddard, A. (2004) *Evaluation of Chemical Bioaccumulation Models of Aquatic Ecosystems: Final Report.* Prepared for U.S. Environmental Protection Agency, Office of Research and Development, National Exposure Research Laboratory, Ecosystems Research Division: Athens, Georgia; http://hspf.com/pdf/FinalReport218.pdf (accessed June 2010).

Inamdar, S. P.; Altier, L. S.; Lowrance, R. R.; Williams, R. G.; Hubbard, R. (1998) The Riparian Ecosystem Management Model: Nutrient Dynamics. *Proceedings of the First Federal Interagency Hydrologic Modeling Conference;* Las Vegas, Nevada; April 19–23; pp 1.73–1.80.

Intergovernmental Panel on Climate Change (2007) *Contribution of Working Group II to the Fourth Assessment Report of the IPCC;* Parry, M. L., Canziani, O. F., Palutikof, J. P.; van der Linden, P. J.; Hanson, C. E., Eds.; Cambridge University Press: Cambridge, United Kingdom, and New York. http://www.ipcc.ch/publications_and_data/ar4/wg2/en/contents.html (accessed Feb 2011).

James, W. (2005) *Rules for Responsible Modeling,* 4th ed.; Computational Hydraulics Inc.: Guelph, Ontario, Canada.

James, W.; Huber, W. C.; Dickinson, R. E.; James, W. R. C. (1999) Water Systems Models: Hydrology, Users Guide to SWMM4 Runoff and Supporting Modules; Computational Hydraulics Inc.: Guelph, Ontario, Canada.

Maidment, D. R. (2002) *Arc Hydro: GIS for Water Resources;* ESRI Press: Redlands, California.

Mays, L. W. (2001) Water Resources Engineering; Wiley & Sons: New York.

McCuen, R. H. (1998) *Hydrologic Analysis and Design,* 2nd ed.; Prentice Hall: Upper Saddle River, New Jersey.

McMillin, W. E.; Omer, T. A. (2000) A Simplified Modeling Approach for Simulating Rainfall-Runoff, Projecting Pollutant Loads and Analyzing Treatment Performance. *Proceedings of the Annual Conference on Stormwater and Urban Water Systems Modeling;* Computational Hydraulics International: Guelph, Ontario, Canada.

Minton, G. R. (2005) *Stormwater Treatment: Biological, Chemical, and Engineering Principles;* RPA Press: Seattle, Washington.

MUSIC (2010) Model for Urban Stormwater Improvement Conceptualisation. http://www.toolkit.net.au/music (accessed June 2010).

MWH Soft (2011) http://www.mwhsoft.com/products/infoworks_cs/infoworks_2d.aspx (accessed Feb 2011).

Nash, J. E.; Sutcliffe, J. E. (1970) River Flow Forecasting through Conceptual Models: Part 1, A Discussion of Principles. *J. Hydrology,* **10** (3), 282.

New York City Department of Environmental Protection (2008) The NYCDEP Climate Change Program Assessment and Action Plan. http://www.nyc.gov/html/dep/html/news/climate_change_report_05–08.shtml (accessed June 2010).

New York State Department of Environmental Conservation (2003) Pathogen Total Maximum Daily Loads for Shellfish Waters in Oyster Bay Harbor and Mill Neck Creek, Nassau County, New York. http://www.dec.ny.gov/docs/water_pdf/oystbaynopic.pdf (accessed July 19, 2011).

Nicklow, J. W.; Boulos, P. F.; Muleta, M. K. (2006) *Comprehensive Urban Hydrologic Modeling Handbook for Engineers and Planners,* 1st ed.; MWH Soft: Pasadena, California.

Ollinger, S. V.; Aber, J. D.; Lovett, G.; Millham, S. E.; Lathrop, R. G.; Ellis, J. M. (1993) A Spatial Model of Atmospheric Deposition in the Northeastern U.S. *Ecol. Applications,* **3** (3), 459.

Pathapati, S.; Sansalone, J. J. (2007) Application of Computational Fluid Dynamics (CFD) to Stormwater Clarification Systems. *Proceedings of the American Society of Civil Engineers/ Environmental and Water Resources Institute World Environmental and Water Resources Conference;* Tampa, Florida; May 15–19; pp 1–9.

Perez-Pedini, C., Limbrunner, J.; Vogel, R. M. (2005) Optimal Location of Infiltration-based Best Management Practices for Storm Water Management. *J. Water Resour. Plann. Manage.*, **131** (6), 441.

Pitt, R. E. (1987) Small Storm Flow and Particulate Washoff Contributions to Outfall Discharges. Ph.D. Dissertation, Department of Civil and Environmental Engineering, University of Wisconsin-Madison, Madison, Wisconsin.

Pitt, R. E.; Lilburn, M.; Nix, S. J.; Durrans, S. R.; Voorhees, J.; Martinson, J. (1999) *The Source Loading and Management Model (SLAMM) Guidance Manual for Integrated Wet Weather Flow (WWF) Collection and Treatment Systems for Newly Urbanized Areas;* U.S. Environmental Protection Association: Edison, New Jersey.

Pitt, R. E.; Voorhees, J. (2000) *The Source Loading and Management Model (SLAMM), A Water Quality Management Planning Model for Urban Stormwater Runoff;* University of Alabama, Department of Civil and Environmental Engineering: Tuscaloosa, Alabama.

Pitt, R. E.; Maestre, A.; Morquecho, R. (2003) Evaluation of NPDES Phase I Municipal Stormwater Monitoring Data. *Proceedings of National Conference on Urban Stormwater: Enhancing the Programs at the Local Level;* Chicago, Illinois; Feb 17–20; EPA-625/R-03–003

Pitt, R. E.; Clark, S. E. (2008) Integrated Storm-Water Management for Watershed Sustainability. *J. Irrig. Drainage Eng.*, **134** (5), 548.

Rangarajan, S. (2005) A Critical Review of BMP Models and Guidance for Selection. *Proceedings of the Water Environment Federation Total Maximum Daily Load 2005 Conference;* Philadelphia, Pennsylvania; June 26–29.

Rangarajan, S.; Mahoney, K.; Simmons, P. (2007) New York City's Wet Weather Discharges in the Long Island Sound TMDL Context. *Proceedings of Engineering Conferences International Conference on Urban Runoff Modeling;* Arcata, California; July 22–27.

Rangarajan, S.; Munson, K. A.; Farley, K. J.; Tedesco, M. (2008) A Decision Support Framework to Facilitate Nitrogen Load Reductions in the Long Island Sound (LIS) Watershed. *Water Practice,* **2** (1), 1.

Schueler, T. (1987) *Controlling Urban Runoff: A Practical Manual for Planning and Designing*

Urban BMPs; Metropolitan Washington Council of Governments, Department of Environmental Programs: Washington, D.C.

Srivastava, P.; Hamlett, J. M.; Robillard, P. D. (2003) Watershed Optimization of Agricultural Best Management Practices: Continuous Simulation Versus Design Storms. *J. Am. Water Resour. Association,* **39** (5), 1043.

Strecker, E. W.; Quigley, M. M.; Urbonas, B. R.; Jones, J. E.; Clary, J. K. (2001) Determining Urban Storm Water BMP Effectiveness. *J. Water Resour. Plann. Manage.,* **127** (3), 144.

Tchobanoglous, G.; Burton, F. L. (1991) *Wastewater Engineering Treatment, Disposal and Reuse;* McGraw-Hill: New York.

Thomann, R. V.; Mueller, J. A. (1987) *Principles of Surface Water Quality Modeling and Control;* McGraw-Hill: New York.

Urbonas, B. R.; Stahre, P. (1993) *Stormwater: Best Management Practices and Detention for Water Quality, Drainage, and CSO Management;* Prentice Hall: Englewood Cliffs, New Jersey.

U.S. Army Corps of Engineers (1977) Storage, Treatment, Overflow, Runoff Model, STORM, Generalized Computer Program 723–58-L77520; U.S. Army Corps of Engineers, Hydrologic Engineering Center: Davis, California.

U.S. Department of Agriculture (1986) *Urban Hydrology for Small Watersheds;* Technical Release 55; U.S. Department of Agriculture, Natural Resources Conservation Service, Conservation Engineering Division: Washington, D.C.

U.S. Department of Agriculture, Natural Resources Conservation Service (2009) Hydraulics and Hydrology Tools and Models—WinTR-55. http://www.wsi.nrcs.usda.gov/products/W2Q/H&H/Tools_Models/WinTR55.html (accessed May 2011).

U.S. Environmental Protection Agency (1983) *NURP—Results of the Nationwide Urban Runoff Program: Volume 1;* Final Report; U.S. Environmental Protection Agency: Washington, D.C.

U.S. Environmental Protection Agency (1997) Compendium of Tools for Watershed Assessment and TMDL Development; EPA-841/B-97–006; U.S. Environmental Protection Agency: Washington, D.C.

U.S. Environmental Protection Agency (1999) *Combined Sewer Overflows: Guidance for Monitoring and Modeling;* EPA-832/B-99–002; http://www.epa.gov/npdes/pubs/sewer.pdf (accessed May 2011).

U.S. Environmental Protection Agency (2002) Stormwater Permitting Memorandum from Robert Wayland in a TMDL Context. http://www.nj.gov/dep/watershedmgt/DOCS/WLAsStormwater.pdf (accessed June 2010).

U.S. Environmental Protection Agency (2004) *Water Quality Trading Assessment Handbook;* EPA-841/B-04–001; U.S. Environmental Protection Agency: Washington, D.C.

U.S. Environmental Protection Agency (2005) *Handbook for Developing Watershed Plans to Restore and Protect Our Waters;* EPA-841/B-05–005; U.S. Environmental Protection Agency: Washington, D.C.

U.S. Environmental Protection Agency (2007) *Watershed-Based National Pollutant Discharge Elimination System (NPDES) Technical Guidance;* EPA-833/B-07–004; U.S. Environmental Protection Agency: Washington, D.C.

U.S. Environmental Protection Agency (2010) Stormwater Discharges from Municipal Separate Storm Sewer Systems (MS4s). http://cfpub.epa.gov/npdes/stormwater/munic.cfm (accessed Dec 2010).

Walker, W. W., Jr. (1990) P8 Urban Catchment Model Program Documentation, Version 1.1; Prepared for IEP, Inc., Northborough, Massachusetts, and Narragansett Bay Project, Providence, Rhode Island.

Walker, W. W., Jr. (2007) P8 Urban Catchment Model. Program for Predicting Polluting Particle Passage thru Pits, Puddles, & Ponds. http://www.wwwalker.net/p8/ (accessed June 2010).

Wanielista, M. P.; Yousef, Y. A.; Harper, H. H. (1983) Hydrology/Hydraulics of Swales; Workshop on Open Channels and Culvert Hydraulics; Orlando, Florida; Oct 22–23.

Wastewater Planning Users Group (1998) Guide to the Quality Modeling of Sewer Systems, http://www.ciwem.org/media/44486/Quality_Modelling_Guide_Version_1–0.pdf (accessed May 2011).

Water Environment Research Foundation (2005a) *Critical Assessment of Stormwater Treatment and Control Selection Issues;* ISBN: 1–84339-741–2; Water Environment Research Foundation: Alexandria, Virginia.

Water Environment Research Foundation (2005b) *Performance and Whole Life Costs of Best Management Practices and Sustainable Urban Drainage Systems;* Project 01-CTS-21Ta; Water Environment Research Foundation: Alexandria, Virginia.

Winer, R. (2000) *National Pollutant Removal Performance Database for Stormwater Treatment Practices,* 2nd ed.; Center for Watershed Protection: Ellicott City, Maryland.

WL Delft (2011) http://delftsoftware.wldelft.nl/ (accessed Feb 2011).

Wong, T. H. F.; Duncan, H. P.; Fletcher, T. D.; Jenkins, G. A.; Coleman, J. R. (2001) A Unified Approach to Modeling Urban Stormwater Treatment; Paper presented at the Second South Pacific Stormwater Conference; Auckland, New Zealand; June 27–29.

XP-SWMM (2011) http://www.xpsoftware.com/products/xpswmm/ (accessed Feb 2011).

Zhen, X.-Y.; Yu, S. L.; Lin, J.-Y. (2004) Optimal Location and Sizing of Storm Water Basins at Watershed Scale. *J. Water Resour. Plann. Manage.,* **130** (4), 339.

11.0 SUGGESTED READINGS

Bicknell, B. R.; Imhoff, J. C.; Kittle, J. L.; Donigian, A. S.; Johanson, R. C. (1997) *Hydrologic Simulation Program-Fortran (HSPF): User's Manual for Release 11;* U.S. Environmental Protection Agency, Office of Research and Development: Athens, Georgia.

Chen, C. W.; Herr, J.; Weintraub, L. (2004) Decision Support System for Stakeholder Involvement. *J. Environ. Eng. (Reston, VA, U.S.),* **130** (6), 714.

Evans, B. M.; Lehning, D. W.; Borisova, T.; Corradini, K. J.; Sheeder, S. A. (2003) A Generic Tool for Evaluating the Utility of Selected Pollution Mitigation Strategies Within a Watershed, Diffuse Pollution and Basin Management. *Proceedings of the 7th International Specialised International Water Association Conference;* Dublin, Ireland; ISBN 1902277767; Bruen, M., Ed.; pp 10–7, 10–12.

Horner, R. R. (1995) Constructed Wetlands for Urban Runoff Water Quality Control. *Proceedings of the National Conference on Urban Runoff Management;* Chicago, Illinois; pp 327–340.

Lee, J. G. (2003) Process Analysis and Optimization of Distributed Urban Stormwater Management Strategies. Ph.D. Thesis, Department of Civil, Environmental and Architectural Engineering, University of Colorado, Boulder, Colorado.

Strecker, E.W.; Kersnar, J. M.; Driscoll, E. D.; Horner, R. R. (1992) The Use of Wetlands for Controlling Storm Water Pollution; The Terrene Institute: Alexandria, Virginia.

Index